M000206684

INCOMPRESSIBLE
AERODYNAMICS

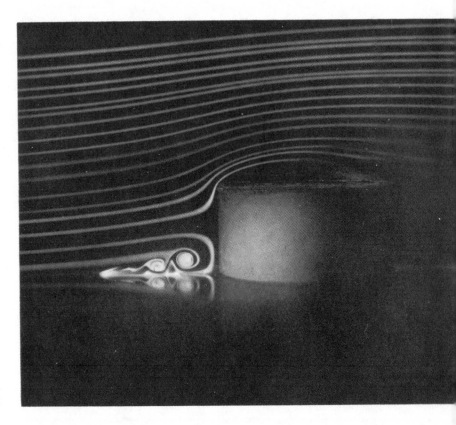

The stubby circular cylinder projects from a plane surface (in which faint reflections can be seen
Air is flowing from left to right, and the pattern of flow is indicated by the thin filaments of smoke

One of the effects of the cylinder is to make the filaments nearest the surface coil up. The tw
largest coils, or vortices, rotate in the clockwise sense and spiral away past the sides of the cylinder
These vortices induce in turn a smaller one, between and beneath them, rotating in the opposit
sense and passing downstream in the same way. A diagrammatic interpretation of this flow wi
be found in Fig. XII. 34.

This flow differs radically from its two-dimensional analogue; for example, the vortices do no
consist always of the same air but draw in fresh supplies constantly from upstream. It is correspond
ingly more difficult to treat analytically.

As a whole, this flow well exemplifies the complexities which face modern studies of low-spee
fluid dynamics.

INCOMPRESSIBLE AERODYNAMICS

*An Account of the Theory
and Observation of the Steady Flow
of Incompressible Fluid past
Aerofoils, Wings, and
Other Bodies*

Edited by
BRYAN THWAITES

DOVER PUBLICATIONS, INC.
New York

The Editor of this work is now Professor Sir Bryan Thwaites, Honorary Professor of Southampton University, formerly Professor of Theoretical Mechanics at that University, and recently retired as Principal of Westfield College, University of London.

Copyright © 1960 by Oxford University Press.
All rights reserved under Pan American and International Copyright Conventions.

Published in Canada by General Publishing Company, Ltd., 30 Lesmill Road, Don Mills, Toronto, Ontario.
Published in the United Kingdom by Constable and Company, Ltd.

This Dover edition, first published in 1987, is an unabridged and unaltered republication of the work first published by The Clarendon Press (Oxford University Press) in 1960 in the *Fluid Motion Memoirs* series. It is reprinted by special arrangement with Oxford University Press, 200 Madison Avenue, New York, N.Y. 10016.

Manufactured in the United States of America
Dover Publications, Inc., 31 East 2nd Street, Mineola, N.Y. 11501

Library of Congress Cataloging-in-Publication Data

Incompressible aerodynamics.

Reprint. Originally published: Oxford, Oxfordshire : Clarendon Press, 1960.
    Bibliography: p.
    Includes index.
    1. Aerodynamics.   2. Fluid dynamics.   I. Thwaites, Bryan.
TL570.I5   1987   629.132′3   87-15458
ISBN 0-486-65465-6 (pbk.)

TO

THE AERONAUTICAL RESEARCH COUNCIL
OF GREAT BRITAIN

*in appreciation of its work for
aeronautical science*

This book is a synthesis of
original contributions by

D. G. AINLEY

L. F. CRABTREE

M. B. GLAUERT

D. KÜCHEMANN

M. J. LIGHTHILL

W. A. MAIR

E. C. MASKELL

T. R. F. NONWEILER

R. C. PANKHURST

J. H. PRESTON

A. G. SMITH

D. A. SPENCE

B. THWAITES

J. WEBER

L. G. WHITEHEAD

L. C. WOODS

PREFACE

THIS particular volume of the Fluid Motion Memoirs is concerned mainly with the uniform flow of fluid past certain kinds of body, and with the methods by which we may predict the physical characteristics of such flow.

The scope of the book is limited in two important respects: the flows chosen for study are all more or less closely related to the problems of the flight of aircraft, and phenomena associated with the compressibility of fluid or with the unsteadiness of its flow are, as a general rule, ignored. Even with these restrictions, many categories of flow have had to be excluded. But in aerodynamics one can discern certain distinct lines of development and it is on these that the book runs, to branch off only occasionally towards those which seem of special interest.

There are few historical perspectives in this account—there is too much to be seen as it is. And by focusing our view sharply only on existing knowledge, we blur that most exciting feature of any science, the leap-frogging of theory and experiment by which our knowledge of the physical world is jerkily advanced. So you are invited to read between the lines and to appreciate the skill by which both theoretician and experimentalist stimulate and react upon each other's efforts.

The general plan of the book was, of course, settled some years ago, and the balance which is struck between the competing claims of the various topics reflects the views of aerodynamic theory current at that time; nevertheless, it has been possible to incorporate into the text many results from researches reported during the last few years and even as recently as 1959.

To those named on the facing page I owe a great personal debt, for they have done much more than offer their original contributions. My editorial task could not possibly have been completed without their sustained patience and sympathetic co-operation, and I am deeply grateful to them all for a most rewarding experience. The shortcomings of this book are entirely my responsibility and for them I apologize as much to my collaborators as to the reader.

I am very specially indebted to E. J. Watson for his valuable commentary on the typescript at a late stage of its preparation, and to N. Gregory, Secretary of the Aerofoil Theory Panel of the A.R.C., whose assistance has vastly exceeded what could reasonably have been asked of him.

I acknowledge most gratefully the work of Miss J. A. Jones, Miss B. D. A. Bankes, and Mrs. M. Franklin who, in their turns, gave me the most expert secretarial help.

Many individuals, too numerous to name, have willingly responded to my appeals for advice during the writing of the book, and my thanks go out to them all. In particular, I would like to thank

The staff of the Clarendon Press for all their help and skill in the production of the book;

J. L. Nayler and R. W. Gandy, successive Secretaries of the A.R.C., for their kindnesses in all sorts of administrative matters;

W. A. Mair, P. R. Owen, R. C. Pankhurst, L. Rosenhead, and A. D. Young for their work as members of the Aerofoil Theory Panel of the A.R.C.;

Miss D. Saxton and the staff of the A.R.C. Office for their work in connexion with the original contributions; and

Miss E. E. Metcalfe for her fine tracing of all the figures.

B. T.

Winchester
August 1958

ACKNOWLEDGEMENTS

WE gratefully acknowledge the assistance given by the following authorities in granting permission to reproduce certain Figures and Tables:

American Institute of Physics for Fig. I. 24 taken from *Journal of Applied Physics*.

Cambridge University Press for Figs. XII. 36 and 43 and Table II. 5 taken from *Journal of Fluid Mechanics*.

Cavendish Laboratory, Cambridge, for Fig. I. 1 provided by Mr. J. Elder.

Chemical Engineering Laboratory, Cambridge, for Figs. XII. 32 and 35 provided by Dr. W. D. Armstrong.

Engineering Laboratory, Cambridge, for the Frontispiece and Fig. III. 5(a) provided by Mr. E. P. Sutton.

David Taylor Model Basin, United States Navy Department, for Figs. III. 6, 7, 9.

Engineering Laboratory, Oxford, for Fig. III. 5(c) provided by Dr. C. J. Apelt.

Fluid Motion Laboratory, Manchester, for Fig. I. 2 provided by Dr. J. Gerrard.

Friedr. Vieweg & Sohn, Braunschweig, for Fig. III. 1 taken from *Zeitschrift für Flugwissenschaften*.

Handley Page Ltd., for Fig. III. 4 provided by Mr. G. H. Lee.

Institute of the Aeronautical Sciences for Figs. II. 5 and 6, X. 8, XI. 6 and 7, XII. 33 taken from *Journal of the Aeronautical Sciences*.

Institution of Mechanical Engineers for Fig. XI. 12 taken from *Proceedings of the Institution of Mechanical Engineers*.

Jet Propulsion Laboratory, California Institute of Technology, for Table II. 3.

Max-Planck-Institut für Strömungsforschung, Göttingen, for Figs. XII. 14, 17.

National Aeronautics and Space Administration, for Figs. I. 6, VI. 4, VIII. 36, X. 13, and Table V. 1 taken from *Research Memoranda, Technical Reports*, and *Wartime Reports* of the National Advisory Committee for Aeronautics.

Nationaal Luchtvaartlaboratorium, Amsterdam, for Fig. I. 22 provided by Dr. H. Bergh.

Royal Aeronautical Society for Figs. II. 1, VIII. 21 and Table II. 1 taken from *Aeronautical Quarterly*, and for Fig. V. 15 taken from *Journal of the Royal Aeronautical Society*.

Royal Society for Figs. IV. 14, XII. 1, 3 taken from *Proceedings of the Royal Society*.

We are also grateful to the Controller, H.M. Stationery Office, for the following Crown Copyright material:

Figs. I. 18–21, III. 2, IV. 2, 10, and 11, V. 2 and 5–8, VI. 9–15, 18, 19, 22, and 23, VII. 11–15, 17, and 19, VIII. 22, 24, 25, 32, and 33, XI. 3 and 10, XII. 21 and 34, and Tables IV. 1 and 2, V. 2, which have been taken in whole or in part from the *Reports and Memoranda* and *Current Papers* of the Aeronautical Research Council, and from the *Proceedings of the Symposium on Boundary Layer Effects in Aerodynamics* of the National Physical Laboratory; Fig. III. 8, which was provided by the Admiralty Research Laboratory, and for Figs. V. 11, VI. 29, VIII. 23 and 37, XII. 8 and 9, which derive from unpublished papers of the Ministry of Supply.

Finally, acknowledgement is made to the following organizations for permission to refer to unpublished papers:

Admiralty Research Laboratory; Cornell Aeronautical Laboratory, New York; David Taylor Model Basin, United States Navy Department; Douglas Aircraft Company, Inc.; Guggenheim Aeronautical Laboratory, California Institute of Technology; Ministry of Supply; National Aeronautics and Space Administration; National Physical Laboratory; Northrop Aircraft, Inc.; United Aircraft Corporation; United States Air Force, Wright Air Development Centre; United States Naval Ordnance Laboratory.

CONTENTS

II. THE CALCULATION OF THE BOUNDARY LAYER

III. THEORETICAL MODELS OF REAL FLOWS

IV. UNIFORM INVISCID FLOW PAST AEROFOILS

XII. SOME MISCELLANEOUS TOPICS

xviii CONTENTS

Figs. I. 22, III. 4, III. 5, III. 6, III. 7, III. 8, VI. 22, XII. 32, and XII. 35 appear as plates facing pages 56, 100, 101, 106, 107, 108, 242, 552 and 553.

NOTES ON ARRANGEMENT

THE systems of cross-reference within the book are as follows:

Chapters are designated by Roman numerals.

Sections and equations are numbered serially within each chapter in Arabic numerals. References to sections and equations within the same chapter do not carry the chapter number; others do.

Figures are numbered serially within each chapter in Arabic numerals, and always carry the chapter number in addition.

The method of referring to original papers follows, in the main, the conventions used by the Royal Society. All references are collected towards the end of the book in a single bibliography, arranged alphabetically by the names of the authors; it is hoped that the advantages of this arrangement offset the rather formidable aspect of the lengthy list.

In assessing the historical development of any topic, the reader should bear in mind that many researches, especially those done in government establishments, are first reported in internal papers given restricted circulation. Thus the date attached to a published paper is not necessarily a reliable guide to the year in which the work was actually done.

The abbreviations used in the list of references follow the methods of the *World List of Scientific Periodicals* (1952) published by Butterworths. A complete list of the abbreviations together with their full versions and originating addresses has been issued as Current Paper 444 of the Aeronautical Research Council, London; this list is designed to remove completely any ambiguities and is strongly recommended to those who wish to consult the original works.

The author index is incorporated in the bibliography in such a way that the reference to a particular work of an author may be found quickly in the text.

A great effort has been made to introduce as much uniformity of notation as possible over the various branches of aerodynamics, which in the past have tended to develop their own specialized notation. No particular success in this can be claimed but perhaps attention should be drawn to three special conventions which have been adopted:

1. The symbols u, v, w and U, V, W are used for the components of velocity in the Cartesian system (x, y, z). Thus a relatively isolated

use of, for example, U normally implies an x-axis parallel to the velocity so designated. A velocity which is not parallel to a coordinate axis is denoted by $\mathbf{v}$ or $\mathbf{V}$, the corresponding symbols for speed being v and V.

2. Suffixes usually denote particular values, occasionally components, and never derivatives, Derivatives are normally written in full, though occasionally a dash, or prime, is used.

3. The z-direction is, in general, taken to be roughly perpendicular to the solid surface under consideration. This is standard practice in wing theory, but it goes against convention for two-dimensional flows; for the latter we now take (x, z) as the coordinates and (u, w) as the velocity components. The usual notation for two-dimensional potential flow—$z = x+iy$ and $w = \phi+i\psi$—is therefore upset, and we have adopted new founts for both the complex potential and the position vector. Thus

$$\mathfrak{z} = x+iz \quad \text{and} \quad \mathfrak{w} = \phi+i\psi.$$

It is suggested that in manuscript $\mathfrak{z}$ and $\mathfrak{w}$ be written with bobbles on them: $\mathfrak{z}$ and $\mathfrak{w}$. In conversation, they could be pronounced 'com-z' and 'com-w' respectively.

I

SOME GENERAL PRINCIPLES

1. Prologue

To begin with, we should bear in mind the inherent limitations of all mathematical analyses of physical events. First, although our aim is to formulate general rules of conduct for fluid in motion, it is the fluid itself and not our analysis which finally decides whether it will conform to those rules; the justification of an analysis, therefore, lies not in its apparent rigour nor in its elegance—though these things count for much—but in its agreement with practical observations. Next, such analysis can account only for those properties of a physical event whose existence our limited knowledge can conceive and which we may hope to observe and measure; its value will depend on the discernment with which we single out certain properties for special attention and on their natural significance. Last, the claim has never been made that the equations, which we construct to express the mutual dependence of these properties, exactly represent physical fact, and that any deviations from observed fact are due to defects in the observations; nor, on the other hand, can the infallibility which we thus deny to theory be claimed by experimental observation.

If we do not refer to these limitations again, it is not because they are, for ordinary practical purposes, unimportant; indeed, they should often be recalled even when the original equations have long since disappeared in a welter of further approximation and hypothesis.

2. Physical scales

It must first be decided with what broad class of fluid flow we intend to deal. This is no pedantry for in all physics many different classes of flow can be distinguished, both by their physical characteristics and by the so-called fundamental equations used to describe them. For an account of some of these different classes and especially of the analogies between gases and liquids, the reader is referred to the first chapter of *LBL*: here it needs only to be remarked that fluid flows can be categorized roughly by their characteristic scales of mass, length, speed, and temperature, and more precisely by the values of certain characteristic non-dimensional quantities. Our interest, as was acknowledged in the Preface, is primarily in the problem of human flight, which at the present time suggests the following scales:

Density	of the order of 10^{-2} pounds mass per cubic foot
Length	of the order of 10^1 feet
Speed	of the order of 10^2 feet per second
Temperature	of the order of 10^2 degrees Kelvin.

Now these are only rough indications of scale; the phrase 'of the order of' as it is used here has no strict meaning, and it certainly does not mean, for example, that a single power of 10 alters the order of magnitude. Indeed our scale of length runs from about 10^{-4} feet (which is roughly the diameter of the hot wire in the most delicate instrument for measuring the velocity of a gas) to about 10^3 feet (which is roughly the length of the largest airship ever built). But even the smallest of these lengths is about 10^3 times the molecular mean free path in air in normal atmospheric conditions at sea-level, and this suggests that, as a reasonable approximation, our fluid can be regarded as a continuum, such that those of its properties in which we are interested are continuous in space and time. This fundamental assumption enables the so-called Navier–Stokes equations to be formulated, and on these equations, which are quoted in Section 4, all the analysis of the following chapters is based. It is worth noting that these equations are not invalidated by the fact that the mean speeds of the fluid may be of the same order as the molecular velocities (which, again in normal atmospheric conditions at sea-level, are roughly 10^3 feet per second).

To regard the fluid as a continuum is not, of course, to imply that its molecular structure is utterly ignored. Many of the most commonly measured properties of a fluid in motion—pressure, temperature, and viscosity, to take three examples—are directly attributable to molecular action; but their interdependence can nevertheless be described within the limitations of the continuum approximation.

This approximation becomes less valid as the molecular mean free path increases in relation to the other lengths typical of a flow. In particular, when applied to the motion of a body through the atmosphere, it becomes increasingly less accurate as the height of the body above the earth's surface increases. At a height of about 2×10^5 feet, where the density is about 3×10^{-4} times that at sea-level and is decreasing roughly exponentially, the mean free path is already about 9×10^{-4} feet and so about 4×10^3 times that at sea-level. For the flow of air at such a height, analytical methods other than those based on the Navier–Stokes equations need to be used and in recent years a start has been made on the study of the dynamics of gases at very low pressures. Meanwhile we recognize that the analysis of this book is limited to flight at heights of less than, say, 5×10^4 feet; further limitations are described later.

Although we have so far drawn attention to certain ranges of length, speed, and so on, in fact it is not so much the absolute limits of these ranges but the relative magnitudes or ratios of various properties which determine the character, and hence the governing equations, of a fluid flow. Thus, as was suggested in the previous paragraph, the ratio of the molecular mean free path to the length of the body is of more importance than the actual size of either. Flows are further characterized by non-dimensional combinations of unlike properties, the importance of which is considered in Section 8.

We have yet to mention scales of time. One time scale is implied by the typical length and speed quoted above; this is of the order of 10^{-1} seconds which, for example, is the time taken for a typical body to travel its own length. Another time scale is manifested as the reciprocal of a typical frequency of oscillation and forms the topic of the next section.

3. Laminar and turbulent flow

The hot-wire anemometer is at present the most sensitive instrument for measuring the velocity of a gas. Its use reveals that the velocity at any fixed point in a gas almost always fluctuates in a random manner, with component frequencies up to 10^5 sec^{-1}. This is as true for a moving stream of gas as for, say, the atmosphere which, as a whole, may be at rest. A mean velocity may be defined by taking an average over a time of the order of one second. Fluctuations about this mean within the frequencey range of 10^2–10^5 sec^{-1} are called turbulence. Fluctuations whose frequencies are of the order of 10^1 sec^{-1} may be regarded as turbulence or as an unsteadiness of the mean velocity; these more detailed distinctions can only be discussed in particular contexts. Frequencies lower than 10^0 sec^{-1} would normally be regarded as characteristic of unsteady rather than of turbulent flow.

The magnitude of the turbulent fluctuations can be as high as 0·3 times the mean speed, is usually between 10^{-2} and 10^{-4} times the mean speed, and sometimes is so small that it cannot be measured. The wake close to the rear of a bluff body, the air stream in a wind tunnel, and the atmosphere on a calm day at some height, exemplify these three magnitudes of turbulence. The random character of turbulent flow is illustrated in Fig. I. 1 which is a record of the downstream velocity component close to a solid surface.

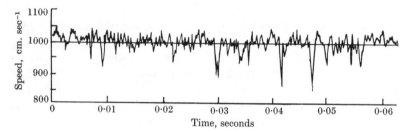

FIG. I. 1. A typical trace of a single velocity component in a turbulent flow.

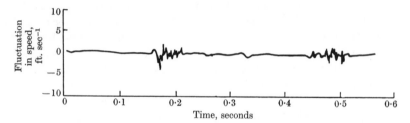

FIG. I. 2. A typical trace of the fluctuation of a single velocity component in intermittent turbulence; in this case, the downstream velocity component was measured near the edge of a jet of air issuing from an orifice.

Turbulence produces a thorough mixing of the fluid. If, however, the turbulence is so small that it cannot be measured, or if the fluctuations are regular, the adjacent layers of fluid do not mix to an appreciable extent and the flow is therefore said to be laminar.

Some parts of a moving fluid may be turbulent, and others laminar. Thus at a fixed point, the fluctuations of velocity may be intermittent in character, as shown in Fig. I. 2, depending on whether turbulent or laminar parts of the fluid are passing the point. This phenomenon is discussed in greater detail in Sections 26 and 28.

Now although turbulent flow comes within the class of flow which was defined in the last section and which is described by the Navier–Stokes equations in the next, the typical scales of turbulence, especially those of length and time, are very different from and usually much smaller than those which typify overall flows past bodies. Consequently, special methods have been developed for the analysis of turbulent flow.

Important developments have been described by Batchelor (1953) and by Townsend (1956).

In this book, therefore, no attempt is made to study the detailed nature of the turbulence in any flow. Especially in the study of the forces which act on a body moving through a gas, it is found that only negligible errors are introduced by the neglect of turbulence over most of the field of flow; in these parts of the flow, therefore, we use the Navier–Stokes equations as though the flow were laminar. For the remaining regions of the flow field, and especially very near the body where account must be taken of the effects of turbulence, approximate methods of calculation are available. Sections 26–29 are thus devoted to a discussion of the physical nature of turbulence as it is found near a body, of which a quantitative analysis is given in Sections II. 4–16.

4. The Navier–Stokes equations of motion

The properties of a gas which interest us and may be measured are its pressure p, density ρ, temperature T, and velocity $\mathbf{v}$; and the four equations which govern these properties are given below as equations (1)–(4). The three scalar equations embodied in the momentum equation (3) are usually referred to in the literature as the Navier–Stokes equations even though the original derivations applied only to incompressible flow. Thus we have:

the equation of state

$$f(p, \rho, T) = 0, \tag{1}$$

the equation of continuity

$$\partial \rho / \partial t + \operatorname{div}(\rho \mathbf{v}) = 0, \tag{2}$$

the equation of momentum

$$\rho D\mathbf{v}/Dt = \rho \mathbf{F} - \operatorname{grad} p - \mu \operatorname{curl} \operatorname{curl} \mathbf{v} + \tfrac{4}{3}\mu \operatorname{grad} \operatorname{div} \mathbf{v}, \tag{3}$$

the equation of energy

$$\rho DE/Dt = \Phi - p \operatorname{div} \mathbf{v} + \operatorname{div}(k \operatorname{grad} T), \tag{4}$$

E being the internal energy per unit mass, Φ the dissipation function, μ the coefficient of viscosity, k the thermal conductivity, and $\mathbf{F}$ the external force per unit mass.

The formulation of these equations is discussed by Howarth (1953) and need not be repeated here; the assumptions which underlie them must, however, be carefully noted:

1. The equation of state is independent of the motion; as Howarth remarks, this assumption is not trivial.

2. The gas is isotropic; namely, its properties of state do not depend on direction.

3. The gas is a continuum; namely, all properties are regarded as being continuous functions of space and time.

4. A linear relation exists between stress and rate-of-strain. (For a monatomic gas, there is a particular relationship between the two coefficients which appear in this linear relation, and this has been incorporated in the derivation of equation (3). For other gases, an additional term has to be added to equation (3) to take into account the effect of the relaxation times of the non-translational degrees of freedom; and further, this procedure is only valid if these times are small in comparison with other time scales of the motion.) For flows in which the density may be assumed constant, equation (3) reduces to equation (6) which is then valid for all gases.

5. The coefficient of viscosity, μ, is constant.

Some of the implications of the first three assumptions have already been discussed in Section 2; the fourth can best be regarded as the typical first approximation for an elastic medium. No experimental evidence, at any rate for the kind of flow discussed in this book, seriously questions the adequacy of these four assumptions.

The fifth assumption is in a different category, in that there is no difficulty in formulating the equations—and they are given by Howarth (1953)—to allow for variations in μ. μ, however, depends only on the temperature and a restriction is shortly to be made to flows in which the temperature may be assumed to be constant.

Howarth's volumes study the equations when changes in the density are appreciable in comparison with the density itself. Under these circumstances the speed of the gas is comparable with the speed of sound in it and specially appropriate approximations enable solutions to be found of the very complicated equations (1)–(4).

In direct contrast to this we might assume that the density and also the temperature are constant. Strictly this would result in a few trivial flows of a gas, whose motion, in general, is necessarily accompanied by change in density; it would also exclude the possibility of externally-applied sources of heat. However, it may be shown that if the density and temperature are taken to be constant in equations (1)–(4), the velocity field is given by the equations with only negligible inaccuracy provided certain conditions hold, of which the major one is that the speed everywhere is sufficiently small in comparison with the speed of sound in the gas. A full discussion of these conditions is given in Chapter I of *LBL* which shows that they are satisfied by large classes of physical flows: practically any liquid flowing at normal temperature and pressure satisfies them as does air at sea-level if its speed is less than, say, 350 m.p.h. The phrases 'incompressible fluid' and 'incompressible flow' usually refer to a liquid or to a gas flowing under these restrictions and are not to be taken literally.

This book is an account of incompressible flow—mainly of uniform streams past aerofoils, wings, and other bodies—and from this point onwards the general assumption of incompressibility will be made.

5. Dynamical equations for an incompressible fluid

The equations describing the velocity field of an incompressible fluid are obtained by putting ρ and T constant in equations (1)–(4). Only equations (2) and (3) are then significant and they become:

the equation of continuity

$$\operatorname{div} \mathbf{v} = 0, \tag{5}$$

the equation of momentum

$$D\mathbf{v}/Dt = \mathbf{F} - (\operatorname{grad} p)/\rho - \nu \operatorname{curl} \operatorname{curl} \mathbf{v}, \tag{6}$$

where $\nu = \mu/\rho$ and is the kinematic viscosity.

Under these restrictions, the linear stress-strain relationships given by Howarth (1953) may be written, in a Cartesian system, as

$$p_{ij} = -p\delta_{ij} + \mu(\partial \mathrm{v}_i/\partial x_j + \partial \mathrm{v}_j/\partial x_i), \tag{7}$$

δ_{ij} being the Kronecker delta which is unity when i and j are equal and zero otherwise. Here, p_{ij} is the stress per unit area in the x_j direction on an element of surface whose outward normal is in the x_i direction. p_{11}, p_{22}, and p_{33} therefore represent tensions while the remaining six stresses are shear stresses. As an example, we pick out the shear stress in the x-direction on an element whose outward normal is in the z-direction; thus

$$p_{zx} = \mu(\partial u/\partial z + \partial w/\partial x) = \tau, \tag{8}$$

τ being the symbol used later for this particular shear stress. The six shear stresses are grouped in pairs such that $p_{ij} = p_{ji}$, an important result which may be derived from first principles by considering the angular momentum of an infinitesimal fluid particle.

6. Conditions at boundaries

A region of flow for which equations (5) and (6) are applicable may be bounded either by solid boundaries or by another region of fluid or it may extend to infinity: any combination of these three types of boundary is also possible. The physical conditions on these boundaries which may, and ideally should, be incorporated into a mathematical analysis are as follows:

Fluid-solid boundaries. The fluid in contact with a solid boundary assumes at any point the instantaneous velocity of the boundary at that point. This statement is usually interpreted in terms of velocity components tangential and normal to the surface. That the normal components of the velocities of the boundary and of the fluid should be equal follows at once from the idea of continuity. The so-called 'no-slip condition', that the tangential components also are equal, stems ultimately from the molecular nature of the fluid; an interesting historical account of it is given by Goldstein (1938), while the physical processes are considered in some detail in Chapter I of *LBL*.

If the boundary is porous, the condition on the velocity normal to the surface has to be adjusted to take into account the speed of the fluid relative to the surface. It is generally assumed that the tangential condition is unchanged by the porosity; this seems reasonable but a careful experimental investigation of conditions very close to a porous surface has yet to be made. Any modification of the no-slip condition would presumably have to take into account the size of the pores and their spacing.

Fluid-fluid boundaries. The kinematic condition is that the normal component of velocity is continuous. The dynamic condition is that any difference of stress is balanced by forces arising from surface tension; if both the fluids are gases, then the stress is continuous at the boundary.

According to our hypothesis that all physical properties are continuous (except, of course, at boundaries between different media), the tangential velocity at a fluid-fluid boundary is also continuous. Nevertheless, flows in which the velocity changes very rapidly from one streamline to another are quite common. Consider, as an example, the flow very near the sharp edge of a plate set facing a uniform stream, illustrated in Fig. I. 4; it is easy to observe a difference of velocity between the up- and the down-stream sides of the edge which amounts almost to a discontinuity. Thus, even if a strict discontinuity of tangential velocity is a physical impossibility, it is nevertheless a mathematical fiction which is very useful, and as a vortex sheet it is discussed further in Section 19.

Boundaries at infinity. No real flow is infinite, but it may happen that the effects of a certain boundary do not depend crucially on its actual position. This clearly is true for most boundaries which are at large distances from the region of flow under examination. Sometimes it is true in other cases: the calculated flow inside a thin boundary layer depends hardly at all on the actual position of its outer edge along which the velocity or pressure is assumed to have specified values. It is a great analytical simplification to regard such boundaries as at infinity where the velocity and pressure are usually prescribed.

Most of the flows considered in this book refer to a body moving with constant velocity through air which is not itself in motion except by virtue of the body's motion. This may be interpreted analytically by the condition that the air velocity is zero at infinity. However, it is nearly always more convenient to work in terms of axes fixed relative to the body, and we then have a flow in which the non-zero velocity, and also the pressure, are assumed constant at infinity. Such a flow is described as a uniform stream, or the uniform flow, past the given body.

7. Streamlines in steady flow. The equation of continuity. Stream functions

In a steady flow, for which all properties are functions of position only and not of time, a particle of fluid travels along a path whose tangent at any point is in the direction of the velocity at that point. Such a line is called a streamline and its equation is

$$d\mathbf{r}/ds = \mathbf{v}/v, \tag{9}$$

$\mathbf{r}$ being the vector radius from a fixed origin and s the distance along the line measured from a fixed point on it. In Cartesian notation equation (9) is

$$dx/u = dy/v = dz/w. \tag{10}$$

In unsteady flow, the tangent at a point of the path actually taken by a certain particle is not in general in the direction of the velocity at that point except instantaneously at the time at which the particle was itself at the point. It is important therefore not to confuse the particle paths with the lines which at any instant satisfy (9): and the concept of streamlines has little practical use in unsteady flow.

A stream surface is formed by the streamlines which pass through all points of a given curve. If (l, m, n) are the direction cosines of the normal to an element, dS, of a stream surface, equation (10) leads to $(lu+mv+nw)dS = 0$ which shows that the flux of fluid through any element, or hence through any area, of a stream surface is zero.

A stream tube is the stream surface formed by the streamlines through a closed curve which is usually, though not necessarily, regarded as infinitesimal. Since there is no flux of fluid through the surface of the tube, the flux is the same through every normal area. Therefore the normal cross-sectional area of any infinitesimal stream tube is inversely proportional to the speed, a result which is a great help in the interpretation of flows which are visualized by smoke filaments or by other means.

The equation of continuity (5) is satisfied identically if

$$\mathbf{v} = \text{curl } \mathbf{\Psi}, \tag{11}$$

$\mathbf{\Psi}$ being a vector function of position.

In two-dimensional flow, two components of $\mathbf{\Psi}$ may be taken as zero and so $\mathbf{\Psi}$ reduces to a scalar function. If derivatives with respect to y are identically zero, and $\mathbf{\Psi} \equiv (0, -\psi, 0)$, equation (11) gives

$$u = \partial\psi/\partial z, \qquad w = -\partial\psi/\partial x. \tag{12}$$

The flux, per unit length in the y-direction, across the curve AB is

$$\int_A^B (u\,dz - w\,dx) = [\psi]_A^B.$$

From this, we see that a line $\psi = $ constant is a streamline. Also, the flux across a closed curve equals the change in ψ round the curve. ψ is therefore single-valued in any region in which there are no sources of fluid, and is singular at a source.

In axi-symmetric flow where $\mathbf{v} \equiv (u, v, w)$ is referred to the cylindrical polar coordinates (r, θ, z), derivatives with respect to θ are identically zero. If $\mathbf{\Psi} \equiv (\psi_r, \psi/r, \psi_z)$, equation (11) becomes

$$u = -(1/r)\partial\psi/\partial z \quad \text{and} \quad w = (1/r)\partial\psi/\partial r, \tag{13}$$

with $v = \partial\psi_r/\partial z - \partial\psi_z/\partial r$ an arbitrary function of r and z. Here again it may easily be shown that ψ is constant on any streamline. Further, $\psi = $ constant represents a stream surface which is a surface of revolution and the total flux between two such surfaces may easily be shown to be $2\pi[\psi]$.

The functions ψ in (12) and (13) are called stream functions, the latter often being given Stokes's name. Their use is often of great convenience since equations (11)–(13) ensure the satisfaction of the equation of continuity.

8. Dynamical similarity. Non-dimensional coefficients. Reynolds number

Laboratory experiments, essential weapons in the physicist's armoury, have broadly two functions. The first is to provide a physical comparison with a theory whose assumptions and limitations are reproduced as closely as possible in the experiment. Often, however, a theory purports to be valid for values of the physical properties which are out of reach of the experimental equipment. The extrapolation of the experimental results which is then necessary is the essence of the second function, and that is to enable a prediction to be made of what will happen in roughly similar circumstances on a different scale, in a different place, and at a different time.

The technique of dimensional analysis goes a long way towards establishing criteria of comparison between different physical circumstances. First, we note that the total force F exerted by a fluid flowing past a body depends strongly on the density, ρ, of the fluid, its speeds characterized by the fixed speed v, and the size of the body characterized by the length c. The dimensions of the four properties mentioned are respectively $\mathbf{MLT^{-2}}$, $\mathbf{ML^{-3}}$, $\mathbf{LT^{-1}}$, $\mathbf{L}$, which make a unique relation possible of the form

$$F = \tfrac{1}{2}\rho v^2 c^2 C_F, \tag{14}$$

where C_F is a number and is called a force coefficient. The factor, $\tfrac{1}{2}$, is trivial from a theoretical viewpoint but convenient since the dynamic pressure, which is so often measured directly in experiments, appears explicitly as $\tfrac{1}{2}\rho v^2$. (We may perhaps remark that to refer to $\tfrac{1}{2}\rho v^2$ as the dynamic pressure is, for incompressible flow, consistent with the recommendations, observed throughout this book, of the Pressure Panel (1956).)

Now if the force on a body of given shape is measured experimentally for a wide variety of values of ρ, v, and c, C_F will be found to vary from one experiment to another but to a far smaller extent than F itself varies. In other words, the major effects of density, speed, and size have been accounted for in the form (14). The remaining effects must be due to other properties of the flow such as the stagnation pressure, the thermal conductivity, the compressibility, the external force field, and the viscosity. For a complete description of the force on the body, we need also to know the dependence of C_F on these five properties, so let us consider each in turn.

The stagnation pressure can be excluded at once as a governing parameter; this is only true of incompressible flow, in which case we can see from equation (6) that the addition of a constant to the pressure does not affect the other properties. Further, owing to the definition of incompressible flow, neither the thermal conductivity nor the speed of sound can directly affect the velocity or pressure field; we may recall, however, that for the general case of compressible flow the two appropriate numerical parameters are the Péclet and Mach numbers respectively. Next, the effect of a field of force depends on its character and here we will consider only the gravitational field, characterized by the gravitational acceleration g; other kinds of force field are uncommon in aerodynamics. The dimensions of g being $\mathbf{LT^{-2}}$, the so-called Froude number $v(cg)^{-\frac{1}{2}}$ may be formed. Now in some types of flow—for example, those with a free surface of liquid or those involving free convection—gravitational effects are clearly of importance. But with the flows in which we are primarily interested, with bodies totally immersed in infinite fluids, gravitational effects are confined mainly to the hydrostatic forces; these are either negligible or can be superimposed upon the dynamic forces. Thus we ignore the effects of Froude number in considering the velocity fields of fluid flows.

Finally there is the viscosity, μ, to be taken into account, whose dimensions are $\mathbf{ML^{-1}T^{-1}}$. The only non-dimensional combination of μ and the original three properties, ρ, v, and c, is the Reynolds number

$$R = \rho v c / \mu = v c / \nu. \tag{15}$$

Thus it appears that in any given configuration of incompressible flow, forces may be represented by force coefficients which depend only on the Reynolds number. For a fuller treatment of this result and of the significance of non-dimensional parameters in general, we may refer to Chapter I of *LBL*.

The effect of the Reynolds number—scale effect, as it is called—needs considering more thoroughly. If the transformation

$$\mathbf{r} = c\bar{\mathbf{r}}, \qquad \mathbf{v} = v\bar{\mathbf{v}}, \qquad t = c\bar{t}/v, \qquad p = \rho v^2 \bar{p} \tag{16}$$

in which $\mathbf{r}$ is the radius vector from a fixed origin, is applied to equations (5) and (6), they become, in the absence of an external force field,

$$\left. \begin{array}{l} \overline{\mathrm{div}}\,\bar{\mathbf{v}} = 0, \\ \overline{D}\bar{\mathbf{v}}/\overline{D}\bar{t} = -\overline{\mathrm{grad}}\,\bar{p} - R^{-1}\,\overline{\mathrm{curl\ curl}}\,\bar{\mathbf{v}}. \end{array} \right\} \tag{17}$$

Here a bar denotes a non-dimensional quantity or operator.

For complete similarity of two flows, the two solutions in terms of the non-dimensional quantities must be identical. This clearly requires more than the equality of Reynolds number: the boundary conditions, geometric or kinematic, must be identical in non-dimensional terms. This latter requirement is often overlooked in practice, and usually with considerable justification; but too facile an acceptance of the criterion of equality of Reynolds number may lead to unexpected errors. Roughness or imperfections on the boundaries of one flow should be reproduced correctly to scale in the other, for these can strongly influence the nature of the flow as will be seen in Section 25 and elsewhere. Boundaries such as wind-tunnel walls should be included in the similarity requirements, though their influence is often ignored if they are far enough away from the region of flow under examination. Similarity should extend also to time variations: vibration of the boundaries, for example, should strictly obey a similarity relation though again this is often ignored in practice. The structure of the turbulence in, say, a stream from infinity should be similar in two cases, and this may be at least as important as the similarity of R: for example, the resistance coefficient of spheres in uniform flows which are otherwise similar depends to a marked degree on the turbulence of the stream.

It is worth remarking that it is not possible to construct a transformation such as (16) so that the Reynolds number does not appear in the non-dimensional equation. Thus calculations from equation (6) have to be repeated for every desired value of R. In contrast, it will be seen that the approximate equation (27) for laminar boundary-layer flow becomes, under the transformation (31) involving R, equation (32) which is independent of R. As a result scale effect is much more easily calculated for boundary layers, even when turbulent, than for whole regions of viscous flow.

The fact that the similarity conditions on roughness, turbulence and so on are, in practice, difficult to satisfy usually leads to an independent assessment of the effects of these phenomena which may themselves be described by further appropriate non-dimensional parameters. The Reynolds number, however, is pre-eminent, partly because of its role in equation (17), partly because its influence is on the whole greater than that of other parameters, partly because its range is large (from, say, 1 to 10^8 for the flows to which equations (5) and (6) are usually applied) and partly because it may be determined with relative ease in practical work. For these reasons, the velocity and pressure and shear-stress fields are often expressed as

$$\left.\begin{aligned}
\mathbf{v} &= \mathrm{v}\bar{\mathbf{v}}(\mathbf{r}/c, R) \\
p &= \tfrac{1}{2}\rho\mathrm{v}^2\bar{p}(\mathbf{r}/c, R)+p_\infty \\
\tau &= \tfrac{1}{2}\rho\mathrm{v}^2\bar{\tau}(\mathbf{r}/c, R)
\end{aligned}\right\} \tag{18}$$

and one practical objective of any analysis of incompressible viscous flow is to derive expressions of this form.

The total force exerted by the fluid on its boundaries may, of course, be found by integrating the pressure and shear stress over its surface, and the appropriate form for the non-dimensional force coefficient has already been given in equation (14).

In the particular case of uniform flow past a closed body, it is usual to resolve the total force into two components perpendicular and parallel to the stream. The latter is called the drag D; the component of the former in the plane of symmetry or in some other suitably defined

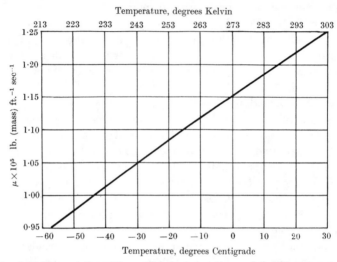

FIG. I. 3. The variation of the coefficient of viscosity, μ, of air with temperature.

plane associated with the body, is called the lift L. These are put in terms of C_D and C_L, the drag and lift coefficients: thus

$$L = \tfrac{1}{2}\rho v_\infty^2\, SC_L; \qquad D = \tfrac{1}{2}\rho v_\infty^2\, SC_D. \tag{19}$$

Here the area S has taken the place of c^2 in equation (14) and is usually some obvious area of the body such as the plan area of a wing or the frontal area of a body of revolution. v_∞, the speed at infinity of the stream, has also replaced v. A great part of this book is devoted to the determination of the lift and drag coefficients of bodies in uniform streams.

Most flows of aeronautical interest correspond to values of R in the range $10^5 < R < 10^8$; for example, the Reynolds number for an aircraft wing, whose chord is 10 feet, flying at 300 m.p.h. at a height of 10,000 feet where the atmospheric temperature is $-5°$ C, is about 2×10^7. Values of R up to 10^7 can be obtained in many existing wind-tunnels though there are only a few which extend the range of R to 10^8.

The variation of the coefficient of viscosity of air is shown in Fig. I. 3 which covers the range of temperature usually to be found in the atmosphere up to a height of 50,000 feet. The values are based on those given in the tables compiled by the Compressible Flow Tables Panel (1952).

9. Vorticity

A dominant characteristic of viscous flow is its vorticity. This is defined mathematically as

$$\boldsymbol{\omega} = \operatorname{curl} \mathbf{v}. \tag{20}$$

It may be given this physical meaning: imagine an infinitesimally small sphere of the fluid as it flows to be suddenly solidified; the vorticity of the fluid element before solidification then equals twice its angular velocity immediately after. Thus the vorticity describes the rotation of fluid elements.

The equation governing the vorticity of an element of fluid as it moves under the action of a conservative external force field is found by taking the curl of the momentum equation (6), which gives

$$D\boldsymbol{\omega}/Dt = \boldsymbol{\omega}.\boldsymbol{\nabla}\mathbf{v} + \nu\nabla^2\boldsymbol{\omega}. \tag{21}$$

The first term on the right-hand side expresses the variation of an element's vorticity due to the velocity field and is interpreted more thoroughly in Section 18, while the second term expresses the rate at which the vorticity is being diffused by the action of viscosity. This diffusion of vorticity is exactly analogous to the diffusion of heat in a homogeneous solid: in two-dimensional flow when, say, the third component of $\mathbf{v}$ and derivatives in the third direction of an orthogonal system are zero, the first two components of $\operatorname{curl} \mathbf{v}$ or of $\boldsymbol{\omega}$ are zero, $\boldsymbol{\omega}.\boldsymbol{\nabla}\mathbf{v}$ is also zero, and equation (21) reduces to $D\omega/Dt = \nu\nabla^2\omega$ which is well known as an equation for the flow of heat.

It is sometimes useful to express the equation of momentum (6) in a form involving the vorticity. If we recall the vector expansion of the gradient of a scalar product, we have $\frac{1}{2}\nabla(\mathbf{v}.\mathbf{v}) = \mathbf{v}.\boldsymbol{\nabla}\mathbf{v} + \mathbf{v}\times(\boldsymbol{\nabla}\times\mathbf{v}.)$ Also, $D\mathbf{v}/Dt = \partial\mathbf{v}/\partial t + \mathbf{v}.\boldsymbol{\nabla}\mathbf{v}$. Substitution in equation (6) then gives

$$\partial\mathbf{v}/\partial t - \mathbf{v}\times\boldsymbol{\omega} = \mathbf{F} - (1/\rho)\operatorname{grad} H - \nu\operatorname{curl}\boldsymbol{\omega} \left.\right\}$$
where
$$H = p + \tfrac{1}{2}\rho\mathbf{v}^2. \tag{22}$$

H is called the total pressure and is recorded by a pitot head, namely a small open-ended tube set facing and parallel to the local velocity.

Equation (21) is satisfied by $\boldsymbol{\omega} \equiv \mathbf{0}$. There are a few highly specialized flows for which this is true: for example, the vorticity may be zero for the laminar flow between two co-axial infinite circular cylinders which are rotating in the same sense, each with peripheral speed inversely proportional to its radius. This is not a type of flow commonly found in engineering applications; and there is further doubt about the uniqueness of such a flow. In almost every real flow, the vorticity is not zero everywhere, as may be verified directly by measurement of the velocity field.

The physical nature of vorticity may be further illuminated by the observation that vorticity cannot be spontaneously generated within a fluid. As may be shown from equation (21), vorticity originates only at boundaries between two media, whence it is diffused by the molecular action of viscosity and convected by the mean flow.

In this connexion, it is interesting to recall the kinematical conditions at a fluid-fluid boundary, given in Section 6. A discontinuous tangential velocity implies, from the definition (20), an infinite vorticity; the rate of diffusion therefore is very large and the velocity field soon adjusts itself to much lower values of vorticity. Thus, if we take again the example of the flat plate set normal to a uniform stream, what appear to be near-discontinuous tangential velocities at the edges of the plate will in any case rapidly disappear downstream.

If the region of flow is finite, it is filled with vorticity which has been generated continuously since the beginning of the motion, and the vorticity may be of the same order of magnitude throughout the whole region. A few examples illustrate this. First, suppose that a moving fluid is enclosed within boundaries which become stationary. The tendency will be for the vorticity which is generated at the boundary to be, on the whole, opposite in sign to the vorticity already in the fluid; as this new vorticity diffuses, the fluid velocities tend to decrease in an exponential manner, and within a short time the fluid is virtually at rest. The original kinetic energy has been transmuted, by the action of viscosity, into heat. Next, let us take the case of fluid initially at rest within a finite circular cylinder which is impulsively given a constant angular velocity Ω about its axis. The vorticity generated on the boundaries will accumulate steadily until the vorticity throughout the fluid is constant; it will then equal 2Ω, and the fluid and cylinder will be rotating as a solid. Last, if this same cylinder is rotated periodically one way and then the other, annuli of vorticity of opposite signs are generated periodically and diffuse towards the centre. In the final quasi-steady state, the magnitude of vorticity at any point varies with the same periodicity as the cylinder's rotary motion, and we may visualize a vorticity wave being propagated inwards from the surface of the cylinder, though in this case the amplitude of the wave decreases exponentially and very rapidly, becoming negligible after only one wavelength. Such finite flows are not considered in this book.

10. The boundary layer and wake

If the region of flow is infinite in extent, the possibility at once arises of vorticity being convected to infinity rather than being accumulated in some finite part of the flow, and therefore of some parts of the flow being unaffected by the vorticity generated at the boundaries. Let us consider, therefore, a uniform stream, of velocity $\mathbf{v}_\infty$, past a closed body. Upstream at infinity the vorticity is zero by virtue of the uniformity of the flow: such vorticity as exists therefore comes only from the body. The vorticity as it is generated diffuses outwards away from the body and at the same time it is convected in the downstream direction. Now the rate of diffusion depends on ν, and that of convection on $\mathbf{v}_\infty$. Provided therefore that the ratio of ν to $\mathbf{v}_\infty$ is small enough— a proviso which is made more precise later on—the vorticity generated at the body is convected so rapidly downstream that it is confined to a relatively small region close to the body and extending downstream of it. One infers that within this region the velocity changes much more rapidly than elsewhere.

This is, of course, largely an argument *a posteriori*. The physical existence of a region, close to a body moving in fluid, in which the speed changes rapidly from that of the solid boundary to that of the main stream is obvious to the traveller who peers over the side of his ship. The more curious observer will distinguish between two kinds of flow near a closed body. In separated flow, the fluid flowing close to the front part of the body seems to detach itself from the body at the so-called separation point, and vorticity is thus carried away from the body not necessarily, to begin with, in the downstream direction. This is exemplified by the flow past a flat plate which is illustrated in Fig. I. 4 and is characterized almost always by a region of highly turbulent flow behind the body. In Fig. I. 4, the flow is roughly symmetrical about the centre line, and the mean flow behind the plate is roughly steady; this contrasts with the flow past a circular cylinder in which the flow in the wake seems to be both highly turbulent and unsteady in the mean, the two separation points having asymmetric periodic oscillations. In general, it may be suggested that a salient point—such as the edge of the flat plate—has, to some extent, a stabilizing influence on the flow; on the other hand, separated flows past bluff or well-rounded bodies tend to be oscillatory. In unseparated flow, however, there is no tendency for the fluid close to the surface to detach itself: such flow is a rare natural phenomenon and only occurs for slender bodies of carefully designed shape or for others on which special pre-

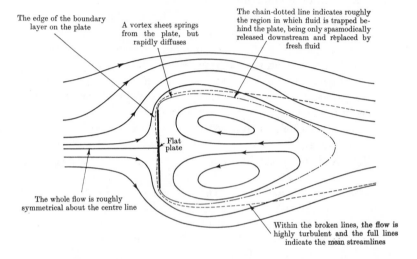

The edge of the boundary layer on the plate

A vortex sheet springs from the plate, but rapidly diffuses

The chain-dotted line indicates roughly the region in which fluid is trapped behind the plate, being only spasmodically released downstream and replaced by fresh fluid

Flat plate

The whole flow is roughly symmetrical about the centre line

Within the broken lines, the flow is highly turbulent and the full lines indicate the mean streamlines

Fig. I. 4. A sketch (not to scale) illustrating the separated flow of a uniform stream past a flat plate normal to the stream. Detailed observations of this flow have been made by Fail, Lawford, and Eyre (1957).

cautions, such as those discussed in Chapter VI, have been taken. Fig. I. 5 illustrates an unseparated flow with the characteristically limited region of vorticity.

The region of flow close to a surface, in which the vorticity is large compared with its values elsewhere, is called the boundary layer. Simple experiments reveal that the boundary layer is also distinguished as a region in which the total pressure is appreciably smaller than for the rest of the flow; and the region downstream of a body in a stream of fluid, in which similar losses of total pressure are observable, is called the wake.

Further definitions and more detailed consideration of the nature of flow in the boundary layer are postponed to Section 24. For the moment we make a few general comments on the boundary layer in an unseparated flow.

The limits of the boundary layer and wake are not precise; strictly the diffusion of vorticity extends to infinity. But it may be shown that in general the vorticity decreases with distance away from the body in an exponential manner, and so for most purposes may be taken as having reached an asymptotic value after some finite distance from the body, which distance is loosely called the thickness of the boundary

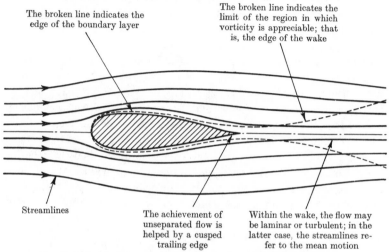

The broken line indicates the edge of the boundary layer

The broken line indicates the limit of the region in which vorticity is appreciable; that is, the edge of the wake

Streamlines

The achievement of unseparated flow is helped by a cusped trailing edge

Within the wake, the flow may be laminar or turbulent; in the latter case, the streamlines refer to the mean motion

FIG. I. 5. A sketch (not to scale) illustrating the unseparated flow of a uniform stream past a thin aerofoil at a low incidence.

layer. A rough estimate of the thickness of a boundary layer in laminar flow may easily be made by the use of dimensional analysis. Consider the vorticity generated at some point near the front of the body. In time t, it has diffused outwards through a distance depending only on ν and t and so of the order of $(\nu t)^{\frac{1}{2}}$; in the same time it has been convected through a distance of the order of $t v_\infty$, v_∞ being the speed of the uniform stream. Thus at the rear end of the body of length c, the vorticity has diffused through a distance of the order of $(\nu c/v_\infty)^{\frac{1}{2}}$ which may be regarded as the thickness of the boundary layer. The ratio of this boundary-layer thickness to the length c of the body is $R^{-\frac{1}{2}}$, R being the Reynolds number $c v_\infty/\nu$; thus we see that a boundary layer can be distinguished from the rest of the flow provided the Reynolds number of the flow is sufficiently large. The vorticity being curl $\mathbf{v}$, its order of magnitude within the boundary layer is $v_\infty \div (\nu c/v_\infty)^{\frac{1}{2}}$ or $R^{\frac{1}{2}}(v_\infty/c)$.

The scale effect on the thickness of the boundary layer as represented above by the factor $R^{-\frac{1}{2}}$ is quite accurate for the flow of a laminar boundary layer, as we shall discover in Section 12. For a turbulent boundary layer, the analysis of the preceding paragraph needs drastic modification since the convective effects of the turbulence in the direction normal to the surface may overwhelm the diffusive effect of viscosity. Thus we would expect that, other things being equal, a turbulent boundary layer is thicker than a laminar one. A very rough result is that the thickness of a turbulent layer equals $0 \cdot 025 c R^{-\frac{1}{5}}$ after a distance c from the leading edge; it also, therefore, is small in comparison with the chord of a wing at a Reynolds number of, say, 10^7.

In the wake near the rear of the body the vorticity is roughly of order $(v_\infty/c) R^{1/n}$, n being a small number between about 2 and 6 according to the particular conditions. Since no further vorticity can be generated in the wake, the effect of diffusion, by viscosity or turbulence, is to reduce the vorticity to zero at distances far downstream: at the same time the width of the wake steadily grows to an unlimited extent. At large distances downstream, the existence of the body can be inferred not by any variation from the free-stream values of velocity, pressure, or vorticity at a particular point, but only by the summed variations of these quantities which mathematically would be put in terms of integrals round circuits far from the body. These matters are discussed more fully in later sections.

11. Prandtl's boundary-layer approximation

The approximation which was first proposed by Prandtl (1904) and which may be said, without exaggeration, to have paved the way for all modern advances in fluid dynamics, is based on the idea that the boundary-layer thickness in laminar flow is proportional to $R^{-\frac{1}{2}}$, for large values of R. This idea is supported by the few existing exact solutions of the equation (6). (In turbulent flow, a rather smaller negative index might be better, but this does not vitiate the approximation.)

We take first a system of Cartesian coordinates in which n is length in the direction of the outward normal to the plane boundary, and write

$$n = c R^{-\frac{1}{2}} \bar{n}, \tag{23}$$

leaving distances parallel to the boundary of zero order in R. Thus the continuity equation requires an expression for the velocity component, v_n, normal to the boundary, in the form

$$v_n = v_\infty R^{-\frac{1}{2}} \bar{v}_n, \tag{24}$$

velocity components perpendicular to v_n being also of zero order in R.

In the equation of momentum (6) with $\mathbf{F} = 0$, we see that in the
n-direction, the term in p is of the highest order, of order $R^{\frac{1}{2}}$, while the
remaining terms are at most of order $R^{-\frac{1}{2}}$: thus

$$0 = -(1/\rho)(\partial p/\partial n) \tag{25}$$

is an approximation good for large Reynolds numbers. The pressure
may therefore be taken to be constant through the boundary layer and
a function only of coordinates in the surface. Considering now the
component of equation (6) in any direction, say **s**, perpendicular to **n**,
we see that the part of highest order in the term ν curl curl **v** is

$$-(\nu \mathbf{v}_\infty R/c^2)(\partial^2 \overline{v}_s/\partial \bar{n}^2) = -(\mathbf{v}_\infty^2/c)(\partial^2 \overline{v}_s/\partial \bar{n}^2);$$

this is of zero order in R and of the same order as the remaining terms
of the equation. The full viscous term is therefore replaced by its
component representing variations in the **n**-direction only, and this is
Prandtl's approximation.

The assumption of a Cartesian system of axes is appropriate to a
plane boundary. A more natural coordinate system for a cylindrical
surface would be based on parallel surfaces and the argument given
above would have to be modified to take into account the curvature, κ,
of the surface; the boundary-layer approximations still hold in the form
given so long as $R^{\frac{1}{2}}$ is large in comparison with κc and $(c^2 d\kappa/ds)$. This
result is justified in *LBL* where the corresponding results for surfaces
of general shape are also derived.

The theory of the general three-dimensional boundary layer has not
yet reached the stage at which the characteristics of the flow may be
derived from the external pressure field by a calculation of a routine
kind. The calculation of the boundary layers in the flows considered
in this book will almost invariably be based on methods developed for
two-dimensional boundary-layer flow. We therefore go on, in the next
section, to formulate the boundary-layer equations appropriate to two-
dimensional flow.

12. General equations for two-dimensional boundary layers

Cartesian coordinates (x, z) are used with the corresponding velocity
components (u, w). If the boundary is $z = 0$, equations (5) and (6)
become, after the boundary-layer approximation,

$$\partial u/\partial x + \partial w/\partial z = 0, \tag{26}$$

$$\partial u/\partial t + u\,\partial u/\partial x + w\,\partial u/\partial z = -(1/\rho)(\partial p/\partial x) + \nu\,\partial^2 u/\partial z^2, \tag{27}$$

$$0 = -(1/\rho)(\partial p/\partial z). \tag{28}$$

It is as well to note explicitly the approximations which are made throughout: (i) the effects due to curvature of the boundary which are ignored are of order $R^{-\frac{1}{2}}$, and (ii) the remaining errors in equations (27) and (28) are of order R^{-1}. The validity of these approximations may be questionable even for large values of R if any coefficients of $R^{-\frac{1}{2}}$ or R^{-1} themselves take large values: this will certainly occur near singularities of any solution of equation (27) and at such points adequate information can only be obtained from the full equation of motion (6).

By the stream velocity, U, is usually meant the velocity in the x-direction at the edge of the boundary layer: this is interpreted as $u \to U(x,t)$ as $z \to \infty$. Thus at this limit, equation (27) is

$$\partial U/\partial t + U\,\partial U/\partial x = -(1/\rho)(\partial p/\partial x)_{z=\infty}. \tag{29}$$

But since, from (28), p is a function of x and t only, (29) gives the value of $\partial p/\partial x$ everywhere in terms of U; substitution of (29) into (27) then gives

$$\partial u/\partial t + u\,\partial u/\partial x + w\,\partial u/\partial z = \partial U/\partial t + U\,\partial U/\partial x + \nu\,\partial^2 u/\partial z^2. \tag{30}$$

This is the usual form of the two-dimensional boundary-layer equation in which $U(x,t)$ is regarded as prescribed.

The application of this equation to turbulent flow is discussed in Section 27. For laminar flow, important results are obtained by the transformation

$$\left.\begin{array}{lll} u = \mathrm{v}\bar{u}, & x = c\bar{x}, & t = c\bar{t}/\mathrm{v} \\ w = \mathrm{v}R^{-\frac{1}{2}}\bar{w}, & z = cR^{-\frac{1}{2}}\bar{z}, & p = \rho\mathrm{v}^2\bar{p} \end{array}\right\}, \tag{31}$$

ρ, v, and c being constants.

Equations (26) and (27) then become

$$\left.\begin{array}{l} \partial\bar{u}/\partial\bar{x} + \partial\bar{w}/\partial\bar{z} = 0, \\ \partial\bar{u}/\partial\bar{t} + \bar{u}\,\partial\bar{u}/\partial\bar{x} + \bar{w}\,\partial\bar{u}/\partial\bar{z} = -\partial\bar{p}/\partial\bar{x} + \partial^2\bar{u}/\partial\bar{z}^2 \end{array}\right\}. \tag{32}$$

This result demonstrates one of the advantageous analytical properties of the boundary-layer equations when they are compared with the corresponding form (17) of the Navier–Stokes equation. Provided the boundary conditions and the prescribed term $\partial\bar{p}/\partial\bar{x}$ do not vary with R, scale effect can be wholly accounted for in a preliminary transformation so that any solution of the equations in the form (32) at once refers to all values of R. A second analytical advantage is the parabolic nature of the equations, which offers prospects of much simpler solutions than the full equation (6) which is elliptic. The interpretation of this in physical terms is that conditions in the boundary layer at any point on a surface depend only on conditions within it upstream of the point and not downstream; even if this appears unlikely at first sight, all experimental evidence gathered since Prandtl first suggested these equations has completely justified their validity within the limitations we have mentioned.

The transformation (31) may be applied both to the expressions for the stresses p_{ij} in equation (7) and to the components of the vorticity given by $\boldsymbol{\omega} \equiv (\xi, \eta, \zeta)$ in equation (20). If only the highest terms in R are retained, we have, in the original variables,

$$p_{xx} = p_{yy} = p_{zz} = -p \qquad (33)$$

for the normal stresses, while for the shear stresses

$$p_{xy} = p_{yz} = 0 \quad \text{and} \quad p_{zx} \equiv \tau = \mu(\partial u/\partial z), \qquad (34)$$

the error, for a plane wall, being of order R^{-1} in both equations. The same error is introduced into the following expressions for the vorticity:

$$\xi = \zeta = 0 \quad \text{and} \quad \eta = \partial u/\partial z. \qquad (35)$$

The boundary layer has no definite limit: its outer edge may be taken as the line on which the vorticity has reached some arbitrarily prescribed small value, or as that on which the velocity u has attained some particular proportion of its value, U, at infinity. The fact that both η and u tend very rapidly towards their asymptotic values is a help in the practical definition of the edge of the boundary layer. But it is useful to have one or two lengths associated with the boundary-layer thickness which are capable of precise definition. The first such length, δ_1, is called the displacement thickness since it represents the distance through which the outer streamlines have been displaced by the viscous retardation of the fluid in the inner streamlines. By comparing the flux in the viscous case with that in the imaginary inviscid case, we have

$$\int_0^{z+\delta_1} u \, dz = \int_0^z U \, dz;$$

with $z \to \infty$, this can be rewritten as

$$\delta_1 = \int_0^\infty (1-u/U) \, dz. \qquad (36)$$

The second length, δ_2, called the momentum thickness, is defined by

$$\delta_2 = \int_0^\infty (u/U)(1-u/U) \, dz \qquad (37)$$

and is associated with the loss of momentum due to the viscous retardation. Both these lengths are clearly of the same order of thickness as
the boundary layer, and so $O(R^{-\frac{1}{2}})$ for laminar flow.

Approximate methods of calculating the main characteristics of steady
flow in a two-dimensional boundary layer, both laminar and turbulent,
are given in Chapter II. An exhaustive treatment of the boundary-
layer equation, though for laminar flow only, is given in *LBL*.

It is worth remarking finally that the physical notion of a boundary
layer as the region within which vorticity generated at the boundary
is confined, is entirely consistent with the mathematical analysis of
flows at high Reynolds numbers.

13. Inviscid flow

The suggestion that, at sufficiently high Reynolds numbers, the vorticity generated at the surface of a body in an infinite fluid is confined
to the relatively small region of the boundary layer and wake is valid
broadly, whether or not the flow is separated. This does not, however,
imply necessarily that the vorticity is zero outside this region. It may
happen, for example, that far upstream the velocity is given by
$\mathbf{v} \equiv (Uz/c, 0, 0)$: this is a parallel shear flow for which the pressure is
constant and the vorticity $\boldsymbol{\omega}$ is $(0,\ U/c, 0)$. Such a flow is called non-
uniform and is rotational everywhere. However, even in such a flow,
a boundary layer may be distinguished from the rest of the flow by
the order of magnitude of the vorticity within it; in the main part of
the flow $\boldsymbol{\omega}$ is of order U/c while in the boundary layer it is, for laminar
flow, of order $R^{\frac{1}{2}}(U/c)$.

Now by the definition of the boundary layer it follows that, outside
it, the order of magnitude of a space-derivative is independent of
direction. Thus the viscous term of equation (6) is of order R^{-1} whereas
the others are of order R^0. Therefore, to the same order of approximations as was accepted for the boundary-layer equations we now write
equation (6) in the form

$$Dv/Dt = \mathbf{F} - (1/\rho)\mathrm{grad}\,p, \tag{38}$$

which is valid in the region outside the boundary layer and wake. This
equation is called the inviscid-flow equation. To emphasize that, in
general, inviscid flow is also rotational, equation (38) is written in the
alternative form

$$\partial v/\partial t - \mathbf{v} \times \boldsymbol{\omega} = \mathbf{F} - (1/\rho)\mathrm{grad}\,H \tag{39}$$

obtained from equation (22).

Whereas classical hydrodynamics largely ignored rotational inviscid flows they are now recognized as being of great importance for some branches of engineering, especially those involving rotating bodies. Chapter XI, for example, is devoted to a discussion of the particular type of rotational flow which has axial symmetry, and its studies are based on the form of (39) appropriate to steady flow under no external force, namely

$$\mathbf{v} \times \boldsymbol{\omega} = (1/\rho)\mathrm{grad}\, H. \tag{40}$$

It may perhaps be worth remarking that, in general, the analysis of inviscid flow is not much simpler than that of viscous flow; rather, it is the possibility of irrotationality that introduces significant simplifications as we shall see in the next section. By taking the curl of both sides of equation (38), we obtain the inviscid form of equation (21), which is

$$D\boldsymbol{\omega}/Dt = \boldsymbol{\omega} \cdot \boldsymbol{\nabla} \mathbf{v}. \tag{41}$$

In terms of the stream function $\boldsymbol{\Psi}$ of equation (11), $\boldsymbol{\omega} = \mathrm{curl}\,\mathrm{curl}\,\boldsymbol{\Psi}$ and equation (41) is a third-order equation in $\boldsymbol{\Psi}$.

The neglect of the viscous term in equation (6) carries with it further and far-reaching implications of a mainly mathematical nature. We can only summarize them very briefly. The viscous terms are the only terms of second order and so their neglect fundamentally alters the nature of the equation. One immediate result is that the prescribed boundary conditions have to be less comprehensive: in general it is now possible to specify only the direction of flow at a boundary, and not the speed as well. This appears a contradiction of the no-slip condition which, in Section 6, was represented as one of the fundamental requirements for any analytical solution; the resolution of this difficulty presents one of the most important problems in fluid dynamics and forms the main topic of Chapter III. Just as serious is the fact that a solution to the inviscid equation is not, in general, the limit of a solution to the viscous equation as $\nu \to 0$. Solutions of the equations are, in other words, singular at $\nu = 0$ (or $R = \infty$), and any attempt to pass from viscous to inviscid solutions by means of a perturbation method based on a power series in R^{-1} will run into the typical difficulties of all singular perturbation techniques. Further problems concern the propagation of disturbances. In inviscid compressible flow the signal speed for a disturbance is finite, whereas the reintroduction of the viscous terms admits infinite signal speeds which are also characteristic of inviscid incompressible flow. The nature of wave propagation is intimately bound up with the characteristics of the differential equation and these change discontinuously at $\nu = 0$. A valuable review of the analytical implications of the assumption of inviscid flow is given by Lagerstrom, Cole, and Trilling (1949).

In the special case of steady flow in which $\mathbf{F}$ is the gradient of a scalar function Ω, we may take the component of equation (39) in the direction of $\mathbf{v}$ as

$$0 = \partial\Omega/\partial s - (1/\rho)(\partial H/\partial s), \qquad (42)$$

s being measured along a streamline. This equation can be integrated in the form

$$H/\rho - \Omega \equiv p/\rho + \tfrac{1}{2}v^2 - \Omega = \text{constant}, \qquad (43)$$

the constant being different, in general, for each streamline.

14. Irrotational flow

For many common flows, the vorticity is zero everywhere outside the boundary layer and wake. For example, in the flow of a uniform stream past a closed body, the vorticity far upstream is zero, since the velocity there is constant; thus the vorticity everywhere is zero, except within the boundary layer and wake.

Thus for this region external to the boundary layer and wake, to take $\boldsymbol{\omega} \equiv \operatorname{curl} \mathbf{v} = \mathbf{0}$ is often a very good approximation; it follows that $\mathbf{v}$ is the gradient of a scalar point function, ϕ, called the velocity potential:

$$\mathbf{v} = \operatorname{grad}\phi. \qquad (44)$$

The equation of continuity (5) then becomes

$$\nabla^2\phi \equiv \partial^2\phi/\partial x^2 + \partial^2\phi/\partial y^2 + \partial^2\phi/\partial z^2 = 0. \qquad (45)$$

Known as Laplace's equation, this is one of the famous equations of mathematical physics. We refer to Jeffreys and Jeffreys (1946) for an account of it in connexion with physical problems, to Whittaker and Watson (1927) for purely mathematical treatment, and to Lamb (1932) for a full account of its applications in classical hydrodynamics.

With equation (44) and the assumption that $\mathbf{F} = \operatorname{grad}\Omega$, equation (39) may be integrated in the form

$$p/\rho + \tfrac{1}{2}v^2 - \Omega + \partial\phi/\partial t = \text{constant}, \qquad (46)$$

which is known as Bernoulli's equation. The constant here refers to the whole field and this should be noted in comparison with equation (43), for steady rotational flow, in which the constant varies from streamline to streamline.

By virtue of the existence of ϕ, such flow is called potential or irrotational flow. The general procedure of solution is to determine ϕ from equation (45) and then the pressure, p, from (46). Some of the more common techniques of deriving solutions of Laplace's equation for irrotational flow are discussed in Sections 20–23.

15. Steady flow

All physical flows inevitably vary with time; not only do boundary conditions alter but sometimes unsteadiness seems to arise quite naturally within the fluid as, for example, in the wake of a bluff body in a uniform stream. However, it often happens that for periods of time very much larger than, say, the periods of turbulent fluctuations or the representative time c/v_∞, all boundary conditions remain fixed; the question then arises whether the velocity field, or at any rate the mean velocity field, itself becomes independent of time—that is, becomes steady.

Experiment suggests a number of different answers to this question which is bound to recur in subsequent chapters. At the moment, it is enough to refer to the possibility of regular sinusoidal waves of small amplitude (as are found in laminar boundary layers or in a sounding organ pipe), and of waves of large amplitude (as in fluid which is rotating), to show that by no means always does the flow fully respond to fixed boundaries. In another category of oscillation is the formation in a wake of eddies of high vorticity which are created at the solid body but which are released into the wake only intermittently. Broadly, these types of oscillation seem inherent in the nature of fluid flow and may not depend crucially on the steadiness or otherwise of the boundary conditions.

Given these occasional exceptions, it remains true that, at any rate outside the boundary layer and wake, most uniform flows past closed bodies are steady if the boundary conditions are steady. This implies that the unsteadiness which must have occurred in the initial stages of the flow is damped once the boundary conditions have become steady. In mathematical analyses, this result often tends to be assumed, rather than to be proved, by the use of exponentials of negative multiples of the time. What therefore tends to be obscured is the possibility of the final steady flow being dependent on the past history; or in other words we question the uniqueness of steady flow under steady boundary conditions.

On this, experiment seems to reveal the uniqueness of the great majority of flows; if, for example, the flow of a uniform stream parallel to the longest axis of a thin ellipsoid is set up at different places and different times, no significant differences are likely to be observed which cannot very plausibly be explained as transgressions of the exact similarity conditions discussed in Section 8. On the other hand, flows of practical importance can occasionally be observed to have at least two possible physical states, and two examples may be mentioned. In Fig. I. 6 is shown a typical relation between the lift coefficient C_L and the incidence α of an aerofoil, obtained experimentally by slowly increasing and then decreasing the incidence as indicated by the arrows. For a certain range of high incidences, two regimes of flow are observed,

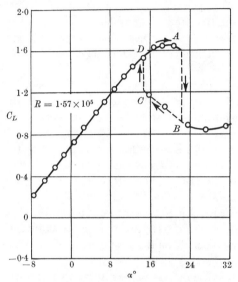

Fig. I. 6. The experimental lift-curve for an NACA 103 aerofoil obtained by Jacobs (1931). It illustrates the possibility of the non-uniqueness of flow past aerofoils. The arrows indicate the sequence in which the incidence was varied.

and this is explained in Section V. 14. Next we may consider the flow in a two-dimensional duct as shown in Fig. I. 7 (a) and (b). At A, slots in the walls continuously withdraw fluid in small quantities from the duct. A steady flow as in (a) may be set up by slowly increasing the speed of the fluid from rest. If the speed is still further increased, the flow takes up the pattern shown in (b) which may then persist if the speed is decreased again to its original value.

These two examples illustrate the crucial role played by the boundary layer in any flow. Certainly, as will be stated in Section 20, potential flow outside the boundary layer and wake is unique under given boundary conditions, but these include, in part, conditions at the edge of the boundary layer and wake; the boundary layer may thus be said to control the flow external to it and, incidentally, such other characteristics of the flow as non-uniqueness. Although this is not a wholly fair description of the state of affairs—for there is clearly an inter-action between the boundary-layer region and the external inviscid region—for most purposes, nevertheless, many of the answers to the problems raised in this section are found to reside in the calculation of the boundary layer.

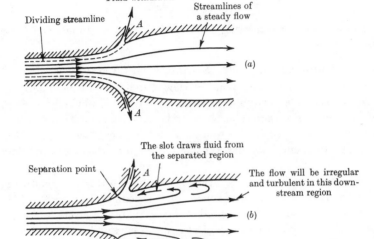

FIG. I. 7. A sketch (not to scale) illustrating the possibility of two configurations of flow in a duct with slots in the walls.

16. The equations for steady incompressible flow

From this point onwards, the restriction will be made that all boundary conditions—either at solid boundaries, or fluid-fluid boundaries or at infinity—are steady. Only in cases where observable un-steadiness is clearly of importance to the overall character of the flow, and especially to the forces acting on the bounding surfaces, will account be taken of unsteadiness.

For convenience, therefore, we collect together the equations of motion for steady incompressible flow, as special cases of equations (6), (30), (39), (45), and (46). As none of the flows to be considered in subsequent chapters will be subject to an external force field, we also put $\mathbf{F} \equiv 0$. Thus:

Navier–Stokes equation for viscous flow

$$\mathbf{v}.\nabla\mathbf{v} = -(1/\rho)\operatorname{grad} p - \nu \operatorname{curl} \operatorname{curl} \mathbf{v}. \qquad (47)$$

Prandtl's two-dimensional boundary-layer equation

$$u\, \partial u/\partial x + w\, \partial u/\partial z = U\, dU/dx + \nu\, \partial^2 u/\partial z^2. \tag{48}$$

Inviscid flow

$$\mathbf{V} \times \boldsymbol{\omega} = (1/\rho)\mathrm{grad}\, H. \tag{49}$$

Bernoulli's and Laplace's equations for irrotational flow

$$\mathrm{grad}\, H = \mathbf{0}; \quad \nabla^2 \phi = 0. \tag{50}$$

The equation of continuity is, of course, $\mathrm{div}\,\mathbf{V} = 0$ under all these circumstances.

17. Two-dimensional flow. Symmetrical flows

From the mathematical point of view, a reduction of the number of independent scalar variables in equations (47)–(50) would be a great help in the solution of the equations; and even if the simplified equations are not obviously applicable to a realizable physical flow, nevertheless solutions to them may increase our insight into the nature of fluid flows.

One device coalesces two variables into one: say, x and z into the single variable $x^{-\frac{1}{2}}z$ which is typical of parabolic problems and which is therefore often used in boundary-layer analysis. Another ignores variations with respect to one of the variables: this has already been used in Section 12 in deriving the two-dimensional boundary-layer equation and now we need briefly to consider the physical validity of this procedure.

The assumption $\partial/\partial y = 0 = v$ implies $\mathbf{V} = \mathbf{V}(x, z)$ and boundaries of the form $f(x, z) = 0$. Since any plane $y = \mathrm{constant}$ consists of streamlines, it might be argued that the plane $y = y_0$ could be replaced by a solid boundary and that the flow in the semi-infinite region $y < y_0$, bounded otherwise by $f(x, z) = 0$, is two-dimensional. This is, of course, not so, since the viscous no-slip condition on $y = y_0$ is that the velocity there is zero and so the original velocity field is no longer found on that plane. However, the flow might be such that the vorticity generated on the plane $y = y_0$ is confined to a boundary layer outside which its influence is so small that the flow in this external region satisfies very closely the two-dimensional conditions. Such a case occurs with a two-dimensional wing spanning a wind tunnel. If the wing is thin, symmetrical, and at zero incidence, then for large values of the Reynolds number, the conditions near the centre of the wing may be taken as two-dimensional provided its chord is a sufficiently small fraction of the distance between the tunnel walls; in addition some allowance should be made for the acceleration of the stream in the centre of the duct due to the decrease in the flux of fluid in the boundary layers on the side walls $y = \pm y_0$. But these two-dimensional conditions would almost certainly be spoiled by the onset of separation which would occur, for example, if this same wing were set at a high incidence.

Unexpected contradictions of these principles sometimes occur, however, and we may quote a celebrated investigation of G. I. Taylor (1923b). If the length of two coaxial rotating circular cylinders is large in comparison with the difference of their radii, it could be expected that the flow in the annulus between the cylinders, at any rate near the centre of their length, would be unaffected by the presence of the two ends and that the flow in the centre region would be independent of distance along the length. This expectation is not realized, the flow taking on a periodic nature in the direction of the length and being fully three-dimensional.

A reconciliation can be made between the two cases just distinguished. Viscous flow appears, in general, to be much more susceptible to disturbances than irrotational flow which indeed is, in general, neutrally stable: as a result, any flow in which no region can be described even approximately as inviscid tends to exhibit fully three-dimensional characteristics quite independently of the geometry of its boundaries. Secondary flow in straight pipes is a well-known phenomenon conforming to this principle.

Another method of simplifying theoretical analysis appeals to symmetry, and it is often assumed that if the undisturbed stream and the body have some common line or plane of symmetry then the flow as a whole will possess the same symmetry. This is a dangerous assumption. Consider a sphere in a uniform stream: the flow in and near the wake is very far from being axi-symmetric and if symmetry is sought, it will be found only far away from the sphere. A similar example is the gravitational rising of a small spherical bubble in a fluid at rest. If the Reynolds number of the bubble based on its diameter, its speed of ascent, and the kinematic viscosity of the liquid, is less than about fifty, the bubble rises in a straight vertical line; for larger Reynolds numbers, the bubble rises in a helical path as was shown by Nisi and Porter (1923) and Saffman (1956). For much larger Reynolds numbers, the bubble does not, of course, maintain its spherical form at all.

We conclude, from both this and Sections 13–15, that it is always necessary to examine the results of theoretical analysis in the light of the behaviour of a real fluid, if the theory has made some overall simplifying assumption.

18. Vortex lines. Vortex tubes. Circulation

A vortex line is such that its tangent at any point is parallel to the vorticity vector at the same point. A vortex tube is a surface bounded by the vortex lines passing through a closed curve, usually but not necessarily of infinitesimal area.

Let us consider a vortex tube whose two cross-sectional areas A_1 and A_2 enclose the volume, V, of the tube; also, let A_3 be the surface area of tube between A_1 and A_2 so that the total surface area of the volume V is $A = A_1 + A_2 + A_3$. Then we have $\int_A \boldsymbol{\omega}.\mathbf{dS} = \int_V \operatorname{div}\boldsymbol{\omega}\,dV = 0$ since $\boldsymbol{\omega} = \operatorname{curl}\mathbf{v}$. Thus $\int_{A_1} \boldsymbol{\omega}.\mathbf{dS} + \int_{A_2} \boldsymbol{\omega}.\mathbf{dS} + \int_{A_3} \boldsymbol{\omega}.\mathbf{dS} = 0$, the differential vectors being taken in the direction of the outward normal. The third integral is zero for, by definition, $\boldsymbol{\omega}$ is parallel to the surface of the tube. The first two terms are then equal (with $\mathbf{dS}$ taken now in the same sense in both integrals), and so the integral $\int \boldsymbol{\omega}.\mathbf{dS}$ taken over any cross-section of the tube is constant. This integral is thus a characteristic of the tube as a whole and called the strength of the tube; an important consequence is that a vortex tube—and so also a vortex line—cannot begin or end in the fluid. If it does not form a closed curve, each of its ends is either on a boundary or at infinity.

Circulation is a property associated with a line joining two points in the fluid; the circulation along the line AB is by definition

$$\Gamma_{AB} = \int_A^B \mathbf{v}.\mathbf{ds}, \tag{51}$$

$\mathbf{ds}$ being the element of length along the line. Circulation is closely associated with the vorticity for, by Stokes's theorem and with the usual conventions about the direction of integration,

$$\Gamma_C = \int_C \mathbf{v}.\mathbf{ds} = \int_S \operatorname{curl}\mathbf{v}.\mathbf{dS} = \int_S \boldsymbol{\omega}.\mathbf{dS}, \tag{52}$$

where the open surface S is bounded by the closed curve C. Thus the circulation round a closed curve equals the total strength of all the vortex tubes which pass through the curve.

In general, the circulation along a line with fixed end points A and B varies as the line AB varies. If, however, $\mathbf{v}$ is the gradient of a scalar function ϕ, we see from (51) that $\Gamma_{AB} = [\phi]_A^B$; thus Γ_{AB} does not change with the path AB (i) if ϕ is single-valued, or (ii) if no singularities of ϕ are crossed as the path AB is deformed. These results have important applications.

Further important results concern the circulation in closed circuits. For a potential flow in which ϕ is single-valued, Γ is zero for any closed circuit and hence is the same for all closed circuits. If ϕ is many-valued, then Γ is the same for all circuits which can be deformed into one another without crossing singularities of ϕ. In contrast to this, for viscous flow Γ varies in general from one closed circuit to another.

Important ideas also arise from the rate of change of circulation in moving and fixed circuits. For a closed curve C which is moving with the fluid, it may be shown from equation (6) that, provided $\mathbf{F}$ is conservative,

$$D\Gamma_C/Dt = -\nu \int_C \mathrm{curl}\,\boldsymbol{\omega}.\mathbf{ds}. \tag{53}$$

For inviscid flow, this reduces to Kelvin's famous theorem that

$$D\Gamma_C/Dt = 0. \tag{54}$$

In other words, the circulation round a circuit moving with the fluid is constant. This last result is true whether the inviscid flow is rotational or not.

For a fixed circuit, the analogous result concerning the rate of change of circulation is most useful when it refers to two-dimensional flow. By forming the scalar product of equation (22) with $\mathbf{ds}$ and integrating along the curve AB in the plane $y = $ constant, we derive the following result, first given by Temple (1943),

$$\partial\Gamma_{AB}/\partial t = (H_B - H_A)/\rho - \int_A^B \eta \mathrm{v}_n\,ds - \nu \int_A^B (\partial\eta/\partial n)\,ds + (\Omega_B - \Omega_A), \tag{55}$$

where $\mathbf{n}$ is the unit normal to the curve AB and Ω is the potential of the force field. For a closed circuit and with a conservative field of force, the equation expresses the rate of change of circulation in a fixed closed circuit as the sum of the rate of convection of vorticity and the rate of viscous diffusion out of the circuit. In steady flow, the result appears that the rate of convection of vorticity out of a fixed closed circuit is exactly balanced by the rate at which vorticity is being diffused into it. This finds serious application in the determination of lift on bodies, as in Section V. 13.

Returning now to the nature of vortex tubes, we remark that those properties which have been mentioned so far are closely analogous to

those of stream tubes. In one important respect, however, there is no
analogy: there is, in general, a flux of fluid through the surface of a
vortex tube, or in other words, the tube does not move with the velocity
of the fluid. But this is seen to be a consequence of viscosity; for
consider, in inviscid flow, a small circuit C lying within the surface of
a vortex tube. The circulation round it is therefore zero and, by Kelvin's
theorem (54), remains zero as the circuit moves; C therefore remains
in the surface of the tube. A further consequence of Kelvin's theorem
arises when it is applied to a circuit enclosing the vortex tube: this
circuit moves with the fluid as we have just seen, and the circulation
remains constant. Thus, for inviscid flow, the strength of a vortex tube
remains constant. For the corresponding results in viscous flow, we
have to refer to equation (21). The change in vorticity of an element
as it moves is due partly to viscous diffusion and partly to the effect
of the term $\boldsymbol{\omega}.\nabla\mathbf{v}$; this term produces such changes of vorticity as would
occur if every vortex line moved with the fluid, the direction of vorticity
rotating as the vortex line rotates and the magnitude of the vorticity
changing in proportion as the vortex line stretches.

19. Concentrated vortices. Vortex sheets. Induced velocity

It often happens in physical flows that there are one, or more, vortex
tubes of small cross-sectional area whose strength is evidently much
greater than that of other tubes of similar size. The spiralling trail
behind the tip of an aircraft wing is well known to most people; a spoon
drawn suddenly through a cup of tea will also create such concentrated
vorticity, while a tornado is a more violent example. Observation of
flows of this kind suggests a mathematical model in which the vorticity
is everywhere zero except along a line on which it is infinite.

To consider such an idealized and irrotational flow, we refer to
Laplace's equation (89) in cylindrical polar coordinates (r, θ, z). A solution of this equation is evidently $\phi = \Gamma\theta/2\pi$, for which the velocity
components are $(0, \Gamma/2\pi r, 0)$ and the vorticity is zero everywhere except
on the straight line $r = 0$ where it is infinite. Any vortex line, such as
$r = 0$ in this example, on which the vorticity is infinite is called a concentrated vortex or simply a vortex.

Now the velocity field $(0, \Gamma/2\pi r, 0)$ is often described as the induced
velocity of the concentrated vortex which lies along $r = 0$; and the idea
of associating the velocity field with the existence of concentrated
vortices has many applications in aerodynamics. To find the induced
velocity of a curved vortex line, use is made of the Biot–Savart law

which states that the velocity, induced by an element **ds** of the line at which the strength is Γ, is

$$(\Gamma/4\pi r^3)\ \mathbf{ds} \times \mathbf{r} \tag{56}$$

at the point whose position from the element is **r**. Thus the induced velocity of the whole line may be calculated by an integration of an expression of this form. As an example which finds frequent application, let us calculate the induced velocity at P of the straight finite

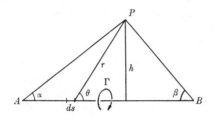

FIG. I. 8. The scheme of notation for a straight vortex
of constant strength.

concentrated vortex BA of constant strength Γ, as shown in Fig. I. 8. From equation (56) we see that the induced velocity is normal to and into the plane of the page, and of magnitude

$$\mathrm{v} = (\Gamma/4\pi)\int_{B}^{A} d(h\cot\theta)\sin\theta/h^2\operatorname{cosec}^2\theta = (\Gamma/4\pi h)(\cos\alpha+\cos\beta), \tag{57}$$

in which the notation of the figure is used. For an infinite line, $\alpha = \beta = 0$ and the velocity field given by (57) reduces to that found in the previous paragraph.

The deduction of the velocity field from a continuous vorticity field is a classical problem which has been fully treated by Lamb (1932). We can see in principle that equation (20) may be inverted to give **v** in terms of **ω**, though the value so obtained is indeterminate to the extent of the gradient of a scalar point function, which represents an irrotational velocity field. Alternatively the term Γ **ds** in (56) may be replaced by **ω** dV, dV being an element of volume of fluid, so that the expression (56) gives the velocity induced by the finite vorticity at a point: an integration over the whole flow gives a value of the total induced velocity.

The concentrated vortex is not a physical possibility, since the kinetic energy of the fluid surrounding and containing it is infinite; and even were this not so, the infinite vorticity would at once diffuse. Indeed, one would expect that unless there is some direct mechanism for maintaining high values of vorticity, these will not long persist in a real flow.

This expectation, based by analogy on the rapid diffusion of a vortex sheet such as that in Fig. I. 4, is not wholly realized. Titchener and Taylor-Russell (1957), investigating vortices of the kind that leave the tips of aircraft wings, found their growth and diffusion remarkably small. This appears characteristic of vortex tubes which are roughly parallel to the direction of convection. Another interesting example of it occurs when a small body is put in a boundary layer, and the Frontispiece vividly shows the formation of a vortex core; a more detailed interpretation of this flow has been given by Gregory and Walker (1951) and reproduced as Fig. XII. 34. This and other experimental evidence suggests that in general the effect of the very high shear stresses is to reduce the vorticity to a constant value in the inner core of such vortex tubes as these; the fluid is rotating there as a solid body. Thus near the centre line of a vortex tube of large strength, the circumferential velocity component is directly proportional to the radial distance, r; farther outwards, the velocity reaches a maximum and then decreases, its gradient being continuous, until eventually it varies inversely with the distance r. It is possible, in the case of the wing-tip vortices, to estimate the diameter of their inner core by considering the energy of the flow and correlating it with the work being done to maintain it.

Vorticity may also tend to an infinite value on a surface, such a surface being called a vortex sheet which is said to have a strength $\boldsymbol{\gamma}$ per unit area, $\boldsymbol{\gamma}$ being a vector lying in the plane of the sheet. The velocity induced at a point P by the vortex sheet is then obtained by integrating, over the sheet, the expression (56) in which $\Gamma\,\mathbf{ds}$ is replaced by $\boldsymbol{\gamma}\,dS$, dS being the element of area. By allowing P to tend to a position on one side of the surface at which $\mathbf{n}$ is the outward unit normal, we find that the induced velocity there is

$$\tfrac{1}{2}\boldsymbol{\gamma}\times\mathbf{n}. \tag{58}$$

Thus $\boldsymbol{\gamma}\times\mathbf{n}_1$ equals $(\mathbf{v}_1-\mathbf{v}_2)$, the difference of the velocities on the two sides denoted by suffixes 1 and 2. $\boldsymbol{\gamma}$ therefore takes the value

$$\boldsymbol{\gamma}=-(\mathbf{v}_1-\mathbf{v}_2)\times\mathbf{n}_1. \tag{59}$$

The whole induced-velocity field is then correctly given if the element of vorticity $\boldsymbol{\gamma}\,dS$ itself moves with the velocity $\tfrac{1}{2}(\mathbf{v}_1+\mathbf{v}_2)$.

A vortex sheet in the strict sense is also a physical impossibility but wherever, according to the principles of Section 6, there is a near-discontinuity of tangential velocity, a good analytical approximation is a vortex sheet. In a uniform medium, vortex sheets always spring from a solid boundary, and tend to deform in shape increasingly with distance from the boundary. When the vortex lines are roughly perpendicular to the main flow—as behind a two-dimensional wing—the sheet tends to concentrate into a regular pattern of discrete vortices. But when the vortex lines are roughly parallel to the main flow, the sheet tends to roll up from its edges in the manner further described in Section III. 4.

Certain further characteristics of vorticity are given in equations (XI. 11–14) where they are relevant to the special case of flows with axial symmetry.

20. The velocity potential in irrotational flow

We are now in a position to discuss certain properties of Laplace's equation (50) which are particularly relevant to the potential flow of fluid and especially to the region outside the boundary layer and wake of a body in a uniform stream. In this region, where it is assumed that the vorticity is zero, there is a velocity potential ϕ.

If ϕ is continuous and single-valued throughout a certain region of flow, the following theorems hold:

(i) ϕ is determined uniquely everywhere by its values on the boundaries of the region, or by the values of $\partial\phi/\partial n$, the normal derivative, on the boundaries. Alternatively ϕ may be prescribed over parts of the boundaries and $\partial\phi/\partial n$ over the remainder.

(ii) If, in a finite region, all the boundaries are at rest, it follows that the fluid is also at rest everywhere.

(iii) If, in an infinite region of flow, the velocity is zero at infinity and the boundaries are at rest, again the velocity is zero everywhere.

(iv) The speed cannot have a maximum value within the fluid, but only on the boundaries. It may, of course, take a minimum value, indeed may be zero within the fluid.

(v) The circulation round all closed circuits is zero.

From (i), it follows that it is not possible to prescribe the velocity on the boundaries: the shape of the given boundaries determines the velocity on them. (ii) and (iii) are valuable mainly for their consequence, that any flow which takes place under the given conditions must be rotational.

A further important consequence of ϕ being single-valued is that no lift force can act on a body in a uniform stream, as is shown for a two-dimensional body in Section 22 and illustrated for a three-dimensional body in Section III. 4. Thus, because we shall often be dealing with bodies experiencing lift, the velocity potential will usually be many-valued, and it is then necessary to distinguish between simply-connected and multiply-connected regions.

For a simply-connected region, ϕ has branch lines or surfaces within the fluid which extend either from boundary to boundary or from boundary to infinity: these correspond to concentrated vortices or to vortex sheets. If their positions are prescribed, then (i) above still holds, (ii) and (iii) do not, and (iv) only holds if it is interpreted to apply to any sub-region of the flow, created by making appropriate cuts, in which ϕ is single-valued; (v) will hold for circuits which neither cross vortex sheets nor enclose concentrated vortex lines. The existence of these sheets and lines is inevitable for a finite wing with lift; their physical counterparts are regions in which the vorticity is significantly non-zero, and these will be discussed in more detail in Chapters III and VIII.

The only type of multiply-connected region which we need to consider is that formed by a two-dimensional body. Here concentrated vorticity need not exist within the fluid since ϕ can pass from one value to another, round circuits enclosing the body. Thus the circulation in any circuit enclosing the aerofoil is not zero, and we have already established in Section 18 the result that the circulation is the same for all circuits enclosing the aerofoil.

It is seen therefore that, at any rate for the flow of uniform streams past closed bodies, singular solutions of Laplace's equation are of the utmost importance. In three-dimensional flow, it is often convenient to work in terms of the velocity field of certain types of singularities rather than the potential. In two-dimensional flow it is best to introduce the so-called complex velocity potential which we now discuss.

21. The complex potential in two-dimensional irrotational flow

For two-dimensional flow, we may assume that $\partial/\partial y = 0$ and $v = 0$, whereupon Laplace's equation becomes

$$\partial^2\phi/\partial x^2 + \partial^2\phi/\partial z^2 = 0, \tag{60}$$

which suggests the use of the complex variable

$$\mathfrak{z} = x + iz, \tag{61}$$

since any function of $\mathfrak{z}$ is then a solution of (60). Now the respective definitions of ϕ and ψ, given in equations (44) and (12), imply that

$$\left.\begin{array}{l} u = \partial\phi/\partial x = \partial\psi/\partial z \\ w = \partial\phi/\partial z = -\partial\psi/\partial x \end{array}\right\} . \tag{62}$$

Ignoring u and w for the moment, we recognize these equations as the Cauchy–Riemann equations which show that $(\phi+i\psi)$ is an analytic function of $\mathfrak{z}$. This function is called the complex potential, $\mathfrak{w}$, so that

$$\mathfrak{w} = \phi+i\psi, \tag{63}$$

and by considering, for example, the derivative in the x-direction and making use of equations (62), we have

$$d\mathfrak{w}/d\mathfrak{z} = u-iw = \mathrm{v}e^{-i\theta}, \tag{64}$$

where v is the speed, and θ is the angle between the velocity vector and the x-axis.

The usefulness of the complex potential depends ultimately upon the theorem that if the real or the imaginary part of a function is known on the boundary of a region in which the function is analytic, the function is determinate throughout the region, apart from an imaginary or real additive constant respectively. For example, the stream function ψ takes a constant value on any solid boundary of the flow and so $\mathfrak{w}$ can be determined. Of course, it is one thing to know that a solution exists or even to be able to write it down, and another to carry out the numerical calculations based on it; in fact, the practical procedures for calculating the velocity field of an aerofoil of given shape are based on further analysis of some complexity and are reserved for Chapter IV.

The complex potential is closely related to the circulation Γ about, and the flux Q through, a curve AB; the proof of the result

$$\Gamma+iQ = [\mathfrak{w}]_A^B \tag{65}$$

is elementary, being based on the definitions of Γ and Q and on equation (64).

22. The two-dimensional irrotational flow of a uniform stream past a closed body

We consider the stream given by $d\mathfrak{w}/d\mathfrak{z} = U_\infty$, namely the stream parallel to the x-axis of speed U_∞. The disturbance to this velocity field due to the presence of a body is represented by an additional function in the expression for $(d\mathfrak{w}/d\mathfrak{z})$ which is analytic and single-valued everywhere in the region of flow. It may therefore be expanded as a Laurent series so that

$$dw/d_3 = U_\infty + \sum_{n=1}^{\infty} a_n {_3}^{-n} = U_\infty + f(_3). \qquad (66)$$

The convenience of this form for dw/d_3 usually depends on $_3 = 0$ lying within the body and this we now assume to be so; in addition,

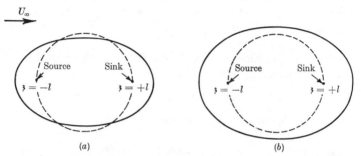

FIG. I. 9. In a uniform stream, these two bodies, of much the same shape, can be represented exactly by a source and a sink. Only for the body (b), however, is the expansion of equation (68) valid over the whole field of flow.

if $_3 = {_3}_s$ is the singularity of $f(_3)$ farthest from the origin $_3 = 0$, the series in (66) only converges for $|_3| > |{_3}_s|$. Thus the series may or may not be valid over the whole region of flow, according to each particular case; but since $_3 = {_3}_s$ must be within the body contour, the series is bound to be valid everywhere outside any circle $|_3| = R$ which completely encloses the body.

To exemplify the region of validity of the series form of dw/d_3 in a particular case also brings out some further ideas important in fluid dynamics. It may easily be verified that

$$dw/d_3 = U_\infty + (Q/2\pi)\{(_3+l)^{-1} - (_3-l)^{-1}\} + i\Gamma/2\pi_3 \qquad (67)$$

represents the uniform flow past a closed body; Figs. I. 9 (a) and (b) refer to this flow when $\Gamma = 0$ and $Q \lessgtr 4U_\infty l$ respectively. dw/d_3, given in equation (67), may be expanded in inverse powers of $_3$ as in (66). In this case, $_{3_s} = l$, and the series is valid everywhere outside the circle $|_3| = l$ which is shown by the dotted line in the two figures; it is therefore valid for the whole region of flow in the second case, but not in the first. Thus in the first case, the series could not be used, for example, to calculate the velocity everywhere on the surface of the body.

The question inevitably arises: is there any physical significance in the singularities of $(d\mathfrak{w}/d\mathfrak{z})$ which lie within the body and so outside the region in which we are interested? It is not possible to give a precise answer to this question. Referring for the moment to the flow given in equation (67), we see that the terms in that equation represent in turn the uniform stream, a concentrated source of strength Q at $\mathfrak{z} = -l$, a similar sink at $\mathfrak{z} = +l$, and a concentrated vortex of strength Γ at $\mathfrak{z} = 0$. It would be accurate to say, therefore, that the body can be represented, or even replaced, by the source, sink, and vortex; and since the velocity fields of such singularities can be so simply expressed, this idea of representing a body by an equivalent distribution of singularities is extensively used in aerodynamics, and constantly recurs in the following chapters.

The power of this approach is due to the fact that, contrary to what might be inferred so far, there are usually many different distributions of singularities which represent the same flow. This can be seen at once from the example of (67); with $\Gamma = 0$ and $Q > 4U_\infty l$, that equation may be written in the form

$$d\mathfrak{w}/d\mathfrak{z} = U_\infty - (Q/\pi l) \sum_{n=1}^{\infty} (l/\mathfrak{z})^{2n} \quad (|\mathfrak{z}| > l), \qquad (68)$$

which is valid over the whole region of flow. We may therefore regard the body as being represented by singularities at $\mathfrak{z} = 0$, all of different orders. This, however, would not be possible for the body in Fig. I. 9 (a) even though it appears, at first sight, similar in most respects to the other body. Equally, the flow may be represented by distributions of singularities of lower order over the surface of the body, and we may refer to Lamb (1932) for general theorems.

That singularities of first order—$d\mathfrak{w}/d\mathfrak{z} \propto \mathfrak{z}^{-1}$—are both very simple and have a definite physical significance—of sources and vortices—puts a premium on their use. It is, however, important to note that whereas the flow about any body can be represented by a continuous distribution of such singularities on its surface, in general it cannot be so represented by such singularities distributed on some arbitrarily chosen surface within it. Nor, in general, can a flow be exactly represented by a finite number of such singularities. This may be exemplified by the flow obtained from equation (67) by allowing $Q \to \infty$ and $l \to 0$ in such a way that $4Ql \to \pi d^2 U_\infty$. We then have

$$d\mathfrak{w}/d\mathfrak{z} = U_\infty (1 - d^2/4\mathfrak{z}^2) + i\Gamma/2\pi\mathfrak{z}. \qquad (69)$$

This is a flow past the circular cylinder $|\mathfrak{z}| = \frac{1}{2}d$ and is constantly used in two-dimensional aerofoil theory. It cannot be represented by a finite number of sources or vortices within the cylinder. The second-order singularity—$d\mathfrak{w}/d\mathfrak{z} \propto \mathfrak{z}^{-2}$—is called a doublet on account of the derivation preceding equation (69); it may easily be verified that a source doublet and a vortex doublet are equivalent if their axes are perpendicular.

The first coefficient, a_1, in the expansion (66) is related to the circulation round and the flux through the surface of the body, for from (65)

$$\Gamma + iQ = 2\pi i a_1. \qquad (70)$$

For a solid body $Q = 0$; a_1 is therefore imaginary and equals $\Gamma/2\pi i$. In equations (67) to (69) Γ is then the circulation about the body, in the clockwise sense.

By theorems due to Blasius (1910) the force, (X, Z), and the clockwise moment, M, about the point $\mathfrak{z} = b$, which act on a body in two-dimensional potential flow are given by

$$\left. \begin{array}{l} X - iZ = \tfrac{1}{2} i\rho \int (d\mathfrak{w}/d\mathfrak{z})^2 \, d\mathfrak{z} \\ M = \tfrac{1}{2}\rho \mathscr{R} \int (\mathfrak{z} - b)(d\mathfrak{w}/d\mathfrak{z})^2 \, d\mathfrak{z} \end{array} \right\}. \qquad (71)$$

It is important to note that the dimensions of $X - iZ$ and M are $\mathbf{MT}^{-2}$ and $\mathbf{MLT}^{-2}$ respectively; in other words, $X - iZ$ and M are force and couple per unit length in the y-direction. These results are always true if the integrals are evaluated round the body contour. In most practical cases, there are no singularities within the fluid and so the integrals may be evaluated round larger contours; it may then be convenient to choose a contour on which an expansion (66) is valid.

For the uniform flow past a solid body for which, from equation (70), $a_1 = \Gamma/2\pi i$, equation (71) gives

$$X = 0; \qquad Z = \rho U_\infty \Gamma. \qquad (72)$$

Z is a lift force perpendicular to the stream, and the crucial importance of circulation as the agency of lift is established. That the force parallel to the stream, namely the drag, is zero is known as d'Alembert's paradox, since a zero drag is never encountered in the flow of real fluid; it is, of course, a consequence of the assumption of inviscid flow. The modifications to equations (72) for viscous flow are the subject of Chapter V.

It should be noted that the existence of lift implies disturbances in the speed of the order of $\mathfrak{z}^{-1}$ at large distances from a solid body; if the lift is zero the disturbances are at most of order $\mathfrak{z}^{-2}$.

23. Singular solutions of Laplace's equation in three-dimensional flow

We saw in the previous section that two-dimensional irrotational flow past a solid closed boundary may be represented by an appropriate distribution of singularities either on or sometimes within the body; this representation is, however, seldom resorted to, owing to the convenience of the complex potential. In three-dimensional irrotational flow there is nothing to correspond to the complex potential, and for this reason the representation of closed bodies, and indeed other boundaries, by suitable singularities is practised more frequently.

The fundamental theorem on this matter is due to Green (1828): any inviscid irrotational flow may be expressed in terms of distributions of sources and doublets over the boundaries. This is of great academic importance but is of restricted utility for the practical problems of, for example, determining the potential flow past a body of given shape. For such problems, alternative theorems which express the velocity field in terms of other properties of the flow are often used and some of these may be found in Lamb's (1932) book.

In later chapters, we shall have to use a variety of methods for representing flows past bodies and it is best to leave the explanation of each of them until its own context is reached. Many of these methods use, as approximations, distributions of sources and vortices on the boundaries and the usual procedure in determining the complete flow, given the boundaries, is to find first the distribution of the strength of these singularities and then to calculate the velocity field from that.

In the final step, no difficulty arises with the vortex distribution, Section 19 having given the induced velocity field of a vortex element. The induced velocity of the source distribution is rather simpler; a source of strength Q at the point $\mathbf{a}$ induces at the point $\mathbf{r}$ a velocity given by

$$\mathbf{v} = (Q/4\pi)|\mathbf{r}-\mathbf{a}|^{-3}(\mathbf{r}-\mathbf{a}), \tag{73}$$

a result which follows at once from a consideration of the flux through a spherical surface centred at the source.

The practical methods for the determination of the source and vortex distribution depend very much on the configuration of the boundaries; special methods for wings are explained in Chapters VII and VIII, for bodies of revolution in Chapter IX, while more complicated surfaces are considered in Chapter X.

24. Some general characteristics of the flow in a boundary layer

The last few sections have been devoted to a consideration of the inviscid region of any fluid flow and in particular of the irrotational flow which occurs outside the boundary layer and wake in a uniform stream. The manner in which theories of potential flow are applied to the flow of real viscous fluid is further explained in Chapter III. Meanwhile we need to pick up the thread from Section 10 and consider more thoroughly the nature of the boundary layer.

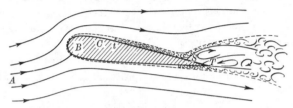

Fig. I. 10. A sketch (not to scale) illustrating the nature of the flow of a uniform stream past an aerofoil when separation occurs near the trailing edge.

It is convenient to have a definite flow in mind and so we refer to Fig. I. 10 which illustrates the two-dimensional flow past a thin aerofoil at a low incidence. AB is the upstream dividing streamline, B the forward stagnation point, BC the region of the upper surface along which the pressure is decreasing in the streamwise direction, and CT the region in which it is increasing. The edge of the boundary layer is represented by the dotted line, which for the time being can be defined as the line along which the vorticity takes some arbitrarily small value.

Almost always, there is a region Bt downstream of a forward stagnation point in which the boundary layer is laminar. Typical distributions of velocity in this laminar region, called laminar profiles for short, are given by curves (a) and (b) in Fig. I. 11. Curve (b) is typical of the laminar flow on a flat plate, for which the pressure is constant everywhere.

When the Reynolds number of the flow is sufficiently high, turbulent fluctuations appear in the boundary layer at some distance from the leading edge; these rapidly develop through the transition region in which the velocity fluctuations at any fixed point are intermittent, similar to the behaviour shown in Fig. I. 2. Downstream of the transition region the boundary layer becomes fully turbulent. Sections 26 and 28 contain discussions of the nature of transition and turbulence. Typical distributions of the mean velocity in a turbulent boundary layer, called turbulent profiles for short, are shown in Fig. I. 12.

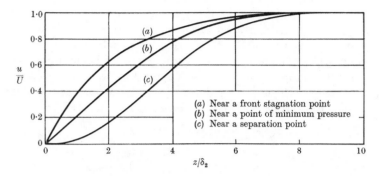

FIG. I. 11. Some typical distributions of velocity in a laminar boundary layer.

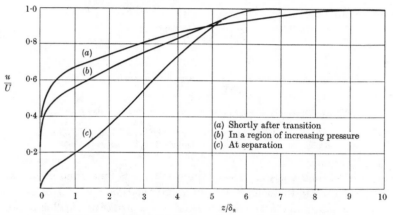

FIG. I. 12. Some typical distributions of mean velocity in a turbulent
boundary layer.

The gradient of the turbulent profiles near the boundary is characteristically greater than that for the laminar profiles of Fig. I. 11; hence,
from equation (34), the shear stress on the boundary is greater for a
turbulent than for a laminar layer of similar thickness. A quantitative
comparison is shown in Fig. I. 13 for a flat plate set parallel to the
stream: from this it is clear that the state of the boundary layer is of
the utmost practical importance. The realization of laminar flow with
its low drag is a topic and an aim which will constantly arise in later
chapters. And although the three stages—laminar flow, transition,
turbulent flow—are characteristic of practically all boundary layers in
flows whose Reynolds numbers are greater than, say, 10^6, much can
be done to mitigate the effect of turbulence.

A further phenomenon, that of separation, occurs only in some cases, not in others, and is associated with a positive pressure gradient along the surface. Let us consider first a laminar boundary layer. In any region in which the pressure is increasing, there are bound to be some stream tubes near the surface whose total pressure is less than the static pressure a little farther downstream. These stream tubes can only reach this farther point if the total shear force on them is tending

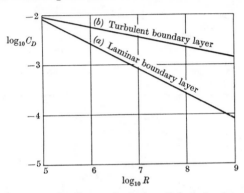

Fig. I. 13. The scale effect on the drag coefficient of a flat plate in a uniform stream with (a) a laminar and (b) a turbulent boundary layer over the whole surface. Usually both types of flow occur on a given plate and then, for any R, the value of C_D lies between the two extreme values indicated in the figure.

to increase their energy; this condition is $\partial \tau / \partial z > 0$ or, from equation (34) according to the boundary layer approximation, $\partial^2 u / \partial z^2 > 0$. This condition must hold in some region close to the surface and is illustrated in curve (c) of Fig. I. 11. It may also be obtained as a general result for a solid surface by putting $z = 0$ in the equation of motion (30) and remembering that $dU/dx < 0$. This process of conversion by viscosity of kinetic energy into pressure energy can continue only to a limited extent and a point is often reached at which the value of τ, or of $\partial u / \partial z$, becomes zero at the surface. Downstream of this point, τ and hence u is negative close to the surface and so the configuration of the stream-lines near a separation point in two-dimensional flow is as illustrated in Fig. I. 14. The character of the region downstream of a separation point depends on a number of factors and especially on the shape of the boundary downstream, and it will be discussed in more detail in Chapter III. For the moment, it is plain that the separation of the boundary layer, which releases into the main body of fluid all the vorticity which has been generated upstream at the surface, has a

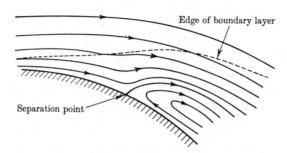

Fig. I. 14. A sketch (not to scale) illustrating the configuration of mean streamlines near a separation-point on a well-rounded surface.

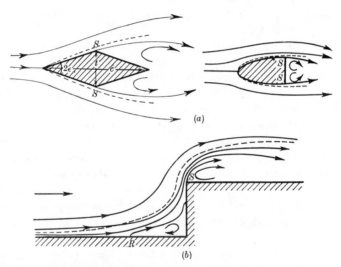

Fig. I. 15. Sketches illustrating the mean streamlines near separation points induced by discontinuities in the slope of the surface. Even under two-dimensional boundary conditions, the flow in such separated regions is usually three-dimensional.

(a) In each of these cases, the flow behind the bodies is highly turbulent, the mean streamlines tending to form a closed bubble in the wake. (b) In this flow past a step, separation which is induced by the first corner occurs upstream of it.

decisive effect on the inviscid region of flow; and it is largely from their potentiality for separation that boundary layers derive their governing influence upon fluid flows.

The process leading up to separation is not always a gradual one. A discontinuity of tangent to the surface, if sufficiently severe, will normally cause separation. Such points as S in Fig. I. 15 (a) are separation points and these are usually characterized by vortex sheets springing from them. The point R in Fig. I. 15 (*b*) illustrates the possibility of separation upstream of a discontinuity of surface gradient.

The physical mechanism of separation for turbulent layers is broadly similar except that the turbulence is more effective than viscosity in transferring energy from the outer to the inner parts of the layer. Thus in otherwise similar circumstances, the separation point of a turbulent layer will be downstream of that of a laminar layer.

25. The laminar boundary layer. Free and forced transition

For a comprehensive description of the stability of laminar boundary layers, the reader is referred to Chapter IX of *LBL*; in this section we are interested more in the ways in which a laminar boundary layer becomes turbulent.

First, we consider the amplification of infinitesimally small disturbances at natural frequencies of oscillation. The results of investigations are usually put in terms of α, the wave number of an assumed sinusoidal disturbance, and R_{δ_1}, the local Reynolds number based on the stream velocity and displacement thickness. Graphs then show the relationship for neutral stability between α and R_{δ_1}; Fig. I. 16 shows three typical curves, for three values of the parameter $\Lambda = (\delta_1^2/\nu)(dU/dx)$, the region outside the looped curve denoting stability. In each case, there is a minimum Reynolds number below which the boundary layer appears to be stable for regular disturbances of any wave number. The physical existence of such waves was doubted when this theory was first proposed, but we now know that, at the high levels of turbulence typical of the free streams of early experiments, the waves were masked by the irregular fluctuations. But ever since Schubauer and Skramstad (1943) detected small regular oscillations in a laminar boundary layer when the free-stream turbulence was reduced to the extremely low level of $(\overline{u'^2}/U_\infty^2)^{\frac{1}{2}} = 0 \cdot 0002$, the theory has been generally accepted and very greatly developed. In recognition of their theoretical origins, these oscillations are usually known as Tollmien–Schlichting waves. In a series of remarkable experiments, Schubauer and Skramstad went on to introduce disturbances of prescribed frequencies; as a result, stability curves, similar to those in Fig. I. 16, were obtained which gave excellent agreement with the theoretical predictions. But it must be recognized that all these findings refer to a boundary layer which is still laminar and they are as yet incapable of predicting the precise moment at which a laminar layer first displays intermittent turbulence.

It may be said quite generally that the mechanism of transition involves a transfer of energy to the developing turbulence, and in a process usually called dynamic instability an intermediate stage seems to exist in which regular patterns of vorticity are set up, which may subsequently degenerate into turbulence if the Reynolds number is increased. For flow between rotating co-axial cylinders this train of events is best

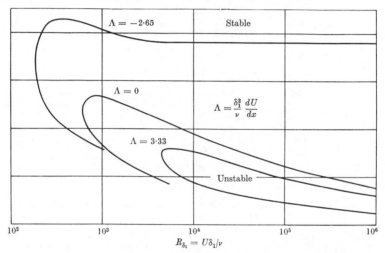

FIG. I. 16. Some typical theoretical curves of neutral stability for a laminar boundary layer in positive, zero, and negative pressure gradients.

described by the very words of G. I. Taylor (1923b): 'A moderate increase in the speed of the apparatus merely increased the vigour of the circulation in the vortices without altering appreciably their spacing or position; but a large increase caused the symmetrical motion to break down into some kind of turbulent motion, which it was impossible to follow by eye.' Görtler (1940) postulated similar effects in flow over a concave surface; while Gregory, Stuart, and Walker (1955) have studied, experimentally and theoretically, similar effects on a rotating disk. The centrifugal effects play an important part in all these flows.

An alternative type of dynamic instability, first described by Rayleigh (1880) for inviscid flow and usually given his name, attacks a boundary layer with an inflexion in its velocity profile. In two-dimensional flow, waves are set up which travel in the direction of the stream; in three-dimensional flow, the vorticity in the boundary layer often seems to form itself into discrete vortices roughly parallel to the streamlines just outside the boundary layer. Fully turbulent flow is the usual

consequence in either case. In recent years this phenomenon has assumed importance owing to its occurrence near the leading edges of
swept-back wings, as was first noticed by Gray (1952).

The principal requisite for these types of instability, which lead to
transition to turbulence, seems to be that the laminar flow should be
rotational. This is not, however, the prerogative of an unseparated

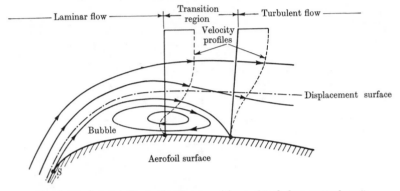

Fɪɢ. I. 17. A sketch illustrating free transition and turbulent reattachment
after laminar separation on an aerofoil.

boundary layer and an important case of transition in the absence of
a contiguous solid boundary occurs for the so-called bubble flows, the
typical characteristics of which are illustrated in Fig. I. 17. These
flows exhibit the phenomenon generally referred to as turbulent reattachment which is considered in more detail in Chapters III and V.
This type of transition, with a bubble as intermediary, is becoming
increasingly common now that very thin wings are in use.

Much more potent causes of transition are external agencies such as
small roughnesses or waves in the surface, which can cause abrupt
transition when in their absence laminar flow would have persisted.
Similarly, a trip-wire whose diameter is only a few thousandths of an
inch placed on the surface, or sound waves, or the passage of an electric
spark, may cause transition. The turbulence in the free stream also
affects the Reynolds number of the boundary layer at which transition
will occur. An important experimental technique is based on these
effects; transition on a model in a wind tunnel can often be fixed
artificially at the same position as on the full-scale wing.

Corrugations in and excrescences on a surface are two particularly
important agencies causing transition. For the former, Fage (1943)

has derived relations for the least size of surface waves sufficient to affect the position of transition in zero and negative pressure gradients. In an analysis of data for isolated excrescences, Klanfer and Owen (1953) argued on dimensional grounds that transition should depend on the parameters $\epsilon u_\tau/\nu$, R_{δ_1}, and $\Lambda = (\delta_1^2/\nu)(dU/dx)$, where ϵ is the height

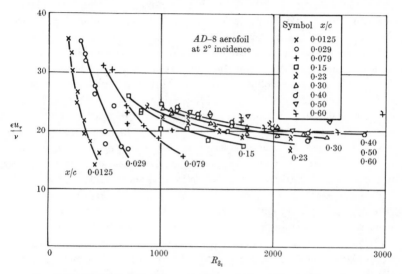

FIG. I. 18. The critical size of an excrescence which causes transition. Experimental relationships between $\epsilon u_\tau/\nu$ and R_{δ_1}, obtained by Gregory and Walker (1957).

of the roughness, and u_τ is the laminar friction velocity defined in equation (79). Thus

$$\epsilon u_\tau/\nu = F(R_{\delta_1}, \Lambda). \tag{74}$$

It was, however, found impossible to take into account the variations of Λ, and the experimental data then available suggested that transition will occur if

$$\epsilon u_\tau/\nu > 20. \tag{75}$$

From more recent experiments Gregory and Walker (1957) deduce that this is too sweeping a simplification, as is indicated by Fig. I. 18 in which the critical value of $\epsilon u_\tau/\nu$ clearly depends on a number of still unknown factors.

Many of the ideas and theories mentioned in this section have been reviewed and correlated in a paper by Smith and Gamberoni (1956) who also propose a method for predicting transition on a smooth surface, for both two-dimensional and axi-symmetric flows.

26. The nature of transition

The principal function of most of the investigations described in the preceding section is to predict the possibility of transition under certain general conditions: it lies beyond their ability to predict when disturbances of a particular kind will occur or the position at which transition will actually take place. For example, a laminar layer which, according to the criteria contained in Fig. I. 16, is unstable may nevertheless remain laminar, given special conditions. On the other hand, a boundary layer, theoretically stable for infinitesimal disturbances, may become turbulent either due to observable finite disturbances or for some less easily accountable reason. This is to say little more than that most of these theories are still in a primitive state. Even so, some of their general conclusions have been of immediate practical importance; thus the idea of the low-drag aerofoil, based on the achievement of a large area of laminar flow, has depended solely on the simple result, first noticed experimentally, that free transition is unlikely to occur on a sufficiently smooth surface in a region of falling pressure.

The actual physical characteristics of a transition region have only recently emerged from the mists of hypothesis. Important contributions to our understanding of these have been made by Emmons (1951) and Mitchner (1954), who studied the flow of a thin sheet of water on a glass table, and by Schubauer and Klebanoff (1955). The most striking discovery is that at any point x of a transition region the flow exhibits turbulent fluctuations only for a proportion $\gamma(x)$ of the time; for the rest of the time it is laminar and a typical record of the fluctuations in such a region would be much the same as that shown in Fig. I. 2. $\gamma(x)$ is known as the intermittency factor; it varies from zero at the upstream, laminar end of the transition region to unity at the downstream, fully turbulent end. Fig. I. 19 correlates a number of experimental observations; the full line represents a Gaussian distribution of $d\gamma(x)/dx$, and as γ varies from 0 to 1, the mean-velocity profiles, shown in Fig. I. 20, change steadily from the laminar to the fully turbulent.

An earlier supposition that transition occurs instantaneously at a spanwise line which oscillates between limits in the streamwise direction could be reconciled with these observations. However, it is now thought that turbulence originates in spots, which occur in a random manner near the upstream limit of the transition region. These spread laterally as turbulent wedges into the surrounding fluid and are swept downstream at the same time at a velocity rather less than that of the free stream. The wedge angle is approximately 10°, the inner 6° being

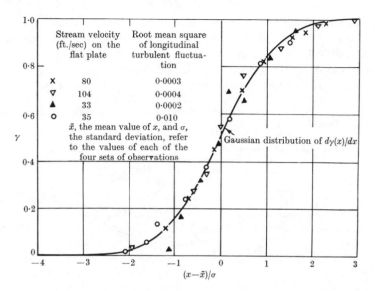

Fig. I. 19. The variation of the intermittency factor, γ, through a transition region.

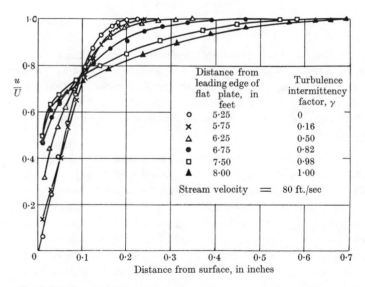

Fig. I. 20. Experimental mean-velocity profiles through a transition region.

occupied by fully turbulent fluid, and the outer 2° on each side by fluid in which the turbulence is intermittent. Fig. I. 21 illustrates the downstream diffusion of a turbulent spot created artificially by an electric spark; the diffusion of a naturally-occurring spot seems to follow the same pattern. Further, spots appear to form only in part of the whole

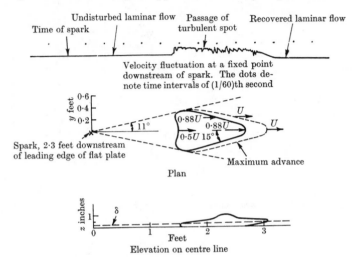

FIG. I. 21. Sketches of a turbulent spot initiated by an electric spark between a needle electrode and the surface.

transition region; in the remaining downstream part of the region, new spots are prevented from appearing by the apparently enhanced stability of the fluid between the already growing spots. Schubauer and Klebanoff are of the opinion that the initial breakdowns arise from random perturbations superimposed on the regularly amplified waves in the laminar layer.

27. Equations for two-dimensional turbulent boundary layers

The Navier–Stokes equations can, despite their non-linearity, be solved exactly for certain special laminar flows, and Prandtl's equation (48) may be solved by a wide variety of methods for laminar boundary layers. For turbulent boundary layers, however, little rigorous analysis can be done which is at all analogous to that for laminar flow; in the past few years, therefore, attempts have been made to extend the methods of analysing homogeneous and isotropic turbulence to shear flows, in which isotropy cannot be expected. In these the velocity is regarded as the sum of the mean and the turbulent velocities; the effects of the latter may be expressed in terms of correlation functions, energy spectra, and so on. For details of the mathematical methods, the original papers should be consulted. We also mention the general reviews by Batchelor (1953) and Townsend (1956); Townsend (1949, 1951) and Schubauer (1954) have done notable work for boundary layers and wakes, and Laufer (1950, 1953) for flow in pipes and channels. But these analyses still fall short of any sort of exact calculation based on the Navier–Stokes equations.

The most pressing need of boundary-layer analysis is a means of relating the stresses, which arise from correlations between the components of the fluctuating velocities, to the mean velocity and pressure, so that a solution of the equation of mean motion would at least be theoretically possible. The mixing length theories reviewed by Goldstein (1938) represent early attempts to obtain such a relation but it is now generally agreed that they are inadequate for quantitative analysis, being based on no more than dimensional reasoning. Despite all this, much information about the overall behaviour of turbulent boundary layers has been collected by experimental studies and in Chapter II we shall see the success of the semi-empirical methods in predicting, with reasonable accuracy, the shear stress and growth of momentum thickness, and in giving some indication of the separation point.

To establish the boundary-layer equation in two dimensions on which these semi-empirical methods are based, we consider the velocity as being made up of the mean velocity (u, w) and the turbulent velocity (u', w'). The mean of the turbulent velocity is, of course, zero. It is assumed that none of the assumptions made in Section 11 is invalidated by the turbulent fluctuations and by taking the time mean of equation (48) we find

$$u \, \partial u / \partial x + w \, \partial u / \partial z = U \, dU / dx + \nu \, \partial^2 u / \partial z^2 - \partial(\overline{u'^2}) / \partial x - \partial(\overline{u'w'}) / \partial z.$$
(76)

In this, bars denote mean values; thus

$$\overline{u'^2} = \lim_{T \to \infty} (1/2T) \int_{-T}^{+T} u'^2 \, dt; \qquad \overline{u'w'} = \lim_{T \to \infty} (1/2T) \int_{-T}^{+T} u'w' \, dt. \quad (77)$$

The quantities $\overline{u'^2}$ and $\overline{u'w'}$ occurring in the last two terms of equation (76) are sometimes called the Reynolds stresses, after that author's paper (1895). The forces they represent, which arise from the momentum changes due to the turbulence, are equivalent to additional stresses. Thus the term in $\overline{u'^2}$ represents a pressure while the effective shear stress p_{zx}, usually written as τ, is given by

$$\tau = \mu(\partial u/\partial z) - \rho\overline{u'w'}, \tag{78}$$

in which the first and second terms represent the viscous and turbulent
contributions respectively. The stress at the boundary, or skin friction,
is therefore

$$\tau_w = \mu(\partial u/\partial z)_{z=0} = \tfrac{1}{2}\rho U^2 c_f = \rho u_\tau^2, \tag{79}$$

since $u' = w' = 0$ at the wall; τ_w thus depends only on the gradient of
the mean velocity and is unaffected by other manifestations of the
turbulence. It is often convenient to work in terms of the local skin
friction coefficient, c_f. The so-called friction velocity u_τ provides an
appropriate velocity scale for the flow very close to the boundary.
Also, the combination zu_τ/ν is an appropriate dimensionless distance
perpendicular to the surface, and from (79) we have, for small values
of z,

$$u/u_\tau = zu_\tau/\nu. \tag{80}$$

28. Physical characteristics of a turbulent boundary layer. Velocity profiles

Three regions of different character may be distinguished in a turbulent boundary layer:

1. In the outer region large-scale eddies predominate, and the flow
closely resembles that in the outer part of a turbulent wake. This
region is characterized by intermittency of the turbulence at any
point; but here the intermittency, while retaining the same definition,
is not the same in character as that found in a transition region and
described in Section 26. It is as though the turbulence sporadically
reaches out into the stream to involve more fluid. Fig. I. 22 vividly
illustrates this idea under rather special conditions of forced oscillation.
For the boundary layer on a flat plate, Schubauer (1954) found that
the intermittency factor varies from zero at a distance from the wall
of about $1\cdot2\delta$ to unity at about $0\cdot4\delta$, where δ is the distance from the
wall at which the mean velocity has reached its maximum or stream
value. δ is capable of being defined, from experimental readings, with
an accuracy of about 5 per cent. Again, the space derivative of γ—
here, $\partial\gamma(z)/\partial z$—lies close to a Gaussian distribution. As γ varies, the
changes in mean velocity are comparatively small, the shear stress is
low, and the length scales of the largest eddies are of the same order
as the boundary-layer thickness. The effect of the wall and the inner
region of the layer on this outer part is to enforce a shear stress, or
mean-velocity gradient, and so to provide the mechanism for energy
transfer.

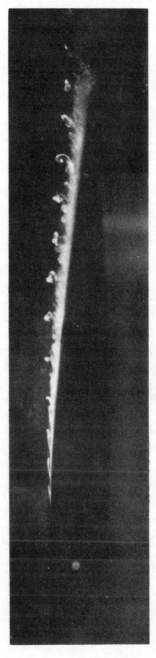

FIG. I. 22. In experiments by Bergh and Berg (1958), smoke, oozing from a hole in the upper surface of an aerofoil in a wind tunnel, gives a good impression of the character of a boundary layer as it becomes turbulent.

2. Nearer the surface, the flow is more strongly influenced by the presence of the surface, and the shear of the mean flow is much greater. Into this region, turbulent energy is transported by the action of the large fluctuations typical of the external intermittent region; this energy has been extracted from the mean flow and about 40 per cent of it is dissipated at once as heat. The remainder is conveyed to the region even closer to the wall where, in fluctuations of much higher frequency, it also is dissipated as heat. In this region, it has been found that the mean velocity distribution is given, to a good approximation, by a universal functional relationship between u/u_τ and zu_τ/ν. The most commonly used relation is the logarithmic law:

$$u/u_\tau = A \log_e(zu_\tau/\nu) + B. \tag{81}$$

The values of A and B, as given by various authors, are given in Table I. 1. For zero and negative pressure gradients, this formula holds

TABLE I. 1

Constants in the universal logarithmic law

Author	A	B
Ludwieg and Tillman (1949) . .	2·5	5·5
Laufer (1950)	2·92	6·0
Coles (1953)	2·5	5·1
Clauser (1954)	2·43	4·9
Eskinazi and Yeh (1956) . . .	2·18	6·5

good in the range $20 < zu_\tau/\nu < 400$ though neither limit is at all precise; in increasing pressure, the upper limit decreases rapidly as separation is approached. Fig. I. 23 shows a typical collection of experimental points which, in this range of zu_τ/ν, lie close to the form (81) with $A = 2·5$ and $B = 5·5$. In this inner region, the shear stress arises almost entirely from the turbulent contribution, $-\rho\overline{u'w'}$, which is several hundred times $\mu(\partial u/\partial z)$.

3. As the wall is approached still closer, $\overline{u'w'}$ tends to zero and there is a region of very small width in which the logarithmic distribution of mean velocity has to give way to the linear distribution of equation (80). This region is called the viscous sub-layer and its outer edge is somewhere in the range $10 < zu_\tau/\nu < 30$, as may also be seen from Fig. I. 23, though these limits again depend on the pressure gradient. The value of u_τ depends, of course, on the upstream history of the boundary layer, and in Chapter II experimental techniques for

measuring u_τ are discussed together with analytical methods of predicting it in terms of the stream velocity U.

Also in Chapter II, the distribution of mean velocity within a turbulent boundary layer is considered in greater detail, and in particular improved versions of equation (81) are given which apply to practically the whole of the boundary layer.

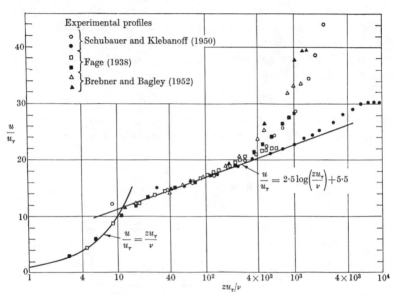

FIG. I. 23. A comparison between experimental velocity profiles and the two forms, (80) and (81), of the universal relationship $u/u_\tau = f(zu_\tau/\nu)$.

29. Turbulent flow in pipes and channels

In circular pipes and two-dimensional channels, at distances sufficiently far downstream of the inlet, a state of fully-developed turbulence is reached in which the mean flow is independent of the longitudinal coordinate x. The distribution of shear stress may be expressed in terms of the longitudinal pressure gradient by the following relations. Considering the equation of momentum in the longitudinal direction, we have for a channel of width $2a$:

$$\partial\tau/\partial z = \tau_w/a = -\partial p/\partial x, \tag{82}$$

and for a pipe of diameter $2a$:

$$\partial\tau/\partial z = \tau_w/a = -\tfrac{1}{2}\partial p/\partial x. \tag{83}$$

The constancy of the mean-velocity distribution makes both these flows simpler to calculate than a boundary layer which continually changes in thickness; further, equations (82) and (83) enable a direct evaluation of skin friction to be made, since it is relatively simple to measure the pressure gradient.

It is remarkable that, apart from the absence of intermittency in pipe flow, the structure of turbulence in a boundary layer is almost the

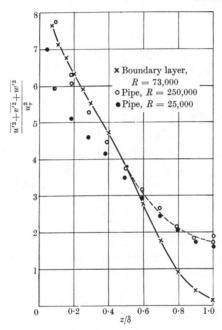

FIG. I. 24. Some experimental distributions of turbulent energy across a boundary layer and a pipe.

same as that in a pipe. Fig. I. 24 shows a comparison, made by Schubauer (1954), between the turbulent energy distribution of the two flows; a comparison between the component distributions, taking intermittency into account, shows even closer agreement. Similarities between the two types of flow extend to nearly every characteristic though whether or not the constants A and B in equation (81) take the same values is still a matter of lively debate. Certainly the distributions of shear stress are markedly different.

30. Equations of motion in general orthogonal coordinates

The equations of steady flow, (47) to (50), are sometimes required in terms of coordinates other than Cartesian which have been used, on the whole, up to now. With orthogonal coordinates (x_1, x_2, x_3) and a vector $\mathbf{F} = (F_1, F_2, F_3)$, the differential operators are as follows:

$$\nabla F \equiv \text{grad}\, F = \left(\frac{1}{h_1}\frac{\partial F}{\partial x_1}, \frac{1}{h_2}\frac{\partial F}{\partial x_2}, \frac{1}{h_3}\frac{\partial F}{\partial x_3}\right), \tag{84}$$

$$\mathbf{\nabla}.\mathbf{F} \equiv \text{div}\,\mathbf{F} = \frac{1}{h_1 h_2 h_3}\left\{\frac{\partial}{\partial x_1}(h_2 h_3 F_1) + \frac{\partial}{\partial x_2}(h_3 h_1 F_2) + \frac{\partial}{\partial x_3}(h_1 h_2 F_3)\right\}, \tag{85}$$

$$\mathbf{\nabla}\times\mathbf{F} \equiv \text{curl}\,\mathbf{F}$$
$$= \left(\frac{1}{h_2 h_3}\left\{\frac{\partial h_3 F_3}{\partial x_2} - \frac{\partial h_2 F_2}{\partial x_3}\right\}, \frac{1}{h_3 h_1}\left\{\frac{\partial h_1 F_1}{\partial x_3} - \frac{\partial h_3 F_3}{\partial x_1}\right\}, \frac{1}{h_1 h_2}\left\{\frac{\partial h_2 F_2}{\partial x_1} - \frac{\partial h_1 F_1}{\partial x_2}\right\}\right), \tag{86}$$

while from (84) and (85),

$$\nabla^2 F \equiv \text{div}\,\text{grad}\, F$$
$$= \frac{1}{h_1 h_2 h_3}\left\{\frac{\partial}{\partial x_1}\left(\frac{h_2 h_3}{h_1}\frac{\partial F}{\partial x_1}\right) + \frac{\partial}{\partial x_2}\left(\frac{h_3 h_1}{h_2}\frac{\partial F}{\partial x_2}\right) + \frac{\partial}{\partial x_3}\left(\frac{h_1 h_2}{h_3}\frac{\partial F}{\partial x_3}\right)\right\}. \tag{87}$$

In these expressions, $(h_1 dx_1, h_2 dx_2, h_3 dx_3)$ are the elements of length in the three orthogonal directions so that the total element of length ds is given by

$$(ds)^2 = \sum_1^3 h_i^2 (dx_i)^2.$$

Since Laplace's equation (50) has been used earlier in this chapter in terms of cylindrical polar coordinates (r, θ, z), we may take this as an example. The elements of length are $(dr, r\,d\theta, dz)$ so that

$$(h_1, h_2, h_3) \equiv (1, r, 1).$$

Equation (87) then gives

$$\nabla^2\phi = \frac{1}{r}\left\{\frac{\partial}{\partial r}\left(r\frac{\partial\phi}{\partial r}\right) + \frac{\partial}{\partial\theta}\left(\frac{1}{r}\frac{\partial\phi}{\partial\theta}\right) + \frac{\partial}{\partial z}\left(r\frac{\partial\phi}{\partial z}\right)\right\}, \tag{88}$$

and so Laplace's equation becomes

$$\frac{\partial^2\phi}{\partial r^2} + \frac{1}{r}\frac{\partial\phi}{\partial r} + \frac{1}{r^2}\frac{\partial^2\phi}{\partial\theta^2} + \frac{\partial^2\phi}{\partial z^2} = 0. \tag{89}$$

Since, from (84), $(u, v, w) = \mathbf{v} = \text{grad}\,\phi = (\partial\phi/\partial r, (\partial\phi/\partial\theta)/r, \partial\phi/\partial z)$, this equation may be written

$$\partial u/\partial r + u/r + (\partial v/\partial\theta)/r + \partial w/\partial z = 0, \tag{90}$$

which is the usual form for the equation of continuity in cylindrical polar coordinates.

II

THE CALCULATION OF THE BOUNDARY LAYER

1. Introduction

THE cardinal importance of the boundary layer in viscous flow has been emphasized in Chapter I. But it was suggested also—and this is considered in greater detail in Chapter III—that for many purposes it is not essential to know the complete velocity field of a boundary layer; often a knowledge of the skin friction, τ_w, of the displacement and momentum thicknesses, and of the separation point (where $\tau_w = 0$) may be enough on which to base a description not only of the main characteristics of the whole flow but also of the controlling mechanisms exerted by the boundary layer. In particular, knowledge of these quantities enables quite accurate calculations to be made of the forces acting on bodies within a fluid flow.

The major part of this Chapter is therefore taken up with the problem of calculating τ_w, δ_1, and δ_2 as functions of x in the two-dimensional flow past a solid boundary over which the stream velocity, $U(x)$, is prescribed. For the remainder, there are brief descriptions of those characteristics of boundary-layer flow which are peculiar to axi-symmetric bodies and to porous surfaces; the general problem of three-dimensional flow in the boundary layer is not touched upon. No attempt is made, either in this or succeeding chapters, to predict the position of transition on any surface in a given flow; the theory is presented in such a way that the value of x at transition is a disposable parameter.

Only the briefest account, in Section 7, is given of the principles underlying the measurement of the characteristics of a boundary layer; of the actual experimental techniques nothing is said, and for these reference should be made to *LBL* in which there is an exhaustive account of laminar boundary layers, or to the work of Pankhurst and Holder (1952) on wind-tunnel techniques in general.

2. The laminar boundary layer

The boundary-layer equation for steady two-dimensional flow, as it stands in (I. 48), is not in an appropriate form for making approximate calculations of the overall quantities τ_w, δ_1, and δ_2. A more convenient equation, used first by Kármán (1921), is obtained by integrating (I. 48) with respect to z from 0 to ∞. Thus we have the momentum integral equation

$$d\delta_2/dx + (H+2)(\delta_2/U)(dU/dx) - w_w/U = \tau_w/\rho U^2 = \tfrac{1}{2}c_f. \tag{1}$$

Here H is the form parameter:

$$H = \delta_1/\delta_2, \tag{2}$$

and the local coefficient of skin friction, c_f, has already been introduced in equation (I. 79). w_w is the value of the normal velocity at the surface of a porous boundary and the effect of an inward velocity in decreasing the boundary-layer thickness is clear from this equation. We shall in fact assume a solid surface hereafter, except in Section 17 in which some general results are quoted for the calculation of the boundary-layer characteristics over a porous surface.

Now if H and $\tau_w/\rho U^2$ are known as functions of δ_2 or of some suitable combination of δ_2 and U, equation (1) can be integrated, at least by a numerical process. Such functions may be found by a method due to Thwaites (1949b) who put (though in slightly different notation)

$$\text{at } z = 0: \quad \partial^2 u/\partial z^2 = -(U/\delta_2^2)\lambda, \quad \partial u/\partial z = (U/\delta_2)l(\lambda), \tag{3}$$

in which λ and $l(\lambda)$ are numerical variables. The function $l(\lambda)$ may be calculated for any particular solution of the boundary-layer equation (I. 48), and it is found that all known functions $l(\lambda)$ adhere reasonably closely to a universal function $l(\lambda)$. In the same way if H is regarded as depending only on λ, a reasonably valid universal function for H can also be found, namely $H(\lambda)$.

By putting $z = 0$ in equation (I. 48) and using equations (3) we find

$$\lambda = (\delta_2^2/\nu)(dU/dx). \tag{4}$$

Also $\qquad \tau_w/\rho U^2 = (\nu/U^2)(\partial u/\partial z)_{z=0} = \nu l(\lambda)/U\delta_2. \tag{5}$

With these two results, equation (1) may be rewritten in the form

$$(U/\nu)(d\delta_2^2/dx) = 2[-\{H(\lambda)+2\}\lambda + l(\lambda)] \equiv F(\lambda), \tag{6}$$

in which $F(\lambda)$ is a universal function. Equation (6) may now be solved numerically; but a consideration of the form of $F(\lambda)$ leads to a simpler result. Fig. II. 1 shows the values of $F(\lambda)$ for four solutions whose accuracy is undisputed; a satisfactory approximation to $F(\lambda)$ is the linear form

$$F(\lambda) = 0.45 - 6\lambda = 0.45 - 6(\delta_2^2/\nu)(dU/dx), \tag{7}$$

with which value, equation (6) is integrable in the form

$$U_0\delta_2^2/c\nu = 0.45(U/U_0)^{-6} \int_0^{x/c} (U/U_0)^5 \, d(x/c). \tag{8}$$

The representative fixed values, U_0 and c, of velocity and length have been incorporated to reduce the equation to non-dimensional form, and $x/c = 0$ is the upstream limit of the boundary layer. The momentum thickness, δ_2, may thus be calculated directly in terms of the given free-stream velocity distribution.

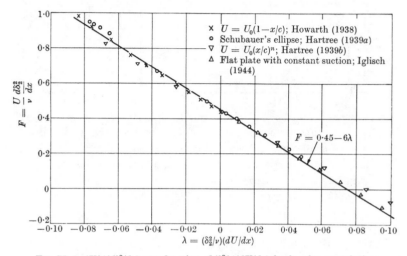

FIG. II. 1. $(U/\nu)(d\delta_2^2/dx)$ as a function of $(\delta_2^2/\nu)(dU/dx)$ for four known solutions of laminar boundary-layer flow.

With δ_2 known, λ can be calculated. The skin friction in equation (5) and the displacement thickness in equation (2) follow from this. The functions $l(\lambda)$ and $H(\lambda)$ necessary for this last calculation which were given originally by Thwaites have been slightly modified by Curle and Skan (1957) in the light of some recent calculations by Görtler (1957). Table II. 1 gives the modified values of these functions, λ being equal to the parameter $(-m)$ of the original papers.

The criterion for separation is seen from the table to be

$$\lambda = \lambda_s = (\delta_2^2/\nu)(dU/dx) = -0.090. \tag{9}$$

This may be put in terms of the stream velocity alone by means of (8); thus separation is predicted to occur at the point $x = x_s$ at which

$$(c/U_0)(dU/dx) \int_0^{x_s/c} (U/U_0)^5 \, d(x/c) = -\tfrac{1}{5}(U/U_0)^6. \tag{10}$$

This has an explicit solution for the case computed in detail by Howarth (1938): if $U = U_0[1-(x/c)]$, equation (10) gives, for the

TABLE II. 1

Functions for the calculation of τ_w and δ_1, from δ_2 and U

λ	$l(\lambda)$	$H(\lambda)$	λ	$l(\lambda)$	$H(\lambda)$	λ	$l(\lambda)$	$H(\lambda)$
$+0\cdot25$	0·500	2·00	$+0\cdot016$	0·244	2·55	$-0\cdot068$	0·095	3·09
$+0\cdot20$	0·463	2·07	0	0·220	2·61	$-0\cdot072$	0·085	3·16
$+0\cdot14$	0·404	2·18	$-0\cdot016$	0·195	2·67	$-0\cdot076$	0·072	3·24
$+0\cdot12$	0·382	2·23	$-0\cdot032$	0·168	2·75	$-0\cdot080$	0·056	3·35
$+0\cdot10$	0·359	2·28	$-0\cdot040$	0·153	2·81	$-0\cdot084$	0·038	3·47
$+0\cdot080$	0·333	2·34	$-0\cdot048$	0·138	2·87	$-0\cdot086$	0·027	3·54
$+0\cdot064$	0·313	2·39	$-0\cdot056$	0·122	2·94	$-0\cdot088$	0·015	3·62
$+0\cdot048$	0·291	2·44	$-0\cdot060$	0·113	2·99	$-0\cdot090$	0	3·70
$+0\cdot032$	0·268	2·49	$-0\cdot064$	0·104	3·04			

separation point, $x_s/c = 1 - (\frac{5}{11})^{\frac{1}{6}} = 0\cdot123$, while Howarth's value, which can be accepted as correct, is $x_s/c = 0\cdot120$. It is at once the strength and weakness of semi-empirical equations that constants can be adjusted especially to suit particular cases: the value $\lambda_s = -0\cdot086$, which in some respects is just as reasonable as that given in equation (9), predicts separation correctly for this particular flow.

3. The transition region

Although the details of the physical processes involved in the transition to turbulence of a laminar boundary layer are slowly being understood and have been described briefly in Section I. 26, the possibility of being able to predict with reasonable accuracy the position of transition on a given surface seems as remote as ever. Sometimes some peculiarity of the surface—say, a line of squashed flies on the wing of an aircraft—will clearly fix the transition point, but normally calculations of the boundary layer in any particular flow are carried out for a number of different points of transition. Of course, if a calculation is being made on the basis of observations from an experiment, the observed transition point should be taken in the analysis.

Once the transition point has been decided upon, the initial values of the characteristics of the turbulent boundary layer have to be deduced from the laminar characteristics which, we may assume, have already been calculated according to the method of Section 2.

Now we shall find in the following sections that, given the stream velocity distribution, an approximate solution of the turbulent layer requires no more than the initial values of the two variables δ_2 and H. The assumption is often made that H takes the initial value 1·4; possibly slightly greater accuracy is obtained by giving H a value which depends on the initial value of δ_2 and this is discussed more fully in Section 14. As to δ_2, if it is assumed that transition occurs instantaneously, then there is no opportunity for external forces to affect the flow at the transition point and so there is no change in the flux of momentum through the transition region. In other words, δ_2 is assumed to be continuous at the transition point. In view of the recent recognition that transition takes place over a definite length of surface, this argument clearly has its flaws; on the other hand, there is no evidence which relates inaccuracies in the prediction of δ_2 by the methods soon to be described to any inaccuracy in its initial value. Experimental evidence on the whole supports the assumption just described, which is illustrated in Fig. II. 2.

A typical value of H for a laminar layer at transition is 2·8, from which we see that the displacement thickness falls sharply during transition to roughly half its value. But thereafter it increases much more rapidly than before and this behaviour, which is illustrated in Fig. II. 2, often has a pronounced effect on the flow outside the boundary layer. For example, in supersonic flow, where the effect is particularly noticeable, the rapid increase in displacement thickness after transition often results in a compression wave which modifies the inviscid velocity field; this in its turn causes a secondary modification to the distribution of boundary-layer thickness and even to the position of transition. Similar effects, but often of greater magnitude, arise from a separation point. The process, just described, of continual adjustment between the viscous and inviscid regions of flow is probably not manifested as an unsteadiness in a real fluid (except possibly in its initial accelerating phase), but is rather the process by which we should attempt to carry out a refined calculation; on the other hand, the stability of any flow pattern is probably governed partly by such mutual interactions—a slight change in the position of transition, for example, induces a change in the pressure distribution which encourages the transition to return to its original position.

In the following sections, therefore, we consider the calculation of τ_w, δ_1, and δ_2 for a turbulent boundary layer in terms of the stream velocity $U(x)$, the initial values at transition being given by the criteria we have discussed.

4. The momentum integral equation in turbulent flow

The equation for turbulent flow which corresponds to (1) is obtained by integrating equation (I. 76) with respect to z between the limits 0 and ∞; thus, for a solid boundary,

$$d\delta_2/dx + (H+2)(\delta_2/U)(dU/dx) = \tau_w/\rho U^2 + \frac{d}{dx}\int\limits_0^\infty (\overline{u'^2}-\overline{w'^2})\,dz/U^2. \quad (11)$$

We may recall from Section I. 27 that on the mean velocity field (u, w) is superimposed the turbulent field (u', w') whose time-mean is zero. The various thicknesses of the boundary layer and the skin friction all retain, in terms of the mean velocity, the same definitions as for laminar flow.

It is usual to neglect the last term in the momentum equation (11); this is partly because its inclusion necessitates some assumption about the distributions of u' and w', and partly because it is, in fact, often much smaller than $\tau_w/\rho U^2$. However, near a separation point, the two terms on the right-hand side are of comparable magnitude, and in all the subsequent analysis which is based on the momentum equation in the form (1), it must be remembered that unknown errors arise in the equation near separation, errors which are further aggravated by the neglect, also, of the pressure gradient across the boundary layer. The methods of the ensuing sections are, however, based more on the form than on the strict equality of the momentum equation, and so the neglect of the terms under discussion is usually acceptable.

Further integral relations similar to (1) may be obtained by multiplying the equation of motion (I. 76) by $z^m u^n$ and then integrating from $z = 0$ to $z = \infty$. Some of those derived for small integral values of m and n have been used in approximate methods of calculation, particularly for the laminar boundary layer. With $m = 0$, $n = 1$ we obtain an equation of energy

$$\frac{1}{U^3}\frac{d}{dx}(\delta_3 U^3) = \frac{2}{\rho U^3}\int\limits_0^\infty \tau\frac{\partial u}{\partial z}\,dz \equiv \frac{2D}{\rho U^3}, \quad (12)$$

in which

$$\delta_3 = \int\limits_0^\infty (u/U)[1-(u/U)^2]\,dz. \quad (13)$$

In the derivation of this equation, terms similar to the last of equation (11) have again been ignored, with similar justification. This energy equation shows the importance of shear in the mean flow in maintaining or increasing turbulence; the right-hand side represents, in non-dimensional form, the work being done by the shear stresses in transferring energy from the mean to the turbulent flow, as well as the energy directly dissipated into heat.

5. Turbulent flow on a flat plate

We consider first the simplest case, of flow for which, according to the boundary-layer equations, the pressure is constant everywhere. This corresponds to the physical flow of a uniform stream past a semi-infinite flat plate set parallel to the stream; for this reason this constant-pressure flow, which has such importance in the analysis of turbulent

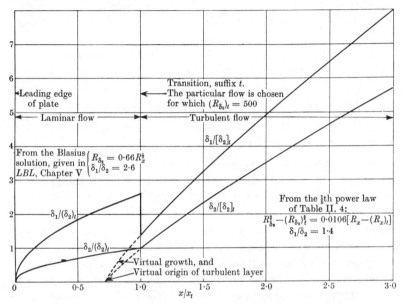

Fig. II. 2. These curves, showing the growth of a boundary layer in a constant pressure, illustrate various theoretical ideas.

boundary layers, is customarily called flat-plate flow. We must be careful not to confuse this term with the fact that the boundary conditions for the boundary-layer equations are always specified, as an approximation, on the plane $z = 0$.

It is usual to represent the laminar flow upstream of transition by a fictitious length of turbulent flow whose momentum thickness at the transition point equals that of the calculated laminar flow. We are thus led to talk of an equivalent flat plate from whose leading edge the downstream distance, x, is measured; $R_x = Ux/\nu$ is then assumed to be the quantity on which depend all other properties of the real turbulent boundary layer, when expressed non-dimensionally. Thus the local Reynolds numbers, $R_{\delta_1} = U\delta_1/\nu$ and $R_{\delta_2} = U\delta_2/\nu$, the skin friction coefficient, c_f, and the velocity profile are all uniquely related to R_x.

The hypothesis of a virtual origin of turbulence some distance up-stream of the observed transition position has been well justified by observations of mean flow. It has even been found to be valid for the description of the structure of the turbulence in the boundary layer: Klebanoff and Diehl (1951) have shown that if a boundary layer is artificially thickened its eddy structure only a few boundary-layer thicknesses downstream of the disturbance resembles that of a boundary layer of the same local Reynolds number which would have formed naturally on a much longer smooth plate.

The idea of the virtual origin of turbulence is illustrated in Fig. II. 2, the numerical values of which are calculated from formulae in Section 8, for the particular case of $R_{\delta_2} = 500$ at the transition point.

6. Velocity profiles in turbulent flow on a flat plate

A dimensional argument suggests that the velocity profile should be of the form
$$u/U = f(z/x, Ux/\nu), \tag{14}$$
where f is a universal function which depends at most on the nature of turbulence. The no-slip condition at the boundary requires $f = 0$ at $z = 0$, and as $z \to \infty$, $f \to 1$. This last condition is usually replaced by
$$f(\delta/x, Ux/\nu) = 1, \tag{15}$$
where δ, loosely called the thickness of the boundary layer, is defined as the minimum value of z for which the velocity takes, for all practical purposes, its stream value. Although this is in no sense a precise definition, δ can be determined, within a variation of about 5 per cent, from experimental observations; further, it is useful in analysis to be able to say that $u = U$ when $z = \delta$.

It follows from equation (14) that δ/x, δ_1/x, and δ_2/x and the form parameter $H = \delta_1/\delta_2$ are functions of $R_x = Ux/\nu$ only. Hence the velocity profile may be written without any loss of generality in the form
$$u/U = h(z/\delta, H). \tag{16}$$
Similarly, the skin friction may be written as
$$\tau_w \equiv \rho u_\tau^2 = \rho U^2 g(Ux/\nu), \tag{17}$$
and a combination of all these results suggests an alternative form for the velocity profile:
$$u/u_\tau = k(z/\delta, zu_\tau/\nu), \tag{18}$$
h, g, and k all being universal functions. The convenience of the forms (16) and (18) is that they involve local quantities only.

A good and convenient approximation to most profiles obtained experimentally is
$$u/U = (z/\delta)^m, \tag{19}$$

where m takes a value between $\frac{1}{5}$ and $\frac{1}{9}$, depending on the Reynolds number, R_x. It may easily be found that, for this profile,

$$\delta_1/\delta = m/(m+1); \quad \delta_2/\delta = m/(m+1)(2m+1); \quad H = 2m+1. \quad (20)$$

Thus it is equivalent to $u/U = (z/\delta)^{\frac{1}{2}(H-1)}$, which is in the form (16). The variation of m with R_x, however, is a disadvantage.

A preferable form, which attempts to take scale effect into account, is the logarithmic profile already given in equation (I. 81). This is only applicable to the inner fully turbulent core and in an attempt to extend the range of its utility, Kármán (1934) suggested

$$u/u_\tau = A \log(zu_\tau/\nu) + \phi(z/\delta), \quad (21)$$

where $\phi(z/\delta)$ is a universal function, taking a constant value in the logarithmic region. Thus

$$U/u_\tau = A \log(\delta u_\tau/\nu) + \phi(1) \quad (22)$$

and, by subtraction of (21) from (22),

$$(U-u)/u_\tau = -A \log(z/\delta) + \phi(1) - \phi(z/\delta) = j(z/\delta), \quad (23)$$

where $j(z/\delta)$ is a universal function for flat plates. Equation (23) is not strictly valid inside the viscous layer, since by taking $z = 0$, we see that it would imply that u_τ/U is a constant; this is not, however, found to be a serious objection to the general form of (23), for Schultz-Grunow (1940), Coles (1953, 1956), and Clauser (1954) have all shown the validity of the relation (23) for profiles obtained in a variety of conditions. That each has preferred his own function $j(z/\delta)$ is shown in Fig. II. 3. If $\eta = z/\delta$, the constants C_1 and C_2, defined by

$$C_1 = \int\limits_0^1 j(\eta)\,d\eta \quad \text{and} \quad C_2 = \int\limits_0^1 [j(\eta)]^2\,d\eta, \quad (24)$$

exemplify the differences between the three functions.

TABLE II. 2

Constants occurring in formulae for velocity profiles

	C_1	C_2
Schultz-Grunow . .	3·34	21·9
Coles (1953) . . .	4·05	29·0
Clauser	3·60	22·0
Coles (1956) . . .	3·88	26·4

The comparatively flat part of Coles's curve for $0·2 < \eta < 0·8$ is characteristic of the results of almost all other investigators. Differences in the definition of the boundary-layer thickness δ account for much of the discrepancy between the various curves. In his second paper Coles (1956) has proposed a definition of δ which is both plausible and useful for turbulent flow in a wide variety of circumstances.

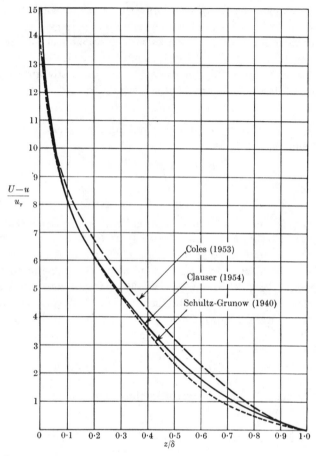

FIG. II. 3. Universal functions for the velocity defect in turbulent flow on a flat plate.

The displacement and momentum thicknesses, and the form parameter, are calculable from equations (23) and (24) as

$$\left. \begin{aligned} \delta_1/\delta &= C_1 u_\tau/U \\ \delta_2/\delta &= C_1 u_\tau/U - C_2(u_\tau/U)^2 \\ H &= (1 - C_2 u_\tau/C_1 U)^{-1} \end{aligned} \right\}. \tag{25}$$

These relations together with the functions in Fig. II. 3 determine the
boundary-layer characteristics completely once one of them is known.
The theoretical determination of u_τ as a function of R_x is discussed in
Section 8, but meanwhile in Section 7 we consider some of the experimental methods of estimating u_τ.

7. Experimental methods of measuring skin friction

To measure accurately the skin friction is an exceedingly difficult
task which stands as a perpetual challenge to the experimenter. We
may list the most common experimental methods of determining c_f.
Some attempt a direct measurement. Others measure the overall coefficient C_f, defined by

$$C_f = (1/x) \int_0^x c_f \, dx = (1/R_x) \int_0^{R_x} c_f \, d(R_x), \qquad (26)$$

for a range of values of R_x and so derive c_f by numerical differentiation.

(i) Measurements of the growth of momentum thickness, or of the
drag forces on whole plates. The latter have usually been obtained by
towing models in water tanks and a comprehensive review of such
experiments has been given by Hughes (1952). Apart from the obvious
uncertainties about transition and surface finish, a hitherto unsuspected
source of error has recently been found in the secondary flow near the
edges of plates of small or moderate aspect ratios; this causes an increase in drag, a theoretical explanation of which has been tentatively
proposed by Townsend (1954).

(ii) Measurements of the shear force on isolated surface elements.
The magnitude of the forces involved, and the disturbance to the
boundary layer caused by the unavoidable gap, however small, between
the measuring element and the remainder of the plate are troublesome,
as indicated by Kempf (1929) and Dhawan (1952). However, Smith
and Walker (1958) show that, with improved techniques, the method
is now reliable.

(iii) The friction velocity may be deduced from the shape of the
velocity profile by means of equation (I. 81). The accuracy of this,
however, is affected by the uncertainty about the constants A and B,
which is reflected in Table I. 1.

(iv) At very low Reynolds numbers it is possible to measure the
velocity profile in the viscous layer, and so to deduce u_τ from (I. 80).

(v) The rate of diffusion of heat away from a heated surface element is proportional to $u_\tau^{\frac{1}{2}}$—that is, to $c_f^{\frac{1}{2}}$—and may be measured electrically as has been shown by Ludwieg and Tillmann (1949).

(vi) Preston (1954b) used a series of geometrically similar pitot tubes placed in contact with the surface. On the assumption of local dynamical similarity of the turbulent flow, a unique relation exists between R^2c_p and R^2c_f, where R is a Reynolds number based on the diameter of the tube and the free-stream speed, and c_p is the pitot pressure coefficient. Preston obtained this relation by measurements in a fully turbulent pipe, in which c_f is known from the pressure drop by equation (I. 83), but Relf, Pankhurst, and Walker (1954) have doubted whether it is correct to use the same relation for flow on a flat plate.

(vii) Schubauer and Klebanoff (1950) attempted to determine skin friction from experimental observations of the Reynolds stress $(-\overline{u'w'})$ and typical experimental results are shown in Fig. II. 7. The curves obtained were extrapolated inwards to $z = 0$ along lines whose slopes were known from the relation $(\partial\tau/\partial z)_{z=0} = -dp/dx$ which is a consequence of equation (I. 76). This method was not successful, mainly because of the difficulty of measuring $(-\overline{u'w'})$ accurately, but it may prove valuable when hot-wire techniques are further advanced.

8. Theoretical methods of predicting the skin friction on a flat plate

To derive analytically a relation between c_f and R_x, it is convenient to use the variable

$$\zeta = U/u_\tau. \tag{27}$$

Thus, in terms of ζ, $c_f = \tau_w/\tfrac{1}{2}\rho U^2 = 2\zeta^{-2}. \tag{28}$

The momentum integral equation (1) may, in the case of the flat plate, be written

$$\tfrac{1}{2}c_f = dR_{\delta_2}/dR_x = \zeta^{-2}. \tag{29}$$

Elimination of δ between equations (22) and (25) gives

$$R_{\delta_2} = K(C_1 - C_2\,\zeta^{-1})\exp(\zeta/A), \tag{30}$$

where $K = \exp[-\phi(1)/A]$ is given the value $0\cdot0424$ by Coles (1953). The equation obtained by the elimination of R_{δ_2} between (29) and (30) may be integrated to give

$$R_x = (a\zeta^2 + b\zeta + c)\exp(\zeta/A) - c. \tag{31}$$

Here it has been assumed that at the virtual origin, $R_x = 0$, the boundary layer is of zero thickness and so, that $\zeta = 0$. The constants a, b, and c are given by

$$a = KC_1, \quad b = -K(2C_1A + C_2), \quad c = 2KA(C_1A + C_2), \tag{32}$$

in terms of the constants defined in equation (24) and given in Table II. 2, of A given in Table I. 1, and of K. Thus, if R_x is given, ζ follows from (31), R_{δ_2} from (30), R_{δ_1} and H from (25). The mean friction coefficient may be calculated from equations (26) and (29) as

$$C_f = 2R_{\delta_2}/R_x. \tag{33}$$

In the above analysis, there are four disposable constants; we may choose suitable values for a, b, c, and A in equation (31), or alternatively take values for C_1, C_2, A, and $\phi(1)$ or K. Following Coles (1953), we adopt the following values:

$$C_1 = 4 \cdot 05, \quad C_2 = 29 \cdot 0, \quad A = 2 \cdot 5, \quad K = 0 \cdot 0424;$$

and the corresponding values for C_f, R_x, c_f, R_{δ_2}, R_δ, and H are given in Table II. 3. These values do not differ significantly from those given more recently by Coles (1956) after more comprehensive investigations.

TABLE II. 3

Properties of the turbulent boundary layer at constant pressure as calculated by Coles (1953)

$10^3 C_f$	R_x	$10^3 c_f$	R_{δ_2}	R_δ	H
5·0	$1 \cdot 05 \times 10^5$	6·26	$3 \cdot 29 \times 10^2$	$2 \cdot 62 \times 10^2$	1·558
4·0	$3 \cdot 64 \times 10^5$	4·92	$8 \cdot 95 \times 10^2$	$7 \cdot 28 \times 10^2$	1·471
3·6	$6 \cdot 78 \times 10^5$	4·39	$1 \cdot 49 \times 10^3$	$1 \cdot 22 \times 10^3$	1·436
3·2	$1 \cdot 40 \times 10^6$	3·87	$2 \cdot 70 \times 10^3$	$2 \cdot 24 \times 10^3$	1·401
3·0	$2 \cdot 11 \times 10^6$	3·60	$3 \cdot 80 \times 10^3$	$3 \cdot 16 \times 10^3$	1·383
2·8	$3 \cdot 30 \times 10^6$	3·35	$5 \cdot 53 \times 10^3$	$4 \cdot 62 \times 10^3$	1·366
2·6	$5 \cdot 43 \times 10^6$	3·09	$8 \cdot 38 \times 10^3$	$7 \cdot 06 \times 10^3$	1·348
2·4	$9 \cdot 43 \times 10^6$	2·84	$1 \cdot 34 \times 10^4$	$1 \cdot 13 \times 10^4$	1·330
2·2	$1 \cdot 76 \times 10^7$	2·58	$2 \cdot 27 \times 10^4$	$1 \cdot 94 \times 10^4$	1·311
2·0	$3 \cdot 55 \times 10^7$	2·33	$4 \cdot 14 \times 10^4$	$3 \cdot 55 \times 10^4$	1·293
1·8	$8 \cdot 00 \times 10^7$	2·08	$8 \cdot 33 \times 10^4$	$7 \cdot 20 \times 10^4$	1·274
1·6	$2 \cdot 07 \times 10^8$	1·84	$1 \cdot 90 \times 10^5$	$1 \cdot 66 \times 10^5$	1·254
1·4	$6 \cdot 43 \times 10^8$	1·59	$5 \cdot 13 \times 10^5$	$4 \cdot 50 \times 10^5$	1·234
1·2	$2 \cdot 58 \times 10^9$	1·35	$1 \cdot 75 \times 10^6$	$1 \cdot 55 \times 10^6$	1·213
1·0	$1 \cdot 52 \times 10^{10}$	1·12	$8 \cdot 48 \times 10^6$	$7 \cdot 60 \times 10^6$	1·191

In Fig. II. 4 is shown this relationship between c_f and R_{δ_2}, together with others soon to be cited. We have deliberately omitted a comparison between these analytical curves and the multitudinous experimental values which from time to time have been found. The scatter in experimental values is roughly the same as the difference between any two analytical values, to choose any one of which is largely a matter of personal preference. We have selected Coles's values for tabulation since the analysis leading up to them has an air of plausibility.

From the large number of other relationships between c_f and R_{δ_2} which have been proposed, we may choose a few of the most well known. Those which use R_x in preference to R_{δ_2} may be read in conjunction with equation (33). Each formula is represented by a curve in Fig. II. 4.

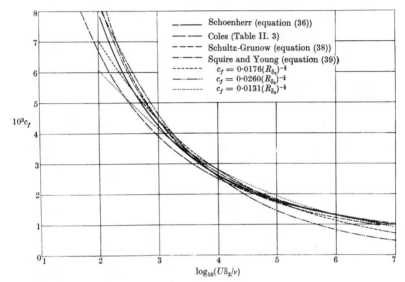

FIG. II. 4. The local skin friction coefficient for a turbulent boundary layer on a flat plate.

1. Kármán (1934). By retaining only the highest-order term in ζ on the right-hand side of equation (31) and taking logarithms, we find that

$$c_f^{-\frac{1}{2}} = A' + B' \log_{10}(R_x c_f),$$

where

$$A' = 2^{-\frac{1}{2}}[\phi(1) - A \log_e(2C_1)]; \qquad B' = 2^{-\frac{1}{2}}A \log_e 10. \tag{34}$$

Values of $A' = 1 \cdot 7$ and $B' = 4 \cdot 15$ were found directly from experiment by Kempf (1929). It is interesting to compare these with the values $A' = 1 \cdot 96$ and $B' = 4 \cdot 07$ which follow from the values of A, C_1, and $\phi(1)$ used by Coles. Equation (34) is often referred to as the Kármán–Schoenherr formula, since a formula was obtained by Schoenherr (1932) for the mean friction coefficient by a similar analysis and approximation. This is

$$C_f^{-\frac{1}{2}} = 4 \cdot 13 \log_{10}(R_x C_f), \tag{35}$$

and it is a result which has been widely used. The corresponding local friction is obtained from equations (34) and (35):

$$c_f = \int d(x C_f)/dx = C_f/(1 + 3 \cdot 58 C_f^{\frac{1}{2}}). \tag{36}$$

2. Prandtl–Schlichting. The implicit form of equation (35) is not convenient, so, using an analysis similar to Kármán's, Prandtl (1935) obtained a numerical result; to this, Schlichting fitted the formula

$$C_f = 0.455(\log_{10} R_x)^{-2.58}. \tag{37}$$

3. Schultz-Grunow (1940). Following Kármán's analysis, but with new experimental results, Schultz-Grunow obtained the formulae

$$\left.\begin{aligned} c_f &= 0.370(\log_{10} R_x)^{-2.584} \\ C_f &= 0.427(-0.407 + \log_{10} R_x)^{-2.64} \end{aligned}\right\}. \tag{38}$$

4. Squire and Young (1938). Corresponding to equation (34), a formula expressing c_f directly in terms of R_{δ_2} is obtained by taking the logarithm of equation (30) with only the first term on the right-hand side retained. This gives

$$c_f^{-\frac{1}{2}} = C' + D' \log_{10}(R_{\delta_2}), \tag{39}$$

where $C' = A' + 2^{-\frac{1}{2}} A \log_e 2$, $D' = B'$, and A' and B' are given by (34). Squire and Young (1938) fitted this formula to values of c_f and R_{δ_2} computed from (37), by taking $C' = 2.54$ and $D' = 4.16$. The values of Coles's constants would give $C' = 3.19$ and $D' = 4.07$.

5. Power laws. A good interpolation to the relation between c_f and R_{δ_2} over any given small range of R_{δ_2} can be provided by power laws of the type

$$c_f = 2C(R_{\delta_2})^{-n}, \tag{40}$$

both C and n being disposable. The corresponding relation between C_f and R_x is found by integrating the momentum equation (29), and is

$$C_f = 2[(1+n)C]^{1/(1+n)} R_x^{-n/(1+n)}. \tag{41}$$

Table II. 4 gives the constants in (40) and (41) for three values of n: from Fig. II. 4 we see that $n = \frac{1}{5}$ gives acceptable results over a wide range of Reynolds number, and this value was used in the compilation of Fig. II. 2.

TABLE II. 4

Power laws for skin friction

n	$2C$	$2[(1+n)C]^{1/(1+n)}$	Author
$\frac{1}{7}$	0.026	0.074	Kármán (1921)
$\frac{1}{6}$	0.0176	0.0450	Young (1953)
$\frac{1}{8}$	0.0131	0.0306	Falkner (1943b)

9. Velocity profiles in turbulent flow in a variable pressure

The variation with x of pressure, p, or of free-stream velocity, U, introduces a complication which the analysis of the preceding sections is not fitted to meet. Most of the results of those sections stemmed originally from dimensional arguments such as those that led to equation (16), though of course the final form of formulae such as equation (35) is obtained and justified by the measure of agreement with experiment. But the details of the dimensional arguments are inadequate for the more general flow since they do not include a parameter such as $\Lambda = (\delta_2^2/\nu)(dU/dx)$ which describes the nature of the pressure variations.

As a start we consider the most general dimensional result for the flat plate:

$$u/U = f(z/\delta, H) \tag{42}$$

from equation (16). Even though the value of H varies from between 1·35 and 1·5 near transition to between 2 and 2·6 at separation, and even though Λ does not appear, the form of this equation seems to describe adequately all measured velocity profiles, even those in a variable pressure. It is strongly supported by experimental data given by Doenhoff and Tetervin (1943) and by Schubauer and Klebanoff (1950). In seeking a definite expression for f, we recall the power law (19) and note that the index is connected with the value of H, as given in equation (20); from those two equations we therefore have

$$\frac{u}{U} = \left(\frac{z}{\delta}\right)^{\frac{1}{2}(H-1)} = \left[\frac{H-1}{H(H+1)} \cdot \frac{z}{\delta_2}\right]^{\frac{1}{2}(H-1)}, \tag{43}$$

and this simple law seems to be reasonably accurate even for the values of H which occur near separation; for the smaller values of H near transition, the index takes the familiar value of about 0·2.

It may be wondered how it is that an external pressure gradient could seriously affect the structure of a turbulent boundary layer, since its typical lengths are so much greater than the lengths associated with the turbulence in the inner core of the layer. In fact, as found by Ludwieg and Tillmann (1949) and already noted in Section I. 28, in the inner part of the layer (but outside the viscous layer) the velocity profile is again expressible in terms of the local friction velocity by the logarithmic law (I. 81). Fig. II. 5 shows a set of velocity profiles in an adverse pressure gradient, plotted semi-logarithmically the better to show the inner region. At first sight the existence of this inner region would appear to rule out the uni-parametric representation of a complete profile; its influence on the values of δ_1, δ_2, and H is, however, very small.

Coles (1956) has achieved a single analytic description of the velocity profile, using universal functions, which is valid over the whole boundary layer. He proposes a form more general than (21), namely

$$u/u_\tau = A \log(zu_\tau/\nu) + B + A\Pi(x)p(z/\delta), \tag{44}$$

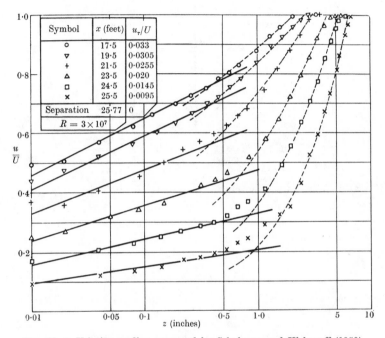

FIG. II. 5. Velocity profiles, measured by Schubauer and Klebanoff (1950), for a turbulent boundary layer in a positive pressure gradient. The formula $U = (u_\tau/U)[A \log(zu_\tau/\nu) + B]$ is represented by the solid lines; power laws are represented by the broken lines.

in which $\Pi(x)$ is a form parameter. By examining extensive experimental results, he finds it possible to specify, numerically, a universal function $p(z/\delta)$ which satisfies the conditions

$$p(0) = 0, \quad p(1) = 2, \quad \int_0^2 (z/\delta)\,dp = 1. \tag{45}$$

He calls $p(z/\delta)$ the law of the wake and it is tabulated in Table II. 5. Four equations can be derived which express the mutual relations between the six quantities (U/u_τ), (δ_1/δ), $(\delta u_\tau/\nu)$, $(\delta_1 U/\nu)$, Π, and H.

In particular, if (U/u_τ) and $(\delta_1 u_\tau/\nu)$ are supposed known, Π is given by

$$2\Pi - \log(1+\Pi) = U/Au_\tau - \log(\delta_1 U/\nu) - B/A + \log A; \qquad (46)$$

the velocity profile can then be deduced from (44) and Table II. 5.

TABLE II. 5

The function $p(z/\delta)$—Coles's law of the wake

z/δ	$p(z/\delta)$	z/δ	$p(z/\delta)$
0	0	0·55	1·149
0·05	0·004	0·60	1·303
0·10	0·029	0·65	1·458
0·15	0·084	0·70	1·600
0·20	0·168	0·75	1·729
0·25	0·272	0·80	1·840
0·30	0·396	0·85	1·926
0·35	0·535	0·90	1·980
0·40	0·685	0·95	1·999
0·45	0·838	1·00	2·000
0·50	0·994		

10. Skin friction in a variable pressure

Ludwieg and Tillmann (1949) use equation (I.81) to infer the existence of a relation for c_f which involves the form parameter as well as the local Reynolds number. Assuming the equation to be valid for the value $z = \delta_2$ — a typical value for δ_2/δ is $\frac{1}{6}$ — we have

$$u_{\delta_2}/u_\tau = A\log(u_\tau \delta_2/\nu) + B, \qquad (47)$$

where u_{δ_2} is the velocity at $z = \delta_2$. We now introduce the parameter

$$\gamma = u_{\delta_2}/U = \gamma(H), \qquad (48)$$

γ being a function of H only, on the assumption of equation (42). The right-hand side of equation (I. 81) is approximated by $C(zu_\tau/\nu)^n$ over a range of z including $z = \delta_2$, and equation (47) is then written as

$$\gamma\zeta = C(U\delta_2/\nu\zeta)^n, \qquad (49)$$

$\zeta = U/u_\tau$ being the parameter already introduced in equation (27). Thus from equations (28) and (49)

$$c_f = 2/\zeta^2 = 2C^{-2/(1+n)}(U\delta_2/\nu)^{-2n/(1+n)}\gamma^{2/(1+n)}. \qquad (50)$$

Remembering that γ is a function of H only, we note that this is of the same form as

$$c_f = 0.246(U\delta_2/\nu)^{-0.268}10^{-0.678H}, \qquad (51)$$

which is an empirical relation designed by Ludwieg and Tillmann to fit experimental values as closely as possible. For all practical purposes, this equation gives results which are indistinguishable, in the particular case of the flat plate for $10^5 < R_x < 10^7$, from those from the formula of Schultz-Grunow given in equation (38).

This formula may be used, among other purposes, to deduce the skin friction from experimental values of δ_2 and H. Fig. II. 6 refers to experiments on an aerofoil by Schubauer and Klebanoff (1950) and equation (51) is represented by the broken line which is probably the

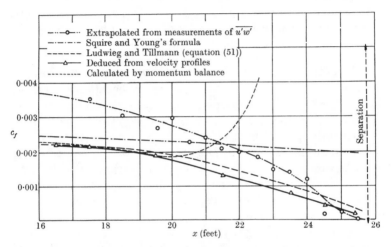

FIG. II. 6. Various evaluations of skin friction on an aerofoil based on data of Schubauer and Klebanoff (1950).

most reliable result. The other curves in the figure were calculated as follows:

1. The solid curve was obtained by fitting the logarithmic profile, that is equation (I. 81) with $A = 2 \cdot 5$ and $B = 5 \cdot 5$, to the measured profiles in the way indicated in Fig. II. 5. A value of u_τ/U, and hence of c_f, is deduced for each profile.

2. The curve for c_f obtained from the momentum equation (1) agrees well with the two previous curves up to $x = 17 \cdot 5$ at which point the positive pressure gradient commenced. The rapid rise of c_f thereafter towards separation is typical of other calculations from the momentum equation in its form (1), and was regarded as genuine by Wieghardt and Tillmann (1944); it is now regarded as a spurious effect arising first from the omission of the last term in equation (11) which takes into account the turbulence distribution and second, from the neglect, common to all boundary-layer theory, of the variation of pressure across the

boundary layer. It is also possible that the very assumption of two-dimensional flow is seriously in error near separation.

3. The curve calculated by the method of Squire and Young (1938) lies close to the others, so long as the values of H are near that for a flat plate but it is inaccurate for values of H typical of those near separation.

4. The remaining curve shows values of c_f calculated from measured distributions of $\overline{u'w'}$ in the way described in Section 7; it is now realized that these values may be in error by as much as half, on account of the difficulties in the hot-wire technique.

11. Theoretical methods of predicting the momentum thickness

The approximate form (1) of the momentum equation for turbulent flow enables δ_2 to be calculated only if functional relationships are known between both c_f and H and the other variables of the equation. This was our starting-point in the analysis for laminar layers in Section 2, and there was no difficulty in formulating the appropriate parameters between which universal functional relationships were to be found. But for turbulent flow, it is not clear which parameters are the best and a large number of methods, each based on different functional relationships and different variables, have been proposed in the past. It is as well, in examining any particular method based on the momentum equation, to bear in mind that it is distinguished from the others only by the two relationships which it assumes involving c_f and H. This is not to say that the accuracy of the final formula of a method can readily be assessed by the accuracy of the two basic assumptions: it is quite possible that relatively serious errors in these may tend to counterbalance each other.

The following analysis, due to Maskell (1951), derives a result first given (though in a less convincing manner) by Buri (1931) and later described by Goldstein (1938). The first assumption is

$$c_f = 2(R_{\delta_2})^{-n} G(H), \tag{52}$$

as was proposed by Ludwieg and Tillmann (1949). The value of n and the function $G(H)$ will be considered later. In terms of the new variables

$$\Theta = \delta(R_{\delta_2})^n \tag{53}$$

and

$$\Gamma = -(\Theta/U)(dU/dx), \tag{54}$$

the momentum equation (1) becomes

$$d\Theta/dx = (1+n)G(H) + \Gamma\{(1+n)H + 2 + n\}. \tag{55}$$

After an exhaustive examination of experimental data, Maskell showed that for the values of n usually associated with equation (52) the right-hand side of (55) is, to a good approximation in all cases, a linear function of Γ only. This is his second assumption, necessary for a solution, and thus

$$d\Theta/dx = \alpha + \beta\Gamma, \qquad (56)$$

α and β being constants. The values of n, α, and β given by Maskell

TABLE II. 6

Constants in the momentum equation (56)

Author	n		α	β
Buri (1931)	(Increasing pressure)	0·25	0·01475	3·945
	(Decreasing pressure)	0·25	0·0175	4·15
Garner (1944) . . .	(Increasing pressure)	0·167	0·0076	3·73
Maskell (1951) . . .		0·2155	0·01173	4·20
Truckenbrodt (1952) . .		0·167	0·0076	3·536
Schuh (1954) . . .		0·268	0·0185	4·27
Spence (1956a) . . .		0·2	0·0106	4·0

and by a number of other authors are listed in Table II. 6. Equation (56) may be integrated to give

$$\Theta U^\beta = \alpha \int U^\beta \, dx, \qquad (57)$$

and with the help of equation (53), of a reference length c and a velocity U_0, this may be rewritten in non-dimensional terms:

$$(\delta_2/c)^{1+n}(U/U_0)^{\beta+n} = \alpha R^{-n} \int_{x_0/c}^{x/c} (U/U_0)^\beta \, d(x/c) + K. \qquad (58)$$

Here $R = U_0 c/\nu$; and the constant, K, is the value of the left-hand side at the starting-point, $x = x_0$, of the integration. Normally, this point is taken at the transition point at which δ_2 takes the final value for the laminar region, given by equation (8). Experience suggests that any of the last four sets of constants in Table II. 6 will give values accurate to within about 5 per cent even up to the separation point.

It may be noted that equation (56) is a direct consequence of equations (1) and (52) provided $(H+2)$ is taken to be constant; thus the values in Table II. 6 proposed by Spence, on which the analysis of later sections is based, are compatible with the $\frac{1}{5}$th-power law for skin friction and the constant value $H = 1·5$. Maskell's work may therefore be regarded as justifying such approximations.

It is also interesting to note the analogy between this analysis and the approximate theory of laminar boundary layers, given in Section 2. With $n = 1$ in equation (53), and with $\alpha = 0.45$ and $\beta = 5$ in equation (56), equation (58) reduces to Thwaites's formula (8).

Perhaps at this stage it is helpful to survey what has so far been achieved, and what still has to be done, for a full solution of a turbulent boundary layer. Equation (58) enables δ_2 to be calculated. Equations (43) and (51) then give the mean velocity distribution and skin friction, in terms, however, of H. The calculation of H is therefore the outstanding task and for this another equation is needed, for we have exhausted the possibilities of the momentum equation. In the following sections we shall see how the energy equation (12) can be used to obtain an equation for H.

12. The distribution of shear stress within a turbulent boundary layer

We have not yet felt the need to define a stress-strain relationship which determines the stress, τ, in terms of the other local fluid properties, but it is unlikely that the remaining boundary-layer characteristics, especially δ_1 and τ_w, can also be found without recourse to an explicit stress-strain relationship. To establish some such relationship was the principal aim of the various mixing length theories, described by Goldstein (1938).

To go farther we might follow Fediaevski (1936) and propose a polynomial representation, in powers of $\eta = z/\delta$. The boundary conditions at $z = 0$ and $z = \delta$, imposed by the equation of motion (I. 76) and its first z-derivative, are:

$$\left. \begin{array}{l} \eta = 0: \quad \tau = \tau_w, \quad \partial\tau/\partial\eta = -\rho U\delta(dU/dx), \quad \partial^2\tau/\partial\eta^2 = 0 \\ \eta = 1: \quad \tau = \partial\tau/\partial\eta = 0 \end{array} \right\} \quad (59)$$

A stress distribution consistent with these conditions is

$$\tau/\rho U^2 = (\tau_w/\rho U^2)(1-4\eta^3+3\eta^4)-(\delta/U)(dU/dx)(\eta-3\eta^3+2\eta^4). \quad (60)$$

The first experimental data with which this formula could be compared came from the work of Schubauer and Klebanoff (1950), and the comparison in three cases is shown in Fig. II. 7. Now it happened in these experiments that the value of $(\delta/U)(dU/dx)$ was almost the same at $x = 22.5$ as at $x = 25$, whereas the values of H at these two points differed considerably, being 1.60 and 2.22 respectively. The observed distributions of shear stress were also markedly different. This suggests

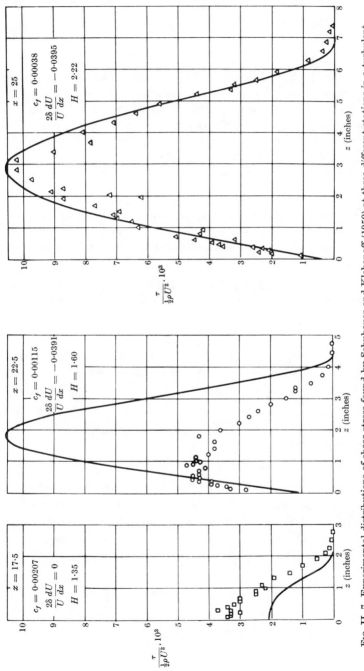

Fig. II. 7. Experimental distributions of shear stress found by Schubauer and Klebanoff (1950) at three different stations in a turbulent boundary layer, compared with the equation (60) of Fediaevski (1936) whose values are shown by the full line.

that equation (60) might be improved by an allowance for a dependence on H; thus

$$\tau/\rho U^2 = (\tau_w/\rho U^2)f_1(z/\delta, H) - (\delta/U)(dU/dx)f_2(z/\delta, H). \qquad (61)$$

Experimental determinations of shear stress in boundary layers are still not sufficiently numerous to enable the numerical values of the functions f_1 and f_2 to be estimated. It should be noted, however, that equation (61) improves on the results of dimensional analysis; on the other hand, the fact that f_1 and f_2 are unknown merely shifts the responsibility of formulating some kind of relationship to a later stage. Nevertheless the form of equation (61) is going to be useful.

13. The energy equation

The energy equation (12) is transformed into a more convenient form through the following steps.

First, δ_3 is put in terms of δ_2 by using the power law (43) which gives

$$\delta_3 = 4\delta_2 H/(3H-1). \qquad (62)$$

This is only one of many similar relations between δ_2 and δ_3, each depending on the particular velocity profile chosen: a slightly more empirical relation of a similar form to (62)—namely

$$\delta_3 = 1 \cdot 269\delta_2 H/(H - 0 \cdot 379)$$

—has, for example, been given by Truckenbrodt (1952). Substituting for δ_3 from equation (62) into equation (12) we obtain

$$d\delta_2/dx - [\delta_2/H(3H-1)](dH/dx) + (3\delta_2/U)(dU/dx)$$
$$= [(3H-1)/4H](2D/\rho U^3). \qquad (63)$$

Second, $d\delta_2/dx$ is eliminated between this equation and the momentum equation (1); thus

$$\delta_2(dH/dx) = -H(3H-1)(H-1)(\delta_2/U)(dU/dx) +$$
$$+ H(3H-1)(\tau_w/\rho U^2) - \tfrac{1}{2}(3H-1)^2(D/\rho U^3). \qquad (64)$$

Third, in the calculation of D in equations (12) and (64), the form (61) for τ is used in conjunction with the form (42) for the velocity distribution and the form (52) for the skin friction. This results in

$$2D/\rho U^3 = (U\delta_2/\nu)^{-n}F_1(H) - (\delta_2/U)(dU/dx)F_2(H), \qquad (65)$$

where

$$F_1(H) = G(H)\int_0^1 f_1(\eta)(df/d\eta)\,d\eta \left. \right\}$$
$$F_2(H) = (\delta_2/\delta)\int_0^1 f_2(\eta)(df/d\eta)\,d\eta \left. \right\} .$$

The final result is obtained by putting this expression for $D/\rho U^3$ and the form (52) for $\tau_w/\rho U^2$ into equation (64). It is

$$\Theta \, dH/dx = \Phi(H)\Gamma - \Psi(H), \qquad (66)$$

where

$$\begin{aligned}
\Phi(H) &= H(3H-1)(H-1) - \tfrac{1}{4}(3H-1)^2 F_2(H) \\
\Psi(H) &= -H(3H-1)G(H) + \tfrac{1}{4}(3H-1)^2 F_1(H)
\end{aligned} \Bigg\}, \qquad (67)$$

and Θ and Γ are defined by (53) and (54).

A knowledge of the functions f_1 and f_2 in the stress relation (61) would determine $\Phi(H)$ and $\Psi(H)$ and so H would follow from equation (66); as it is, Φ and Ψ have to be determined empirically and we review in the following section the methods of a number of investigators.

Integral relations such as the momentum or energy equations are valuable to use as checks of the accuracy of either theoretical approximations or experimental results. Rupert and Persh (1951) have shown that the values of τ_w, D, $\delta_2(dH/dx)$, and $(\delta_2/U)(dU/dx)$ as evaluated from the measurements of Schubauer and Klebanoff (1950) satisfy equation (64) remarkably well and suggest that the errors might at least be diminished by retaining the last term in the full momentum equation (11).

14. Empirical equations for the form parameter

The first major advance from the early formulae described by Goldstein (1938) was made by Doenhoff and Tetervin (1943). They analysed a large amount of aerofoil data collected in the N.A.C.A. wind-tunnels and obtained empirically a linear relation between $\delta_2 \, dH/dx$ and a parameter $4(\delta_2/U)(dU/dx)(1/c_f)$, the coefficients in the relation being functions of H. This relation was used simultaneously with the momentum equation and the formula (39) of Squire and Young (1938) to evaluate the three variables δ_2, H, and c_f. Garner (1944) reanalysed the data used by Doenhoff and Tetervin; he disregarded all the data from regions in which H was decreasing on the grounds that the flow there was not completely turbulent and therefore not subject to the same analysis. He also assumed the $\tfrac{1}{6}$th-power law for skin friction given by Falkner (1943b) and exhibited in Table II. 4, and his final equation was the first to have the form (66).

The inadequacies of both these methods were revealed when the results of the tests by Schubauer and Klebanoff (1950) became available: these were made at a Reynolds number of 3×10^7 which was much greater than that of the data analysed by Doenhoff and Tetervin, the failure of whose method at high Reynolds numbers is exemplified in

Fig. II. 8. When Ludwieg and Tillmann (1949) published their relation between c_f and H, given in equation (51), a number of authors proposed new forms for the empirical functions $\Phi(H)$ and $\Psi(H)$ of equation

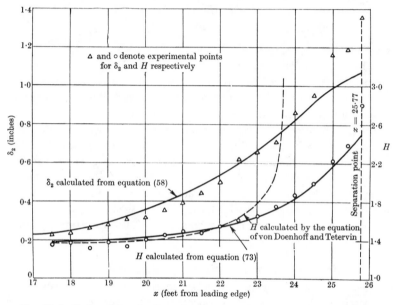

Fig. II. 8. Various determinations of momentum thickness and form parameter for the aerofoil of Schubauer and Klebanoff (1950).

(66) and these are listed in Table II. 7. In addition, Truckenbrodt (1952) and Spence (1956a) have given more elaborate expressions for Φ and Ψ, for which their original papers should be consulted.

TABLE II. 7

Functions used in the equation for the form parameter

(The notation refers to equations (52), (53), (54), and (66))

Author	n	$\Phi(H)$	$\Psi(H)$
Garner (1944) .	0·167	$\exp(5H-7)$	$0{\cdot}0135(H-1{\cdot}4)\Phi(H)$
Zaat (1951) .	0·268	$\exp[10^{1{\cdot}1475(H-0{\cdot}6)(H-1{\cdot}87)}\log_e 10]$	$0{\cdot}1[2{\cdot}214+\sin(14{\cdot}8H-21{\cdot}6)]$ $\times(H-1{\cdot}302)\Phi(H)$
Maskell (1951) .	0·268	$(0{\cdot}3H-0{\cdot}32)\exp(1{\cdot}561H)$ for small Γ, or $0{\cdot}15(2H-1)\exp(1{\cdot}561H)$ for large Γ	Tabulated function or $0{\cdot}15(H-1{\cdot}2)$
Schuh (1954) .	0·268	$10^{1{\cdot}535H-2{\cdot}17}$	$10^{-3}\Phi(H)$

Each of these methods has something to commend it and no one method gives the best results under all conditions, though it seems to be true that the methods of Maskell, Schuh, and Spence are better constructed for flows in which the pressure gradient changes sign. We therefore proceed to derive a kind of portmanteau equation which draws on all the previous analysis so that something approaching the best possible result is obtained.

To begin with, we ensure that good results are given for the flat plate. When U is constant, equation (66) is

$$\Theta\, dH/dx = -\Psi(H). \tag{68}$$

With the one-fifth power law for skin friction from Table II. 4 the momentum equation (1) is

$$\nu\, dR_{\delta_2}/dx = 0{\cdot}0088 U(R_{\delta_2})^{-\frac{1}{4}}, \tag{69}$$

and eliminating x from these two equations and remembering to take $\Theta = \delta_2(R_{\delta_2})^{\frac{1}{4}}$, we find

$$-\Psi(H) = 0{\cdot}0088\, dH/d(\log R_{\delta_2}). \tag{70}$$

This derivative may be calculated from equations (25) and (30), and with Coles's numerical values, equation (70) becomes

$$\Psi(H) = 0{\cdot}00307(H-1)^2. \tag{71}$$

This simple value ensures the accuracy of equation (63) when applied to the flow past a flat plate on which the boundary layer is turbulent from the leading edge.

It remains to choose $\Phi(H)$ and this may be taken as

$$\Phi(H) = 9{\cdot}524(H-1{\cdot}21)(H-1). \tag{72}$$

This is an artificially constructed function which enables equation (66) to be integrated explicitly and which fits well the results of the three methods we particularly mentioned earlier in the section.

So with these values of Φ and Ψ, equation (66) can be integrated to give

$$H = 1 + \left[4{\cdot}76 + kU^{-2} + 0{\cdot}00307 U^{-2} \int_{x_t} (U^2/\Theta)\, dx\right]^{-1}, \tag{73}$$

in which the value of the constant k is fixed by the initial values. This result is due to Spence who, earlier in his paper of 1956, derived an equation, similar in general form to this, using the equations of motion with an assumed distribution of shear stress.

15. Summary of the calculation of the characteristics of a turbulent boundary layer

δ_2 is first calculated from equation (58) which, with the values $n = \frac{1}{5}$, $\beta = 4$, $\alpha = 0\cdot0106$ and $\Theta = \delta_2(U\delta_2/\nu)^{\frac{1}{4}}$, is

$$\Theta U^4 = 0\cdot0106 \int_{x_t}^{x} U^4 \, dx + \text{constant}; \tag{74}$$

also equation (53) becomes, with these values,

$$\delta_2 = \Theta(U\Theta/\nu)^{-\frac{1}{4}}. \tag{75}$$

With the values of Θ so calculated, equation (73) gives H. Then $\delta_1 = H\delta_2$ and c_f is calculated from equation (51).

An example of this procedure was given in Fig. II. 8 where it is seen to give very satisfactory results.

Any criterion for separation is bound, in the present state of knowledge, to be a rough and ready one. Little more can be said than that the value of H seems always to be between 2 and 3 at separation, and as often as not between $2\cdot4$ and $2\cdot6$.

If the criterion for separation is to be put in terms of H, clearly the initial value of H—that is, its value at the transition point—has some importance. The rough suggestions in Section 3 about the value of H must eventually give way to something superior and Maskell (1951) has proposed an empirical relation between the values at transition of Γ, R_{δ_2}, and H, for $R_{\delta_2} < 2500$; this is, however, based on scanty and uncertain data.

16. The turbulent boundary layer in a linear pressure gradient

This particular case of boundary-layer flow, in which

$$U/U_0 = 1 - (x/c) = t, \tag{76}$$

has assumed a classical importance, largely due to the calculations of Howarth (1938) for the case of laminar flow. When this flow is turbulent from the leading edge, the equations of the last section may be integrated exactly. If Θ_0 is the initial value of Θ, at $x = 0$, equation (74) gives

$$\Theta/\Theta_0 = (\lambda^5 - t^5)/t^4(\lambda^5 - 1), \tag{77}$$

where

$$\lambda = (1 + 472\Theta_0/c)^{\frac{1}{5}}, \tag{78}$$

and H follows from equation (73).

We select for illustration, in Fig. II. 9, the distribution of H with x. The initial value of H is obviously of critical importance. For a plate whose leading edge is at $x = 0$ and on which the flow is impinging, a good initial value for H is $H_0 = 1\cdot4$. But the solutions found should be a useful guide in other cases. Often the part of a flow in an adverse pressure gradient can be well represented by a velocity distribution of the form (76); in that case, Θ_0 could be taken as the value of $\delta_2 R_{\delta_2}^{\frac{1}{4}}$ at, say, the point of maximum velocity of the free stream. Or if the boundary layer is known to be still laminar there, Θ_0 could take the appropriate value at an assumed transition point. If we take the value

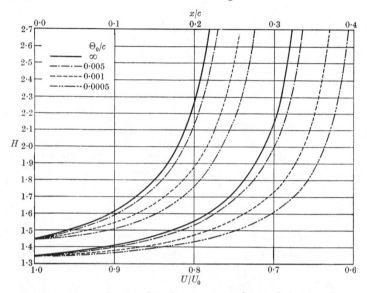

FIG. II. 9. The distribution of the form parameter for a turbulent boundary layer in a linear pressure gradient, calculated in Section 16.

$H = 2\cdot 5$ to denote separation, we see that the point of separation varies widely for only a small change in H_0. This seems unlikely to happen in practice and serves to show that the theory of turbulent boundary layers is still in an infant state.

17. The boundary layer on a porous surface

All the foregoing theory needs drastic modification when the boundary conditions include a non-zero normal velocity. The physical conditions for which a porous boundary is advantageous are fully discussed in Chapter VI and we need only remark at the moment on the obvious advantages of being able to convect vorticity into the boundary rather than to allow it to diffuse into the mainstream.

Although the problem of calculating the boundary layer under such conditions has received considerable attention over the past fifteen years, no method suitable for routine use has been fully tested by experiment. For laminar flow, Thwaites (1949c) has extended his simple result (8) to obtain

$$U_0 \delta_2^2/c\nu = (U/U_0)^{-6} \int_0^{x/c} (U/U_0)^5 (0\cdot45 - 1\cdot28\sigma + 0\cdot76\sigma^2)\, d(x/c), \quad (79)$$

where

$$\sigma = -w_w \delta_2/\nu, \quad (80)$$

w_w being the normal velocity at the boundary; he has also given approximate solutions for a number of different types of flow.

An asymptotic theory, valid for large values of w_w, has been given by Watson (1947) whose main result is that

$$u/U = 1 - \exp(w_w z/\nu) \quad (81)$$

is not only an exact solution of the full equation of motion (I. 6) if U and w_w are constant, but also the limit to which the velocity profiles tend as the suction velocity w_w increases indefinitely, whatever the distribution of $U(x)$. From this it appears that a sufficient suction velocity ought always to be able to prevent separation, a proposition which is examined in the light of experimental evidence in Chapter VI. The outcome of the analysis is that the boundary-layer characteristics at a point may be expressed in terms of the values of w_w and of $U(x)$ and its derivatives at that point only. This then is the physical meaning of the asymptotic theory, that conditions at any point are not controlled by what has happened elsewhere (except in so far as the values of the derivatives of $U(x)$ represent conditions elsewhere). The results of the theory may be summarized in the following expressions for τ_w, δ_1, and δ_2:

$$\left. \begin{aligned}
-\tau_w/\rho U w_w &= 1 + (\nu/w_w)^2 (2U' - \tfrac{1}{2}Uw_w'/w_w) + O(w_w^{-4}) \\
-w_w \delta_1/\nu &= 1 - (\nu/w_w)^2 (3U' - \tfrac{5}{4}Uw_w'/w_w) + O(w_w^{-4}) \\
-w_w \delta_2/\nu &= \tfrac{1}{2} - (\nu/w_w)^2 (\tfrac{7}{4}U' - \tfrac{5}{6}Uw_w'/w_w) + O(w_w^{-4})
\end{aligned} \right\}. \quad (82)$$

As a rough guide to the range of applicability, equation (79) should be used when σ is less than about 3 whereas equations (82) begin to be valid for values greater than this.

More recently, Head (1957) has discussed the problem, combining these earlier ideas with fresh functional relationships and numerical techniques. His paper also includes complete sets of graphs which enable the main characteristics of the boundary layer to be computed relatively rapidly.

There is, at present, no satisfactory theory for turbulent flow over a porous surface. The inward convection has an unknown effect on the stress distribution within the boundary layer and so on the velocity profile. The flow over a flat plate has been studied by Kay (1948) and Dutton (1958). The latter observed the possibility of obtaining, for a single value of w_w, different values of δ_2 according to the initial state of the turbulent layer. This contrasts with the result for a laminar layer that, on a flat plate, $-w_w\delta_2/\nu \to \frac{1}{2}$ as $x \to \infty$. Now in the laminar case, the asymptotic state represents a unique balance between the inward convection of vorticity by suction and the outward diffusion by viscosity; in the turbulent case, however, the convective effects of turbulence introduce what amounts to a degree of freedom into the relation between w_w and δ_2. The consequent theoretical problems are fully discussed by Black and Sarnecki (1958) who propose a bilogarithmic law as an extension to (I. 81) for solid boundaries.

18. The boundary layer in axi-symmetric flow

In this section, the principal results are given which enable the main characteristics of a boundary layer on a body of revolution to be calculated; these, therefore, should be read in conjunction with Chapter IX which considers uniform flow past such bodies.

We take the axis of the body to lie on the x-axis, $0 \leqslant x \leqslant c$, and the radius of its surface is $r_w = r_w(x)$. The uniform stream is assumed to be parallel to the axis of the body.

For laminar flow, the transformation given first by Mangler (1946) puts the boundary-layer equation into a form identical to that for two-dimensional flow. Rott and Crabtree (1952) use this transformation to show that the analysis given in Section 2 for two-dimensional flow can be adapted for axi-symmetric flow. The momentum equation (1) becomes

$$r_w^{-1}d(r_w\delta_2)/dx+(H+2)(\delta_2/U)(dU/dx) = \tau_w/\rho U^2, \tag{83}$$

while formula (8) for the momentum thickness becomes

$$U_0\delta_2^2/c\nu = 0\cdot45(U/U_0)^{-6}(r_w/c)^{-2}\int_0^{x/c} (r_w/c)^2(U/U_0)^5\,d(x/c). \tag{84}$$

τ_w and δ_1 follow, as in Section 2, from the functions $l(\lambda)$ and $H(\lambda)$ tabulated in Table II. 1. For flow on a circular cylinder, r_w is constant and the boundary-layer growth is the same as on a two-dimensional surface, provided $U(x)$ is the same in the two cases.

For turbulent flow, no attempt has yet been made to adapt the analysis given in Sections 4–16 to axi-symmetric flow. The assumption is always made that the radius of the body is so large that two-dimensional formulae can be applied without serious loss of accuracy.

THEORETICAL MODELS OF REAL FLOWS

1. Introduction

ONE of the major difficulties of describing any physical phenomenon—
and the flow of fluid is no exception—arises from the analytical necessity
of separating as far as possible the effects of certain influences, and
yet of recognizing at the same time their inevitable interdependence.
Much of Chapter I was taken up with a discussion of certain very general
types of flow and with a description of the circumstances and the regions
of a real flow peculiar to each of them; of their interactions, little was
said.

For any flow whose Reynolds number is large, the general approach
has already been implied: the boundary layer, the separated-flow region,
and the wake are calculated by appropriate versions of boundary-layer
theory—the first, in particular, by the methods of Chapter II—and for
the region of inviscid flow, if it is also irrotational, manifold resources
are at our disposal for solving Laplace's equation. But a solution for
the velocity field in either region depends on the geometric, kinematic,
and dynamic conditions at their common boundary; not all these
conditions, however, can be specified in advance, since some are bound
to be the end-products of the final compatible solutions. Thus many
idealizations and simplifications of these boundary conditions have to
be made before any analysis is embarked upon. The object of this
chapter is thus to survey the various considerations which enable such
idealizations to be made in the case of a body placed in a uniform
stream. Many of the underlying ideas are applicable also to other kinds
of viscous flow.

2. Unseparated flow. The first approximation for the inviscid flow

Suppose we are analysing the flow past a body whose boundary layer
is observed not to separate. The thickness of the boundary layer is
small if the Reynolds number is sufficiently large and as an approximation its outer edge may be taken to coincide with the surface of the
body. Thus for the first approximation the inviscid region is assumed
to be bounded by the body itself, rather than by the edge of the
boundary layer. The viscous condition of no slip at the surface has to

be relaxed; the kinematic condition at the surface is now that the component of the fluid velocity normal to the surface equals that of the surface.

This technique of transferring boundary conditions from one surface to another close to it is a common one; it is used, for example, in linearized theories of potential flow such as that described in Section IV. 8. If the equations governing the flow are linear, the error in this shift of the boundary can sometimes be estimated; if they are not, as in the present case, it is much more difficult to judge the error. The abandonment of one of the kinematic boundary conditions also involves errors which cannot be estimated.

The first inviscid approximation has often in the past been justified by a reference to the smallness of the fluid's viscosity (or to the correspondingly large Reynolds number). This view has its dangers: it suggests that, in the limit of zero viscosity, the approximation is a very good one. This is only so, of course, for unseparated flow; in general, separation occurs and persists no matter how small the viscosity, and to take the surface of the body itself as the boundary of the inviscid region may then lead to severe inaccuracies.

Now for the calculation of the first approximation to the inviscid flow, we need to know the nature of the singularities of the velocity potential or, physically, to know of the existence within the fluid of, among other things, concentrated vorticity in lines or sheets, or of circulation in circuits enclosing the body. At this stage, two- and three-dimensional flows exhibit radically different features which must be carefully distinguished.

3. Unseparated uniform flow past aerofoils. The first inviscid approximation

In two-dimensional unseparated flow, nothing in the nature of a vortex sheet can be observed to extend from the aerofoil into the wake; certainly the boundary layer near the trailing edge as it leaves the upper surface may be likened to a vortex sheet, but this is counter-balanced by that from the lower surface. Sometimes the impingement of two laminar boundary layers convecting vorticity of large magnitude and of opposite sign seems to result in a fluctuating flow in which the vorticity, instead of rapidly disappearing, becomes concentrated into lumps; very little is known about the spacing and strength of such lumps of vorticity in the wake of an unseparated flow, and even if it were, to take them into account would probably introduce unacceptable complications into the analysis. Further, the total sum of vorticity in any length of the wake is small, as will be shown in Section V. 9; so we conclude that there is no need to make any representation of vorticity in the first approximation to the inviscid flow, which may therefore be taken to be a potential flow, regular over the whole field. At the same time, any unsteadiness which may be observable in the real wake is deemed, again for the first inviscid approximation, to be of no account. It is odd that wakes in unseparated flow have been investigated experimentally in rather less detail, in some respects, than those in well-separated flow whose characteristics are discussed in Section 9.

Even if we assume that the two-dimensional flow is everywhere irrotational for the first inviscid approximation, there is still the possibility of a non-zero circulation in any circuit enclosing the aerofoil. For this approximation, the result of equation (I. 72) is relevant for it shows that if the aerofoil experiences lift, a circulation must exist. Now if we are attempting to explain theoretically what is observed experimentally on a particular aerofoil, the value of the circulation may be taken as that which follows, by equation (I. 72), from the observed lift. If, on the other hand, we attempt to predict the lift on a given aerofoil, we then determine the circulation for the first inviscid approximation by what is known as the Kutta–Joukowski condition. This arose from the ideas of Kutta (1902) and Joukowski (1912) and is most readily explained for an aerofoil with a sharp trailing edge; for all values of the circulation except one, the speed at the sharp trailing edge is infinite, and therefore that value is chosen for which the speed is, more realistically, finite. The extension of this condition to viscous flow and more detailed investigations concerning the circulation about an aerofoil are reserved for Chapter V.

Now that the inviscid flow is uniquely prescribed, we can calculate the distribution of velocity by the methods of Chapter IV, and hence of pressure using Bernoulli's equation (I. 46). The lift force, calculated according to the Kutta–Joukowski condition, is usually sufficiently accurate to make empirical corrections worthwhile. For the drag, equation (I. 72) gives the value $C_D = 0$ which, for engineering purposes, is valueless; even so, it strongly suggests that a body, past which the flow is largely irrotational, may have a drag coefficient much less than unity, which is the order of C_D for a bluff body. This has been strikingly illustrated by a figure of R. T. Jones (1956); this Fig. III. 1 shows an aerofoil and a circular cylinder which have the same drag per unit span.

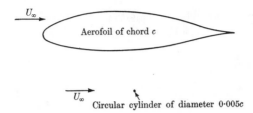

FIG. III. 1. At high Reynolds numbers, the drags of these two bodies
are roughly equal; this is an illustration of the effectiveness of a field
of flow which is largely irrotational.

4. Unseparated uniform flow past wings. The first inviscid approximation

Whereas the first inviscid approximation for two-dimensional flow
past an aerofoil has no need of concentrated vorticity, an essential
feature of the three-dimensional flow past a wing is the existence of
vorticity. In both cases the neglect of the boundary layer may be
regarded as equivalent to neglecting the component of vorticity in any
direction perpendicular to the stream; further, in the streamwise direction, the vorticity component is identically zero in the two-dimensional
case, as may be seen from equation (I. 86). But in the more general
flow this latter component is not zero, as is illustrated in Fig. III. 2 in
which are drawn contours of the streamwise vorticity, ω_x, behind a
rectangular wing. In these experiments by Fage and Simmons (1925)
it was verified that the total strength of streamwise vorticity leaving
one semi-span of the rectangular wing was equal to the circulation round
the centre section, and that the variation of the streamwise component
of vorticity was closely related to the distribution of lift along the
span.

The inextricable connexion between the lift on a wing and streamwise
vorticity in the wake seems first to have been contemplated by Lanchester (1907), though it was some years before quantitative relationships were proposed. For the moment, we only notice that any idealization of a three-dimensional flow must take this vorticity into account.
Now for many wings, as indicated by Fig. III. 2 (a), this trailing vorticity
is confined nearly to a plane; thus for the purposes of determining the
flow near such wings it may be assumed that the vorticity behind
the wing is confined to a plane downstream of the wing. Elsewhere the
flow is irrotational, and the classical theory of Chapter VIII unravels
the complicated threads by which solutions are obtained on the basis
of this assumption. We shall see in Section 6 that, for some other types

of wings, it is necessary to make quite different assumptions about the distribution of vorticity, and such wings are considered in Sections XII. 6–10.

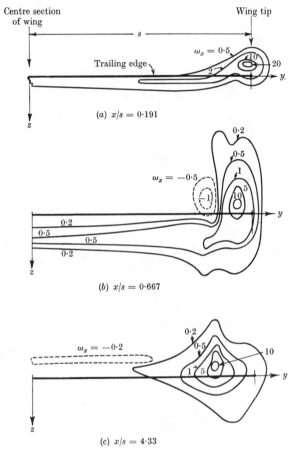

Fɪɢ. III. 2. Contours of equal streamwise vorticity in three transverse planes at a distance x behind the trailing edge of a rectangular wing of aspect ratio 6 at an incidence of 6°.

Once this first approximation to the inviscid flow is known, the force on the wing due to the pressures only may be calculated. In contrast with the two-dimensional case, there is a drag component called the induced drag which is associated with the kinetic energy of the vorticity of the wake. For unseparated flow on wings of large aspect ratio, the induced drag is roughly proportional to $(C_L)^2$: for more complicated kinds of flow, it is found to vary according to a power rather lower than the second.

From Fig. III. 2 (c) may be deduced the tendency of a vortex sheet to roll up; that is, for the vorticity to adhere, after some distance downstream of the wing, to a pattern similar to that for a concentrated vortex. This led the earliest investigators to assume, in their analysis, concentrated vortices extending from the trailing edge. Now it was remarked in Section I. 19 that an inviscid vortex implies an infinite kinetic energy, and in fact, careful observation reveals that the centre region of large vorticity must be dominated by the action of viscosity. The question then arises whether it is possible for this central core to have been formed at the wing and to have been swept back with the flow. This question has been answered in the negative by Betz (1950) and it appears that the vortex-like motion, with a small inner core rotating as a solid body, can only arise from the rolling-up of an existing vortex sheet, by a process of accumulation of vorticity.

There are no similar difficulties in considering the creation of a vortex sheet, since its induced velocities and hence kinetic energy are characteristically much less than those of a concentrated vortex; but the maintenance of a sheet in a nearly plane form is vitiated by the conditions at any of its edges which may be roughly parallel to the vorticity. There must be an outward force at such an edge due to the highly curved flow around it. So long as the edge touches a solid body, this force can be provided by the body; but a free vortex sheet has no alternative to deformation. Kaden (1931) and Westwater (1936) have both carried out calculations which show that a plane sheet in an inviscid fluid will deform so that the edge wraps itself into a spiral; some way downstream a cross-section of the sheet is similar to that shown in Fig. III. 3. There is irrotational flow between the spiralling sheet with the velocity rising roughly in proportion to the inverse of the radius, and a velocity jump at each intersection equal to the circulation per unit length of the vortex sheet. In real flow, the effect of viscosity is to diffuse the vortex sheet, so that the velocity and its gradient are continuous. Near the centre, the diffusion will result in a wholly viscous core, outside which the velocity field is similar to that of a concentrated vortex, as has already been mentioned in Section I. 19.

The theory of the first inviscid approximation to the unseparated flow past wings, which is described in Chapter VIII, takes no account of the rolling-up of the trailing vortex sheet. Nor does it consider the effects

of the displacements of the sheet in the lift direction. These matters
are briefly treated in Sections XII. 6, 7, and 20.

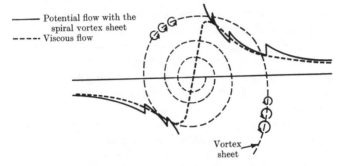

—————— Potential flow with the
          spiral vortex sheet
- - - - - Viscous flow

Vortex
sheet

Fig. III. 3. A sketch of the velocity induced by a spiral vortex sheet.

5. The first approximation for the boundary layer

The first inviscid approximation does not satisfy the viscous condition
of no slip at the boundary; indeed it specifies a tangential velocity there.
But if we now revert to the original physical boundary of the inviscid
flow, this tangential velocity may be regarded as the stream velocity—
$U(x)$, in the notation of Chapter II, for two-dimensional flow—for the
boundary-layer flow. On this assumption, the solution of the boundary-
layer equations according to the methods of Chapter II is called the
first approximation for the boundary layer.

Now if this calculation reveals an unseparated boundary layer, then
the first approximation for the inviscid flow may be said to be justified
a posteriori. We now have a more complete estimate of the forces—
pressure and shear—acting on the surface. First, the pressure distribution is unaltered by the first approximation for the boundary layer,
since one of the assumptions of boundary-layer theory is that the
pressure is constant through the boundary layer. Thus, at this stage
of the approximations, the contributions to the lift and drag of the
normal pressures equal the lift and drag as given by the first inviscid
approximation. For two-dimensional aerofoils this drag—the form
drag—is zero, while for wings it equals the induced drag. Considering
now the shear stresses, we note that they contribute to the lift but, in
general, only by a negligible amount. The integral of their components
in the stream direction, however, gives a first approximation to the
drag which in most cases it is not worth attempting to improve. In
any event, it is found to be better to calculate the skin-friction drag by

considering the loss of momentum at infinity, rather than by integrating the shear stresses on the surface; Chapter V deals with such calculations in detail for two-dimensional flow.

If, on the other hand, separation is predicted, then the first inviscid approximation is called into question and the flow past a two-dimensional aerofoil usually falls into one of three categories:

1. Separation near the trailing edge is usually assumed not to have a serious effect on the validity of the calculation made so far. The wake is not so thick that the pressure distribution on the aerofoil, as given by the first inviscid approximation, is seriously affected except possibly near the trailing edge.

2. Separation near the mid-chord position is uncommon. If it occurred in the operating condition of a wing or aerofoil, then the design of the aerofoil would have been bad. On most well-designed aerofoils, there is a small range of incidence, above the operating incidence yet below the stalling incidence, within which the separation point is somewhere near the mid-chord; the behaviour in this range of incidence is discussed in Section V. 14.

3. If separation is predicted, by the first approximation to the boundary layer, to occur near the leading edge, there may be a number of possible configurations of the flow. First, the boundary layer might reattach itself to the surface, so forming a bubble. If the separated boundary layer is laminar (as is normally the case) and the aerofoil is sufficiently thin, a rough criterion for reattachment within a short distance, say $10^2\delta_2$, is $R_{\delta_2} = U\delta_2/\nu > 500$. This has been given by Owen and Klanfer (1953) and is considered more fully in Section 8. If, secondly, the value of R_{δ_2} at separation is much less than this value, the separated region may form a larger bubble—of the order of $10^4\delta_2$ in length—or include the whole of the upper surface of the aerofoil in which case there is a large eddying wake behind it; Section 9 follows this latter case. In fact, these distinctions may prove to be of doubtful value since the physical phenomena involved in separation near the leading edge of an aerofoil are only now coming within range of our understanding; they are more fully described in Section V. 14.

Our last remark applies even more forcibly to the flow past wings and other types of body. The fact that it is not at present feasible to calculate a three-dimensional boundary layer by a practical routine makes it equally difficult to justify *a posteriori* the validity of the first inviscid approximation for wings. Thus careful observation by experimental methods has largely to take the place of the first approximation to the boundary-layer flow, and the implications of this are considered in the following section.

6. The interaction of theory and experiment

The discussion of the previous section implicitly presupposed that a purely theoretical attempt was being made to predict the type of flow about the aerofoil or wing. While success in such an attempt is probably the final aim of all our analysis, it must be recognized that experimental observations form an essential part of the construction of any theoretical model.

As our knowledge increases, so do our theoretical models become more realistic, but almost always they lag behind the observed character of fluid flow. Indeed the very adoption of any particular model often precludes its modification. To illustrate the possibility of a flow not conforming at all to the rationale proposed in Section 4, we may consider the flow past a highly swept-back wing at moderate incidence. It would be quite reasonable to expect the streamlines of this flow to adopt the smooth pattern sketched in Fig. III. 4 (a), but it would be wrong. What actually happens is shown in Fig. III. 4 (b), there being a large spiralling vortex lying along the upper surface of each side of the wing. No theoretical model with which we are familiar would enable this behaviour to be predicted, and only recently have models been proposed for it—for example, those given by Legendre (1952–3), by Brown and Michael (1955), and by Mangler and Smith (1957)—which enable satisfactory calculations to be performed.

If we stress the importance of a good theoretical model, we also have to admit that often its inherent mathematical difficulties render it useless. Then resort may be made to another model which, while seemingly remote from physical reality, not only is simple enough for the analysis to be completed, but also gives results which have a clear and valid physical interpretation. This kind of model represents, possibly, the highest art of the theoretical physicist; not many such models will appear in later chapters but one example is the brief paper by Squire (1956) to which reference will be made in Section 8.

Often, theoretical models are proposed solely because they can be developed mathematically, even though they are recognized to be physically unrealistic; many of the so-called exact solutions of the boundary-layer equations, as given, for example, in *LBL*, come into this category. Occasionally, however, some advance in engineering techniques or in our physical understanding enables flows to be set up

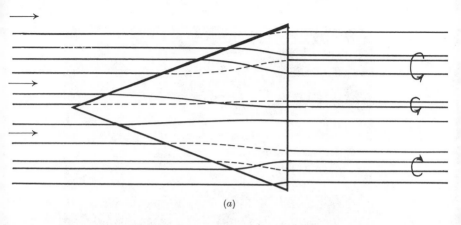

(a)

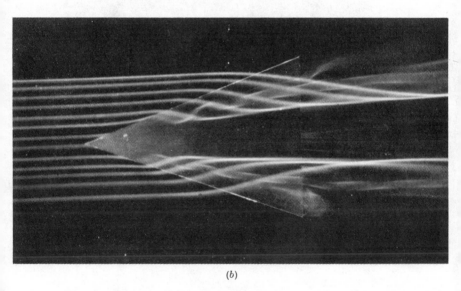

(b)

FIG. III. 4. An illustration of the difficulty of proposing theoretical models. The streamlines in the flow past a delta wing (a) as we might expect them, and (b) as they really are.

(a)

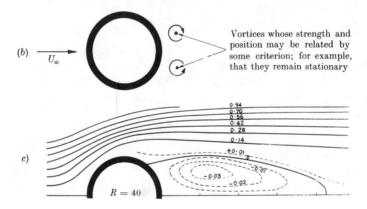

(b) U_∞

Vortices whose strength and
position may be related by
some criterion; for example,
that they remain stationary

c)

0.94
0.70
0.56
0.42
0.28
0.14
+0.01
-0.07
-0.03
-0.02

R = 40

FIG. III. 5. Various views of uniform flow past a circular cylinder at low
Reynolds numbers:

(a) The visualization of a real flow at a Reynolds number of 40.

(b) A possible theoretical model in inviscid flow, whose realism suffers from,
among other things, the concentration of vorticity in the bubble.

(c) Calculated streamlines, based on the assumption that $\partial/\partial t \equiv 0$ in equations
(I. 6); this assumption would not be realistic for higher Reynolds numbers.

to correspond to such models. Examples of this will be found through-out the book and especially in Chapter VI.

In referring to purely mathematical difficulties associated with certain types of models, we should perhaps mention the possibilities opened up for the future by the development and use of high-speed digital computers. It is possible that a computer would cope with a model which has, up to now, been rejected on account of the complication of, say, the shape of its boundary. It is further possible that such computers may render unnecessary the analytical distinctions we have had to make between the boundary layer and inviscid regions of flow, though it may be doubted whether at present any case but that of incompressible two-dimensional flow can be treated fully.

7. The iterative procedure. The second approximations

To continue the discussion of the flow past a body in a uniform stream we see that the first approximation to the inviscid flow may be improved if the boundary of the inviscid region is taken at the distance δ_1 from the surface instead of at the surface; here the displacement thickness is deliberately chosen by virtue of the argument preceding equation (I. 36) and its value is given by the first boundary-layer approximation. This new hypothetical boundary for the inviscid region should be extended to infinity downstream to take into account the displacement thickness of the wake. Thus we could proceed to a second approximation for the inviscid flow, in the newly defined region; and with the revised velocity distribution which it would produce at the edge of the boundary layer, the boundary-layer calculation could be repeated. Thus one imagines an iterative procedure passing to and fro between the boundary layer and the inviscid region.

Now the necessity for this iterative procedure arises solely from the fact that the solution of the Navier–Stokes equations over the whole region of a physical flow is at present beyond our capacities, though we have mentioned the potentialities of electronic computers. But it is important to realize that the iteration does not converge to a solution of those equations, since the errors implicit in the boundary-layer approximation affect the iteration equally. Thus as soon as the difference between two stages of the iteration is of the same order as these boundary-layer errors, no further advantage is gained by proceeding to the next iterative stage. In practice this usually means that the results of the second stage—namely, the second approximation—are as good as may be obtained.

For two-dimensional flow, there are two serious difficulties in the way of this second approximation. First there is the purely mathematical one of finding a convenient method of computing the solution of Laplace's equation in a region external to a specified boundary extending to infinity. In the particular case of thin aerofoils and wakes progress has been made by Spence (1954); he has continued the work of Preston (1949) who, latterly, has concerned himself with the second difficulty, namely the determination of the circulation about the aerofoil at each stage of the iteration. Chapter V deals with these matters.

For three-dimensional flow, the practical calculation of the second approximation for the inviscid flow cannot yet be contemplated, both the difficulties just mentioned for two-dimensional flow being still more serious.

Apart from such practical difficulties, the concepts of the iteration may obviously be applied to cases other than unseparated flows once a mathematical model of a separated flow has been decided upon.

For the rest of the book, the first and second approximations to the inviscid and boundary-layer flows will be referred to without any further definition.

8. Limited separation. Bubbles

The possibility of a separated boundary layer reattaching itself to the surface has already been illustrated in Fig. I. 17 which shows one of the cases mentioned in Section 5 in which the first inviscid approximation is inadequate. If the Reynolds number of the boundary layer at separation is sufficiently great, the layer is already susceptible to transition; thus, after the free transition, the transfer of energy from the outer part of the separated layer enables a substantial increase of pressure to be sustained; reattachment may occur if R_{δ_2} at separation exceeds the critical value, quoted earlier, of about 500. This result is not based entirely on experiments on thin aerofoils; some of the supporting data were derived from measurements in a boundary layer which reattached to a flat surface having separated on passing through a shock wave. It may therefore be valid for regions other than those near the leading edge of a thin aerofoil, but since the shape of the body behind the separation must be of decisive importance, it is unwise to apply the result to other types of flow before further experimental data are available.

Little is known about the conditions inside a short bubble, and we may refer to the paper by McCullough and Gault (1951) as representative of the work which has been done on bubble flows in recent years. The velocities within a bubble may be comparable with those outside it, and it is possible that future investigations will establish a firm distinction between a central region in which the vorticity is more or less constant and an outer region in which a type of boundary-layer flow occurs. A flow inside a circular region displaying these characteristics has been considered theoretically by Squire (1956). What seems certain is that the pressure is not constant but, rather, increases steadily along the inner edge of the separated layer, or along the outer edge of the bubble. The main function of the bubble is to encourage transition so that the boundary layer then gains energy from the mainstream by turbulent action; another, though probably less important, effect is that the separated layer no longer loses energy by contact with a solid surface. When the separated boundary layer has undergone this treatment for a short distance it may feel sufficiently rejuvenated to rejoin the surface. The pressure at the point of reattachment is greater than that at separation, though not so great as that for the hypothetical flow in the absence of the bubble; the bubble could therefore be regarded as the device adopted by the fluid for diminishing the positive pressure gradients on the boundary.

For a recalculation of the inviscid flow when a bubble is suspected, one might take, as the boundary of the potential flow, part of the aerofoil together with a line representing, in some way, the outer edge of the bubble. A mathematical theory which yields solutions for this type of potential flow is given in the next chapter: but inevitably there is some indeterminacy in the solution. If the shape of the outer streamline is known, then it is possible to deduce the velocity on it, and conversely; but there is at present no known principle for determining, *ab initio*, either the one or the other. Even if the velocity, or pressure, is assumed constant, any value of the pressure inside the bubble may be taken without complicating the analysis and there is nothing inherent in the idealization to indicate which pressure in fact occurs in the fluid. Nor is experimental evidence sufficient to enable empirical conditions to be formulated. In connexion with these difficulties, an interesting account of experiments on bubbles on aerofoils, together with a discussion of their influence on the stalling characteristics of thin wings, is given by Crabtree (1957b).

9. Well-separated flow. Wakes

It is just as difficult to devise a good theoretical model for the flow downstream of bluff bodies, and we first consider flows whose

Reynolds numbers are low. The main effects of separation are then confined to a limited region of the flow, and we exemplify the difficulties of mathematical models by considering the flow past a circular cylinder.

For Reynolds numbers between about 1 and 50, two stationary closed regions, of vortex-like flow, occur symmetrically behind the cylinder; these can be seen in Fig. III. 5 (a), which is a photograph of air flowing slowly past hypodermic tubing at $R = 40$. A model of this flow is shown in Fig. III. 5 (b) but it has serious inadequacies and recent work has concentrated on solving numerically the Navier–Stokes equations. Such solutions usually assume the time-derivatives to be zero, even though the real flow is not wholly steady. Apelt (1957) extended the earlier computations of Thom (1933) and gave a numerical solution for $R = 40$; the result, shown in Fig. III. 5 (c), closely matches the real flow of the photograph.

At higher Reynolds numbers, stationary vortices no longer occur in real flow; thus, although steady-state mathematical solutions are generally thought to exist for all values of R, they are not necessarily good mathematical models. The solutions which Allen and Southwell (1955) obtained, using a relaxation technique, have been questioned on account of the coarseness of the mesh used; further, they did not show the increase of bubble length with Reynolds number which is typical of all other theoretical and experimental results.

These figures emphasize one of the difficulties of theoretical prediction based on idealization. If the scale effect happens to be large for the real flow in the range of Reynolds numbers to be considered, there is a danger that a particular idealization chosen is insufficiently realistic, and some kind of iterative procedure will not necessarily improve the solution. We may explain this by saying that idealizations, especially of the kind so far considered, ignore some of the processes of interaction in the fluid, and this is often manifested in the arbitrariness of certain parameters in an idealized solution.

At much larger Reynolds numbers, flow which separates and does not reattach is usually wildly irregular; this is as true of a bluff body as for a thin aerofoil which is set at a high incidence. Any detailed description of the velocity field within the separated region is still impossible. But from the point of view of the external inviscid flow, the separated region may often be likened to a closed bubble. This has already been anticipated in Fig. I. 4 which indicated a closed bubble behind a flat plate set normal to a stream; but the theoretical models of such well-separated flow suffer from the same indeterminacy as was discussed in the preceding section for bubbles.

Sometimes, in the flow past bluff bodies, a regular pattern of concentrated vortices is observed in the wake, though this usually occurs within a restricted range of Reynolds number. For the representation of this, the vortex street, whose stability was investigated by Kármán (1911) and which is usually given his name, has yet to be improved upon, and the spacing of these vortices and the frequency with which they form are among the classical problems still unsolved. In connexion with this, Shaw (1956) has given further evidence to support his earlier idea that the frequency with which eddies are shed into the wake of a bluff body is associated with regular acoustic pulses originating at certain points on the surface, and in particular at the separation points. From a very simple argument he derives a formula for the flow past a circular cylinder of diameter d: $Nd/U_\infty = \frac{3}{4}\pi(U_w/U_\infty)$ where N and U_w are the frequency and speed of the pairs of vortices, and U_∞ the speed at infinity. The value so given of the Strouhal number, Nd/U_∞, agrees remarkably well with experimental values. However, the theoretical basis of his thesis, at any rate in its present form, is unacceptable to most workers in the field, who are also sceptical of the significance of the high natural frequencies, at roughly the harmonics of a fundamental, which Shaw found to exist in the flow past a two-dimensional aerofoil. Attempts on rather more conventional lines, to correlate the characteristics of the Kármán vortex street with the drag and with theoretical models of a first inviscid approximation, continually appear in the literature, and for an interesting account we may refer to Roshko (1955).

An important phenomenon is that the character and unsteadiness of the wake may be changed significantly by the introduction of physical boundaries along lines of geometrical symmetry. For example, the introduction of a long thin plate, extending radially downstream from a circular cylinder and parallel to the stream, has a marked effect on the flow: vortices are no longer shed alternately from the two separation points, the distribution of pressure in the wake is quite altered, and the drag coefficient is decreased by about one-third. This is another example of what was discussed in general terms in Section I. 17 and although it is easy to give a broad explanation of such effects—namely that such a plate acts as a constraint upon certain modes of periodic disturbance—it is much more difficult to produce a satisfactory analysis.

Returning now to the analytical problems associated with bubbles, we see that, in contrast to the case of reattachment, the bubble to which a well-separated wake is likened may be approximated by a region extending from the body downstream to infinity. This approximation leads to the traditional approach of free-streamline theory of which an interesting survey has been given by Birkhoff and Zarantonello (1957).

Helmholtz (1868) and Kirchhoff (1869) laid the foundations underlying the conventional assumptions for the free streamlines when they assumed that the pressure on the streamlines is constant and equal to the pressure of the uniform stream at infinity. This amounts to assuming that the whole wake consists of fluid moving only very slowly, even if in a random manner. One welcome consequence of the flow so calculated is a non-zero drag force. For the case of a two-dimensional flat plate set normal to the stream, the quite unrealistic potential flow bounded by both sides of the plate gives $C_D = 0$, on which Kirchhoff's value of $C_D = 0.88$, based on free streamlines springing from the edges of the plate, is a tremendous improvement; the latter nevertheless compares unfavourably with an experimental value obtained by Fage and Johansen (1927) of $C_D = 1.95$. Further, a grave defect of this classical theory is that it does not make any allowance for scale effect.

The severity of this inaccuracy in predicting the drag of the flat plate is due largely to the assumption that the static pressure, p_c, on the bounding streamlines is equal to the static pressure, p_∞, at infinity. The possibility of these two pressures being different is usually put in terms of a pressure coefficient, σ, defined by $\sigma = (p_\infty - p_c)/\frac{1}{2}\rho v_\infty^2$. Fage and Johansen (1927) found that in the region close behind their flat plate the value of σ was about 1.4, while at infinity $\sigma = 0$. This suggests the more plausible assumption that the pressure varies along the bounding streamline, which would also allow the Reynolds number to be taken into account. But although mathematical methods are available to solve the external inviscid flow once this pressure distribution is known, they do not indicate how it is to be determined at the start. This is the greatest immediate difficulty in the theory of well-separated flows: if it could be overcome it is likely that the concept of the free streamline would survive for a long time to give way only to a detailed theory of the flow within the wake and its interaction with the inviscid region.

Except in the special case of axi-symmetric bodies, the theory of well-separated flows in three dimensions has hardly been initiated, on account of the analytical difficulties. Even in a region bounded by two-dimensional boundaries, significant three-dimensional effects are often observed in well-separated flow.

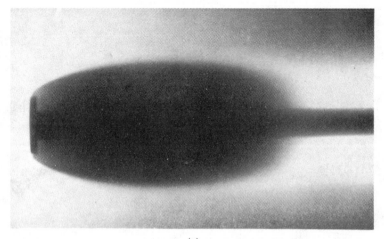

(a)

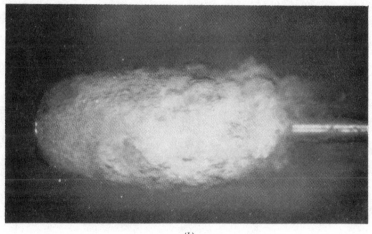

(b)

Fig. III. 6. The cavity behind a circular disk for the pressure coefficient $\sigma = 0 \cdot 188$ and photographic exposures of (a) 2 sec, and (b) 10^{-4} sec.

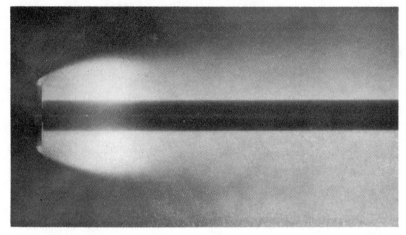

(a)

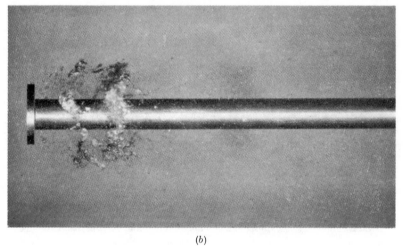

(b)

Fig. III. 7. The cavity behind a circular disk for the pressure coefficient $\sigma = 0.5$ and photographic exposures of (a) 2 sec, and (b) 10^{-4} sec.

10. Cavities in liquids

The theoretical models of separated flow, discussed in the last two sections, together with the mathematical methods of Chapter IV dealing with the inviscid regions of such flows, are of immediate application to some of the phenomena of cavitation in liquids. One of the distinguishing features of a cavity in liquid is that the pressure within the cavity is nearly constant; thus the pressure coefficient σ is also constant and it is usually called the cavitation number. It follows from this that the velocity on the boundary of the cavity is constant. The word bubble will be retained for the idealization of Section 8 and also for the more recent models of a wake mentioned in Section 9.

Cavitation, in its strictest sense, refers to the growth of bubbles within the liquid, due to reductions of pressure. Gas nuclei, which are normally present in a liquid, have the greatest tendency towards growth at the points of minimum pressure in a flow; and if the value of the pressure at such a point approaches the vapour pressure of the liquid, the growth of incipient bubbles is very greatly encouraged. Thus for flow past a streamlined body, a rough criterion for cavitation is that the minimum pressure, as calculated by the first inviscid approximation, should be equal to, or less than, the vapour pressure. This type of cavitation is of the greatest importance in some branches of hydrodynamical engineering—the continual creation and collapse of bubbles, for example, often damages or fatigues a solid surface; nevertheless, it is not very relevant to the topics of this book.

Of greater interest to the aerodynamicist is the type of cavity which is primarily due to the separation of the boundary layer from the surface of the body, especially that due to a sharp edge on the body. The cavity may contain either the vapour of the liquid of the main flow—as in Figs. III. 6 and 7—or some entirely different medium—as in Fig. III. 8. We may cite as an example of the first kind of cavity the flow past a circular disk set normal to the stream of liquid. A photograph, of relatively long exposure, of a vapour-filled cavity usually reveals it as opaque; this is shown in Figs. III. 6 (a) and 7 (a), taken from a valuable review of cavitation by Eisenberg (1950). High-speed photographs of the same flows, shown in Figs. III. 6 (b) and 7 (b), reveal rapid fluctuations which may be characteristic of vapour-filled cavities. These two figures indicate further that there are at least two types of flow possible within such a vapour-filled cavity. For values of the pressure coefficient, as defined in Section 9, of less than about 0·45, the cavity is filled with a mass of jostling bubbles whereas for higher values it is likely that so-called vortex cavitation occurs, in which circular cavitating vortices are shed periodically from the edge of the disk.

Cavities filled with a gas other than the liquid vapour may be obtained easily in experiment. For example, the supporting rod in Figs. III. 6 and 7 may be hollow and air may be introduced through it into

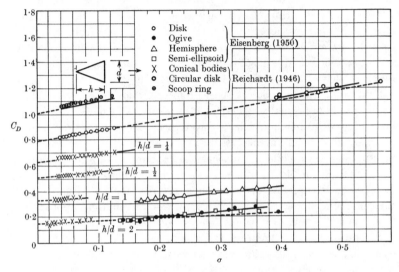

Fig. III. 9. The variation of the drag of various bodies with the pressure coefficient of the cavity behind them. The curves extended to $\sigma = 0$ are of the form $C_D(\sigma) = (1+\sigma)C_D(0)$.

the region behind the rod. The cavitation number may be varied in this way, and the cavities so obtained are often transparent, especially if the interface is quite smooth. This type of flow is similar to that due to the entry of a missile into a liquid, which is illustrated in Fig. III. 8. The speckled nature of the surface of the cavity, which is still filled mostly with air entrained with the sphere from the water surface, is due to a number of factors, the predominant one being, in all probability, the fine spray which is directed forwards at high speed from the rear of the cavity in what is commonly called the re-entrant jet.

What is remarkable is that the overall shapes of the cavities, as between one kind of cavitating flow and another past the same body, differ very little. Thus the assumption that the pressure in the cavity is constant, which is obviously sound for the air-filled cavity, is probably reasonably valid for the vapour-filled cavity; and the various aero-

Fɪɢ. III. 8. An air-filled cavity behind a sphere dropped into water. Diameter: 2 inches; entry speed: 19·6 ft sec⁻¹; depth: 8·5 inches.

dynamic theories which refer to bubbles and wakes of constant pressure are equally applicable to the types of cavitation we have considered.

Much experimental work has been done on cavities formed by separation, especially on air-filled cavities in which the pressure coefficient may be controlled. In an exhaustive series of tests, Reichardt (1946) found that the drag coefficient for most bodies is very nearly a linear function of the pressure coefficient provided that the latter is less than, say, one-half; thus $C_D(\sigma) = (1+\sigma)C_D(0)$, and Fig. III. 9 is an impressive corroboration of this law. It may be mentioned that the two classical models of closed cavities of constant pressure behind two-dimensional bodies—those of Riabouchinsky (1920) and of the re-entrant jet described, for example, by Birkhoff and Zarantonello (1957)—yield results which, in approximate form, are the same as this equation. They are described in Section IV. 24. The slopes of the experimental lines in Fig. III. 9 for the rounded bodies seem rather greater than those for the sharp-edged bodies; this may be due partly to the change in separation point for different values of σ for the first group but is probably mostly due to the curvature of the surface.

11. Unsteadiness

One of the striking characteristics of some of the flows mentioned in the preceding sections, and especially of the well-separated flows, is their unsteadiness, which occurs in spite of the bounding surfaces and conditions at infinity being fixed. Some general remarks on this were made in Section I. 15 and these may be amplified now in connexion with the problem of devising theoretical models of real flows.

The extent to which unsteadiness, for example in the wake of a thin two-dimensional aerofoil which remains fixed at a small incidence in a uniform stream, affects the overall character of the flow outside the boundary layer cannot be estimated; in other words, it is not possible to make any allowance for the unsteadiness in the calculation of, say, the lift and drag. Occasionally, irregularities in the shedding of a wake react in a noticeably unsteady manner on the aerofoil itself; but this event would usually be regarded as a fault in design, and normally the measurement or calculation of lift and drag seldom leads to the suspicion that the unsteadiness is an important factor. In this way we excuse the neglect of the unsteady fluctuations in later chapters. This unsteadiness may have more noticeable, and even serious, effects on other bodies in or near the wake: for example, care has to be taken that the tailplane of an aircraft is not affected adversely by the wake of the main planes.

In the case of flows past bluff bodies or past aerofoils at large incidence, the unsteady character of the flow may have a direct effect on
the mean flow. It is true that certain features of the flow past a flat
plate set perpendicular to a stream may be predicted with remarkable
accuracy by a theory of steady flow, but such a theory must, at present,
be highly empirical. It may amount to little more than the creation
of a highly idealized flow some of whose features—for example, the
boundary condition on the upstream side of the plate, or even the drag
itself—coincide with the corresponding features of the real flow. The
extent of the approximations inherent in such a model might only be
revealed by the comparison with experiment of other features of the
flow, such as the pressure distribution over the downstream side of the
plate. It is at this point that we are handicapped by the fact that
experimental techniques are, at the moment, lagging behind the advance
of theory. The conditions within a short bubble and the fluctuating
pressures over the rear of a circular cylinder are only two examples out
of many indicating the need for more physical knowledge on which to
base further theoretical models. It is, however, remarkable that, even
in cases for which the unsteadiness seems to be an important feature
of the flow, some theoretical success can still be achieved on the assumption of steady flow. That this is a possibility is seen, for example, in
Fig. III. 7. Here, although the cavity is oscillating at a high frequency
and with a large magnitude, its outer envelope is, in shape, very similar
to the boundary of a steady cavity.

So far we have considered unsteadiness only as it arises as a natural
result of the fluid being in motion. Other types of unsteadiness arise
when the various conditions at the boundaries of the flow are unsteady,
and two main classes of such unsteadiness should be distinguished.

If the boundary conditions execute very small random oscillations,
then the mean flow can usually be calculated as though it were steady,
the effect of the oscillations being taken into account empirically, if at
all. For example, the level of turbulence in a uniform stream past an
aerofoil might be interpreted as fixing the points of transition on the
aerofoil surface; the random vibration of the surface could be taken into
account in a similar way. Such effects are not yet amenable to satisfactory theoretical treatment.

On the other hand, if the boundary conditions have large or regular
time-variations, then not only may they produce equally significant
variations over the whole field of flow, but also their effects may be
amenable to analysis. Two particular examples may be cited here.

First, the problem of the impulsive start from rest of a two-dimensional aerofoil at incidence, associated with the name of H. Wagner (1925), has been successfully treated and for an account with further references of both this and more general problems of unsteady motion we may refer to Robinson and Laurmann (1956). The physical character of this flow is well known: in the initial stages of near-potential flow, all the vorticity is confined to a very thin boundary layer which could well be represented by a vortex sheet. Later, a separated region is formed near the trailing edge enclosing a vortex-like motion, and this is convected into the wake. Second, solutions to the problem of the aerofoil whose incidence is oscillating regularly have, according to linearized theories, been well developed under the generic description of oscillatory derivatives. The discussion of such oscillatory flows is, however, outside the scope of this book.

IV

UNIFORM INVISCID FLOW PAST AEROFOILS

1. Introduction

THIS chapter is concerned with the details of the first inviscid approximation, discussed in Section III. 2, as it is applied to closed solid bodies in uniform two-dimensional flow. The work is therefore purely mathematical, once the boundary conditions have been settled by the physical character of the flow. If the real flow does not separate from the body—as in the case of a thin aerofoil at low incidence—then the body itself is taken to be the boundary of the potential flow. This leads to the problem of so-called unmixed boundary conditions in which the velocity normal to the given boundary is zero, and the analysis for such a flow is given in Sections 2–22. If, on the other hand, the real flow separates, then the potential flow of the first inviscid approximation is bounded partly by the body and partly by some hypothetical line representing the edge of the separated region; on this line, it is usually the velocity rather than the shape that is regarded as known. As a result the boundary conditions are mixed and Sections 23–39 deal with this problem.

The distinction between irrotational flows with unmixed and mixed boundary conditions has to be made because the analytical details of their solution differ. However, investigations do not necessarily fall neatly into one of these two categories: for example, the practical problem of designing an aerofoil to have a prescribed distribution of velocity over the front half and a prescribed shape over the rear, might be handled by techniques of either category.

It is often impracticable to compute the whole velocity field, but theories which give values only on the boundary are of great interest, as our main concern is the pressure distribution over the surface.

2. Unmixed boundary conditions

This category of boundary conditions includes the important class of unseparated flows past aerofoils at low incidence, and two mathematical problems associated with such flows may be distinguished. In the direct problem, the shape of the aerofoil and its attitude in relation to the stream are given, and the velocity distribution on the surface is required, whereas the inverse problem refers to the design of an aerofoil, whose shape is unknown but on which the velocity distribution is prescribed.

Fundamentally, the direct problem is straightforward. The complex potential, $\mathfrak{w}$, which determines the irrotational velocity field is an analytic function of position in the region of the plane outside the aerofoil on which its imaginary part, ψ, takes a constant value as discussed in Sections I. 21 and 22. If the magnitude and direction of the stream velocity at infinity are given, then the solution for $\mathfrak{w}$ is unique, apart from a term corresponding to an arbitrary circulation. Nearly all techniques used for the direct problem are variants of the basic one, exemplified in Section 5, in which the region outside the given contour is conformally transformed into the region outside a circle; the irrotational flow past a circular cylinder is known for any value of the circulation, and has been given in equation (I. 69).

As for the inverse problem, it is not immediately obvious that it has a unique solution for a prescribed distribution of velocity, or indeed a solution at all. In fact, we shall see in Section 20 that there is an exact solution provided the velocity distribution satisfies certain integral conditions.

3. Technical terms, notation, and geometrical properties of aerofoils

On an aerofoil, there are usually two points, L and T, such that LT is greater in length than any other straight line joining two points on the aerofoil. These points are called the leading and trailing edges respectively, the former being the one facing the oncoming stream when the aerofoil is in a normal attitude. The line LT is the chord, of length c.

We shall always take $\mathfrak{z} = x + iz$ as the plane of the aerofoil, and it is usual to take L as the origin and the chord as part of the positive x-axis. The whole aerofoil then lies in $0 \leqslant x \leqslant c$.

If $z = z(x)$ represents the contour of the aerofoil, dz/dx is infinite, in general, at both the leading and trailing edges. It is almost always assumed that, near the leading and trailing edges of an aerofoil,

$$\left. \begin{array}{l} z(x) \sim (2\rho_L x)^{\frac{1}{2}}[1 + A_1(x/c)^{\frac{1}{2}} + O(x)] \\ z(x) \sim [2\rho_T(c-x)]^{\frac{1}{2}}[1 + B_1\{(c-x)/c\}^{\frac{1}{2}} + O(c-x)] \end{array} \right\}, \tag{1}$$

ρ_L and ρ_T being the radii of curvature at the two edges respectively. The most common exception occurs when the trailing edge is sharp, namely $\rho_T = 0$. For one side of a wedge-shaped trailing edge,

$$z(x) \sim C_1(c-x)/c,$$

while for a cusp the index of $(c-x)$ is greater than unity.

It is often convenient to work in terms of an angular coordinate, ϕ, defined by
$$x = \tfrac{1}{2}c(1+\cos\phi), \tag{2}$$
rather than x. The trailing and leading edges are given by $\phi = 0$ and $\phi = \pi$ respectively.

Two surfaces of an aerofoil are distinguished as follows:

$$\left.\begin{array}{l}\text{upper surface, suffix } u: \quad 0 < \phi < \pi, \quad z = z_u \\ \text{lower surface, suffix } l: \quad \pi < \phi < 2\pi, \quad z = z_l\end{array}\right\}. \tag{3}$$

Then the camber line and fairing are defined as follows:

$$\left.\begin{array}{ll}\text{camber line, suffix } c: & z_c = \tfrac{1}{2}(z_u+z_l) \\ \text{fairing,} \qquad \text{suffix } s: & z_s = \tfrac{1}{2}(z_u-z_l)\end{array}\right\}. \tag{4}$$

Thus the two aerofoil surfaces are given by $z = z_c \pm z_s$, the alternative signs always being understood to refer to the upper and lower surfaces respectively. The camber line is the mean line of the aerofoil, while $2z_s(x)$ represents the chordwise distribution of thickness of the aerofoil. The thickness, t, of the aerofoil is the maximum value of $2z_s(x)$.

If $z_c \equiv 0$, the aerofoil is symmetrical; otherwise it is cambered.

The incidence, α, is measured from the downstream chordwise direction to the direction of the uniform flow at infinity.

4. The lift slope

Consider the irrotational flow in the ζ-plane past the circle $|\zeta| = a$. If at infinity the velocity has magnitude V and is at an angle α to the real axis, the complex potential is

$$\mathfrak{w} = V(\zeta e^{-i\alpha}+\zeta^{-1}a^2e^{i\alpha})+(i\Gamma/2\pi)\log\zeta, \tag{5}$$

where Γ is the circulation about the circle. On the circle itself, let $\zeta = ae^{i\phi}$; then the speed v_c on the surface is $|d\mathfrak{w}/d\zeta|_{\zeta=ae^{i\phi}}$, or

$$v_c = |2V\sin(\phi-\alpha)+\Gamma/2\pi a|. \tag{6}$$

The circulation is related to the lift and to the lift coefficient by equations (I. 19) and (I. 72): thus

$$\Gamma = \tfrac{1}{2}Vc\,C_L, \tag{7}$$

c being the chord of the body which has been derived from the circle by a conformal transformation whose derivative is unity at infinity. Then (6) may be written as

$$v_c/V = 2|\sin(\phi-\alpha)+(c/4a)(C_L/2\pi)|. \tag{8}$$

A primary task of this and the next chapter is to determine the dependence of C_L on α. For the moment we quote the Kutta–Joukowski condition which asserts that in the ζ-plane the speed, v_c, must be zero at the point, say $\phi = -\beta$, which corresponds to the trailing edge of the aerofoil. This ensures that the velocity is finite at a sharp trailing edge. This condition, from (8), gives

$$C_L = 2\pi(4a/c)\sin(\alpha+\beta). \tag{9}$$

For the small values of α for which the flow is unseparated, C_L may be regarded as linearly dependent on α, as seen, for example, in Fig. I. 6. Thus, bearing in mind also the inherent errors of the first inviscid approximation, we may as well write (9) as

$$C_L/(\alpha+\beta) = 2\pi(4a/c).$$

This is called the theoretical lift slope; $(-\beta)$ is called the no-lift angle, for obvious reasons.

The discovery that C_L depends linearly on incidence was of the greatest importance in the eventual achievement of winged flight. It confounded the pessimists who, even up to about 1900, trusted to the idea of the destruction of the momentum of particles which were supposed to impinge on the body. This reasoning, attributed to Newton, leads to $C_L = 2\alpha^2$. Lanchester, in 1897, was the first to propose, in a qualitative way, the effect of circulation, though his paper was never published. Interesting historical surveys of these and related topics have been given by Pritchard (1957) and Kármán (1958).

Returning to the magnitude of the lift slope, we remark that the chord c of the body never exceeds $4a$, being equal to it only in the limiting case of a flat plate. 2π is often called the classical value of the lift slope; it is increased, in two-dimensional inviscid flow, by the aerofoil being thick, and significantly decreased by the action of viscosity as is discussed in Section V. 11. It is decreased still further for three-dimensional wings of finite span, as shown in Chapter VIII.

Since real flows do not conform strictly to the Kutta–Joukowski condition, most aerofoil theory is put in terms of a_0, an assumed value of the lift slope. Thus

$$C_L = a_0\sin(\alpha+\beta) \quad \text{and} \quad \Gamma = \tfrac{1}{2}Vca_0\sin(\alpha+\beta). \tag{10}$$

5. Some special flows

Consider the transformation

$$\mathfrak{z} = \zeta+b^2\zeta^{-1} \quad (b \leqslant a). \tag{11}$$

The circle $|\zeta| = a$ becomes the ellipse given by

$$x = (a+b^2a^{-1})\cos\phi, \qquad z = (a-b^2a^{-1})\sin\phi, \tag{12}$$

whose thickness-chord ratio is $t/c = (a^2-b^2)/(a^2+b^2)$. From this equation, together with (9) and (12), we obtain

$$C_L/\alpha \simeq C_L/\sin\alpha = 2\pi(1+t/c). \tag{13}$$

This is an indication that, in general, the lift slope increases with the thickness of the aerofoil.

By taking $b = a$, we derive the flow past a flat plate given, from (12), by $x = 2a\cos\phi$, $z = 0$. The chord c now equals $4a$. The speed, v, on the plate is obtained from equations (8) and (11) as

$$v = |d\mathfrak{w}/d\zeta||d\zeta/d\mathfrak{z}| = V\operatorname{cosec}\phi|\sin(\phi-\alpha)+C_L/2\pi|.$$

The Kutta–Joukowski condition gives $C_L = 2\pi\sin\alpha$, and the speed may then be written as

$$v = V\cos\alpha \pm V\sin\alpha[(c-x)/x]^{\frac{1}{2}}, \tag{14}$$

in which x is now measured from the leading edge and given by equation (2). The first term in (14) is the component of the uniform stream along the plate, while the second represents the effect of the plate. v is finite at the trailing edge $x = c$, whereas at the leading edge $x = 0$, v tends to infinity proportionally to $x^{-\frac{1}{2}}$. This is characteristic of the velocity near any sharp edge and although the infinity is, of course, absent for a rounded leading edge, the latent singularity is manifested on thin aerofoils by high maxima in the velocity near the leading edge for large incidences.

The Joukowski transformation extends (11) by replacing ζ^{-1} by $(\zeta-\zeta_0)^{-1}$. The transformation has singularities at the points $\zeta = \zeta_0 \pm b$, and so, for a physically significant flow, neither of these points may lie outside the circle $|\zeta| = a$. If (ζ_0+b) lies on the circle, the transformation gives an aerofoil with a cusped trailing edge, and a circular arc in the particular case of ζ_0 being imaginary. Numerous examples have, in the past, been worked out in detail and a full discussion is given in many standard books on aerodynamics.

6. Poisson's integral formulae

We now go on to consider more general conformal transformations in which the region exterior to the aerofoil in the $\mathfrak{z}$-plane is mapped into the exterior of the circle $|\zeta| = a$ in the ζ-plane. In addition we require the derivative of the transformation, $d\mathfrak{z}/d\zeta$, to be unity at infinity; this ensures that the velocity at infinity is unaltered. Fig. IV. 1 illustrates the correspondence between the two planes. The transformation may be written as a Laurent series, $\mathfrak{z}-\zeta = \sum\limits_{n=0}^{\infty} c_n \zeta^{-n}$, where the coefficients c_n

are constants. The expansion will be valid for sufficiently large values of ζ. Indeed, since ʒ is an analytic function of ζ everywhere outside the circle $|\zeta| = a$, the series will be valid right up to the circle itself. Some properties of such series are of great value, and they will now be described.

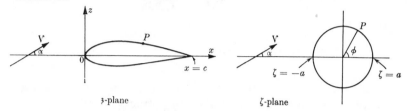

ʒ-plane ζ-plane

Fig. IV. 1. A sketch showing the notation used in the transformation between an aerofoil and a circle.

Consider the function $f(\zeta)$ such that

$$f(\zeta) = U - iV = \sum_{n=0}^{\infty} c_n \zeta^{-n}, \qquad (15)$$

where U and V are real and the coefficients $c_n = a_n + ib_n$ are complex constants. Let $\zeta = re^{i\phi}$; then, taking the real and imaginary parts of equation (15), we have

$$\left.\begin{aligned}
U(r,\phi) &= \sum_{n=0}^{\infty} r^{-n}(a_n \cos n\phi + b_n \sin n\phi) \\
V(r,\phi) &= \sum_{n=0}^{\infty} r^{-n}(a_n \sin n\phi - b_n \cos n\phi)
\end{aligned}\right\}. \qquad (16)$$

Thus, on the circle $r =$ constant, U and V are represented by conjugate Fourier series, the coefficients of the cosine and sine terms being interchanged with appropriate changes of sign. Further, if (16) defines V as the Fourier conjugate of U, then the Fourier conjugate of V is $-U$. If the real part, U, of $f(\zeta)$ is known on the circle $|\zeta| = r$, the coefficients a_n and b_n can be calculated and so the imaginary part, $-V$, of $f(\zeta)$ deduced, apart from an arbitrary constant, the only proviso being that $f(\zeta)$ is finite at infinity. Integral formulae for $f(\zeta)$ in terms of U on $|\zeta| = a$ may be derived as follows.

Taking values in equation (16) on $r = a$, we have by the usual formulae for the coefficients of a Fourier series,

$$n \geqslant 1; \; a_n = (a^n/\pi) \int_0^{2\pi} U(a,t)\cos nt\, dt, \quad b_n = (a^n/\pi) \int_0^{2\pi} U(a,t)\sin nt\, dt, \qquad (17)$$

and $\qquad a_0 = U_\infty = (1/2\pi) \int_0^{2\pi} U(a,t)\, dt, \qquad b_0 = -V_\infty. \qquad (18)$

These values may be put in equation (16) and the order of integration and summation interchanged; summing the geometric series and taking the real and imaginary parts, we finally obtain

$$U(r,\phi) = \frac{1}{2\pi} \int\limits_0^{2\pi} U(a,t) \frac{r^2-a^2}{r^2-2ra\cos(t-\phi)+a^2}\, dt, \qquad (19)$$

$$V(r,\phi)-V_\infty = -\frac{1}{2\pi} \int\limits_0^{2\pi} U(a,t) \frac{2ra\sin(t-\phi)}{r^2-2ra\cos(t-\phi)+a^2}\, dt. \qquad (20)$$

These are Poisson's integral formulae. Equation (20) may be used to obtain the value of V on the circle itself by putting $r = a$. The result is

$$V(a,\phi)-V_\infty = (1/2\pi)P \int\limits_0^{2\pi} U(a,t)\cot \tfrac{1}{2}(\phi--t)\, dt \qquad (21)$$

which is Poisson's integral. The P indicates that the Cauchy principal value must be taken at the singularity $t = \phi$ in the integrand; in other words, the integral $\int\limits_0^{2\pi}$ is to be interpreted as $\lim\limits_{\epsilon \to 0} \left(\int\limits_0^{\phi-\epsilon} + \int\limits_{\phi+\epsilon}^{2\pi} \right)$. Alternatively, equation (21) may be written in the form

$$V(a,\phi)-V_\infty = (1/2\pi) \int\limits_0^{2\pi} \{U(a,t)-U(a,\phi)\}\cot \tfrac{1}{2}(\phi-t)\, dt, \qquad (22)$$

which avoids the singularity. This is admissible since

$$P \int\limits_0^{2\pi} \cot \tfrac{1}{2}(\phi-t)\, dt = 0.$$

If U is an even function of ϕ, so that $U(\phi) = U(-\phi) = U(2\pi-\phi)$, then all the coefficients b_n in (16) are zero; thus V is an odd function of ϕ, again apart from an arbitrary constant. Equation (21) can then be written in the form

$$V(a,\phi)-V_\infty = -\frac{\sin\phi}{\pi}P \int\limits_0^{\pi} \frac{U(a,t)}{\cos\phi-\cos t}\, dt, \qquad (23)$$

the convenience of which is that the range of integration is now from 0 to π. Similarly, if U is an odd function of ϕ, V is even and given by

$$V(a,\phi)-V_\infty = -\frac{1}{\pi}P \int\limits_0^{\pi} \frac{U(a,t)\sin t}{\cos\phi-\cos t}\, dt. \qquad (24)$$

7. Computation of Fourier conjugates and associated formulae

In many of the treatments of aerofoil theory, it is necessary to calculate the Fourier conjugate $V(\phi)$ of a given function $U(\phi)$, and sometimes also the derivative or integral of the conjugate. If $U(\phi)$ has a sufficiently simple analytic form, the integral (21) may be evaluated exactly and no problem arises. But in most cases this is not possible, and for these a powerful computational technique was introduced by Germain (1945) and further developed by Watson (1945). The values of the given function $U(\phi)$ at $2N$ equally-spaced values of ϕ are written as

$$U_m = U(m\pi/N), \quad m = 0, 1, 2, ..., 2N-1, \qquad (25)$$

the suffix m here and later denoting a value at $\phi = m\pi/N$. $U(\phi)$ is now approximated by the trigonometric polynomial

$$U^*(\phi) = A_0 + \sum_{r=1}^{N-1} (A_r \cos r\phi + B_r \sin r\phi) + A_N \cos N\phi \qquad (26)$$

in which the $2N$ constants are chosen so that $U^*(\phi) = U_m = U(\phi)$ at the points $\phi = m\pi/N$. In plainer language, we approximate to $U(\phi)$ by the function $U^*(\phi)$ which takes the correct values at $2N$ equally-spaced points. The Fourier conjugate of $U^*(\phi)$ is

$$V^*(\phi) = \sum_{r=1}^{N-1} (A_r \sin r\phi - B_r \cos r\phi) + A_N \sin N\phi \qquad (27)$$

and this is taken as the corresponding approximation to $V(\phi)$. V may also contain an additive arbitrary constant, but the value of (27) corresponds to that obtained from Poisson's integral.

Using standard properties of trigonometric series, Watson deduces the following results on the basis of the approximation (26):

$$V_m = - \sum_{\substack{1 \leqslant p \leqslant N-1 \\ p \text{ odd}}} N^{-1} \cot(p\pi/2N)(U_{m+p} - U_{m-p}), \qquad (28)$$

$$(dV/d\phi)_m = \tfrac{1}{2}N U_m - \sum_{\substack{1 \leqslant p \leqslant N-1 \\ p \text{ odd}}} (2N)^{-1} \operatorname{cosec}^2(p\pi/2N)(U_{m+p} + U_{m-p}) + {}$$
$$+ \begin{cases} +0 & \text{if } N \text{ is even} \\ -U_{m+N}/2N & \text{if } N \text{ is odd,} \end{cases} \qquad (29)$$

$$(dU/d\phi)_m = \sum_{p=1}^{N-1} (-1)^{p+1} \tfrac{1}{2} \cot(p\pi/2N)(U_{m+p} - U_{m-p}), \qquad (30)$$

$$\int^{m\pi/N} U \, d\phi = (m\pi/2N^2) \sum_{n=0}^{2N-1} U_n + \sum_{p=1}^{N-1} \delta_p (U_{m+p} - U_{m-p}), \qquad (31)$$

$$\int^{m\pi/N} V \, d\phi = \zeta_0 U_m + \sum_{p=1}^{N-1} \zeta_p (U_{m+p} + U_{m-p}) + \zeta_N U_{m+N}, \qquad (32)$$

where
$$\delta_p = -N^{-1} \sum_{r=1}^{N-1} r^{-1} \sin(rp\pi/N)$$

and
$$\zeta_p = -N^{-1} \sum_{r=1}^{N-1} r^{-1} \cos(rp\pi/N) + \tfrac{1}{2}(-1)^{p+1} N^{-2}.$$

Watson has computed the values of the coefficients of U_{m+p} for the case $N = 20$. These are given in Table IV. 1 and apply to the use of 40 points round the aerofoil contour; this number is usually sufficient for full advantage to be taken of any approximate theory.

TABLE IV. 1

The coefficients of U_{m+p}, for $N = 20$, in the formulae (28) to (32)

p	V_m	$(dV/d\phi)_m$	$(dU/d\phi)_m$	$\int^{m\pi/N} U \, d\phi$	$\int^{m\pi/N} V \, d\phi$
0	0	10	0	0	−0·1786370
1	−0·6353102	−4·061191	+6·353102	−0·0886371	−0·0962953
2	0	0	−3·156876	−0·0631191	−0·0569600
3	−0·2082650	−0·458743	+2·082650	−0·0718586	−0·0386245
4	0	0	−1·538842	−0·0590318	−0·0237441
5	−0·1207107	−0·170711	+1·207107	−0·0618980	−0·0135788
6	0	0	−0·981305	−0·0525390	−0·0046772
7	−0·0815926	−0·091573	+0·815926	−0·0530816	+0·0020875
8	0	0	−0·688191	−0·0454095	0·0081774
9	−0·0585425	−0·059272	+0·585425	−0·0446562	0·0130021
10	0	0	−0·5	−0·0380230	0·0173909
11	−0·0427040	−0·043236	+0·427040	−0·0364082	0·0209084
12	0	0	−0·363271	−0·0305095	0·0241082
13	−0·0306400	−0·034388	+0·306400	−0·0282536	0·0266436
14	0	0	−0·254763	−0·0229260	0·0289265
15	−0·0207107	−0·029289	+0·207107	−0·0201520	0·0306621
16	0	0	−0·162460	−0·0153024	0·0321828
17	−0·0120039	−0·026441	+0·120039	−0·0120807	0·0332234
18	0	0	−0·079192	−0·0076562	0·0340699
19	−0·0039351	−0·025155	+0·039351	−0·0040252	0·0344716
20	0	0	0	0	0·0346886

Note. The coefficients for $\int^{m\pi/N} U \, d\phi$ do not include the non-periodic term $(m\pi/2N^2) \sum_{n=0}^{2N-1} U_n$.

8. Thin aerofoils. Linearized theory

There is a practical limit to the amount of useful information to be obtained from the explicit specification of conformal transformations such as (11), since the complexity of the calculations increases rapidly with the number of additional terms. An alternative approach is to simplify the mathematical conditions of the problem in some way.

The most comprehensive simplification is a thorough-going linearization leading to what has been known as thin-aerofoil theory. The theory has been studied in many different forms since the early days of aerodynamics, some of the earlier workers being Munk (1922), Birnbaum (1923), and H. Glauert (1926). Our discussion here will point out only the essential features of the theory, and provide a basis of comparison with the more accurate theories to be described later.

We note first that the equation governing the fluid flow needs no simplification: Laplace's equation for the complex velocity potential is already linear. It is only through the boundary conditions that non-linearity enters the problem, and to resolve the difficulties so created, we consider the perturbations in the velocity rather than the total velocity itself. If the components of the total velocity are $(V \cos \alpha + u)$ and $(V \sin \alpha + w)$, the condition of tangential flow at the aerofoil surface is

$$(V \sin \alpha + w)/(V \cos \alpha + u) = dz/dx. \qquad (33)$$

The first assumption is that u, w, and αV are all small in comparison with V; thus (33) reduces to

$$dz/dx = \alpha + w/U, \qquad (34)$$

in which, for convenience of notation, we have written U, the velocity component in the x-direction, in place of V since they are indistinguishable under the assumptions of linearized theory. The next assumption is that this boundary condition holds on the chord-line $z = 0$, $0 \leqslant x \leqslant c$, and not on the surface of the aerofoil. Equation (34) is therefore split into two parts, using equation (4):

$$w/U = w_s/U = \pm z_s'(x) \quad \text{on } z = \pm 0, \, 0 \leqslant x \leqslant c; \qquad (35)$$

$$w/U = w_c/U = z_c'(x) - \alpha \quad \text{on } z = 0, \quad 0 \leqslant x \leqslant c. \qquad (36)$$

Also, u and w tend to zero as $\mathfrak{z} \to \infty$. It may be shown that the appropriate solutions for the perturbation velocity are respectively

$$u_s - i w_s = \frac{U}{\pi} \int_0^c \frac{z_s'(\xi)}{\mathfrak{z} - \xi} \, d\xi, \qquad (37)$$

$$u_c - i w_c = U\left(\frac{c - \mathfrak{z}}{\mathfrak{z}}\right)^{\frac{1}{2}} \left\{ \frac{1}{\pi} \int_0^c \frac{[z_c'(\xi) - \alpha]}{\mathfrak{z} - \xi} \left(\frac{\xi}{c - \xi}\right)^{\frac{1}{2}} d\xi + \frac{cC}{c - \mathfrak{z}} \right\}. \qquad (38)$$

In (38), C is an arbitrary real constant and that branch of the square root is taken which is positive on $z = +0$, $0 < x < c$. For practical purposes, these two formulae require further elucidation and this is given in Sections 9 and 10. Alternatively, they may be regarded as a first approximation in a formal expansion of the perturbation velocity field in powers of some small quantity and this is taken up again in Section 14.

The solutions (37) and (38) are not in fact the most general expressions satisfying the stated boundary conditions, as may be seen from Muskhelishvili (1946), but all others include singularities in $d\mathfrak{w}/d\mathfrak{z}$ like $\mathfrak{z}^{-n-\frac{1}{2}}$ and $(\mathfrak{z}-c)^{-n-\frac{1}{2}}$, where n is a positive integer. These are unacceptable because they involve an infinite flux between either the leading or trailing edge and any nearby point.

The final stage in this linearized theory is to calculate from (37) and (38) the value of u on the strip $z = \pm 0$, $0 \leqslant x \leqslant c$, and then to regard this as the increment of velocity (over U) on the aerofoil surface itself. Thus, if v denotes the speed on the aerofoil, the final result of this theory is:

$$\mathrm{v} = U + \frac{U}{\pi} P \int\limits_0^c \frac{z_s'(\xi)}{x-\xi}\, d\xi \pm U\left(\frac{c-x}{x}\right)^{\frac{1}{2}} \left\{ \frac{1}{\pi} P \int\limits_0^c \frac{[z_c'(\xi)-\alpha]}{x-\xi}\left(\frac{\xi}{c-\xi}\right)^{\frac{1}{2}} d\xi + \frac{cC}{c-x} \right\}. \tag{39}$$

U here is probably best taken as the value of the stream speed V, but in Sections 9 to 11, and later in Chapters VII and VIII, this notation will be retained as a reminder that linearized theory is being used.

9. Linearized theory. The fairing

Considering first the contribution to the perturbation velocity due to the thickness of the aerofoil, we see from (37) that $(u_s - i w_s)$ is the field due to a source distribution on the chord-line $z = 0$, $0 \leqslant x \leqslant c$, of strength $q(x)$ per unit length given by

$$q(x) = 2U z_s'(x). \tag{40}$$

This therefore may be said to be the source distribution which, according to the ideas of Section I. 22, represents a symmetrical aerofoil at zero incidence. The total source strength is

$$\int\limits_0^c q(x)\, dx = \int\limits_0^c 2U z_s'(x)\, dx = 2U[z_s(x)]_0^c = 0;$$

therefore the source flow has a closed dividing streamline which approximately coincides with the surface of the aerofoil.

This source distribution (40) could have been inferred directly from the boundary condition (35) since only a source-singularity gives equal values of the outward normal velocity on the two sides of the strip. Its magnitude follows from a consideration of the flux of fluid away from the strip.

For a numerical computation of u_s, we note that $u_s \sin \phi$ is the Fourier conjugate of $(2U/c)(dz_s/d\phi)$. This follows at once on writing

$$x = \tfrac{1}{2}c(1+\cos \phi), \qquad \xi = \tfrac{1}{2}c(1+\cos t)$$

in the first integral in (39): thus

$$u_s \sin \phi = -\frac{\sin \phi}{\pi} P \int_0^\pi \frac{(2U/c)z_s'(t)}{\cos \phi - \cos t} \, dt, \tag{41}$$

which may be compared with (23). Given $z_s(\phi)$, u_s can therefore be calculated by the methods of Section 7.

10. Linearized theory. The camber line

To interpret the velocity field given by equation (38), we adopt a physical approach to the boundary condition (36). A velocity component w which takes the same value on either side of the slit is consistent with a vortex sheet in $z = 0$, $0 \leqslant x \leqslant c$. If the strength of the sheet is $\gamma(x)$ per unit length, the velocity field is given by

$$u-iw = (i/2\pi) \int_0^c \gamma(\xi)(\mathfrak{z}-\xi)^{-1} \, d\xi, \tag{42}$$

and on $z = \pm 0$ this gives

$$u = \pm \tfrac{1}{2}\gamma(x) \quad \text{and} \quad w = -\frac{1}{2\pi}P \int_0^c \frac{\gamma(\xi)}{x-\xi} \, d\xi. \tag{43}$$

The boundary condition (36) then becomes

$$z_c'(x)-\alpha = -\frac{1}{2\pi U}P \int_0^c \frac{\gamma(\xi)}{x-\xi} \, d\xi \tag{44}$$

the general solution of which has already been given by the last term in equation (39).

To enable computations to be carried out easily, we again work in terms of ϕ, and put

$$z_c'(x) = \sum_{n=0}^\infty B_n \cos n\phi, \tag{45}$$

which is valid provided the slope of the camber line is finite at the leading and trailing edges. The last term of (39) then gives

$$u_c(x) = U\Big\{(\alpha-B_0)\tan \tfrac{1}{2}\phi - \sum_{n=1}^\infty B_n \sin n\phi\Big\}+2UC \operatorname{cosec} \phi, \tag{46}$$

from which $u_c(x)$ appears correctly as an odd function of ϕ. The sum in (46) is the Fourier conjugate of that in (45) and therefore the methods of Section 7 are again applicable in the determination of the velocity from the given shape.

The constant C in equations (38), (39), and (46) represents, of course, the arbitrariness of the circulation. When the Kutta–Joukowski condition is applied, we see from (46) that $C = 0$.

Two special cases are worth mentioning. For the case of the flat plate, $z_c = 0$ and so $B_n = 0$ for all n; that the linearized theory is then correct to the first order in α may be checked by comparing equations (46) and (14). D. S. Jones (1955) has considered camber lines given as polynomials in x; these may be useful in cases for which the form (45) is not valid. The velocity distribution follows at once from the last term in equation (39). Keune (1938) devised a method of computing the whole velocity field by preparing diagrams for certain basic source and vortex distributions, suitable combinations of which could represent, approximately, any given aerofoil.

11. Linearized theory. Overall aerodynamic properties

The total circulation about the aerofoil is

$$\Gamma = \oint u \, dx = 2 \int_{\pi}^{0} u_c(-\tfrac{1}{2}c \sin \phi) \, d\phi; \tag{47}$$

hence, from (7) and (46),

$$C_L = 2\Gamma/Uc = 2\pi(\alpha - B_0 - \tfrac{1}{2}B_1 + 2C). \tag{48}$$

When the Kutta–Joukowski condition is applied, $C = 0$ and so

$$C_L = 2\pi(\alpha - B_0 - \tfrac{1}{2}B_1), \tag{49}$$

from which it follows that the no-lift angle, $-\beta$, is given by

$$-\beta = B_0 + \tfrac{1}{2}B_1. \tag{50}$$

This is usually fairly close to the experimental value, even if the experimental lift slope, a_0, differs considerably from 2π.

The velocity at the leading edge $\phi = \pi$, as given by (46), is infinite unless $\alpha - B_0 + C = 0$, which, with (10), (48), and (50), defines $C_{L \text{ opt}}$. This is the lift coefficient at which, on linearized theory, the flow attaches itself smoothly to the leading edge. Thus

$$C_{L \text{ opt}} \left(\frac{1}{2\pi} + \frac{1}{a_0} \right) = -B_1. \tag{51}$$

The pressure over the aerofoil surface is given by Bernoulli's equation, which on linearization takes the form

$$p - p_\infty = -\rho U u, \tag{52}$$

p_∞ being the pressure at infinity. On integrating the pressure along the chord, we obtain a force normal to the chord line; also, the singularity at the leading edge contributes a force parallel to the chord. These two forces combine to give a force perpendicular to the stream, as required by equation (I. 72).

The pitching moment, in the nose-up direction, about the leading edge is dependent only on u_c, and from (46) and (52) is found to be

$$C_m = \tfrac{1}{4}\pi(B_1+B_2)-\tfrac{1}{4}C_L \tag{53}$$

provided the no-lift angle has the theoretical value from (50). This is often written as $C_m = C_{m0}-\tfrac{1}{4}C_L$, where $C_{m0} = \tfrac{1}{4}\pi(B_1+B_2)$ is the moment coefficient at zero lift. The centre of pressure is distant $(C_m/C_L)c$ from the leading edge; it is at the quarter-chord point for all values of C_L, according to the linearized theory, if $B_1+B_2 = 0$ or if the aerofoil is symmetrical.

The aerodynamic quantities considered above depend solely on a knowledge of B_0, B_1, and B_2. From equation (45), these Fourier coefficients may be found directly in terms of the shape of the camber line as

$$B_0 = (1/\pi) \int_0^\pi z_c'(x)\,d\phi, \quad B_n = (2/\pi) \int_0^\pi z_c'(x)\cos n\phi\,d\phi \quad \text{for} \quad n \geqslant 1.$$
$$\tag{54}$$

12. The velocity distribution on an arbitrary aerofoil. Theodorsen's theory

The calculation of the pressure distribution on a given aerofoil when there are no restrictions as to thickness, camber, or incidence is one of some complexity in practice. A systematic series of approximations has been developed by Goldstein, who deduces his results from an exact theory due to Theodorsen (1932). The fundamental ideas of Theodorsen's treatment are as follows.

The region outside the aerofoil in the $\mathfrak{z}$-plane is to be mapped into the region outside a circle by a transformation whose derivative is unity at infinity. The first stage is to transform the aerofoil into a contour which does not differ greatly from a circle, by means of the transformation (11) with $b = a$. Thus

$$\mathfrak{z} = \zeta+a^2\zeta^{-1}. \tag{55}$$

This gives an exact circle if the aerofoil is an ellipse with its foci at $\mathfrak{z} = \pm 2\alpha$; hence it is best to position the aerofoil in the $\mathfrak{z}$-plane so that its leading and trailing edges enclose the points $\mathfrak{z} = \mp 2a$. More precisely, as is suggested by Lighthill's analysis described in Section 14, these points should be half their radius of curvature distant from $\mathfrak{z} = \mp 2a$ and on the real axis.

Since our aim is to determine only the velocity on the surface of the aerofoil—the original paper gives the analysis for the whole field—we can confine attention to values on the boundaries. This will be understood for the remainder of this section.

Now on the pseudo-circle, we write

$$\zeta = a \exp[\psi(\phi)+i\phi] \tag{56}$$

This, with the transformation (55), gives the parametric coordinates of the aerofoil as

$$x = 2a \cosh\psi \cos\phi, \qquad z = 2a \sinh\psi \sin\phi, \tag{57}$$

so that $\psi(\phi)$ is determinable from the given aerofoil shape.

The pseudo-circle is next transformed into a circle in the ζ_1-plane, on which

$$\zeta_1 = a \exp[C_0+i\{\phi+\epsilon(\phi)\}], \tag{58}$$

the radius being ae^{C_0}. Corresponding points on the boundaries in the ζ- and ζ_1-planes differ by the angular distance $\epsilon(\phi)$. We now have to determine C_0 and $\epsilon(\phi)$. To do this, we note that $[\{\psi(\phi)-C_0\}-i\epsilon(\phi)]$ is the value on the circle of $\log(\zeta/\zeta_1)$ which is an analytic function of ζ_1 outside the circle and is zero at infinity. Thus by Poisson's integral (21),

$$\epsilon(\phi) = \frac{1}{2\pi} P \int_0^{2\pi} \psi\{t+\epsilon(t)\}\cot\left(\frac{\phi+\epsilon(\phi)-t-\epsilon(t)}{2}\right) d\{t+\epsilon(t)\}. \tag{59}$$

C_0, being a constant, does not contribute to $\epsilon(\phi)$ and is given by

$$C_0 = \frac{1}{2\pi} \int_0^{2\pi} \psi\{\phi+\epsilon(\phi)\} \, d\{\phi+\epsilon(\phi)\} = \frac{1}{2\pi} \int_0^{2\pi} \psi\{\phi+\epsilon(\phi)\}\{1+\epsilon'(\phi)\} \, d\phi. \tag{60}$$

Unfortunately, (59) is an implicit equation for $\epsilon(\phi)$. Theodorsen's method is an iteration which is started by ignoring $\epsilon(\phi)$ in the integral. But his technique, which involves the estimation of derivatives by graphical means, is not recommended; the numerical methods of Section 7 are preferable. In any event, we now regard $\epsilon(\phi)$ as having been determined; this then relates points on the pseudo-circle to those on the exact circle and so we can go on to evaluate the moduli of the various transformations.

From equation (55), first, we have $d\mathfrak{z}/d\zeta = 1-a^2\zeta^{-2}$, and so with the boundary values from (56),

$$|d\mathfrak{z}/d\zeta| = 2a|\zeta|^{-1}\{\sinh^2\psi+\sin^2\phi\}^{\frac{1}{2}}. \tag{61}$$

On the pseudo-circle, logarithmic differentiation of equation (56) gives

$$\zeta^{-1} d\zeta = d\psi + i\, d\phi, \tag{62}$$

while on the true circle, from equation (58),

$$\zeta_1^{-1} d\zeta_1 = i(1+\epsilon')\, d\phi. \tag{63}$$

The combination of equations (58), (61), (62), and (63) then gives the modulus of the transformation between the aerofoil and the circle in the form:

$$\left| \frac{d\mathfrak{z}}{d\zeta_1} \right| = \left| \frac{d\mathfrak{z}}{d\zeta} \right| \cdot \left| \frac{d\zeta}{d\zeta_1} \right| = \frac{2e^{-C_0}}{1+\epsilon'} [1+(\psi')^2]^{\frac{1}{2}} (\sinh^2\psi + \sin^2\phi)^{\frac{1}{2}}. \tag{64}$$

Now the chord, c, of the aerofoil is given from equation (57) as

$$c = 2a(\cosh\psi_L + \cosh\psi_T). \tag{65}$$

The speed on the circle is given in equation (8) with the radius a replaced by ae^{C_0} and ϕ by $(\phi+\epsilon)$. Using equation (65), we then have

$$\mathrm{v}_c = 2\mathrm{V} |\sin(\phi+\epsilon-\alpha) + \tfrac{1}{4}(\cosh\psi_L + \cosh\psi_T)e^{-C_0}C_L/\pi|. \tag{66}$$

The final result for the speed v on the aerofoil, given by $\mathrm{v} = \mathrm{v}_c |d\zeta_1/d\mathfrak{z}|$, is obtained by eliminating α between equations (10) and (66), and using (64); thus

$$\frac{\mathrm{v}}{\mathrm{V}} = \frac{e^{C_0}(1+\epsilon')}{[1+(\psi')^2]^{\frac{1}{2}}(\sinh^2\psi + \sin^2\phi)^{\frac{1}{2}}} \times$$
$$\times \left| \left(1 - \frac{C_L^2}{a_0^2}\right)^{\frac{1}{2}} \sin(\phi+\epsilon+\beta) - \frac{C_L}{a_0}\cos(\phi+\epsilon+\beta) + \frac{C_L(\cosh\psi_L + \cosh\psi_T)}{4\pi e^{C_0}} \right|. \tag{67}$$

Since this is one of the very few exact results of any generality in this book, it is worth recapitulating the two basic steps which must be taken for a numerical calculation. First, with the given aerofoil suitably placed in the $\mathfrak{z}$-plane, the function $\psi(\phi)$ is determined from equation (57); second, ϵ and C_0 are evaluated from (59) and (60).

The Kutta–Joukowski condition demands, from (67), that

$$C_L/\sin(\alpha+\beta) = 2\pi e^{C_0}/(\cosh\psi_L + \cosh\psi_T) \quad \text{and} \quad \beta = -\epsilon(0). \tag{68}$$

The practical accuracy of Theodorsen's formula (67) depends, of course, on the efficiency of the method used for evaluating the Fourier conjugates. It may also be remarked that agreement with the velocity distribution measured in experiment will be most satisfactory if a_0 and β take their experimental values rather than those in (68). The theoretical value, $\beta = -\epsilon(0)$, is often quite accurate, but the value of a_0 rarely exceeds 85 per cent of its theoretical value. With a reduced value of a_0, equation (67) gives an infinite velocity at the trailing edge and a stagnation point near it. This is, of course, not observed in practice, but provided the flow is unseparated, the value of v as given by (67) is usually satisfactory over the greater part of the chord.

13. Goldstein's approximations to Theodorsen's theory

The essence of the approximations made in 1942 by Goldstein (1952) to Theodorsen's theory is the assumption that the differences between the pseudo-circle in the ζ-plane and the true circle in the ζ_1-plane are small. The best of his approximations neglects, where necessary, squares and products of ϵ and ψ in comparison with unity; this imposes some assumptions about the thickness and camber of the aerofoil, but makes no demands on the incidence.

As a start the chord is $c = 4a$ from (65) and so the parametric equations (57) reduce to

$$x = \tfrac{1}{2}c(1+\cos\phi), \qquad z = \tfrac{1}{2}c\psi(\phi)\sin\phi, \tag{69}$$

the origin in the $\mathfrak{z}$-plane having been moved so that the chord extends from $x = 0$ to $x = c$. We note, once again, the appearance of the form (2) for x. The expression (67) for the velocity on the aerofoil surface becomes

$$\frac{\mathrm{v}}{\mathrm{V}} = \frac{e^{C_0}(1+\epsilon')}{(\psi^2+\sin^2\phi)^{\frac{1}{2}}} \left| \left(1-\frac{C_L^2}{a_0^2}\right)^{\frac{1}{2}} \sin(\phi+\epsilon+\beta) - \frac{C_L}{a_0}\cos(\phi+\epsilon+\beta) + \frac{C_L}{2\pi e^{C_0}} \right|. \tag{70}$$

$\epsilon(\phi)$ is now given explicitly in terms of $\psi(\phi)$ by the appropriate approximation to equation (59):

$$\epsilon(\phi) = (1/2\pi)P \int_0^{2\pi} \psi(t)\cot\tfrac{1}{2}(\phi-t)\, dt, \tag{71}$$

while, from (60), C_0 is given by

$$C_0 = (1/2\pi) \int_0^{2\pi} \psi(\phi)\, d\phi. \tag{72}$$

The lift coefficient may still be given by equation (10), and if the Kutta–Joukowski condition is satisfied, equation (68) gives

$$C_L/\sin(\alpha+\beta) = 2\pi e^{C_0}, \qquad \beta = -\epsilon(0). \tag{73}$$

The approximations considered so far constitute Goldstein's Approximation III. For aerofoils whose contour is given by suitable algebraic expressions, $\epsilon(\phi)$ may be calculated explicitly. Otherwise the calculations may be carried out by the formulae of Section 7 with the ordinates of the aerofoil taken at a set of equally-spaced values of ϕ. An illustration of the accuracy of the method is shown in Fig. IV. 2 where the exact and approximate velocity distributions are compared for the aerofoil EQH 1250/4050. Approximation III is seen to be highly satisfactory, even for an aerofoil of considerable thickness and camber.

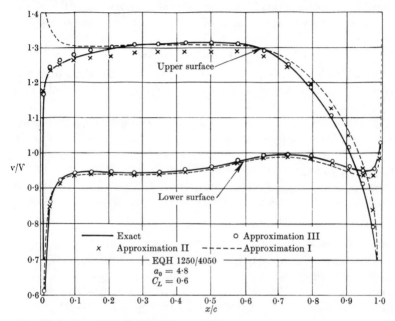

FIG. IV. 2. Computed velocities on the surface of a 12 per cent thick aerofoil with 4 per cent camber.

Further approximations for the velocity distribution enable the effects of thickness, camber, and incidence to be studied separately. The simplest involves rendering equation (70) linear in ψ, ϵ, C_L/a_0 and $C_L/2\pi$; it may be verified that the result is identical with the linearized theory of Sections 8–11. This, Goldstein's Approximation I, may be written in the form

$$v/V = 1+g$$
$$= 1+g_s+g_i+\tfrac{1}{2}\left(\frac{1}{a_0}+\frac{1}{2\pi}\right)(C_L-C_{L\,\mathrm{opt}})\tan\tfrac{1}{2}\phi-\tfrac{1}{2}\left(\frac{1}{a_0}-\frac{1}{2\pi}\right)C_L\cot\tfrac{1}{2}\phi.$$
(74)

Then Vg_s is identifiable with u_s of Section 8, and so from Section 9 we have that $g_s\sin\phi$ is the Fourier conjugate of $(2/c)\,dz_s/d\phi$. Also g_i, an odd function of ϕ, which is the contribution due to the camber line when $C_L = C_{L \, \text{opt}}$ and $a_0 = 2\pi$, is the Fourier conjugate of $(-dz_c/dx)$. A detailed analysis of the results is given by Goldstein.

A serious defect of linearized theory is the prediction of an infinite velocity at the leading edge. In Approximation I, this is due to the replacement of $(\psi^2 + \sin^2\phi)^{\frac{1}{2}}$ in (70) by $\sin\phi$ in (74), which is clearly invalid when $\sin\phi$ is small, however thin the aerofoil. Accordingly, the expression for v/V in equation (74) is corrected by a suitable factor and becomes

$$v/V = (1 + \tfrac{1}{2}C_0^2)|\sin\phi|(\psi^2 + \sin^2\phi)^{-\frac{1}{2}}(1+g), \qquad (75)$$

which is Goldstein's Approximation II. The inclusion of the term $\tfrac{1}{2}C_0^2$ is not completely logical, but does not involve any significant extra labour.

Thus we have three approximations numbered in order of increasing accuracy. To use Approximations I and II it is necessary to calculate g_s, g_i, and the constants $C_{L \, \text{opt}}$ and C_0, while for Approximation III we need ϵ, ϵ', and C_0. All these quantities are given explicitly by suitable expressions involving Fourier conjugates. The velocity distributions over the aerofoil EQH 1250/4050 given by Approximations I and II are also shown in Fig. IV. 2.

14. Non-linear theories. Lighthill (1951)

Numerous attempts to improve directly upon linearized theory have been made, the main aim being to modify the singular form of the solution near the leading edge. A fundamentally satisfactory treatment has been given by Lighthill (1951) as an application of his general technique for rendering approximate solutions to physical problems uniformly valid.

It is assumed that the incidence and the aerofoil ordinates are all of order ϵ, where ϵ is a small constant. The whole velocity field is expanded in powers of ϵ, the Kutta–Joukowski condition being satisfied. The terms linear in ϵ are those of linearized theory, and the terms in ϵ^2 and ϵ^3 are evaluated explicitly, in order to determine the analytical nature of the singularities in the successive approximations. In accordance with the general technique, a new coordinate system is sought in which the terms in the series no longer become successively more singular at the leading edge as they do in the original system. In fact, in this case, it can be shown that the velocity field as obtained by a straightforward expansion may be rendered a valid first approximation near the leading edge, as well as a valid first or second order approximation away from it, if the whole velocity field is shifted downstream by a distance of half the leading-edge radius of curvature ρ_L. Thus, equations (37) and (38) are radically improved for the region of the leading edge if $\tfrac{1}{2}\rho_L$ is subtracted from $\mathfrak{z}$. This result also puts on a firmer footing the choice of origin and scale in Theodorsen's theory.

The original paper discusses various approximations to the velocity distribution and the simplest suggestion for a uniformly valid first approximation is to multiply the velocity on the aerofoil surface, as given by linearized theory, by the factor $[x/(x+\tfrac{1}{2}\rho_L)]^{\frac{1}{2}}$, where $x = 0$ is the leading edge. This agrees with Goldstein's Approximation II to within the approximation used. Lighthill's final result is the following expression for the velocity distribution on the surface, which is a second approximation valid even near the leading edge:

$$(v/V)[x/(x+\tfrac{1}{2}\rho_L)]^{-\frac{1}{2}} = 1-\tfrac{1}{2}\alpha^2+(1/\pi)P\int_0^c s'(\xi)(x-\xi)^{-1}\,d\xi\,\pm$$

$$\pm[(c-x)/x]^{\frac{1}{2}}\left[\alpha+(1/\pi)P\int_0^c r'(\xi)(x-\xi)^{-1}[\xi/(c-\xi)]^{\frac{1}{2}}\,d\xi\right]+$$

$$+(z_c\pm z_s)(z_c''\pm z_s'')+\tfrac{1}{2}(z_c'\pm z_s')^2+\rho_L/4x. \tag{76}$$

Here $r(x) = az_c+bz_s$ and $s(x) = az_s+bz_c$, where

$$a(x) = 1+\frac{1}{\pi}P\int_0^c \frac{z_s'(\xi)}{x-\xi}\,d\xi, \quad b(x) = \left(\frac{c-x}{x}\right)^{\frac{1}{2}}\left[\alpha+\frac{1}{\pi}P\int_0^c \frac{z_c'(\xi)}{x-\xi}\left(\frac{\xi}{c-\xi}\right)^{\frac{1}{2}}d\xi\right],$$

$$\tag{77}$$

and the notation is otherwise as in previous sections. It may be noted that $a(x)\pm b(x)$ is the value (39) of v/U given by linearized theory. The integrals in (76) and (77) could be computed by the methods of Section 7.

The extension of the method to compressible flow past an aerofoil was originally envisaged by Lighthill, but it has not yet proved possible.

15. Non-linear theories. Weber (1953, 1955)

This method of calculation is based on those of Riegels and Wittich (1942) and of Riegels (1948), and its primary aim is to formulate the theory in such a manner as to be readily extensible to three-dimensional flow. This rules out the exclusive use of conformal transformations. Instead, the perturbations of the uniform stream are explained in terms of suitable distributions of sources and vortices which have extensions to three-dimensional flow, as we shall see especially in Chapters VII and VIII.

The basic idea is to transform the region outside the aerofoil in the $\mathfrak{z}$-plane into the region outside a slit on the x^*-axis in the $\mathfrak{z}^*$-plane, where $\mathfrak{z}^* = x^* + iz^*$. Since the transformation of a straight slit into a circle is elementary, the mathematical problem is not essentially different from that in Theodorsen's method.

Consider first a symmetrical aerofoil at zero incidence, extending from $x = 0$ to $x = c$. At a point on the aerofoil surface $z = z_s(x)$, the tangential and normal components of a uniform stream U in the x-direction are respectively

$$V_t = U[1+(z_s')^2]^{-\frac{1}{2}}, \qquad V_n = -Uz_s'[1+(z_s')^2]^{-\frac{1}{2}}. \qquad (78)$$

Now, in a conformal transformation, the tangential and normal directions on the surface correspond; hence

$$V_n^* = V_n |d\mathfrak{z}/d\mathfrak{z}^*|. \qquad (79)$$

For a symmetrical aerofoil these normal velocities at the slit are of equal magnitude on the upper and lower surfaces, and can be reduced to zero with a source distribution on the x^*-axis of strength

$$q(x^*) = -2V_n^*. \qquad (80)$$

The tangential velocity at the slit produced by this source distribution is

$$v_t^*(x^*) = (1/2\pi)P \int q(\xi^*)(x^*-\xi^*)^{-1} d\xi^*, \qquad (81)$$

where the integral is taken over the length of the slit. The corresponding increment of velocity on the aerofoil surface is

$$v_t = v_t^* |d\mathfrak{z}^*/d\mathfrak{z}|. \qquad (82)$$

Now on the surface,

$$|d\mathfrak{z}/d\mathfrak{z}^*| = [1+(z_s')^2]^{\frac{1}{2}} |dx/dx^*| \qquad (83)$$

and hence the total tangential velocity over the aerofoil surface is

$$v = V_t + v_t = \frac{U}{\{1+(z_s')^2\}^{\frac{1}{2}}} \left\{ 1 + \frac{1}{\pi} P \int_0^c \left[\frac{dx^*}{dx} \frac{x-\xi}{x^*-\xi^*} \right] \frac{z_s'(\xi)}{x-\xi} d\xi \right\}, \qquad (84)$$

use being made of the relations established above.

The essence of the method lies in replacing the term in square brackets in equation (84) by unity. It may be shown that this term differs from unity by an amount only of the order of the thickness-chord ratio, and that for an ellipse the approximation is exact. Equation (84) then becomes comparable with Goldstein's Approximation II, being the formula (37) of linearized theory multiplied by a factor which suppresses the singularity at the leading edge; it may be written as

$$v(x, z) = v_x(x, 0)[1 + (z'_s)^2]^{-\frac{1}{2}}, \tag{85}$$

where $v_x(x, 0)$ is the total velocity on the chord and $v(x, z)$ the velocity on the aerofoil surface.

Consider now the effect of incidence on a flat plate extending from $x^* = 0$ to $x^* = c^*$ at incidence α in a stream of speed V. The strength of the vortex sheet representing the difference of the velocities on the two surfaces is, from equation (14),

$$\gamma(x^*) = 2V \sin \alpha [(c^* - x^*)/x^*]^{\frac{1}{2}}, \tag{86}$$

the Kutta–Joukowski condition having been satisfied. The distribution $\gamma(x^*)$ produces a z^*-component of velocity on the plate given by

$$w^*(x^*, 0) = -(1/2\pi) P \int_0^{c^*} \gamma(\xi^*)(x^* - \xi^*)^{-1} d\xi^*, \tag{87}$$

and it can be verified that this takes the constant value $(-V \sin \alpha)$ when γ is given by (86); thus the normal component of the stream velocity is counteracted.

For an aerofoil of non-zero thickness in the $\mathfrak{z}$-plane, the vortex distribution given by equation (86) does not satisfy exactly the boundary condition on the aerofoil surface. To the first power of the thickness only, the boundary condition is satisfied to the degree of accuracy required if the vortex strength on the chord line is $\gamma(x) + \Delta\gamma(x)$, where

$$\Delta\gamma(x) = \frac{2}{\pi} V \sin \alpha \left(\frac{c - x}{x}\right)^{\frac{1}{2}} P \int_0^c \left\{z'_s(\xi) - \frac{cz_s(\xi)}{2\xi(c - \xi)}\right\} \frac{d\xi}{x - \xi}. \tag{88}$$

Defining now, for convenience,

$$\left. \begin{aligned} S^{(1)}(x) &= (1/\pi) P \int_0^c z'_s(\xi)(x - \xi)^{-1} d\xi \\ S^{(2)}(x) &= z'_s(x) \\ S^{(3)}(x) &= \frac{1}{\pi} P \int_0^c \left\{z'_s(\xi) - \frac{cz_s(\xi)}{2\xi(c - \xi)}\right\} \frac{d\xi}{x - \xi} \end{aligned} \right\}, \tag{89}$$

we find the velocity on the aerofoil surface to be

$$v = V\{\cos \alpha [1 + S^{(1)}(x)] \pm \sin \alpha [(c - x)/x]^{\frac{1}{2}} [1 + S^{(3)}(x)]\}[1 + \{S^{(2)}(x)\}^2]^{-\frac{1}{2}}, \tag{90}$$

which is the final result.

TABLE IV. 2. *Values of the Weber coefficients*

$$s^{(1)}_{\mu\nu}$$

μ\ν	1	2	3	4	5	6	7	8
1	82·013	−15·061	0	−0·651	0	−0·136	0	−0·051
2	−29·544	41·810	−11·203	0	−0·705	0	−0·180	0
3	0	−16·265	28·799	−8·980	0	−0·690	0	−0·201
4	−2·360	0	−11·430	22·627	−7·698	0	−0·674	0
5	0	−1·532	0	−9·052	19·243	−6·954	0	−0·673
6	−0·646	0	−1·147	0	−7·727	17·318	−6·563	0
7	0	−0·462	0	−0·935	0	−6·968	16·314	−6·442
8	−0·260	0	−0·362	0	−0·810	0	−6·569	16·000
9	0	−0·196	0	−0·301	0	−0·735	0	−6·442
10	−0·124	0	−0·157	0	−0·262	0	−0·692	0
11	0	−0·095	0	−0·130	0	−0·236	0	−0·673
12	−0·062	0	−0·075	0	−0·111	0	−0·217	0
13	0	−0·045	0	−0·059	0	−0·094	0	−0·201
14	−0·026	0	−0·031	0	−0·044	0	−0·076	0
15	0	−0·013	0	−0·017	0	−0·026	0	−0·051
16	0	0	0	0	0	0	0	0

$$s^{(2)}_{\mu\nu}$$

μ\ν	1	2	3	4	5	6	7	8
1	25·769	17·917	−4·703	2·016	−1·104	0·706	−0·506	0·398
2	−68·941	6·309	14·908	−4·993	2·499	−1·531	1·071	−0·828
3	38·144	−31·420	2·694	12·636	−4·844	2·680	−1·780	1·336
4	−26·486	17·048	−20·468	1·414	11·224	−4·718	2·816	−2·000
5	20·046	−11·798	10·849	−15·519	0·804	10·411	−4·704	2·993
6	−15·836	8·922	−7·411	8·054	−12·854	0·448	10·043	−4·828
7	12·797	−7·033	5·548	−5·418	6·546	−11·318	0·203	10·055
8	−10·453	5·657	−4·330	4·000	−4·330	5·657	−10·453	0
9	8·551	−4·581	3·439	−3·075	3·143	−3·675	5·126	−10·055
10	−6·946	3·696	−2·739	2·398	−2·369	2·613	−3·261	4·828
11	5·548	−2·937	2·158	−1·862	1·800	−1·918	2·259	−2·993
12	−4·295	2·266	−1·654	1·414	−1·347	1·405	−1·598	2·000
13	3·143	−1·654	1·203	−1·021	0·963	−0·991	1·104	−1·336
14	−2·060	1·082	−0·785	0·664	−0·622	0·634	−0·697	0·828
15	1·020	−0·535	0·388	−0·327	0·305	−0·310	0·338	−0·398

$$s^{(3)}_{\mu\nu}$$

μ\ν	1	2	3	4	5	6	7	8
1	82·013	7·458	0	4·031	0	2·006	0	1·256
2	−41·024	41·810	−4·134	0	1·068	0	0·716	0
3	0	−21·134	28·799	−5·362	0	0·313	0	0·340
4	−3·652	0	−14·273	22·627	−5·365	0	0·016	0
5	0	−2·349	0	−11·036	19·243	−5·215	0	−0·132
6	−1·098	0	−1·750	0	−9·293	17·318	−5·121	0
7	0	−0·811	0	−1·433	0	−8·326	16·314	−5·136
8	−0·515	0	−0·662	0	−1·260	0	−7·850	16·000
9	0	−0·424	0	−0·584	0	−1·176	0	−7·749
10	−0·323	0	−0·380	0	−0·551	0	−1·160	0
11	0	−0·298	0	−0·369	0	−0·557	0	−1·215
12	−0·271	0	−0·305	0	−0·391	0	−0·609	0
13	0	−0·301	0	−0·351	0	−0·465	0	−0·742
14	−0·369	0	−0·403	0	−0·485	0	−0·660	0
15	0	−0·686	0	−0·776	0	−0·966	0	−1·357
16	−0·063	0	−0·068	0	−0·080	0	−0·105	0

$s_{\mu\nu}^{(1)}$, $s_{\mu\nu}^{(2)}$, and $s_{\mu\nu}^{(3)}$ for $N = 16$

$$s_{\mu\nu}^{(1)}$$

9	10	11	12	13	14	15	16	ν/μ
0	−0·026	0	−0·017	0	−0·013	0	−0·012	1
−0·076	0	−0·044	0	−0·031	0	−0·026	0	2
0	−0·094	0	−0·059	0	−0·045	0	−0·041	3
−0·217	0	−0·111	0	−0·075	0	−0·062	0	4
0	−0·236	0	−0·130	0	−0·095	0	−0·086	5
−0·692	0	−0·262	0	−0·157	0	−0·124	0	6
0	−0·735	0	−0·301	0	−0·196	0	−0·172	7
−6·569	0	−0·810	0	−0·362	0	−0·260	0	8
16·314	−6·968	0	−0·935	0	−0·462	0	−0·378	9
−6·563	17·318	−7·727	0	−1·147	0	−0·646	0	10
0	−6·954	19·243	−9·052	0	−1·532	0	−1·052	11
−0·674	0	−7·698	22·627	−11·430	0	−2·360	0	12
0	−0·690	0	−8·980	28·799	−16·265	0	−4·890	13
−0·180	0	−0·705	0	−11·203	41·810	−29·544	0	14
0	−0·136	0	−0·651	0	−15·061	82·013	−132·103	15
0	0	0	0	0	0	0	32	16

$$s_{\mu\nu}^{(2)}$$

9	10	11	12	13	14	15	ν/μ
−0·338	0·310	−0·305	0·327	−0·388	0·535	−1·020	1
0·697	−0·634	0·622	−0·664	0·785	−1·082	2·060	2
−1·104	0·991	−0·963	1·021	−1·203	1·654	−3·143	3
1·598	−1·405	1·347	−1·414	1·654	−2·266	4·295	4
−2·259	1·918	−1·800	1·862	−2·158	2·937	−5·548	5
3·261	−2·613	2·369	−2·398	2·739	−3·696	6·946	6
−5·126	3·675	−3·143	3·075	−3·439	4·581	−8·551	7
10·453	−5·657	4·330	−4·000	4·330	−5·657	10·453	8
−0·203	11·318	−6·546	5·418	−5·548	7·033	−12·797	9
−10·043	−0·448	12·854	−8·054	7·411	−8·922	15·836	10
4·704	−10·411	−0·804	15·519	−10·849	11·798	−20·046	11
−2·816	4·718	−11·224	−1·414	20·468	−17·048	26·486	12
1·780	−2·680	4·844	−12·636	−2·694	31·420	−38·144	13
−1·071	1·531	−2·499	4·993	−14·908	−6·309	68·941	14
0·506	−0·706	1·104	−2·016	4·703	−17·917	−25·769	15

$$s_{\mu\nu}^{(3)}$$

9	10	11	12	13	14	15	16	ν/μ
0	0·914	0	0·742	0	0·659	0	0·635	1
0·507	0	0·398	0	0·341	0	0·317	0	2
0	0·276	0	0·234	0	0·211	0	0·204	3
0·175	0	0·169	0	0·155	0	0·147	0	4
0	0·084	0	0·108	0	0·108	0	0·107	5
−0·224	0	0·026	0	0·066	0	0·074	0	6
0	−0·293	0	−0·019	0	0·032	0	0·042	7
−5·287	0	−0·360	0	−0·061	0	−0·005	0	8
16·314	−5·609	0	−0·437	0	−0·112	0	−0·062	9
−8·006	17·318	−6·162	0	−0·544	0	−0·193	0	10
0	−8·694	19·243	−7·068	0	−0·716	0	−0·376	11
−1·365	0	−10·031	22·627	−8·587	0	−1·068	0	12
0	−1·692	0	−12·599	28·799	−11·395	0	−2·220	13
−1·076	0	−2·479	0	−18·273	41·810	−18·064	0	14
0	−2·279	0	−5·334	0	−37·580	82·013	−65·410	15
−0·155	0	−0·281	0	−0·742	0	−6·505	16	16

To simplify the computational labour, Weber established trigonometric formulae of the type discussed in Section 7. Defining cz_μ as the ordinate at $x = cx_\mu = \frac{1}{2}c[1+\cos(\mu\pi/N)]$, we may write her formulae in the forms

$$
\left.
\begin{aligned}
S^{(1)}(cx_\nu) &= \sum_{\mu=1}^{N-1} s_{\mu\nu}^{(1)} z_\mu + s_{N\nu}^{(1)}(\rho_L/2c)^{\frac{1}{2}} \\
S^{(2)}(cx_\nu) &= \sum_{\mu=1}^{N-1} s_{\mu\nu}^{(2)} z_\mu \\
S^{(3)}(cx_\nu) &= \sum_{\mu=1}^{N-1} s_{\mu\nu}^{(3)} z_\mu + s_{N\nu}^{(3)}(\rho_L/2c)^{\frac{1}{2}}
\end{aligned}
\right\}.
\tag{91}
$$

Tables of relevant values of the coefficients $s_{\mu\nu}^{(1)}$, $s_{\mu\nu}^{(2)}$, and $s_{\mu\nu}^{(3)}$ are given by Weber for $N = 8$, 16, and 32. The formulae with $N = 16$ should give adequate accuracy for most purposes, and her tables are reproduced in Table IV. 2.

For cambered aerofoils, the various integrals are again represented by finite sums, and tables are given of the appropriate coefficients. Some consideration is also given to the problem of designing an aerofoil to have a specified pressure distribution, and tables of coefficients for functions required in the calculations are provided.

16. Non-linear theories. Spence and Routledge (1956)

One of the aims of this method was to permit the calculation of the velocity at points near the aerofoil surface as well as on it; here we shall outline the means of introducing the second-order terms by considering the velocity on a symmetrical aerofoil in the $\mathfrak{z}$-plane. As in Weber's method, this is transformed into a slit extending from $x^* = 0$ to $x^* = c^*$ in the $\mathfrak{z}^*$-plane, and Spence and Routledge show by a study of the appropriate integral equation that, on the corresponding surfaces,

$$
dx/dx^* = 1-(1/\pi)P \int_0^c z_s'(\xi)(x^*-\xi^*)^{-1} \, d\xi.
\tag{92}
$$

Integration of this equation leads to

$$
x^* = x+(1/\pi)P \int_0^{c^*} z_s(\xi^*)(x^*-\xi^*)^{-1} \, d\xi^* + \text{constant}.
\tag{93}
$$

The speed v on the aerofoil surface is given by

$$
\mathrm{v}/\mathrm{v}^* = |d\mathfrak{z}^*/d\mathfrak{z}| = (dx^*/dx)[1+(z_s')^2]^{-\frac{1}{2}},
\tag{94}
$$

in which v^* is the speed on the slit; with the Kutta–Joukowski condition satisfied, v^* is given by equation (14) with x^* written for x and c^* for c. The velocity distribution on the aerofoil is thus immediately known if equation (92) or (93) has been solved. For an aerofoil at zero incidence, equation (94) with the value of dx/dx^* given by equation (92) is identical with equation (84) obtained by Weber on the basis of source distributions.

The next step is to put $z_s(x) = \epsilon z_1(x)$, where ϵ is the thickness-chord ratio, supposed small. By equating successive powers of ϵ in equation (93), the solution may be obtained in the form

$$\left. \begin{array}{l} x^* = x + \epsilon\{f_1(x) - f_1(0)\} + \epsilon^2\{f_2(x) - f_2(0)\} + O(\epsilon^3) \\ dx^*/dx = 1 + \epsilon f'_1(x) + \epsilon^2 f'_2(x) + O(\epsilon^3) \end{array} \right\}. \tag{95}$$

The equation for f_1 is immediately obtained as

$$f_1(x) = (1/\pi)P \int_0^c z_1(\xi)(x-\xi)^{-1} \, d\xi. \tag{96}$$

Hence f_1 is the Fourier conjugate of $(-z_1)$. Clearly this must be equivalent to the result of linearized theory. By use of (96) it can now be shown from a consideration of terms in ϵ^2 in equation (93) that

$$f_2(x) = (1/\pi) \int_0^c [f_1(x) - f_1(\xi)]z'_1(\xi)(x-\xi)^{-1} \, d\xi. \tag{97}$$

Since z_1 in an odd function of the angle ϕ of equation (2), appropriate Fourier expansions are

$$z_1 = \sum_{n=1}^{\infty} a_n \sin n\phi, \qquad f_1 = \sum_{n=1}^{\infty} a_n \cos n\phi. \tag{98}$$

The computational method was designed to take advantage of electronic computers and the following technique has in fact been programmed. First, the coefficients a_n are calculated from the standard formula $a_n = (2/\pi) \int_0^\pi z_1 \sin n\phi \, d\phi$ and these integrals are approximated by summing the values of the integrand at $\phi = m\pi/N$, $m = 1, 2,...,$ $N-1$. This approximation is shown to be exact if the Fourier series (98) for z_1 terminates at $n = N$. The value $N = 18$ is considered to give satisfactory accuracy. Spence and Routledge assert that in practice it is usually permissible to round off to zero all but the first few of the coefficients a_n, and as a result subsequent calculations are considerably simplified. Trigonometric series for f_2, f'_2, f'_1, and z'_1 are established, and values are readily computed once the rounded-off values of the coefficients a_n have been determined. Further rounding-off is possible at certain intermediate stages of the calculations.

This method of computation provides an interesting alternative to the method of Section 7. The latter is superior if great accuracy is required, but for an answer correct to perhaps three significant figures the present technique is attractive.

17. Aerofoil design

We now turn to the problem of designing an aerofoil with a prescribed distribution of velocity, or of pressure, on its surface. The difficulties in the problem are partly inevitable, in that only for certain broad types of velocity distribution is there a solution at all. But there is also the fact that most methods involve the guessing of the values of certain constants or functions which play a part, perhaps only a subsidiary one, in the calculations. It might appear that a prolonged iterative procedure is necessary; but experience in carrying out the calculations, together with the assembled particulars of aerofoils previously designed, does in fact enable satisfactory designs to be made without undue labour, and even specifications of considerable detail to be met.

From these remarks it will be seen that practical experience is as important as a knowledge of basic theory. Consequently only a brief discussion of design procedures will be given here. For successful design a full study of the worked examples in the original papers is essential. As a corollary, we shall deal, in the following three sections, only with those methods which, in Great Britain, form the stock-in-trade of the practical aerodynamicist.

The multifarious considerations which confront the aircraft designer usually resolve themselves, as far as the aerofoil sections are concerned, into the following requirements:

  (i) low drag within a specified range of C_L;
  (ii) as low a maximum velocity as possible, within this range;
  (iii) a given thickness-chord ratio.

We may translate these, very roughly, into corresponding requirements for the velocity distribution:

  (ia) a camber line whose $C_{L\,\mathrm{opt}}$ lies within this C_L-range, and
  (ib) a velocity which increases, for all values of C_L within the specified range, over a large part of the front of the aerofoil;
  (ii) a velocity over this front part of the upper surface which is roughly constant at the highest value of C_L;
  (iii) this is largely a matter of experience in choosing the appropriate magnitudes of velocity. It is however relevant that, for an

elliptical fairing, the value of g_s of Section 13 is constant and
equal to the thickness-chord ratio.

Concerning condition (ib), we recall from Section I. 25 that an increasing velocity, or decreasing pressure, encourages the boundary layer
to remain laminar; the advantage gained by a laminar layer over the
front part of the aerofoil must not, however, be destroyed by separation

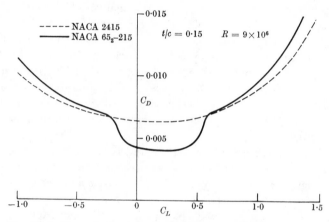

Fig. IV. 3. The variation of C_D with C_L for an early aerofoil and for a
low-drag aerofoil.

over the rear part, which might occur if the rise in pressure towards
the trailing edge were too great. Thus, on balance, there is a practical
limit, for a conventional aerofoil, to the length of laminar flow; this
would not normally be designed to exceed half the chord. Chapter VI
will, however, discuss special methods of controlling the boundary layer
and so of increasing the length of laminar flow.

If the condition (ib) is achieved in a design and the manufacturing
problems of obtaining a smooth surface solved, then the aerofoil should
in practice reveal low drag over a clearly marked range of C_L. Fig. IV. 3
indicates what can be achieved in this way, and an aerofoil exhibiting
this characteristic drag curve is called a low-drag aerofoil. As the lift
coefficient increases out of the low-drag range, a maximum in velocity
appears on the upper surface near the leading edge; this corresponds to
the infinity in velocity at the leading edge obtained in the linearized
theory for all values of C_L other than $C_{L\,\text{opt}}$. This maximum quickly
induces transition far forward, which is responsible for the rapid rise in
C_D with C_L.

The practical objective of low drag has inspired much of the work in aerofoil theory since 1940, besides being the spur to boundary-layer control, to be described in Chapter VI. We should recognize, however, that as the speeds of aircraft increase into the sonic range, factors other than those just discussed begin to predominate.

18. Aerofoil design. Goldstein (1952)

This method of design is based on the analysis of Section 13. The first step is to deduce suitable values for Approximation I from the prescribed velocity distribution, the difference between the two being determined in each case from previous experience. In particular, if the given velocity distribution is regarded as Approximation II, the modifications can be estimated fairly simply and accurately. The symmetrical part, g_s, of g may then be used to design the fairing of the aerofoil, and the anti-symmetrical part may be used to design the camber line.

As discussed in Sections 9 and 13, $g_s \sin \phi$ is the Fourier conjugate of $(2/c)dz_s/d\phi$; hence, if g_s is known, z_s may be determined, either by direct integration (if g_s is given by a sufficiently simple analytic expression) or by means of the numerical formulae of Section 7 (if g_s is specified numerically, at a set of equally-spaced values of ϕ). Now from equations (1), (69), and (23),

$$\left.\begin{aligned} (2\rho_L/c)^{\frac{1}{2}} = \psi_L = -(2/c)[dz_s/d\phi]_{\phi=\pi} = (1/\pi) \int_0^\pi g_s(t)(1-\cos t)\, dt \\ (2\rho_T/c)^{\frac{1}{2}} = \psi_T = -(2/c)[dz_s/d\phi]_{\phi=0} = (1/\pi) \int_0^\pi g_s(t)(1+\cos t)\, dt \end{aligned}\right\}, \quad (99)$$

which show that g_s must be so chosen that neither of these integrals is negative. These are the most important analytical restrictions on the form of g_s.

Goldstein (1952, Pt. III) considers in detail cases in which the chord is divided into a number of segments, in each of which g_s is a polynomial in x. The roof-top family of aerofoils is given by the simplest case in which g_s is linear in each of two segments; for these the numerical calculations are put in a standard form. The aerofoil depends on four parameters, one giving the junction $x = X$ of the two segments and the other three the values of g_s at $x = 0$, X, and c. These parameters may be used to fix ρ_L and ρ_T, the position of the point of maximum thickness, largely governed by X, and the overall thickness, largely governed by $g_s(X)$.

The roof-top type of aerofoil is found to have a relatively small low-drag range of C_L. Fig. IV. 4 illustrates a modification to the front linear part of g_s derived by a method of Thwaites (1945b), which greatly improves the C_L-range; this aerofoil satisfies condition (ii) of the previous section. For the experimental results on the extensive range of N.A.C.A. low-drag aerofoils, we should refer to Abbott and Doenhoff (1949).

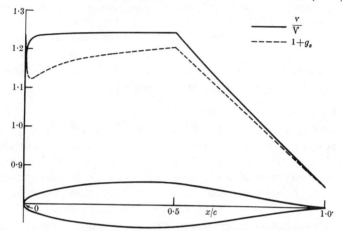

Fig. IV. 4. A symmetrical low-drag aerofoil, MR523–015, and the theoretical velocity distribution on its upper surface at $C_L = 0.23$.

The design of the camber line depends upon a knowledge of the quantity g_i of equation (74), which is the same as the u_c/U of equation (46) when $C_L = C_{L\,\text{opt}}$ and the Kutta–Joukowski condition is satisfied. If, therefore,

$$g_i = -\sum_{n=1}^{\infty} B_n \sin n\phi, \qquad (100)$$

then from (45), $\quad dz_c/dx = B_0 + \sum_{n=1}^{\infty} B_n \cos n\phi. \qquad (101)$

Also C_m, $C_{L\,\text{opt}}$, and β are given at once by the relations given in Section 11. If g_i is known, only the coefficient B_0 remains undetermined, and this is found from the fact that $z_c = 0$ at $x = 0$ and at $x = c$. As before, the Fourier conjugate may be calculated analytically or numerically. It may be noted that g_i must be zero at $x = 0$ and $x = c$ if z_c is to be free from singularities. Goldstein (1952, Pt. IV) carries out explicit calculations for distributions of g_i along the chord, which are linear or quadratic in each of a number of segments. In spite of the objection mentioned above, g_i is often taken to have a non-zero value at the leading edge, as the resulting logarithmic infinity in z_c' is not considered important.

When z_s and z_c have both been determined, the velocity distribution over the whole cambered aerofoil at any C_L may be calculated according to Approximation III, and the suitability of the design finally assessed.

A summary of the method, as applied to low-drag and suction aerofoils, was given by Goldstein (1948) in a valuable review of the existing knowledge of aerofoil design at that time.

The method was used in deriving the R.A.E. 100–104 series of aerofoils, described by Pankhurst and Squire (1952); these have been used extensively in wind-tunnel tests at the Royal Aircraft Establishment and will be frequently quoted in Chapters VII and VIII.

19. Aerofoil design. Thwaites (1945a)

Goldstein, in his method, concentrated on forms of g_s and g_i which are linear in a small number of segments along the chord. This simplifies the calculations if they are to be performed analytically, but may set an unwelcome limit on aerodynamic efficiency. If Fourier conjugates and related functions are to be calculated numerically, there is no need to choose analytically simple functions, and Thwaites (1945a) has devised a development of Goldstein's treatment which takes advantage of this.

For a symmetrical aerofoil, Goldstein's Approximation II is written in the form

$$g_s \sin\phi = -\sin\phi + \frac{\mathrm{v}}{\mathrm{V}} \frac{(\psi^2 + \sin^2\theta)^{\frac{1}{2}}}{1 + \frac{1}{2}C_0^2} - C_L\left(\frac{1}{2\pi} - \frac{\cos\phi}{a_0}\right). \qquad (102)$$

For a given thickness-chord ratio, the value of v/V and the C_L-range obtainable are known within narrow limits from previous experience. If v/V, a_0, and C_L are supposed known, then it only remains to guess the value of ψ in equation (102). Over the front part of an aerofoil, ψ is roughly constant and equal to the thickness-chord ratio—it is exactly constant for an ellipse—while further back ψ decreases steadily, becoming zero at a sharp trailing edge.

The choice of v/V is not entirely arbitrary, for equations (99) for ρ_L and ρ_T continue to apply. The value of g_s over the rear half of the chord may be chosen to give suitable values for these integrals. With experience, one can achieve the required properties with considerable accuracy. When the values of $g_s \sin\phi$ have been fixed thus, the aerofoil ordinates are calculated directly by the formula (32). Approximation III may then be calculated to verify the design.

An important feature of the method is that, in the case of a cambered aerofoil, the fairing and camber line need not be designed separately. Instead, we prescribe the velocity distribution on the upper and lower surfaces at the upper and lower limits of the C_L-range. Again Goldstein's Approximation II is used, in the form

$$g_s \sin \phi + g_i \sin \phi = \frac{\mathrm{v}}{\mathrm{V}} \frac{(\psi^2 + \sin^2 \theta)^{\frac{1}{2}}}{1 + \frac{1}{2}C_0^2} - C_L \left(\frac{1}{2\pi} - \frac{\cos \phi}{a_0} \right) +$$

$$+ C_{L\,\mathrm{opt}} \left(\frac{1}{a_0} + \frac{1}{2\pi} \right)(1 - \cos \phi) - \sin \phi, \quad (103)$$

but before g_s and g_i can be determined from the data, the value of $C_{L\,\mathrm{opt}}$ is required. Now from (51) and (100),

$$C_{L\,\mathrm{opt}}(a_0^{-1} + \tfrac{1}{2}\pi^{-1}) = (2/\pi) \int_0^\pi g_i \sin \phi \, d\phi. \quad (104)$$

This formula usually enables $C_{L\,\mathrm{opt}}$ to be calculated to sufficient accuracy from a rough estimate of g_i; at worst, it may be necessary to carry out one stage of an iteration between equations (103) and (104). Once g_i is determined, a numerical formula similar to those of Section 7 enables a direct calculation of z_c to be made.

As a whole, this method proves flexible, practical, and accurate for the design of aerofoils of small camber and not too great thickness, and a full discussion of the various problems which arise in the course of design is given in the original papers. Douglas (1947) has used the method to design several aerofoils embodying a camber line of a type which is considered to have more favourable aerodynamic properties than Goldstein's camber lines. The fairing is, in all these cases too, designed specifically to suit the camber. Curtis (1949) has discussed some further details of technique in designing cambered aerofoils.

20. Aerofoil design. The theory of Lighthill (1945b)

Whereas in the direct problem of computing the velocity distribution on a given aerofoil, the method of Theodorsen, described in Section 12, is always ultimately available and free from any restriction on thickness and camber, it cannot be used effectively to design aerofoils. No full solution of the inverse problem has yet been given, but what comes nearest to it is the method of Lighthill (1945b); this determines exactly the shape of the aerofoil in terms of a velocity distribution prescribed not as a function of distance along the aerofoil surface, but as a function of ϕ, the angular coordinate round the circle into which the aerofoil may be transformed. In practice, this restriction is not of too great importance.

The region outside the aerofoil in the $\mathfrak{z}$-plane is transformed into the region outside the circle $\zeta = ae^{i\phi}$ by the unique conformal transformation in which $d\mathfrak{z}/d\zeta \to 1$ as $\zeta \to \infty$ and the trailing edge of the aerofoil corresponds to $\zeta = a$. At zero incidence, denoted by suffix 0, and without circulation,

$$d\mathfrak{w}_0/d\zeta = V(1-a^2\zeta^{-2}), \tag{105}$$

while on the aerofoil $d\mathfrak{w}_0/d\mathfrak{z} = v_0 e^{-i\theta}. \tag{106}$

Taking the value of (105) on the circle and eliminating $d\mathfrak{w}_0$, we find

$$d\mathfrak{z} = dx+i\,dz = -(2Va/v_0)e^{i\theta}\sin\phi\,d\phi, \tag{107}$$

whence the coordinates of the aerofoil surface are obtained in the form

$$\left.\begin{array}{l} x = -\displaystyle\int (2Va/v_0)\sin\phi\cos\theta\,d\phi \\[2mm] z = -\displaystyle\int (2Va/v_0)\sin\phi\sin\theta\,d\phi \end{array}\right\}. \tag{108}$$

To carry out these integrations v_0 and θ must be known as function of ϕ. We assume $v_0(\phi)$ to be prescribed, and so it only remains to find $\theta(\phi)$. Now $\log(d\mathfrak{w}_0/d\mathfrak{z})$ is an analytic function of ζ outside the circle $|\zeta| = a$, on which its value is $\log v_0 - i\theta$; it also tends to a constant value at infinity. Hence we may apply Poisson's integral (21) to obtain

$$\theta(\phi) = (1/2\pi)P\int_0^{2\pi} \log v_0(t)\cot\tfrac{1}{2}(\phi-t)\,dt. \tag{109}$$

No constant appears in this equation since θ is zero at infinity. Up to now, the only forms of $v_0(\phi)$ to be investigated in detail are those which enable $\theta(\phi)$ to be evaluated analytically. The integrals (108) giving the aerofoil contour are, however, always evaluated numerically. As was remarked in Section 4, the chord c will always be found to be rather less than $4a$.

The question arises: can $v_0(\phi)$ be prescribed quite arbitrarily, and is there always an aerofoil to correspond to any $v_0(\phi)$? In fact, there are three integral conditions on $v_0(\phi)$, as may be shown as follows. The mapping of the $\mathfrak{z}$- and ζ-planes must be of the form $\mathfrak{z} = \zeta + \sum\limits_{n=0}^{\infty} a_n \zeta^{-n}$, in which the coefficients a_n are constants; hence

$$d\mathfrak{z}/d\zeta = 1 - \sum_{n=1}^{\infty} na_n \zeta^{-(n+1)}. \tag{110}$$

Combining (105) and (110), we see that

$$d\mathfrak{w}_0/d\mathfrak{z} = V\left(1 + \sum_{n=2}^{\infty} b_n \zeta^{-n}\right), \tag{111}$$

and hence $$\log[(1/V)(d\mathfrak{w}_0/d\mathfrak{z})] = \sum_{n=2}^{\infty} c_n \zeta^{-n}, \tag{112}$$

where the coefficients b_n and c_n are further constants. It follows from the discussion of Section 6 that the Fourier series for the value of $\log[(1/V)(d\mathfrak{w}_0/d\mathfrak{z})]$ on the circle, and hence for $\log(v_0/V)$ and θ on the circle, have no constant terms, nor terms in $\cos\phi$ and $\sin\phi$. This implies the following relations:

$$\int_0^{2\pi} \log(v_0/V)\, d\phi = 0; \quad \int_0^{2\pi} \log(v_0/V)\cos\phi\, d\phi = 0; \quad \int_0^{2\pi} \log(v_0/V)\sin\phi\, d\phi = 0. \tag{113}$$

The first is a consequence of the requirement that the velocity at large distances is V, and the other two ensure that the aerofoil is a closed contour when equations (108) are integrated from $\phi = 0$ to $\phi = 2\pi$.

Now let us consider flow at a non-zero incidence denoted by suffix α. If the circulation is given by

$$\Gamma = 4\pi V a \sin\gamma = \tfrac{1}{2}Vc\, C_L, \tag{114}$$

then the speed on the circle is, from (6), $2V|\sin(\phi-\alpha)+\sin\gamma|$, and hence on the aerofoil surface

$$v_\alpha/v_0 = |[\sin(\phi-\alpha)+\sin\gamma]\mathrm{cosec}\,\phi|. \tag{115}$$

Once the circulation is fixed, by whatever criterion, a knowledge of $v_\alpha(\phi)$ thus immediately implies a knowledge of $v_0(\phi)$, and vice versa.

If the Kutta–Joukowski condition is satisfied, v_α is finite at the trailing edge $\phi = 0$; hence $\gamma = \alpha$ and equation (115) becomes

$$v_\alpha/v_0 = |\sec\tfrac{1}{2}\phi \cos(\tfrac{1}{2}\phi-\alpha)|. \tag{116}$$

Expressions for the moment coefficient and other aerodynamic properties are given by Lighthill in the original paper. It may also be shown that when Poisson's integral is used in the form (109), the aerofoil as calculated is in the theoretical no-lift attitude. Thus the no-lift angle $(-\beta)$ follows directly from the computation of equations (108) and the lift is then given by equation (9).

21. Applications of Lighthill's theory

The exposition of the theory and of useful techniques of design was illustrated, in the original paper, by a large number of worked examples. M. B. Glauert (1947), in a full discussion of the practical application of the method, also gave an extensive list of functions and their Fourier conjugates, and tabulated values of several integrals which occur frequently in the calculations. Further refinements have been considered by Williams (1950a).

The most satisfactory procedure in practice is the method of design at incidence, the velocity on the upper surface being specified at an incidence α_1 and on the lower surface at a smaller incidence α_2. With the Kutta–Joukowski condition satisfied, the velocity distribution is taken in the form

$$\log v_0 = \begin{cases} \log|\cos \tfrac{1}{2}\phi \sec(\tfrac{1}{2}\phi - \alpha_1)|; & \alpha_1 + \alpha_2 \leqslant \phi \leqslant \pi + \alpha_1 + \alpha_2, \\ \log|\cos \tfrac{1}{2}\phi \sec(\tfrac{1}{2}\phi - \alpha_2)|; & \pi + \alpha_1 + \alpha_2 \leqslant \phi \leqslant 2\pi + \alpha_1 + \alpha_2, \\ \qquad\qquad + S; & 0 \leqslant \phi \leqslant 2\pi. \end{cases} \tag{117}$$

Here S is the value of $\log v_{\alpha_1}$ on the upper surface of the aerofoil and of $\log v_{\alpha_2}$ on the lower surface, and there are no discontinuities of velocity due to the first two terms. The Fourier conjugate and the contributions to (113) of the first two terms of (117) are fully tabulated by Glauert.

As an example, a symmetrical low-drag aerofoil may be designed by taking $\alpha_1 = -\alpha_2 = \alpha$ and

$$S = \begin{cases} l; & 0 \leqslant \phi \leqslant \pi, \\ +k(\cos\beta - \cos\phi); & 0 \leqslant \phi \leqslant \beta. \end{cases} \tag{118}$$

The velocity on the upper surface at incidence α is constant over the front part of the aerofoil and thereafter decreases more or less linearly, since x is roughly proportional to $\cos\phi$. Once the values of α and β have been chosen, the conditions (113) may be used to determine l and k, the third condition being automatically satisfied for a symmetrical aerofoil. The result of this procedure is an aerofoil very similar to that shown in Fig. IV. 4. The low-drag range is appreciably greater than that of aerofoils of similar thickness obtained by the methods of Sections 18 or 19; on the other hand, as a consequence of the fact that the velocity gradient is discontinuous at the leading edge, the curvature of the aerofoil's surface becomes logarithmically infinite at the leading edge, and this may result in a low maximum lift. This defect may be removed by the addition of suitable terms to S, as discussed by M. B. Glauert (1947).

Another choice for a symmetrical aerofoil is

$$S = \begin{cases} l; & 0 \leqslant \phi \leqslant \pi, \\ -k; & 0 \leqslant \phi \leqslant \beta. \end{cases} \tag{119}$$

There is a discontinuity in velocity at $\phi = \beta$, and here suction must be applied at a slot to prevent the flow separating, as is discussed in detail in Section VI. 17. The form of the surface near the discontinuity is a logarithmic spiral, but the integration of equations (108) can still be carried out without difficulty. This aerofoil is of the kind shown in Fig. VI. 23 (a), while Fig. VI. 23 (b) shows a cambered aerofoil designed for a discontinuity of velocity on the upper surface only. For this, one of the most successful of the very thick suction aerofoils, the C_L-range extends from $C_L = 0$ to $C_L = 2 \cdot 004$, the moment coefficient at $C_L = 0$ is zero and the thickness-chord ratio is $0 \cdot 315$; full details of its design are given by M. B. Glauert (1945, 1947).

The withdrawal of the boundary layer which must, in practice, take place at the discontinuity is equivalent to a sink of fluid at the corresponding point in the circle into which the aerofoil may be transformed. Glauert has shown how the effect of this sink can be included in the prescribed velocity distribution, and as a result the shape of the suction slot can be all part of the design. Examples of aerofoils incorporating this idea have been given by Williams (1950a).

Lighthill's method has been applied to a variety of other flows, including the design of aerofoil cascades as mentioned in Section XII. 17 and of contractions and bends in two-dimensional channels. Its use in the design of high-lift aerofoils with a suction slot at the leading edge is discussed in Section VI. 15, while its application to the design of aerofoils suitable for obtaining lift independent of incidence is discussed briefly in the next section.

For the design of moderately thin conventional aerofoils, the method is probably inferior to those described in Sections 18 and 19, unless an exactly known velocity distribution is particularly required, since the approximate methods have greater flexibility for dealing with detailed requirements. However, for thicker aerofoils Lighthill's method has the advantage, and for slot-suction aerofoils it is unrivalled, since all the approximate methods are unacceptably inaccurate in the neighbourhood of the velocity discontinuity.

22. Aerofoils for which the lift is independent of incidence

The device for producing lift independently of the incidence of an aerofoil, known as the Thwaites flap, is discussed in Section VI. 10. Its efficiency depends, however, on the suitability of the aerofoil shape, and the design of such aerofoils was discussed by Thwaites (1947b). His analysis extended the theories of Sections 13, 18, 19, and 20, and not much needs to be added to these earlier discussions.

For the direct problem, the analysis of these sections has already been arranged so that an arbitrary value of the circulation may be taken at any given incidence. For the indirect problem, we may concentrate on symmetrical aerofoils at zero incidence, since no extensive practical experience has yet suggested the need for greater complication. Under these conditions the exact theory is just as simple as the approximate. The former is therefore summarized.

Equation (115) gives the relation between the speeds at lift and at no-lift:

$$v_\gamma/v_0 = |1 + \sin \gamma \operatorname{cosec} \phi|, \tag{120}$$

where v_γ is the speed at zero incidence and at a lift corresponding to the value γ of equation (114). The conditions (113) on v_0 then reduce to

$$\left. \begin{array}{r} \displaystyle\int_0^\pi \log(v_\gamma/V)\, d\phi = 2 \int_0^\gamma \log \cot \tfrac{1}{2} t \, dt \\[2ex] \displaystyle\int_0^\pi \log(v_\gamma/V)\cos \phi \, d\phi = 0 \end{array} \right\}. \tag{121}$$

Thus for a given C_L, γ is estimated from (114), and v_0 follows by (120) from a specified distribution of v_γ which must satisfy (121). The shape of the aerofoil is derived from v_0 by the same analysis as that given in Section 20.

It can be seen, most easily from the linearized theory of Section 8, that incidence contributes as much as circulation to the velocity maxima near the leading edge; this suggests that the low-drag range of an aerofoil operating always at zero incidence should be roughly twice that for a conventional aerofoil and this is borne out by calculations.

It might be thought that an increasing velocity over the whole of the upper surface is possible under these new circumstances; but, from the second of equations (121), we have

$$\int_0^\pi \left(\frac{\sin \phi}{v_\gamma}\right)\left(\frac{dv_\gamma}{d\phi}\right) d\phi = 0, \tag{122}$$

which shows that $dv_\gamma/d\phi$ cannot be everywhere positive. Indeed the optimum design appears to require v_γ to be constant.

A full discussion of the properties of aerofoils such as these is given in Thwaites's original paper, together with the design of some cambered aerofoils. We may, however, mention that for symmetrical aerofoils at zero incidence, the centre of pressure is constant as is also the moment about the centre of pressure, for all values of C_L. For doubly-symmetrical aerofoils at zero incidence, the centre of pressure is at mid-chord, about which point the moment is zero.

23. Mixed boundary conditions

We now consider the inviscid approximations for two-dimensional flows in which separation is a significant feature. We recall the various types of separated flow on well-rounded bodies which have been exemplified by the limited bubble of separation on a thin aerofoil shown in Fig. I. 17, and by the flow past a circular cylinder shown in Fig. III. 5. But flows past sharp-edged bodies are also of practical importance: air-brakes on aircraft may be likened to the flat plate of Fig. I. 4 while the flow up a step shown in Fig. I. 15 (b) has yet to be treated fully. A discussion of the theoretical models of such flows has already been given in Sections III. 8–10.

It is assumed that a region of separated flow is divided from the main stream by steady streamlines which we shall call the free streamlines. Even though this assumption completely ignores the fact that the flow is usually highly turbulent and unsteady in the mixing region, it often enables useful information to be obtained about the flow near the body.

The classical assumption is that the velocity is constant on these free streamlines; probably the most detailed single account of this mathematical model is by Greenhill (1910), while full treatments are also given by Milne-Thomson (1949) and by Birkhoff and Zarantonello (1957). Section 27 briefly exemplifies the analytical methods of what are called Kirchhoff flows.

Subsequent sections describe the applications of theories, mainly due to Woods, designed to allow for variable velocities on the free streamlines. What, at present, limits the utility of these theories is the lack of criteria for determining the distribution of the velocity or pressure along the free streamlines, as was discussed in Sections III. 8 and 9. For this reason, our treatment is almost exclusively mathematical: the interpretation of experimental results and their correlation with theory needs most careful thought in each particular case.

Certain considerations in the mathematical models of separated flows arise, additional to those already discussed in Chapter III. First, in the choice of the separation point on a rounded body, its position might be taken from experiment; but whether this is known or unknown, the two possibilities shown in Fig. IV. 5 must be avoided. If S is fixed too near the front stagnation point, as at S_1, the free streamline might be found, on calculation, to trespass within the body; equally, if it is too far back, at S_2, the two free streamlines might intersect. The fact of the boundary conditions being mixed is not necessarily the cause of such difficulties: for example, by the method of Section 20 one can design an aerofoil so that it crosses itself. The importance of reckoning with the shape of the body downstream as well as upstream of the separation point is further illustrated in Fig. IV. 6; entirely different models have to be used for the bent plate according to the length of the rear part.

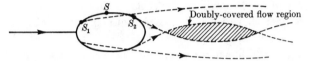

FIG. IV. 5. Two types of mathematical model of a wake to be avoided.

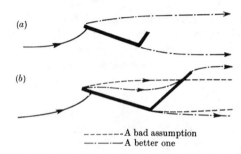

FIG. IV. 6. A sketch of the flow past a bent plate, showing how a mathematical model may depend on the geometry of the body.

It is important, in such flows, to consider the behaviour of the boundary layer; this has been overlooked too frequently in the literature. The position chosen for S should coincide with the separation point predicted by a calculation of the first boundary-layer approximation; this in itself would normally involve an iteration between the inviscid and viscous approximations to the flow. Little work has been done on the relation between the boundary layer and the inviscid model but researches relevant to this, and to the other points raised, have been made by Squire (1934), Weinstein (1949), Stewartson (1953), and Lighthill (1953).

24. Separated wakes

Consider first the classical model of a wake bounded by two stream-lines along which the pressure, p, is constant and equal to that at infinity, p_∞. As mentioned in Section III. 9, this does not accord well with the experimental fact that the pressure coefficient

$$Q = (p_\infty - p)/\tfrac{1}{2}\rho V_\infty^2$$

is significantly positive within most of a separated wake just behind

a body. But further, the distance between two such streamlines tends
to infinity downstream, as shown in Section 34, and this goes against
the idea of the displacement thickness of a wake tending to a finite
value downstream which is, as Section V. 3 shows, proportional to the
drag of the body. Therefore, when the flow far downstream is of special
interest, the classical model is unsuitable.

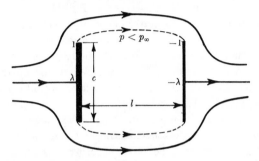

FIG. IV. 7. Riabouchinsky's model of the flow past a flat plate.

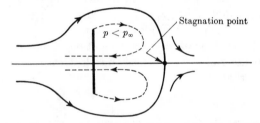

FIG. IV. 8. The re-entrant jet as a model for a closed wake or cavity.

The first attempts at improving the classical model were directed at
the value of the constant pressure on the free streamlines. With a non-
zero value of Q, the cavity cannot extend to infinity downstream.
Riabouchinsky (1920) found it possible to obtain a closed cavity with
a positive value of Q by introducing a second, fictitious, body in the
wake as shown in Fig. IV. 7. Many investigators have sought to obtain
a finite cavity ending in a cusp, and examples have been given by
Lighthill (1945c) and by Southwell and Vaisey (1946); unfortunately,
Q is necessarily negative for such models. Positive values of Q lead
to what is known as a re-entrant jet, shown in Fig. IV. 8 and first
discussed by Gilbarg and Rock (1945); though this model appears unrealistic in that the jet passes back through the plate, it nevertheless
gives a satisfactory representation of the actual flow near the body.

More recent investigations have broken away from the assumption of constant pressure on the free streamlines. As shown in Section 34, the streamlines can be made to tend to a finite distance apart at infinity, by a suitable choice of pressure distribution. Also, by this means, closed cavities of various types can be obtained.

Referring again to the choice of the position, S, of the separation point on a rounded body, as illustrated in Fig. IV. 5 and discussed in the previous section, we note that, in general, the curvature of the free streamline is infinite at the body. If the streamline is convex when viewed from outside, it then cuts into the body; if, on the other hand, it is concave, then the positive pressure gradient just upstream of S is infinite, which suggests that the boundary layer would separate not at S, but upstream of it. Thus we are led to seek a position of S such that the curvature of, and pressure gradient along, the bounding streamline are continuous at S; the mathematical condition for this is given in Section 33. It is doubtful, however, whether this idea, followed by Squire (1934) for a wake of constant pressure behind a circular cylinder, leads to a superior theoretical model, since a calculation of the first boundary-layer approximation will not necessarily predict separation at the point S so chosen from the inviscid model.

A detailed discussion of the technique of mathematical models, and of the apparent paradoxes which such models sometimes seem to create, is given by Birkhoff (1950).

25. The function σ

In the application of the complex potential $\mathfrak{w}(\mathfrak{z})$ to flows with free streamlines whose shape is unknown, $\mathfrak{z}$ is inappropriate as the independent variable; $\mathfrak{w}$ is preferable in this role since each boundary is given by $\psi = $ constant and so is represented by a line parallel to the real axis in the $\mathfrak{w}$-plane. But a more useful function than $\mathfrak{z} = \mathfrak{z}(\mathfrak{w})$ is

$$\sigma = \sigma(\mathfrak{w}) = \log(U \, d\mathfrak{z}/d\mathfrak{w}) \tag{123}$$

in which U is a fixed reference speed. From equation (I. 64), it follows that

$$\sigma = \tau + i\theta \tag{124}$$

where

$$\tau = \log(U/v) \quad \text{or} \quad v = U e^{-\tau}, \tag{125}$$

and θ is the direction of the velocity vector.

It is convenient to take the real axis parallel to the velocity far upstream, and to take U as the speed there; thus

$$\lim_{\phi \to -\infty} \sigma = 0. \tag{126}$$

The usefulness of σ in general problems with mixed boundary conditions is that its real part can be regarded as known on some parts of the boundaries and its imaginary part on the remainder. Appropriate theorems on functions whose boundary conditions are specified in this manner are given in Section 30.

Nearly all methods use an intermediate plane, say the ζ-plane, such that the boundaries in the $\mathfrak{w}$- and σ-planes transform into a particular contour in the ζ-plane. Thus it may be assumed that the two functions

$$\mathfrak{w} = \mathfrak{w}(\zeta) \quad \text{and} \quad \sigma = \sigma(\zeta) \tag{127}$$

are known, and from equation (123) it follows that

$$\mathfrak{z}(\zeta) = (1/U) \int e^{\sigma(\zeta)}(d\mathfrak{w}/d\zeta)\, d\zeta. \tag{128}$$

The elimination of ζ from $\mathfrak{z}(\zeta)$ and $\mathfrak{w}(\zeta)$ gives the final solution as a relation between $\mathfrak{w}$ and $\mathfrak{z}$; in practice, it is often convenient to retain ζ as a parameter.

The speed v is given by

$$\mathrm{v}^2 = |d\mathfrak{w}/d\mathfrak{z}|^2 = |d\mathfrak{w}/d\mathfrak{z}|\,|d\overline{\mathfrak{w}}/d\overline{\mathfrak{z}}| = U^2 e^{-(\sigma+\bar{\sigma})} \tag{129}$$

a bar denoting the complex conjugate. From this, the pressure may be deduced in the form

$$p = p_\infty + \tfrac{1}{2}\rho U^2[1 - e^{-(\sigma+\bar{\sigma})}], \tag{130}$$

where p_∞ is the static pressure when $\mathrm{v} = U$.

26. The formula of Schwarz–Christoffel

This result is essential to the classical theory described in the following section, as it enables polygonal boundaries in the $\mathfrak{w}$- and σ-planes to be transformed into the real axis of the ζ-plane. Its proof may be found in, for example, the treatise by Nehari (1952) on conformal mapping.

Let $a_1, a_2, ..., a_n$ be n points on the real axis in the ζ-plane such that $a_1 < a_2 < ... < a_n$, and let $\alpha_1, \alpha_2, ..., \alpha_n$ be the interior angles of a simple closed polygon of n vertices in the t-plane, so that $\sum_{r=1}^{n} \alpha_r = \pi(n-2)$. Then the transformation defined by

$$dt/d\zeta = A \prod_{r=1}^{n} (\zeta - a_r)^{-1+\alpha_r/\pi} \tag{131}$$

transforms the interior of the polygon in the t-plane into the upper half of the ζ-plane. Furthermore, the boundary of the polygon maps on to the real axis of the ζ-plane in such a way that the vertex at which the interior angle is α_r corresponds to the point $\zeta = a_r$. A is a constant which may be complex. Equation (131) holds if none of the points a_r coincides with the point at infinity; this restriction may, however, be removed by considering the transformation $\zeta = a_n - (1/\zeta^*)$ which transforms $\zeta = a_n$ into the point at infinity. It is then found that equation (131) is of the form

$$dt/d\zeta^* = A^* \prod_{r=1}^{n-1} (\zeta^* - a_r^*)^{-1+\alpha_r/\pi}, \tag{132}$$

where A^* and a_r^*, $r = 1, 2, ..., (n-1)$, are new constants. Thus the effect on (131) of one of the points a_r being at infinity consists in the corresponding term being omitted from the formula. Finally, the relation $t = t(\zeta)$ derived from (131) involves two arbitrary complex constants, and so the coordinates of two corresponding points in the t- and ζ-planes can be assigned.

27. The classical theory for rectilinear boundaries

This theory, founded by Helmholtz (1868) and Kirchhoff (1869), is fully described in the literature; in particular, reference may be made to Lamb (1932), Milne-Thomson (1949), and Birkhoff and Zarantonello (1957). It refers to rectilinear boundaries on which θ takes constant values except for discontinuities, and to streamlines of constant pressure on which τ is constant. Thus the boundaries are represented by polygons in the σ-plane whose sides are parallel to the two axes. These polygons are not usually closed; a stagnation point, for example, is at infinity in the σ-plane. The boundaries in the $\mathfrak{w}$-plane are of the same type. The bounding contour in the ζ-plane is chosen as the real axis so that the functions $\mathfrak{w}(\zeta)$ and $\sigma(\zeta)$ of (127) are then determinable by the Schwarz–Christoffel formula.

It is, of course, essential that a given point in the $\mathfrak{z}$-plane corresponds to the same point in the ζ-plane whichever intermediate transformation —$\mathfrak{w}(\zeta)$ or $\sigma(\zeta)$—is used. In practice, the boundaries in the $\mathfrak{w}$- and σ-planes are first transformed into the real axes of two separate planes, say the ζ_1- and ζ_2-planes; the (ζ_1, ζ_2) relation is then uniquely determined by just three pairs of corresponding points on the real axes. The algebraic relations which then express the correspondence between other pairs of points either give information about the flow under consideration or place restrictions on its generality.

We exemplify the analytical procedure by considering the flow past a bent plate, shown in Fig. IV. 9. The figure shows the four basic planes and corresponding points are labelled by the same letter. The free streamlines are indicated by broken lines and the body's surface by a heavy continuous line, which conventions are adopted throughout the chapter. Without further explanation of the notation contained in the figure, we state the results of applying the Schwarz–Christoffel formula as follows:

$$\mathfrak{w} = \phi_s \zeta^2 \tag{133}$$

and

$$\sigma = i\epsilon + (2\epsilon/\pi)\log[\zeta^{-1} + (\zeta^{-2} - 1)^{\frac{1}{2}}], \tag{134}$$

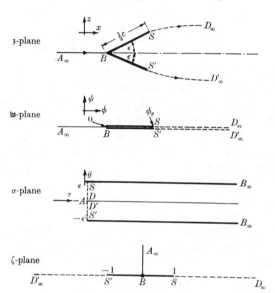

Fig. IV. 9. Notation for the Kirchhoff flow past a symmetrical wedge.

in which that branch of the logarithm is chosen for which $\log i = \frac{1}{2}i\pi$. Substituting this value of σ into (128), we have

$$\mathfrak{z} = \frac{2\phi_s}{U} e^{i\epsilon} \int_0^\zeta \left\{ \frac{\zeta}{1 + (1 - \zeta^2)^{\frac{1}{2}}} \right\}^{-2\epsilon/\pi} \zeta \, d\zeta. \tag{135}$$

Equations (133) and (135) provide the solution of the problem in terms of the parameter ζ. The length of the plate is related to ϕ_s by taking $\zeta = 1$ as the upper limit in equation (135). The pressure distribution on the wedge follows from equation (130) and the drag coefficient may easily be calculated.

The classical result for a flat plate normal to the stream is given by $\epsilon = \frac{1}{2}\pi$; for this case,

$$C_D = 2\pi/(4 + \pi) \simeq 0.88. \tag{136}$$

This is the value quoted in Section III. 9, where its malagreement with experiment was discussed.

Another interesting case arises when ϵ is a small quantity, as for example in the double-wedge aerofoil shown in Fig. I. 15 (a). To the lowest order in ϵ, we now find

$$C_D = 4\epsilon^2/\pi = (4/\pi)(t/c)^2. \tag{137}$$

This suggests that the form drag of a double-wedge aerofoil may vary as the square of the thickness-chord ratio, as was proposed by Squire and Young (1938) for the conventional shape of aerofoil.

28. Curved boundaries. Inverse methods

The essential feature of the classical theory is that the boundaries in the $\mathfrak{w}$- and σ-planes are determined from the geometrical characteristics of the flow. This is not so for flows in which any part of the body's surface is rounded; the distribution of speed on the surface being initially unknown, τ is an unknown function of θ and the corresponding line in the σ-plane is unknown. There appears, therefore, no hope of modifying the preceding analysis, except possibly in the form of a laborious iteration, to flows with given curved boundaries.

Flows with curved boundaries may, however, be constructed by specifying types of boundaries in the σ-plane, which are transformable into the real ζ-axis. This amounts to specifying $\sigma(\zeta)$ in the first place, from which the whole flow can be deduced by equations (127) and (128). Experience is required if plausible shapes are to be derived, and if physical unrealities such as doubly-covered regions in the $\mathfrak{z}$-plane are to be avoided.

This inverse method has by no means been exploited to the full. A great variety of flows is obtainable with polygonal boundaries in the σ-plane for which the Schwarz–Christoffel formula is available: only one side which is not parallel to either of the axes is enough to produce a curved boundary in the z-plane. As an extension to this, Leathem (1916) introduced into the formula (131) 'curve-factors' designed to deform the sides of the polygon. But many other shapes of boundary in the σ-plane lead to very simple analysis and the following example is taken from Lighthill (1945e) to illustrate what is known as the Coanda effect. If a body is partially inserted into a jet—say, a finger into the jet from a tap—it is found that the body tends to be sucked into the jet while the corresponding reaction on the jet deflects it towards the body, as shown in Fig. IV. 10.

The lettering in the figure is so chosen that the ζ-plane is again as shown in Fig. IV. 9. 2α is the total deflexion of the jet while 2β is the angular distance on the surface SBS'. The (ζ, σ) relation is

$$\zeta = -i(\sigma/\beta - \beta/\sigma). \tag{138}$$

For the $\mathfrak{w}$-plane, the Schwarz–Christoffel formula gives

$$\zeta = (\alpha + \beta^2/\alpha)\tanh(\pi\mathfrak{w}/2hU). \tag{139}$$

On the surface SBS', $-1 \leqslant \zeta \leqslant 1$ and the shape is found by substituting σ and $\mathfrak{w}$ from (138) and (139) into (128), the integral of which

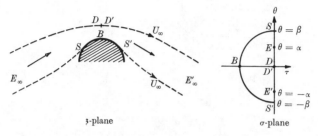

Fig. IV. 10. The deflexion of a jet flowing past an obstacle.

must be evaluated numerically. Lighthill found that for $\alpha = \frac{1}{2}\pi$ the solution was meaningless, the jet crossing itself on the inside, upstream and downstream of the obstacle. This is not to say, however, that with a different boundary in the σ-plane a deflexion of $180°$ is not possible for this type of flow.

For such a flow as this to be realistic, a boundary-layer calculation should predict separation at, or near, the point S'. This may preclude large angles of deflexion under the conditions so far considered, but a simultaneous contraction of the jet towards E' could counteract the rise of pressure along BS' and could be achieved by constraining the flow within solid boundaries. Thus we might produce a contracting bend in a channel—for a wind-tunnel, say—along whose walls the pressure falls monotonically; the boundary layer therefore would have no tendency to separate. With the same general distribution of lettering, Fig. IV. 11 represents this modification of Fig. IV. 10. The velocity is constant on $E_\infty D$, and the boundary $D'E'_\infty$ is straight; the velocity is constant on each of the two parts, $E'_\infty S$ and $SBS'E'_\infty$, of the inner wall. There is a discontinuous increase of speed at S; this could be avoided by bringing S to a finite part of the σ-plane. Similarly, the angle of deflexion and the contraction ratio can be varied by the choice of E' in the σ-plane. The calculations for this flow are very simple.

The hodograph plane, $d\mathfrak{w}/d\mathfrak{z} = u - iw$, may also be used to construct flows: indeed, any relation between $\mathfrak{w}$ and its derivatives determines a flow though it needs some experience to derive flows of any interest. As an example of the use of the hodograph plane, Thwaites (1954) has

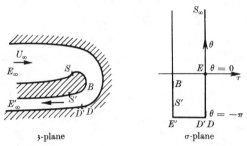

$\mathfrak{z}$-plane σ-plane

FIG. IV. 11. A flow in a contracting bend.

given an exact solution of flow past a semi-infinite body with a rounded front part faired into a straight parallel rear part. For this,

$$\mathfrak{w} = \frac{c}{2(r-1)U^2}\left[\frac{1}{d\mathfrak{w}/d\mathfrak{z} - U} - \left(\frac{r}{2-r}\right)^2 \frac{1}{d\mathfrak{w}/d\mathfrak{z} - rU/(2-r)}\right],$$

r being a real parameter determining the thickness-length ratio of the front part. This flow, in the hodograph plane, is due to a source doublet at $d\mathfrak{w}/d\mathfrak{z} = U$ within the circle $|d\mathfrak{w}/d\mathfrak{z} - \tfrac{1}{2}rU| = \tfrac{1}{2}rU$. If the length of the curved front part is $\tfrac{1}{2}c$, its shape and the speed on it are given by

$$\left.\begin{array}{l}x/c = \tfrac{1}{2}\sin^2\lambda \\[4pt] z/c = \tfrac{1}{2}(r-1)(\lambda + \tfrac{1}{2}\sin 2\lambda) \\[4pt] \mathrm{v}/U = r[1 + (r-1)^2\cot^2\lambda]^{-\frac{1}{2}}\end{array}\right\}, \quad -\tfrac{1}{2}\pi \leqslant \lambda \leqslant \tfrac{1}{2}\pi.$$

From this special case may be verified the general result that, if the front of an aerofoil is faired into a semi-infinite straight part, the maximum increment in velocity is roughly halved.

29. Curved boundaries. The methods of Levi-Cività and Villat

An important theoretical development for the flow past a body, with two free streamlines, was given by Levi–Cività (1907). In the $\mathfrak{w}$-plane, for the notation of which we refer to Fig. IV. 12, the origin is taken at the front stagnation point B and the flow is assumed to separate from the upper and lower surfaces at $\phi = \phi_1$, and $\phi = \phi_2$, respectively. The $(\mathfrak{w}, t)$ relation, from equation (131), is

$$\mathfrak{w} = 4a(t - \sin\tfrac{1}{2}\lambda)^2, \tag{140}$$

where $a = (\phi_1^{\frac{1}{2}} + \phi_2^{\frac{1}{2}})^2/16$ and $\sin\tfrac{1}{2}\lambda = (\phi_2^{\frac{1}{2}} - \phi_1^{\frac{1}{2}})/(\phi_2^{\frac{1}{2}} + \phi_1^{\frac{1}{2}}).$ (141)

The upper half of the t-plane is now mapped on to the upper half of the unit circle in the ζ-plane by $t = -\frac{1}{2}(\zeta + 1/\zeta)$, so that finally

$$\mathfrak{w} = a(\zeta + \zeta^{-1} + 2\sin\tfrac{1}{2}\lambda)^2. \tag{142}$$

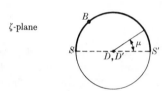

Fig. IV. 12. The scheme of Levi-Città's method.

It remains to determine $\sigma(\zeta)$. Levi-Città's method was simply to assign a function $\sigma(\zeta)$, and then to use (142) and (128) to determine the corresponding shape of the boundary. He did, however, obtain a general formula for the force acting on the obstacle with the aid of the reflection principle mentioned below. Although this method does not permit the shape of the obstacle to be prescribed in advance, Brodetsky (1923) managed to devise an iterative process based on it for circular and elliptic cylinders. A full account of the analytical details is given by Milne-Thomson (1949); the procedure, however, is superseded by the more general method of Section 31.

Villat (1920) extended Levi-Città's method in the following way. Suppose $v = U$ on the free boundaries; then the real part of σ vanishes on the real axis in the ζ-plane. $\sigma(\zeta)$ may be continued analytically by the Schwarzian reflection principle into the lower half of the unit circle, so that $\sigma(\bar{\zeta}) = -\overline{\sigma(\zeta)}$; in particular, on the unit circle at $\zeta = e^{i\mu}$, θ may be regarded as an even function of μ. Thus, from Poisson's integrals (19) and (20),

$$\sigma(\zeta) = \frac{i}{\pi} \int_0^\pi \theta(\mu) \frac{1 - \zeta^2}{1 - 2\zeta\cos\mu + \zeta^2}\, d\mu. \tag{143}$$

Thus to prescribe $\theta(\mu)$—and ϕ_1 and ϕ_2—determines a unique Kirchhoff flow. This is still an inverse method but its significance lies in the fact that it can be made the basis of a direct method.

On the surface, $\zeta = e^{i\mu}$ and so, from (143) and (125), the speed is given by

$$\mathrm{v}(\mu) = U \exp\left\{-(1/\pi) \int\limits_0^\pi \theta(\mu')\sin\mu \, d\mu'/(\cos\mu-\cos\mu')\right\}. \qquad (144)$$

Also, from (142) and from the streamline condition that $d\mathfrak{w} = d\phi = \mathrm{v}\,ds$,

$$s(\mu) = \int d\phi/\mathrm{v} = -8a \int\limits^\mu (\cos\mu+\sin\tfrac{1}{2}\lambda)\sin\mu \, d\mu/\mathrm{v}(\mu), \qquad (145)$$

s being the distance measured along the surface. Further, with a specified body, we know or can easily calculate

$$\theta = \theta(s). \qquad (146)$$

Thus equations (144) to (146) constitute complicated integral equations for $\theta(\mu)$. An iterative procedure of solution would assume a distribution $\mathrm{v}(\mu)$ which determines from equation (145) a corresponding $s(\mu)$; then from (146) and (144), $\theta(\mu)$ and $\mathrm{v}(\mu)$ follow in turn and we are back at our starting-point with a new distribution $\mathrm{v}(\mu)$. There is no known proof of the convergence of this iteration.

This idea of relating one part of the boundary of the subsidiary ζ-plane—here, the semicircular arc—to the imaginary part of σ and the rest—here, the diameter—to the real part of σ forms the basis of the theory of free-streamline flows past curved obstacles which is due to Woods (1955b). His approach, which is closely related to Villat's, uses an infinite strip in preference to a semicircle, on one side of which the imaginary, and on the other the real, part of an analytic function is known. The appropriate forms of Cauchy's integral are given in the next section.

30. Two theorems concerning functions analytic within an infinite strip

THEOREM 1. *If $\gamma(\mathfrak{z}) = \alpha+i\beta$ is a function analytic in the strip $-\infty < x < \infty,\ 0 \leqslant z \leqslant h$, such that*

(i) $\lim\limits_{R\to\infty} \gamma(\pm R, z)e^{-\pi R/2h} = 0$, *and*

(ii) *$\gamma(\mathfrak{z})$ has, at most, logarithmic singularities at a finite number of points on $z = 0$ and $z = h$,* *then the value of $\gamma(\mathfrak{z})$ within the strip is given by*

$$\gamma(\mathfrak{z}) = (1/2h) \int_{-\infty}^{\infty} \{\beta_0(x')\mathrm{cosech}[\pi(x'-\mathfrak{z})/2h] + \alpha_h(x')\mathrm{sech}[\pi(x'-\mathfrak{z})/2h]\}\, dx',$$

$$(147)$$

where the suffixes 0 and h denote values on $z = 0$ and $z = h$ respectively.
The contour of integration, here and later, is understood to be indented to exclude any singularities of $\gamma(x)$.

We summarize the proof which is given in full by Woods (1955b). $\gamma(\mathfrak{z})$ is an analytic function within and on the indented rectangle $0 \leqslant z \leqslant h$, $-R \leqslant x \leqslant R$; thus, from Cauchy's theorem when n is a non-zero integer and from Cauchy's integral when n is zero, we have

$$\left.\begin{matrix} \text{for } n = 0, & \gamma(\mathfrak{z}) = \\ \text{for } n \neq 0, & 0 = \end{matrix}\right\} \frac{1}{2\pi i} \int_{-R}^{R} \left\{\frac{\gamma(x',0)}{x'+2nih-\mathfrak{z}} - \frac{\gamma(x',h)}{x'+(2n+1)ih-\mathfrak{z}}\right\} dx' +$$

$$+ \frac{1}{2\pi} \int_{0}^{h} \left\{\frac{\gamma(R,z')}{R+2nih+iz'-\mathfrak{z}} - \frac{\gamma(-R,z')}{-R+2nih+iz'-\mathfrak{z}}\right\} dz'. \quad (148)$$

Multiplying these equations by $(-1)^n$, summing over $-\infty < n < \infty$, using the identity

$$\sum_{n=-\infty}^{\infty} (-1)^n(a+inb)^{-1} = (\pi/b)\mathrm{cosech}(\pi a/b), \quad (149)$$

and finally letting $R \to \infty$, we obtain

$$\gamma(\mathfrak{z}) = (1/4ih) \int_{-\infty}^{\infty} \{\gamma(x',0)\mathrm{cosech}[\pi(x'-\mathfrak{z})/2h] +$$

$$+ i\gamma(x',h)\mathrm{sech}[\pi(x'-\mathfrak{z})/2h]\}\, dx', \quad (150)$$

the second integral in (148) vanishing by virtue of condition (i).

If the same argument is applied to the conjugate point $\bar{\mathfrak{z}}$, an equation similar to (150) is obtained, but with $\mathfrak{z}$ replaced by $\bar{\mathfrak{z}}$, and with the left-hand side of the equation replaced by zero, since the points $(\bar{\mathfrak{z}}-2inh)$ lie outside the rectangle $-R \leqslant x \leqslant R$, $0 \leqslant z \leqslant h$, for all integral n. Hence

$$0 = (1/4ih) \int_{-\infty}^{\infty} \{\gamma(x',0)\mathrm{cosech}[\pi(x'-\bar{\mathfrak{z}})/2h] +$$

$$+ i\gamma(x',h)\mathrm{sech}[\pi(x'-\bar{\mathfrak{z}})/2h]\}\, dx'. \quad (151)$$

The theorem now follows by adding the complex conjugate of (151) to (150), and noting that

$$\gamma(x,0) - \bar{\gamma}(x,0) = 2i\beta_0(x) \quad \text{and} \quad \gamma(x,h) + \bar{\gamma}(x,h) = 2\alpha_h(x).$$

THEOREM 2 *retains condition* (ii) *but relaxes* (i) *so that* γ *may be non-zero but finite at infinity; then*

$$\gamma(\mathfrak{z}) = (1/2h) \int_{-\infty}^{\infty} \{\beta_0(x')\coth[\pi(x'-\mathfrak{z})/2h] - \\ -\beta_h(x')\tanh[\pi(x'-\mathfrak{z})/2h]\} \, dx' + \tfrac{1}{2}(\alpha_\infty + \alpha_{-\infty}), \quad (152)$$

where the suffixes ∞ *and* $-\infty$ *denote* $\lim_{\mathfrak{z}\to\infty}$ *and* $\lim_{\mathfrak{z}\to-\infty}$ *respectively.*

The proof follows the same lines as the first proof except that equations (148) are summed as they stand; the required identity, corresponding to (149), is

$$\sum_{n=-\infty}^{\infty} (a+inb)^{-1} = (\pi/b)\coth(\pi a/b).$$

If the conjugate of (151) is subtracted from (150), there results an equation similar to (147) (termed its conjugate equation) but with α and $i\beta$ interchanged throughout. The same interchange results in a conjugate equation for (152).

To evaluate $\gamma(\mathfrak{z})$ on the boundary $z = 0$, it is not sufficient merely to put $\mathfrak{z} = x$ in equations (147) and (152); the limit $\mathfrak{z} \to x+i0$ must be properly evaluated. The Cauchy principal values must then be taken of the resulting improper integrals. Similar remarks apply to $\mathfrak{z} = x+ih$, and $\mathfrak{z} = \pm\infty$.

31. The general integral equation for infinite wakes

Let us reconsider the problem defined in Fig. IV. 12. By the Schwarz–Christoffel formula, the upper-half t-plane is mapped on to the infinite strip $-\infty < \delta < \infty$, $0 \leqslant \chi \leqslant \tfrac{1}{2}\pi$ in the plane of $\epsilon = \delta+i\chi$, shown in Fig. IV. 13, by

$$t = \tanh\epsilon \qquad (153)$$

in such a way that the surface becomes $\chi = 0$, and the free streamlines $\chi = \tfrac{1}{2}\pi$. Hence, from equation (140),

$$\mathfrak{w} = 4a(\tanh\epsilon - \sin\tfrac{1}{2}\lambda)^2. \qquad (154)$$

In the ϵ-plane, we apply Theorem 1 to $\sigma = \tau+i\theta$; thus

$$\sigma(\epsilon) = (1/\pi) \int_{-\infty}^{\infty} \{\theta_0(\delta')\operatorname{cosech}(\delta'-\epsilon)+\tau_{\frac{1}{2}\pi}(\delta')\operatorname{sech}(\delta'-\epsilon)\} \, d\delta', \quad (155)$$

where

$$\theta_0(\delta) = \theta(\delta,0) \quad \text{and} \quad \tau_{\frac{1}{2}\pi}(\delta) = \tau(\delta,\tfrac{1}{2}\pi). \qquad (156)$$

This is the fundamental result. For an inverse method, knowledge of the functions $\theta_0(\delta)$ and $\tau_{\frac{1}{2}\pi}(\delta)$ determines a flow from (154) and (155). For a direct problem, the shape of the body does not, of course, specify immediately $\theta_0(\delta)$ since the relation between δ and s, distance along the surface, is as yet unknown. The determination of $\theta_0(\delta)$ is considered in the following section. $\tau_{\frac{1}{2}\pi}(\delta)$, on the other hand, refers to the velocity distribution on the free streamlines and the fact that this is arbitrary is the distinguishing feature of Woods's method.

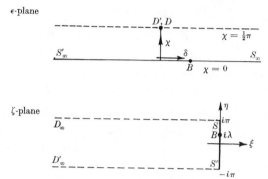

FIG. IV. 13. The scheme of Woods's method.

Of course, ϵ is no more than a parameter and not a convenient one since the infinite range of integration in (155) makes numerical integration difficult. It is more convenient to use $\zeta = \xi + i\eta$ such that

$$t = -i \sinh \tfrac{1}{2}\zeta. \tag{157}$$

This ζ-plane, which is of course distinct from that of Fig. IV. 12, is shown in Fig. IV. 13; the body corresponds to $\xi = 0$, $-\pi \leqslant \eta \leqslant \pi$, and the upper and lower streamlines to $-\infty < \xi \leqslant 0$, $\eta = \pm\pi$.

The relation between ζ and ϵ comes from equations (157) and (153), and enables equations (154) and (155) to be put in terms of ζ. The final results are

$$\mathfrak{w} = 4a(i \sinh \tfrac{1}{2}\zeta + \sin \tfrac{1}{2}\lambda)^2 \tag{158}$$

and

$$\sigma(\zeta) = \frac{\cosh \tfrac{1}{2}\zeta}{2\pi} \left[\int_{-\pi}^{\pi} \frac{\theta_0(\eta')\,d\eta'}{\sin \tfrac{1}{2}\eta' + i \sinh \tfrac{1}{2}\zeta} + \right.$$
$$\left. + \int_{-\infty}^{0} \frac{\tau_1(\xi')\,d\xi'}{\cosh \tfrac{1}{2}\xi' + i \sinh \tfrac{1}{2}\zeta} + \int_{-\infty}^{0} \frac{\tau_2(\xi')\,d\xi'}{\cosh \tfrac{1}{2}\xi' - i \sinh \tfrac{1}{2}\zeta} \right], \tag{159}$$

where now the suffixes 1 and 2 refer to the two free streamlines $\eta = \pm\pi$ respectively.

It is convenient to integrate the first integral in equation (159) by parts and express it as a Stieltjes integral, θ_0 having simple discontinuities at stagnation points. Then

$$\sigma(\zeta) = i\theta_0(-\pi) - (1/\pi) \int_{\eta'=-\pi}^{\pi} \log[\sin\tfrac{1}{4}(\eta'+i\zeta)\sec\tfrac{1}{4}(\eta'-i\zeta)] \, d\theta_0(\eta') +$$

$$+ \frac{\cosh\tfrac{1}{2}\zeta}{2\pi} \int_{-\infty}^{0} \left\{ \frac{\tau_1(\xi')}{\cosh\tfrac{1}{2}\xi'+i\sinh\tfrac{1}{2}\zeta} + \frac{\tau_2(\xi')}{\cosh\tfrac{1}{2}\xi'-i\sinh\tfrac{1}{2}\zeta} \right\} d\xi'. \quad (160)$$

The only property of Stieltjes integrals we need to recall is the following one: if $g(x)$ has a simple discontinuity of h at $x = x_0$, then the discontinuity contributes $hf(x_0)$ to the integral of $f(x)\, dg(x)$.

32. The iterative solution of the integral equation

First, $\tau_1(\xi)$ and $\tau_2(\xi)$ are assumed known. So also is the curvature of the body's surfaces, $\kappa(s)$, as a function of s, the distance along the surface. Now on the body $\zeta = i\eta$ and

$$d\theta_0(\eta) = \frac{d\theta_0}{ds}\frac{ds}{d\phi}\frac{d\phi}{d\eta}\, d\eta = -\frac{\kappa}{v_0}\frac{d\phi}{d\eta}\, d\eta, \quad (161)$$

v_0 being the speed on the surface. $(d\phi/d\eta)$ follows from (158) as

$$v_0(\eta)(ds/d\eta) = d\phi/d\eta = 4a(\sin\tfrac{1}{2}\eta - \sin\tfrac{1}{2}\lambda)\cos\tfrac{1}{2}\eta, \quad (162)$$

while (160) becomes, with the use of both (161) and (162),

$$\left. \begin{aligned} \tau_0(\eta) &\equiv \log\left(\frac{U}{v(\eta)}\right) \\ &= \frac{4}{\pi} \int_{-\pi}^{\pi} \frac{a\kappa}{v_0(\eta)}\cos\tfrac{1}{2}\eta'(\sin\tfrac{1}{2}\eta' - \sin\tfrac{1}{2}\lambda)\log\left|\frac{\sin\tfrac{1}{4}(\eta'-\eta)}{\cos\tfrac{1}{4}(\eta'+\eta)}\right| d\eta' \end{aligned} \right\} \quad (163)$$

plus other terms independent of v_0 due to the discontinuities in θ_0 and to the speed on the free streamlines.

Equations (162) and (163) are complicated integral equations for $v_0(\eta)$.

The iterative solution starts with an assumed $v_0(\eta)$; say, $v_0(\eta) = U$. Equation (162), with $\sin\tfrac{1}{2}\lambda$ neglected, defines s, and so κ, as a function of η. (163) then gives a new value of $v_0(\eta)$. At any stage of this process, ϕ_1 and ϕ_2 may be estimated as $\int_0^{\pm\pi} v_0(\eta)(ds/d\eta)\, d\eta$ and so the corresponding value of $\sin\tfrac{1}{2}\lambda$, given by (141), may be used in the two equations. The process may be repeated as often as is necessary. Tables which enable the integral in (163) to be evaluated rapidly at thirty-six equally-spaced values of η are given by Woods (1955b) who found the process converged reasonably quickly in the case of a circular cylinder.

33. The free streamlines near a separation point

We now express mathematically the discussion in Section 24 concerning the nature of the inviscid flow near a separation point.

Let us consider the neighbourhood of S', the lower separation point, where $\zeta = -i\pi$. Then equation (160) may be written as

$$\sigma(\zeta) = \sigma(-i\pi) - (i/2\pi)A'(\zeta + i\pi) + O(\zeta + i\pi)^3, \qquad (164)$$

where

$$A' = \int\limits_{\eta = -\pi}^{\pi} \tan\tfrac{1}{4}(\pi - \eta)\, d\theta_0(\eta) - \int\limits_{\xi = -\infty}^{0} \tanh\tfrac{1}{4}\xi\, d\tau_1(\xi) + \int\limits_{\xi = -\infty}^{0} \coth\tfrac{1}{4}\xi\, d\tau_2(\xi). \qquad (165)$$

In the same way, on the streamline $\psi = 0$, equation (158) gives

$$\zeta + i\pi = -(\phi - \phi_2)^{\frac{1}{2}}[a + a\sin\tfrac{1}{2}\lambda]^{-\frac{1}{2}} + O(\phi - \phi_2)^{\frac{3}{2}}. \qquad (166)$$

Combining (164) and (166), we have for the free streamline $\phi \geqslant \phi_2$,

$$\theta = \theta(\phi_2) + (A'/2\pi)[a + a\sin\tfrac{1}{2}\lambda]^{-\frac{1}{2}}(\phi - \phi_2)^{\frac{1}{2}} + O(\phi - \phi_2)^{\frac{3}{2}}. \qquad (167)$$

The curvature of the free streamline is then given by

$$\kappa = -\frac{d\theta}{ds} = -\frac{d\theta}{d\phi}\frac{d\phi}{ds} = -\frac{A'\mathrm{v}}{4\pi}[a + a\sin\tfrac{1}{2}\lambda]^{-\frac{1}{2}}(\phi - \phi_2)^{-\frac{1}{2}} + O(\phi - \phi_2)^{\frac{1}{2}}, \qquad (168)$$

being positive if the streamline is convex to the body.

Now the pressure gradient on the surface of the body is

$$\frac{dp}{ds} = -\rho\mathrm{v}\frac{d\mathrm{v}}{ds} = \rho\mathrm{v}^2\frac{d\tau}{d\phi}\frac{d\phi}{ds} = \rho\mathrm{v}^3\frac{d\tau}{d\phi}.$$

$\tau(\phi)$ follows analogously to (167), as the real part of (164) with (166) and $\phi < \phi_2$, and it is easy to show that

$$dp/ds = -(A'\rho\mathrm{v}^3/4\pi)[a + a\sin\tfrac{1}{2}\lambda]^{-\frac{1}{2}}(\phi_2 - \phi)^{-\frac{1}{2}} + O(\phi_2 - \phi)^{\frac{1}{2}}. \qquad (169)$$

Concerning the value of A', which from (165) depends on the velocity distribution chosen for the free streamlines, it seems that $A' \leqslant 0$ follows from (168) as the condition that the free streamline should not cut into the body and that $A' \geqslant 0$ follows from (169) if an infinite positive pressure gradient is to be avoided. Thus $A' = 0$ appears as a sensible condition on the mathematical model, and results in what is known as smooth separation in which it may be shown that both the curvature and the pressure gradient are continuous on $\psi = 0$ through S'. Smooth separation on the upper surface leads to $A = 0$, A being defined by an equation similar to (165). Hence it may be desirable to choose $\tau_1(\xi)$ and $\tau_2(\xi)$ to satisfy $A = A' = 0$. But the effect of viscosity is to blur these clear-cut mathematical distinctions and we cannot say with any certainty that smooth separation is the best model.

The concept of smooth separation can be used to relate the position of separation to the under-pressure in the wake. Suppose, for example, the pressure on the lower streamline is progressively reduced; $\tau_2(\xi)$ is also decreased so that the last integral in (165), which is positive, is increased. The counterbalancing decrease in the first integral in (165) involves a downstream movement of the separation point.

Finally, this analysis cannot show whether the free streamline will intersect the body well away from the separation point, but Leray (1935) has proved that this cannot occur for symmetrical convex bodies whose curvature steadily increases with distance from the front stagnation point.

34. The free streamlines far downstream

The possibility, discussed in Section 23 and shown in Fig. IV. 5, of the free streamlines crossing each other may be analysed mathematically by expanding previous results for large values of ζ. First, from (158), $\mathfrak{w} = \infty$ corresponds to $\zeta = -\infty$, and so

$$\mathfrak{w}/a = -e^{-\zeta}\{1 + 4i\sin\tfrac{1}{2}\lambda\, e^{\frac{1}{2}\zeta} + O(e^{\zeta})\}, \tag{170}$$

and similarly, from equation (159),

$$\sigma(\zeta) = iE + Be^{\frac{1}{2}\zeta} + iCe^{\zeta} + O(e^{\frac{3}{2}\zeta}) \tag{171}$$

in which

$$\left.\begin{aligned}
E &= (1/2\pi)\int_{-\pi}^{\pi}\theta_0(\eta)\,d\eta + (1/2\pi)\int_{-\infty}^{0}(\tau_1 - \tau_2)\,d\xi \\[4pt]
B &= (1/\pi)\int_{-\pi}^{\pi}\theta_0(\eta)\sin\tfrac{1}{2}\eta\,d\eta + (1/\pi)\int_{-\infty}^{0}(\tau_1 + \tau_2)\cosh\tfrac{1}{2}\xi\,d\xi \\[4pt]
C &= (1/\pi)\int_{-\pi}^{\pi}\theta_0(\eta)\cos\eta\,d\eta - (1/\pi)\int_{-\infty}^{0}(\tau_1 - \tau_2)\cosh\xi\,d\xi
\end{aligned}\right\}. \tag{172}$$

With the reference speed U equal to that at infinity, equation (126) holds and so, from (171), $E = 0$. This result is analogous to the first of the conditions (113) for closed aerofoils. The two expansions (170) and (171) give

$$\sigma = iB(a/\mathfrak{w})^{\frac{1}{2}} - i(C + 2B\sin\tfrac{1}{2}\lambda)(a/\mathfrak{w}) + O(a/\mathfrak{w})^{\frac{3}{2}}, \tag{173}$$

so that on the free streamlines

$$\theta = \pm B(a/\phi)^{\frac{1}{2}} + O(a/\phi). \tag{174}$$

Now, far downstream, $(dz/dx) \sim \theta$ and $\phi \sim Ux$; hence an integration of equation (174) gives for the distance Δz between the free streamlines far downstream:

$$\Delta z = 4B(ax/U)^{\frac{1}{2}} + \text{constant} + O(x^{-\frac{1}{2}}). \tag{175}$$

Near the body $\Delta z > 0$ and so if $B < 0$ the streamlines cross each other. A necessary condition of physical reality is thus that B, as given in equation (172), should be positive or zero. It is possible to deduce from this that separation must be upstream of a certain limiting point for a given body.

For Kirchhoff flows, $\tau_1 = \tau_2 = 0$, and B is inevitably positive; thus the wake increases indefinitely in width, which, as was mentioned in Section 24, is a serious defect of Kirchhoff's representation. In the following section, we discuss the improvements on this which Woods's theory makes possible.

35. The pressure distribution in the wake

According to the second inviscid approximation of a flow discussed in Section III. 7, the distance between the bounding streamlines of the wake equals the displacement thickness, which remains finite at infinity. Thus, in considering suitable forms for the pressure distribution in the wake—or for $\tau_1(\xi)$ and $\tau_2(\xi)$—we regard the result $B = 0$ of the previous section as a necessary condition.

Now, from (173), $\sigma \sim \mathfrak{w}^{-1}$ at infinity and in particular $\tau_1 \sim \phi^{-1}$ on the free streamlines, while from (158), $\phi \sim \cosh^2 \tfrac{1}{2}\xi$. A function having the required asymptotic behaviour is $\tau_1(\xi) = -K_1[1+b_1^2\sinh^2\tfrac{1}{2}\xi]^{-\frac{1}{2}}$, K_1 and b_1 being constants; $\tau_2(\xi)$ may be given similarly. This form is chosen for its mathematical simplicity; from the physical point of view it is no more than plausible.

To continue, we consider a symmetrical body with a symmetrical wake such that $\tau_1 = \tau_2$, and put

$$\tau_1(\xi) = \tau_2(\xi) = -K[1+b^2\sinh^2\tfrac{1}{2}\xi]^{-\frac{1}{2}}. \tag{176}$$

The constants K and b may be estimated as follows.

First, the condition $B = 0$ leads, from (172) and (176), to

$$b^{-1} = (1/2\pi K) \int_{-\pi}^{\pi} \theta_0(\eta)\sin\tfrac{1}{2}\eta \, d\eta. \tag{177}$$

K is the value of $(-\tau) = -\log(U/v)$ at separation and so is expressible in terms of the pressure coefficient C_{ps} at separation; it is found that

$$C_{ps} = 1-e^{2K}. \tag{178}$$

The theory has therefore now been put in terms of the single arbitrary parameter C_{ps}.

Woods (1955b) applied the theory to the flow past a circular cylinder, and obtained very satisfactory agreement with experiment as is shown in Fig. IV. 14. The variable α in this figure is the angular displacement in degrees around the cylinder from the front stagnation point. The experimental results for laminar and turbulent separation given in the figure are due to Fage and Falkner (1931). The theoretical results shown are the Kirchhoff flows separating at $\alpha_s = 56°$ (the case of smooth separation), $60°$, $80°$, $100°$, and $120°$, and the flow calculated by the

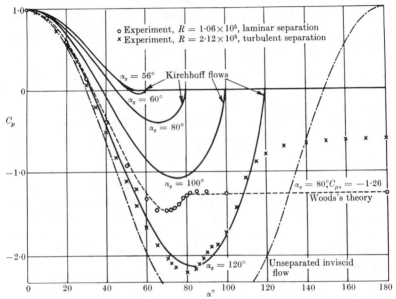

Fig. IV. 14. Various determinations of the pressure coefficient on a circular cylinder.

present method for $\alpha_s = 80°$, $C_{ps} = -1·26$. With $C_{ps} = -1·26$, which is the experimental value for laminar separation, smooth separation was calculated to occur for $\alpha_s = 76°$, and the corresponding curve differs only slightly from that shown in the figure. This suggests that, at any rate for flows expected to be laminar, the criterion of smooth separation is useful.

36. Lift and drag in Kirchhoff flow

In the particular case of $\tau_1 = \tau_2 = 0$, $C_p = 0$ in the wake and simple expressions can be derived for the lift and drag coefficients, C_L and C_D. Now

$$C_L - iC_D = (1/c) \int_C C_p e^{i\theta}\, ds = (2/\rho U^2 c) \int_C (v^2 - U^2)\, d\mathfrak{z},$$

where c is a length typical of the body, and C is any open contour lying on the surface and extending some distance along both the free streamlines. With equations (123) and (129), this can be written

$$C_L - iC_D = (1/cU)\left[\int_C e^\sigma \, d\mathfrak{w} - \int_C e^{-\bar\sigma} \, d\mathfrak{w}\right]. \qquad (179)$$

If the $\mathfrak{w}$-plane is now transformed into the upper half of the t-plane by

$$\mathfrak{w} = at^2, \qquad (180)$$

the wetted surface and the free streamlines transform into the real axis of the t-plane. As $\sigma = -\bar\sigma$ on the free streamlines, $\sigma(t)$ is extended analytically to the lower half of the t-plane by $\sigma(\bar t) = -\overline{\sigma(t)}$. The second integral in (179) can now be taken as the integral of $e^{\sigma(t)}(d\mathfrak{w}/dt)$ along the lower edge of the real axis in the t-plane. Hence

$$C_L - iC_D = (1/cU)\int_C e^{\sigma(t)}(d\mathfrak{w}/dt) \, dt \qquad (181)$$

where, since the integrand is analytic, C is now any contour enclosing the strip representing the surface in the t-plane. The integral may be evaluated by putting the asymptotic value of σ from equation (173) in terms of t from (180); equating real and imaginary parts, we then find

$$C_L = (4\pi a/cU)(C + 2B\sin\tfrac{1}{2}\lambda) \quad \text{and} \quad C_D = 2\pi a B^2/cU, \qquad (182)$$

C and B now taking, from (172), the values

$$B = (1/\pi)\int_{-\pi}^{\pi} \theta_0(\eta)\sin\tfrac{1}{2}\eta \, d\eta, \qquad C = (1/\pi)\int_{-\pi}^{\pi} \theta_0(\eta)\cos\eta \, d\eta. \qquad (183)$$

Levi-Cività (1907) gave similar but less explicit results for these coefficients, and Brodetsky (1922) found a corresponding but more complicated expression for the moment coefficient.

As a comparatively simple example we take a model of the flow, considered in Section III. 3, in which separation occurs somewhere in the middle of the upper surface of an aerofoil. To simplify still further, we assume the aerofoil may be taken as a flat plate and Fig. IV. 15 illustrates this case. If α is the incidence of the plate,

$$\left.\begin{array}{ll} \theta_0 = -\alpha, & -\pi \leqslant \eta < \lambda \\ \theta_0 = \pi - \alpha, & \lambda < \eta < \lambda + \lambda_1 \\ \theta_0 = -\alpha, & \lambda + \lambda_1 < \eta \leqslant \pi \end{array}\right\},$$

where $\eta = \lambda + \lambda_1$ at the sharp leading edge. The fact that E is zero in equation (172) leads to $\lambda_1 = 2\alpha$; to the lowest orders in α, equations (182) and (183) become

$$C_L = 2\pi\alpha(4a/Uc); \qquad C_D = 2\pi\alpha^2(4a/Uc)\sin^2 \tfrac{1}{2}\lambda. \qquad (184)$$

If $(1-f)$ is the fraction of the chord c lying between the separation points, then approximately $\phi_2 = Uc$ and $\phi_1 = fcU$; equations (141) and (184) then give

$$C_L = 2\pi\alpha[\tfrac{1}{2}+\tfrac{1}{2}f^{\frac{1}{2}}]^2; \qquad C_D = 2\pi\alpha^2[\tfrac{1}{2}-\tfrac{1}{2}f^{\frac{1}{2}}]^2. \qquad (185)$$

For a complete theory, the relationship between f and α is needed, but this can only come from boundary-layer calculations and also

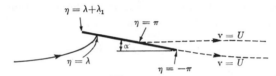

FIG. IV. 15. A theoretical model for separated flow past a flat plate.

depends very much on the shape of the aerofoil. A more elaborate theory would take into account the fact that the values of C_p on the free streamline near the separation point are usually appreciably negative; because of this, C_L is underestimated in equation (184), It is interesting to note that, for $f = 1$, equations (185) give the same values as those for unseparated flow past a flat plate satisfying the Kutta–Joukowski condition, as discussed in Section 5.

37. The design of aerofoils with mixed boundary conditions

The shape of an aerofoil, especially near the leading and trailing edges, is often governed by considerations not primarily aerodynamic; for example, structural problems might lead to a specified shape of trailing edge. Although the methods of Sections 18–21 can be adjusted, with experience, to meet such requirements in design, the underlying theory is not fully suitable. In this section, therefore, we indicate how a theory of Woods (1955a) may be applied to the particular problem of a symmetrical aerofoil whose chord is divided into three parts in which shape, pressure, and shape are specified respectively.

The notation being set out in Fig. IV. 16, it is easily verified that

$$\mathfrak{w} = a(1-\coth \epsilon), \qquad \epsilon = \delta+i\chi. \qquad (186)$$

From what is given, τ is known on the upper side of the strip in the

ϵ-plane and θ on the lower. $\sigma(t)$ is therefore given at once from (155) as

$$\sigma = \sigma_s + (2/\pi) \int_{\delta'=-\infty}^{\infty} \tanh^{-1}\exp(\delta'-\epsilon)\, d\theta_0(\delta') -$$

$$- (2/\pi) \int_{\delta'=-\infty}^{\infty} \tan^{-1}\exp(\delta'-\epsilon)\, d\tau_{\frac{1}{2}\pi}(\delta'), \quad (187)$$

where σ_s is the value of σ at the separation point, the point S in Fig. IV. 16, given by $\mathfrak{w} = 0$.

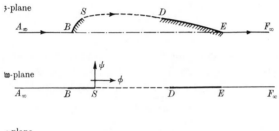

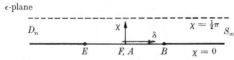

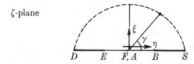

FIG. IV. 16. The scheme of notation for the design of a symmetrical aerofoil with mixed boundary conditions.

The infinite integrals are not convenient for numerical calculation and can be avoided by using the variable $\zeta = \xi + i\eta$ given by

$$\epsilon = \log[(1+\zeta)/(1-\zeta)].$$

If $\zeta = e^{i\gamma}$ on $\chi = \frac{1}{2}\pi$, equations (186) and (187) become

$$\sigma = \sigma_s + \frac{1}{\pi} \int_{\eta'=-1}^{1} \log\left(\frac{1-\eta'\zeta}{\zeta-\eta'}\right) d\theta_0(\eta') + \frac{2}{\pi} \int_{\gamma'=0}^{\pi} \tan^{-1}\left(\frac{1-\zeta}{1+\zeta}\cot\tfrac{1}{2}\gamma'\right) d\tau_{\frac{1}{2}\pi}(\gamma'),$$

$$(188)$$

and

$$\mathfrak{w} = a[1 - \tfrac{1}{2}(\zeta + \zeta^{-1})]. \quad (189)$$

$\theta_0(\eta)$ and $\tau_{\frac{1}{2}\pi}(\gamma)$ are not entirely arbitrary and two conditions, analogous to equations (113), are immediately derivable from (188). First the speed at infinity must equal U so that, from (126), $\sigma \to 0$ as $\mathfrak{z} \to \infty$ or $\zeta \to 0$; second, the aerofoil must be closed, which together with the condition for zero circulation is expressed by $\mathfrak{w} - U\mathfrak{z} = O(\mathfrak{z}^{-1})$ or $\sigma\zeta^{-1} \to 0$ as $\zeta \to 0$. A further desirable condition is that the flow at S and D should be smooth. The equations expressing these various conditions are given in Woods's original paper.

The practical design of an aerofoil is based on equation (188), the real part of which is

$$\tau_0(\eta) = \tau_s + \frac{1}{\pi} \int\limits_{\eta'=-1}^{1} \log\left|\frac{1-\eta\eta'}{\eta-\eta'}\right| d\theta_0(\eta') + \frac{2}{\pi} \int\limits_{\gamma'=0}^{\pi} \tan^{-1}\left(\frac{1-\eta}{1+\eta}\cot\tfrac{1}{2}\gamma'\right) d\tau_{\frac{1}{2}\pi}(\gamma'). \tag{190}$$

This must first be solved for $\theta_0(\eta)$ by an iteration similar to that for equation (163). σ can then be calculated from (188) and inserted in equation (128) which, with $\mathfrak{w}(\mathfrak{z})$ from (189) and $\zeta = e^{i\gamma}$ on SD, becomes

$$\mathfrak{z}(\gamma) = (a/U) \int e^{\sigma(\gamma)}\sin\gamma \, d\gamma, \tag{191}$$

which determines the shape of SD. In all this, $\tau_{\frac{1}{2}\pi}(\gamma)$ follows from a given distribution of speed $\mathrm{v}(s)$ on SD from the relation between γ and s, which, from (189), is $d\phi = \mathrm{v} \, ds = a\sin\gamma \, d\gamma$.

The generalization of this analysis to aerofoils with porous surfaces has been given by Woods (1956).

38. Riabouchinsky flow

The flow past two bodies between which there is a bubble or cavity at constant pressure was proposed by Riabouchinsky (1920) as a representation of the flow past a single body behind which the pressure is less than the pressure at infinity. All symmetrical Riabouchinsky flows can be calculated simply by putting $d\tau_{\frac{1}{2}\pi} = 0$ in the theory just given for aerofoil design.

The pressure coefficient is

$$Q = (p_\infty - p_s)/\tfrac{1}{2}\rho U^2 = (\mathrm{v}_s/U)^2 - 1 = e^{-2\tau_s} - 1.$$

τ_s follows from (188) by putting $\mathfrak{z} = \infty$ or $\zeta = 0$ and using (126); thus

$$Q = \exp\left[-(2/\pi) \int\limits_{\eta=-1}^{1} \log|\eta| \, d\theta_0(\eta)\right] - 1. \tag{192}$$

The simplest example is the flow past two symmetrically-placed plates as shown in Fig. IV. 7. There are discontinuities of $\tfrac{1}{2}\pi$ in θ_0 at $\eta = \pm\lambda$, where $0 < \lambda < 1$, so from equation (192), λ is related to Q by

$$Q = \lambda^{-2} - 1, \tag{193}$$

while equation (188) yields, for the present example,

$$\sigma = \tfrac{1}{2}\log[(1-\lambda^2\zeta^2)/(\zeta^2\lambda^{-2}-1)].$$

Then, from equations (128) and (189), we have for the shape of the free streamlines

$$\mathfrak{z} = \frac{a\lambda}{2U}\int\left(\frac{1-\lambda^2\zeta^2}{\zeta^2-\lambda^2}\right)^{\!\frac{1}{2}}\!\!\left(\frac{1-\zeta^2}{\zeta^2}\right)d\zeta,$$

which can be evaluated in terms of elliptic functions. The parameter a can be expressed in terms of c, the length of the plate, while λ is given, from (193), by the assumed pressure coefficient.

39. Flow through channels

The immense literature on flows bounded by two streamlines at a finite distance apart includes a great diversity of analytical method. But many of these methods are bound to use versions of what deserve now to be regarded as the fundamental results which follow directly from Theorem 2 in Section 30. These, given originally by Woods (1954), we shall now establish.

Let the axes and scales of the flow be fixed so that

$$\lim_{\phi\to-\infty}\sigma = 0 \quad\text{and}\quad \lim_{\phi\to+\infty}\sigma = \log(U/V)+i\alpha. \tag{194}$$

Thus U and V are the speeds at infinity upstream and downstream, and α is the total deflexion of the flow. If the width of the channel upstream is h, the bounding streamlines may be taken as $\psi = 0$ and $\psi = hU$.

Since σ is an analytic function of $\mathfrak{w}$ within the strip $-\infty < \phi < \infty$, $0 \leqslant \psi \leqslant hU$, Theorem 2 states that

$$\sigma(\mathfrak{w}) = (1/2hU)\int_{-\infty}^{\infty}\theta_0(\phi')\coth[\pi(\phi'-\mathfrak{w})/2hU]\,d\phi' -$$

$$-(1/2hU)\int_{-\infty}^{\infty}\theta_h(\phi')\tanh[\pi(\phi'-\mathfrak{w})/2hU]\,d\phi' +\tfrac{1}{2}\log(U/V), \tag{195}$$

of which the limit as $\phi \to \infty$ gives

$$\log(U/V) = (1/hU)\int_{-\infty}^{\infty}[\theta_h(\phi)-\theta_0(\phi)]\,d\phi. \tag{196}$$

This represents the solution of the direct problem in which the shapes of the boundaries are given. By taking $\psi = 0$ and $\psi = hU$ in (195), and remembering that $d\theta = -\kappa v^{-1}\,d\phi$ and $ds = v^{-1}\,d\phi$ on these boundaries, the equations represent integral equations for v_0 and v_h which may be solved by methods similar to those already described.

For the inverse or design problem, in which τ rather than θ is known on the boundaries, the conjugate form of Theorem 2 states

$$\sigma(\mathfrak{w}) = \tfrac{1}{2}i\alpha - (i/2hU) \int_{-\infty}^{\infty} \tau_0(\phi')\coth[\pi(\phi'-\mathfrak{w})/2hU]\, d\phi' +$$

$$+ (i/2hU) \int_{-\infty}^{\infty} \tau_h(\phi')\tanh[\pi(\phi'-\mathfrak{w})/2hU]\, d\phi', \quad (197)$$

from which follows, as $\phi \to \infty$,

$$\alpha = (1/hU) \int_{-\infty}^{\infty} [\tau_0(\phi)-\tau_h(\phi)]\, d\phi. \tag{198}$$

$\theta_0(\phi)$ and $\theta_h(\phi)$ are given by the imaginary part of (197) when $\mathfrak{w} = \phi$ and $(\phi+ihU)$ respectively, and the shape of the streamlines is given by

$$x = \int \cos\theta\, d\phi/\mathrm{v}; \qquad z = \int \sin\theta\, d\phi/\mathrm{v}.$$

These two results (195) and (197)—which, we note, determine the whole velocity field and not only values on the boundaries—have been applied by Woods (1954) to a number of different types of flow and especially to problems of wind-tunnel interference.

40. Concluding remarks

Within the strict limitations of a first inviscid approximation, the various theories described in this chapter are remarkably accurate and complete. Indeed there seems little need for new theories, since the fundamental problem in the analysis of two-dimensional irrotational flow—that of relating the real to the imaginary part of an analytic function, on a boundary—is now fully appreciated and has been put in practical forms for both types of boundary condition.

We can be confident about the validity and even the accuracy of the various analyses of unseparated flows; for these flows, the most frequently used methods are those of Sections 2–22. It is also profitable to consider the first boundary-layer approximation and the higher approximations, and Chapter V deals with these.

But for separated flow, to which the methods of Sections 23–39 are most relevant, the mathematical models are often so crude that not only is it difficult to choose between several alternative models, but also there is little point in proceeding to a boundary-layer approximation. The most significant future advances are bound to be in the consideration of viscous effects and their relation to the inviscid approximation. Developments on other lines should, however, be mentioned.

First, Leray (1935), Weinstein (1949), Gilbarg (1952a), and Serrin (1952) are among those who have done important work aimed at establishing the existence and uniqueness of physically possible configurations of irrotational separating flow past bodies and in channels of fairly general shape. We, in the preceding sections, have tacitly assumed both these properties of the solution sought; at present there is no alternative, as the established theorems cover only a limited range of shapes of obstacle.

Woods (1955b) has shown how his theory can be applied approximately to subsonic compressible flow, and the same modification may be made to all the analysis of the chapter.

Unsteady flows in which bubbles and wakes are present have only comparatively recently received the attention of theoretical workers. Kármán (1940) and Gilbarg (1952b) have considered cavity flows in which the cavity length is a function of time, and Woods (1953) has generalized their results. All the models used by these authors are, however, of doubtful validity since they incorporate some of the unsteady characteristics of the flow and neglect others. Woods (1955c) considered unsteady Kirchhoff flow in which the unsteady perturbations of the obstacles are comparatively small, as is assumed in classical flutter theory; Curle (1956), on the other hand, considered the establishment of a steady state of free-streamline flow from rest.

Three-dimensional and axi-symmetric separating flows have so far resisted exact theoretical treatment. Garabedian, Lewy, and Schiffer (1952) have established some existence and uniqueness theorems for axi-symmetric flows, and suggest two methods of calculating such flows. Armstrong and Dunham (1953), who give a useful bibliography, describe two methods of calculating axi-symmetric cavity flows of the Riabouchinsky type. The first is exact in principle but very laborious to compute, while the second, described further by Armstrong (1954), is a simpler but approximate method. The latter seeks to establish a correspondence between axi-symmetric and two-dimensional flows which is difficult to justify except by its moderate success in a number of cases.

V

UNIFORM VISCOUS FLOW PAST AEROFOILS

1. Introduction

WE now have to apply the procedures outlined in Chapter III. These are essentially approximate and the precision characteristic of the mathematics of Chapter IV can no longer be expected. But a brief explanation must first be given of the difficulties and doubts which at present surround the Navier–Stokes equations when they are considered in connexion with the two-dimensional flow past an aerofoil. No existence or uniqueness theorems have yet been established for these equations under the following boundary conditions:

(i) the flow is uniform at infinity,
(ii) the speed is zero on a closed interior surface, and
(iii) the flow is two-dimensional and steady.

Numerical solutions, of the kind mentioned in Section III. 9, suggest that there may be just one solution for a body such as a circular cylinder, but they throw no light on two further difficulties.

The first of these concerns the shape of the body. Does the character of solutions depend on the shape? In particular, does a salient point —such as a sharp trailing edge—impose an additional condition on the solution? In fact, much of the analysis of this chapter is based on an assumption concerning the effect of a sharp trailing edge, but we should emphasize that there is, at present, no purely mathematical answer to the question.

The second mathematical difficulty concerns the value of the circulation at infinity. Is this a disposable parameter in the same way that it is in an irrotational flow? Opinion on this is divided. Some would say that the boundary conditions specified above imply a definite value of the circulation; others hold that the circulation can be independently assigned while the opposite extreme opinion is that there may be some boundary conditions for which a steady-flow solution could not be found at all.

One cannot foresee to what extent these questions may be answered in the next few years. So for the present we have to assume that there is a unique flow past a given aerofoil, and our main aim in this chapter is to predict the values of lift and drag for this one flow.

Methods for calculating these values follow fairly naturally the lines laid down in previous chapters, but only after the value of the circulation in each inviscid approximation has been specified. Thus the central problem underlying the discussion of this chapter is the determination of the circulation. For the first inviscid approximation, the Kutta–Joukowski condition has already been described in Chapter IV, but for the higher approximations to the flow, it is found that the simple condition that the velocity is finite at the trailing edge is not sufficient to determine a value for the circulation; for example, it is inherent in all the viscous approximations that the velocity is zero at all points of the surface of an aerofoil.

The analytical criterion for the determination of the circulation in any inviscid approximation will be given in equations (30) and (34), for unseparated and for separated flows respectively. When one comes, however, to formulate a general physical hypothesis, from which the analytical criterion is deducible, no consensus of opinion is to be found. On the one hand, it is argued that the flow of vorticity governs the configuration of flow and that only certain types of vorticity distribution are possible. On the other, appeal is made more to the topological character of the streamlines.

We have chosen to develop the subject of this chapter according to the latter ideas, which are more explicitly described in Section 2.

In Sections 2–11 which refer to unseparated flow past two-dimensional aerofoils, much of the analysis of the wake applies strictly only to laminar flow, and the corresponding treatment for turbulent flow has yet to be established. Nevertheless, the theoretical results obtained for such overall characteristics as lift and drag accord well, on the whole, with experiment.

2. Thin aerofoils at low incidence. The extended Kutta–Joukowski hypothesis

Aerofoils are usually designed to have wedge-shaped or cusped trailing edges for the practical reason that, in this way, very low values of the drag can be achieved. But it is also thought that the tendency of the fluid to adopt one and only one configuration of flow past such an aerofoil is due largely to the influence of the sharp trailing edge. While we have seen that it is not possible to give a theoretical explanation for this, an attempt to construct configurations of flow near a sharp trailing edge soon leads to an intuitive conclusion, of use in the iterative procedure.

First, suppose that the rear dividing streamline leaves the upper surface as sketched in Fig. V. 1 (*a*). This is reminiscent of the flow shortly after an impulsive start when the circulation in a circuit far from the aerofoil is still zero. It is not easy to imagine a steady flow of this type, even though in viscous flow the velocity very near the trailing edge would not be large, as it is in inviscid flow. In practice

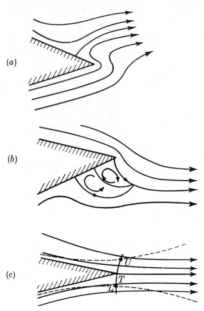

Fig. V. 1. Sketches of some hypothetical patterns of flow near the trailing edge of a thin aerofoil at low incidence.

it is unlikely that such a flow could remain steady and it would probably develop by forming a bubble and by 'casting-off' a vortex.

Next, we might suppose the dividing streamline springs from the trailing edge at a large angle to the two surfaces. This might result in a decelerating flow on one surface and so in the formation of a bubble as shown in Fig. V. 1 (*b*). But again the flow near the dividing stream-line is difficult to visualize and one cannot readily cite any example of this type of flow occurring in practice.

The difficulties suggested by these two configurations might be avoided by postulating the flow sketched in Fig. V. 1 (*c*) which has the added merit of representing what often appears to happen in practice. We interpret this figure in the following terms:

'*The extended Kutta–Joukowski hypothesis.* The rear dividing stream-line leaves the aerofoil at the trailing edge. Its tangent at the trailing edge, in general, passes through the interior of the aerofoil.'

The first part of this, when applied to the first inviscid approxima-tion, is precisely what is generally known as the Kutta–Joukowski hypothesis. The whole is an extension of this hypothesis to viscous flow. We defer detailed experimental support for it until opportunities arise. Interpretations of, and deductions from it will constantly be made in Sections 3–11, and it will also be shown to be consistent with the alternative physical hypotheses mentioned in the previous section.

It should be emphasized that the hypothesis is only strictly applicable to unseparated flow. The calculation of lift and drag in well-separated flow is considered briefly in Sections 12 and 13.

3. Drag. The first approximation

If experimental results are being used to help the calculation of the first inviscid approximation, then the circulation may be given the value $\frac{1}{2}cU_\infty C_L$ which follows from equations (I. 19) and (I. 72); much of the analysis of Sections IV. 4–22 is, in fact, arranged in such a way that an observed value of C_L may be inserted. If, on the other hand, we are required to predict entirely theoretically the forces on a given aerofoil at a given incidence, we may determine the circulation, for the first inviscid approximation, by the extended Kutta–Joukowski hypothesis which reduces for this case to the condition that the velocity is finite at the trailing edge. In either event, for the purpose of calculat-ing the drag, it is now assumed that the first approximation to the inviscid flow is known.

The drag could then be calculated by the integration of the stresses at the aerofoil surface. The shear stresses are calculable from equations (II. 74, 73, and 51), and from them the total skin-friction drag also. The form drag is zero according to the approximation so far, but once the boundary layer has been calculated, an allowance could be made by equation (19) for the variation of pressure through it; thus a revised pressure distribution may be calculated, leading to a second approxima-tion for the form drag. But these two calculations are most tedious to perform and a better procedure is based on the fact that skin friction and form drag are together manifested finally by a loss of momentum at infinity downstream.

Suppose the uniform flow upstream is $(U_\infty, 0, 0)$ while far downstream at, say, $x = X$, the velocity field is (u, v, w). Then the mass per unit span which passes per unit time through an element dz of the plane $x = X$ is $\rho u\, dz$ and its loss of momentum in the x-direction during its passage from far upstream is $\rho u\, dz(U_\infty - u)$. If the pressure is assumed to be constant on $x = X$ and equal to its value far upstream, the total drag force on the body equals the total loss of momentum in the x-direction of the fluid; thus the drag force per unit span of the aerofoil is

$$D = \lim_{x \to \infty} \int_{-\infty}^{\infty} \rho u (U_\infty - u)\, dz. \tag{1}$$

The drag coefficient is therefore

$$C_D = 2\delta_{2\infty}/c, \tag{2}$$

where $\delta_{2\infty}$ is the momentum thickness of the wake at infinity and c the chord of the aerofoil.

This derivation of equation (2) is by no means rigorous. It has violated the rule that an equation of momentum must be applied to a closed surface and it has ignored pressure variations; it has also glossed over the fact that the velocity, u, far downstream is indistinguishable from U_∞. But the result is nevertheless correct, as is shown by the more accurate treatments of G. I. Taylor (1925) and B. M. Jones (1936). Fage (1938) has shown the importance of taking the pressure variations into account when the technique of the wake traverse is used experimentally to determine drag.

To calculate $\delta_{2\infty}$ in terms of values on the aerofoil, we write the momentum equation (II. 1) as

$$d \log \delta_2 / dx + (H+2)(d \log U / dx) = 0, \tag{3}$$

τ_w having been omitted since there is no external stress in the wake. It is recalled, here, that terms involving turbulent fluctuations have been neglected. This equation may be integrated from the trailing edge, denoted by the suffix T, to infinity downstream in the form

$$\delta_{2\infty} = \delta_{2T}(U_T/U_\infty)^{H+2} \exp\left[\int_{H_T}^{H_\infty} \log(U/U_\infty)\, dH\right], \tag{4}$$

which would be convenient if experiments had yielded the functional relationship between U and H. Squire and Young (1938) deduced a value for the integral from some limited experimental data, but the same value is obtained by taking H, in equation (3), as the mean of its values at the trailing edge and infinity. Thus, if

$$H \simeq \tfrac{1}{2}(H_T + H_\infty), \tag{5}$$

equation (3) is integrable as

$$\delta_{2\infty} = \delta_{2T}(U_T/U_\infty)^{\frac{1}{2}(H_T+H_\infty+4)}. \tag{6}$$

Now it may be shown that integrals of the form $\int_{-\infty}^{\infty}(1-t)\,dz$ and $\int_{-\infty}^{\infty}t(1-t)\,dz$ tend to a common limit as $t \to 1$ uniformly over the range $-\infty < z < \infty$. Thus $\delta_1 \to \delta_2$ as $x \to \infty$ and so $H_\infty = 1$. Putting this value into (6) and substituting into (2), we have finally

$$C_D = 2(\delta_{2T}/c)(U_T/U_\infty)^{\frac{1}{2}(H_T+5)}. \tag{7}$$

This formula, the first approximation to the drag, is almost invariably used for numerical calculations.

Any improvement on this formula, which might be made by some relation other than (5), would be counterbalanced by the inaccuracy in the determination of δ_{2T} and H_T. Indeed, it appears at first sight that the accuracy of C_D in (7) would depend critically on the accuracy of the values of δ_{2T} and U_T; but it happens that changes in these two quantities are related in such a fashion that C_D is relatively insensitive to them. From equation (II. 74), it follows that $(\delta_{2T})^{6/5}(U_T)^{21/5}$ is proportional to the integral of U^4 over the aerofoil surface and so is insensitive to local inaccuracies in U near the trailing edge. Thus $\delta_{2T}(U_T)^{7/2}$ is insensitive to changes in U_T and this is precisely the combination of δ_{2T} and U_T which occurs in equation (7) if $H_T = 2$. The latter is a very plausible value for those cases in which the turbulent layer is approaching separation. The final result is not really surprising since uncertainties in local values of U could not be expected to affect seriously the overall changes of momentum.

In a similar way it may be argued that C_D does not depend critically on the value of H_T and a very simple formula for C_D may be obtained by putting $H_T = 2$ as a universal approximation. The error so introduced is, to the first order in $[1-(U_T/U_\infty)]$, $50(H_T-2)[1-(U_T/U_\infty)]$ per cent, which is negligible for practical purposes. Equation (7) may then be written as

$$C_D = 2 \sum [(\delta_{2T}/c)^{6/5}(U_T/U_\infty)^{21/5}]^{5/6}, \tag{8}$$

where the summation refers to the upper and lower surfaces of the aerofoil. Now the term in square brackets follows at once from equation (II. 74) with $x = x_T$, and so we obtain

$$C_D = 2R^{-\frac{1}{5}} \sum \left[\left(\frac{\delta_{2t}}{c}\right)^{\frac{6}{5}}\left(\frac{U_t}{U_\infty}\right)^{\frac{21}{5}}R^{\frac{1}{5}} + 0\cdot0106 \int_{x_t/c}^{1}\left(\frac{U}{U_\infty}\right)^4 d\left(\frac{x}{c}\right)\right]^{\frac{5}{6}}.$$

Here R is the Reynolds number for the whole aerofoil and equals $U_\infty c/\nu$; the lower limit in the integral is taken, for each surface, at the transition point denoted by the suffix t. The term involving δ_{2t} may be calculated by using the formula (II. 8) for the laminar region, and so finally we may write in terms of $U(x)$ of the first inviscid approximation:

$$C_D = \sum \left[\frac{1 \cdot 422}{R^{\frac{1}{2}}} \left\{ \frac{U_t}{U_\infty} \int_0^{x_t/c} \left(\frac{U}{U_\infty} \right)^5 d\left(\frac{x}{c} \right) \right\}^{\frac{3}{5}} + \frac{0 \cdot 02429}{R^{\frac{1}{5}}} \int_{x_t/c}^1 \left(\frac{U}{U_\infty} \right)^4 d\left(\frac{x}{c} \right) \right]^{\frac{5}{6}}. \quad (9)$$

The form of this equation is very convenient for investigating scale effect and the effect of transition on a given aerofoil. Numerical results are compared with experiment in Table V. 1 and with the results of the two earlier methods to be described in Section 4. The experimental data were obtained by Doenhoff (1940) and refer to an NACA 0012 aerofoil.

TABLE V. 1

A comparison of some calculated and experimental values of the drag coefficient of an NACA 0012 aerofoil

	C_D			
$R \times 10^{-6}$	Experiment. Doenhoff (1940)	Equation (9)	Squire and Young (1938)	Tetervin (1944)
2·68	0·0071	0·0067	0·0074	0·0069
3·78	0·0070	0·0068	0·0072	0·0070
5·35	0·0068	0·0068	0·0071	0·0070
7·56	0·0067	0·0067	0·0071	0·0069

The formula tends to be insensitive to small errors in the value of the circulation assumed for the first approximation to the inviscid flow; a change in circulation alters the velocity distribution by amounts of opposite sign on the two surfaces of the aerofoil. Thus an increased contribution from the upper surface is offset to some extent by a decreased contribution from the lower surface: the effect is not, of course, strictly of the second order.

It has been mentioned already that the first approximation to the boundary layer could be used to predict the skin-friction drag or C_f. The form drag would then be $(C_D - C_f)$; however, no great reliance can be placed on this value since C_D and C_f are close in value and the errors inherent in their separate calculations may well be of the same order as $(C_D - C_f)$, especially for thin aerofoils. Fig. V. 2 illustrates the relative

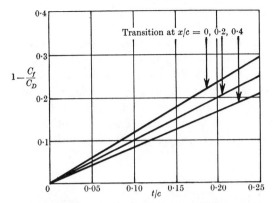

FIG. V. 2. A typical variation of form drag with thickness-chord ratio and transition point for an aerofoil of conventional shape.

magnitudes of the skin-friction and form drags for a typical NACA aerofoil, as calculated by Squire and Young (1938).

It is interesting to note the accuracy of equation (9) in the special case of the flat plate for which $U = U_t = U_\infty = $ constant. For fully turbulent flow $x_t/c = 0$, while for wholly laminar flow $x_t/c = 1$. Thus we find that, for a single surface,

$$\left.\begin{array}{ll} \text{for laminar flow:} & C_D = 1 \cdot 34 R^{-\frac{1}{2}} \\ \text{for turbulent flow:} & C_D = 0 \cdot 0452 R^{-\frac{1}{5}} \end{array}\right\}. \tag{10}$$

The first result is close to Blasius's value $C_D = 1 \cdot 33 R^{-\frac{1}{2}}$ while the second compares favourably with the value $C_D = 0 \cdot 0450 R^{-\frac{1}{5}}$, given in Table II. 4 for $n = \frac{1}{5}$.

The effect of the position of transition on the drag of an aerofoil is illustrated in Fig. V. 4, the curves referring to a flat plate and calculated from equation (9): the practical importance of delaying transition to a position as far downstream as possible is clear from this figure, and the next chapter discusses some of the techniques used in achieving laminar flow.

Finally, it is of some importance to inquire at what stage the Kutta–Joukowski hypothesis entered into this analysis of drag. Now in the equation of momentum, the term representing the streamwise pressure gradient is $U \, dU/dx$; this is a direct consequence of the assumption that the pressure may be taken to be constant across the boundary layer or wake: when applied to the wake it implies that the velocity takes the same value on opposite sides of the wake right up to the trailing edge.

That is the point at which the extended Kutta–Joukowski hypothesis is invoked.

This interpretation of the hypothesis in terms of the velocities at the edges of the boundary layer is supported reasonably well by experiment. Fig. V. 3 shows the ratio of U_U to U_L, the velocity at the edges of the upper and lower boundary layers at the trailing edge, in a number of different cases; the significance of the departure of this ratio from unity is difficult to assess and it will be necessary to return to this point in Section 8 since it is a crucial factor in the calculation of lift.

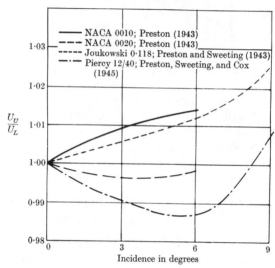

Fig. V. 3. The ratio of the velocities just outside the boundary layer at the trailing edge, for various aerofoils.

4. Drag. Other methods for the first approximation

Although the formula (9) for C_D is the latest synthesis of existing knowledge for the calculation of drag, it has not yet been extensively tested by comparison with experiment. Some earlier methods, which have been widely used over the past years, will be described briefly.

A reference has already been made to the work of Squire and Young (1938) whose method was based entirely on experimental results from flat plates. They used the variable ζ, defined by

$$\zeta^2 = \tfrac{1}{2}c_f, \tag{11}$$

which is the reciprocal of the variable ζ of equation (II. 28). With the relation

$$U\delta_2/\nu = 0 \cdot 2454 \exp(0 \cdot 3914\zeta) \tag{12}$$

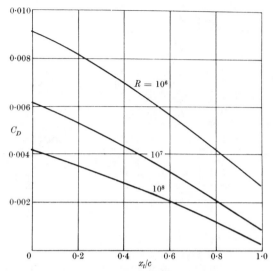

FIG. V. 4. The variation of the drag of a flat plate with the position of the transition point, for various Reynolds numbers.

which is equivalent to equation (II. 39), the momentum equation becomes

$$d\zeta/dx + 6 \cdot 13(d \log U/dx) = 10 \cdot 411(U/\nu\zeta^2)\exp(-0 \cdot 3914\zeta). \qquad (13)$$

With an assumed transition point, the laminar layer may be calculated, as in the previous section, by equation (II. 8); thus the initial values of δ_2 and, from (12), ζ for the turbulent layer are known. Equation (13) is then solved by a step-by-step process to give ζ and hence δ_2 at the trailing edge. C_D follows from (7). Extensive calculations, based on these equations, were collated as charts, of which three are given in Fig. V. 5. These are interesting in showing the typical trends of C_D for aerofoils whose maximum thickness occurs between 20 per cent and 35 per cent of the chord from the leading edge; for more modern types of low-drag aerofoil, for which the maximum thickness occurs nearer the mid-chord position, the flat-plate data on which the charts were based cannot describe accurately the turbulent flow in the pressure gradient towards the trailing edge. Numerical results for a particular aerofoil were given in Table V. 1. Lock (1946) produced revised charts for such aerofoils but a method which has been in common use since about that time is due to Tetervin (1944).

He assumed the power law

$$c_f = 2C(U\delta_2/\nu)^{-n} \qquad (14)$$

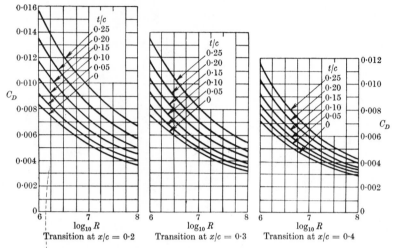

FIG. V. 5. The calculated variation of drag with Reynolds number, thickness-chord ratio, and transition point, for the NACA 24 series of aerofoils.

between c_f and R_{δ_2} as in equation (II. 40) and took a constant value for H. Under these circumstances, the momentum equation may be integrated to give δ_2 explicitly. The final formula obtained for the drag coefficient is

$$C_D = 2\left(\frac{U_\infty}{U_T}\right)^{\frac{1}{2}(H-1)}$$

$$\times \sum \left[\left\{\frac{\delta_{2t}}{c}\left(\frac{U_t}{U_\infty}\right)^{H+2}\right\}^{n+1} + \frac{C(n+1)}{R^n}\int_{x_t/c}^{1}\left(\frac{U}{U_\infty}\right)^{(H+2)(n+1)-n}d\left(\frac{x}{c}\right)\right]^{1/(n+1)}, \quad (15)$$

where again suffix t refers to transition. Typical values for $2C$ and n are given in Table II. 4 while Tetervin was prepared to take values

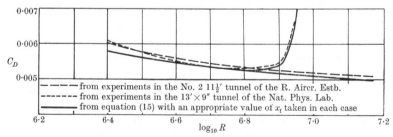

FIG. V. 6. Scale effect on the drag coefficient of the Boulton–Paul low-drag wing NACA 653–018, as given by theory and experiment.

of H between 1·4 and 1·6 according to the thickness of the aerofoil. This formula was the first of a line of which the latest has been given in equation (9). A comparison of equation (15) with some tests on an 18 per cent thick low-drag wing by Preston, Gregory, and Kimber (1946) is shown in Fig. V. 6. Further comparisons between theory and experiment have been given by Tetervin (1944) and were incorporated in Table V. 1.

5. The second inviscid approximation for symmetrical aerofoils at zero lift. Displacement flux method

To start on the iterative process of the calculation of viscous flow past an aerofoil, it is usual to displace the surface outwards by the amount of the displacement thickness, δ_1, at each point, as was suggested in Section III. 7. This procedure is based on the definition of δ_1 given in equation (I. 36) for which it was assumed that, in the hypothetical absence of the boundary layer, the velocity could be regarded as constant throughout the region of the boundary layer. The accuracy of this assumption depends mainly on the curvature of the surface; in a region of large curvature even the velocity of the potential-flow field may change rapidly near the surface. To generalize the conception of displacement thickness, a displacement flux, ψ^*, is defined by

$$\psi^* = \int_0^\delta (U-u)\, dn, \tag{16}$$

n being distance measured along the outward normal to the surface, and U and u being the velocity components parallel to the surface in the first approximation to the inviscid and boundary-layer flows respectively. When the Reynolds number is large, and so δ small, it is usual to approximate ψ^* by $U\delta_1$, U now being the velocity on the surface according to the first inviscid approximation. We may then equate the effect of the boundary layer on the inviscid flow to that of a source distribution of strength $d\psi^*/ds$ per unit length of surface.

This approach was given first by Preston (1945) who also discussed other methods of allowing for the boundary layer. His method was to transform the aerofoil into a flat plate. If (ξ, η) are the coordinates in the new plane, the velocity component in the ξ-direction, v_ξ, is given by

$$\frac{v_\xi}{U_\infty} = 1 + \frac{1}{\pi U_\infty} \int_0^\infty \frac{d\psi^*(\xi')}{d\xi'} \frac{\xi-\xi'}{(\xi-\xi')^2+\eta^2}\, d\xi'. \tag{17}$$

A form more convenient for numerical calculations is obtained by an integration by parts: thus

$$\frac{v_\xi}{U_\infty} = 1 - \frac{1}{\pi} \int_0^\infty \frac{\psi^*(\xi')}{U(\xi')} \frac{U(\xi')}{U_\infty} \frac{(\xi-\xi')^2 - \eta^2}{[(\xi-\xi')^2+\eta^2]^2} \, d\xi'. \tag{18}$$

For most purposes, and certainly in the case of a purely theoretical prediction, the factor (ψ^*/U) would be taken equal to δ_1.

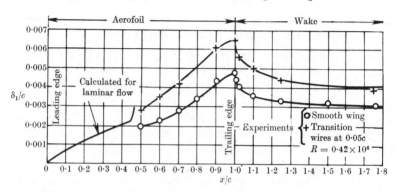

FIG. V. 7. The variation of displacement thickness with distance along the chord of a Joukowski aerofoil at zero lift.

The ease with which the velocity field induced by the displacement flux is written in the form (17) depends on the flow being symmetrical, the outward flux on the upper surface combining with the equal flux on the lower surface to produce a source distribution of ψ^* along $\xi = 0$.

The experimental distribution of δ_1 on the symmetrical Joukowski aerofoil investigated by Preston is shown in Fig. V. 7. This distribution was used in the calculations of the velocity distribution, shown in Fig. V. 8. Curve (a) shows the velocity distribution at the surface for the first inviscid approximation. Curve (b) is the velocity, according to the first inviscid approximation, calculated at the edge of the measured boundary layer. Curve (c) is the velocity given by the second inviscid approximation, again calculated at the edge of the measured boundary layer, with which may be compared the experimental value given in curve (d). These results may be regarded as highly satisfactory; the discrepancies in the wake were traced at the time of the experiment to the interaction of the boundary layers on the aerofoil and the walls of the wind tunnel. Similar but more recent experiments on a typical modern aerofoil section have been made by Brebner and Bagley (1952).

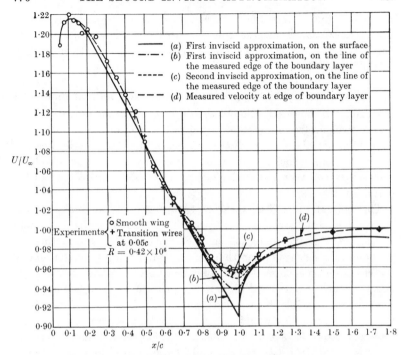

Fig. V. 8. A comparison of computed and observed velocities at the edge
of the boundary layer, for a Joukowski aerofoil at zero lift.

6. The second inviscid approximation for symmetrical aerofoils at zero lift. Other methods

Preston (1945) has also given two methods of allowing for the boundary layer based on the idea of calculating the induced velocity of the vorticity in the boundary layer. The more complicated method makes no approximation to the distribution of vorticity and is correspondingly difficult to calculate. Alternatively the total vorticity in the boundary layer which, according to the boundary-layer approximation of equation (I. 35), equals $\int_{0}^{\delta} (\partial u/\partial z)\, dz = U$, is concentrated at its centre of weight in a vortex sheet; this position is easily shown to be at a distance δ_1 from the surface.

The three methods so far given—the displacement flux, the vorticity field, and the vortex sheet methods—have been used to calculate the velocity at the trailing edge of the symmetrical Joukowski aerofoil previously mentioned; expressed as a ratio of the free-stream velocity, the values found were 1·0093, 1·0088, and 1·0105 respectively. From the practical standpoint, the differences between these results are very small, and as it is much the simplest to compute, the displacement flux method is preferable.

7. The second inviscid approximation for aerofoils at incidence

In general, the distribution of the displacement thickness will differ on the two surfaces of an aerofoil and so its effect on the inviscid flow cannot be calculated as easily as in Section 5. This complicates the analysis of the velocity induced by the source distribution $d\psi*/ds$ to such an extent that the reader is referred to the original papers for details of it.

The method adopted by Preston (1949) regarded $d\psi*/ds$ as the sum of even and odd distribution: the even distribution included the whole of the effect of the wake and may be calculated by the method of Section 5 on the assumption that the wake lies along the extension of the chord. This is equivalent to assuming that the wake has an equal effect on each surface, and to be more accurate it would be necessary to assume a plausible shape for the centre line of the wake along which the source distribution would be placed. The odd distribution of $d\psi*/ds$ arises from the effects of both camber and incidence, and the assumption was made that the two effects could be separated and recombined linearly. This method, in its essentials, does not involve a recalculation of the circulation or lift; it is primarily designed to enable the influence of the boundary layer on the external inviscid flow to be calculated.

A preferable procedure of calculation is given by Spence (1954) who avoids the splitting of the displacement source distribution but simplifies the analysis by other approximations. If the incidence is small, simple results are obtained. There is little doubt that for most practical purposes the second approximation, calculated by this method, gives results which need not be improved. Unlike the earlier method just described, Spence's considers the change of circulation involved in the second stage of the iteration. This involves further consideration of the Kutta–Joukowski condition and Sections 9 and 10 are devoted to this.

8. Drag. The second approximation

A revised value of the drag may now be calculated by inserting in equation (9) the value of $U(x)$ obtained from the second inviscid approximation. The difference between the values of the drag as given by the first and second approximations is likely to be very small if we may judge from Fig. V. 8. This shows, admittedly in a particular case, that differences between the first and second approximations for $U(x)$ are likely to be significant only in the region of the trailing edge.

In calculating the second approximation to the pressures on the aerofoil surface, the boundary-layer approximation

$$\kappa \rho u^2 = -\partial p/\partial n \qquad (19)$$

should be used wherever the curvature, κ, of the streamlines is appreciable. A simple technique for this calculation has been given by Spence (1954) and normally it would only be necessary in the region of the trailing edge. The fact that the pressure fails to reach its stagnation value at a trailing edge of non-zero angle may be attributed to this effect and not, as is sometimes supposed, to a local separation.

It is clear that a cusped trailing edge will, in general, result in a lower form drag than a wedge-shaped trailing edge; not only are the pressures on the surface closer to the inviscid-flow values, owing to the streamlines being less curved, but the drag components of surface pressures are smaller owing to the cusped shape. These considerations, however, do not suggest that a cusped trailing edge has necessarily an advantage from the point of view of drag, since the cusped shape may have the counterbalancing effect of increasing the skin-friction drag.

9. The calculation of lift and its relationship with circulation

One possible expression for the lift on an aerofoil would involve the integration of the appropriate components of the pressure and shear forces on the surface. But while in the calculation of drag it is best to consider the integral of momentum at infinity, so in the case of lift it is better to consider the circulation in a large circuit enclosing the aerofoil.

For the first inviscid approximation, we have the familiar equation

$$L = \rho U_\infty \Gamma, \qquad (20)$$

Γ being, of course, the circulation round any circuit enclosing the aerofoil. The same equation holds for the higher inviscid approximations: once the inviscid flow is known, it may be expressed in the form of equation (I. 66) from which follows Γ, as the coefficient of $(i/2\pi_3)$.

Thus at each stage of the inviscid approximations we need a criterion for Γ, and the formulation of this on the basis of the extended Kutta–Joukowski hypothesis is the underlying topic of Sections 10, 11, and 13.

Meanwhile, it is interesting to consider the successive viscous approximations and the extent to which equation (20) has to be modified in the case of viscous flow. Now in this connexion the important feature of viscous flow is that the circulation varies from one closed circuit to another. Thus equation (20) is itself meaningless unless accompanied by the specification of the circuit for which Γ is measured. Two main questions pose themselves, the second as a consequence of the first.

First then, for what class of circuits is equation (20) true for viscous flow? The answer to this has been given by Temple (1943) generally for compressible flow and we now summarize his analysis for an incompressible fluid. The z-equation of motion for an element of fluid may be written

$$\frac{\partial}{\partial x}(\rho uw - p_{zx}) + \frac{\partial}{\partial z}(\rho w^2 - p_{zz}) = 0, \tag{21}$$

the stress components being given in equation (I. 7). By integrating this over the whole region of fluid between the aerofoil and a circuit C enclosing it, and applying Green's theorem, we may obtain

$$L = \int_C [\rho uw\, dz - \rho w^2\, dx - p\, dx - \mu\eta\, dz], \tag{22}$$

which is exact. η is the vorticity. To progress, a linearization is made in the quantities $(U_\infty - u)$, w, and $(p_\infty - p)$ which are taken as $O(1/r)$ on C, now regarded therefore as a circuit far from the aerofoil. As a result (22) may be written as

$$L = \rho U_\infty \Gamma - \int_W (H - H_\infty)\, dx, \tag{23}$$

the integral referring to that part of C lying within the wake. If C is such that $dx \equiv 0$ in equation (23), then the classical equation (20) is obtained. Thus the first question is answered: for circuits which cut the wake at large distances from the aerofoil and perpendicularly to the stream direction—such as C in Fig. V. 9—the circulation is such that $L = \rho U_\infty \Gamma$.

This immediately raises the second question, which concerns the importance of the proviso that C should be far from the aerofoil. More definitely, we ask what would the error be in equation (20) if the circuit D, as shown in Fig. V. 9, were chosen instead of C. The following analysis is due to Spence and Beasley (1958) who based it on the work of Preston (1954c) concerning jets. Let Γ_W be the circulation in the circuit $U U_\infty L_\infty L U$ enclosing the wake; then

$$\Gamma_C = \Gamma_D + \Gamma_W, \tag{24}$$

and we define $C_{LW} = \rho U_\infty \Gamma_W / \frac{1}{2}\rho U_\infty^2 c$ as the error in the lift coefficient if the lift is computed as $\rho U_\infty \Gamma_D$ and not as $\rho U_\infty \Gamma_C$. Now Γ_W may be estimated as follows. Each element of the wake is supposed to consist of concentric circular-arc streamlines as indicated in Fig. V. 10. The

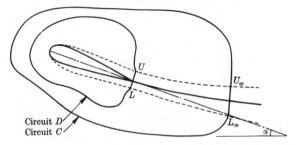

FIG. V. 9. A sketch illustrating the notation used in considering circuits for measuring the circulation about an aerofoil.

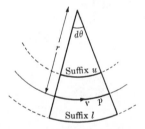

FIG. V. 10. The notation for the analysis of an element of wake.

pressure gradient in the radial direction is $\partial p/\partial r = \rho v^2/r$; integration of this together with the fact that the total pressure is the same on either side of the element of wake gives

$$(v_u^2 - v_l^2)(r_u + r_l) = \int_{r_u}^{r_l} v^2 \, dr. \qquad (25)$$

The circulation $d\Gamma_W$ about the element is given by $d\Gamma_W = (v_u r_u - v_l r_l) \, d\theta$ and it is found that this may be written with the help of (25) as

$$d\Gamma_W = \tfrac{1}{2}(\delta_1 + \delta_2)(v_u + v_l) \, d\theta. \qquad (26)$$

We proceed by further approximations. First, it was shown in Section 3 that $\delta_1 \to \delta_2$ as $x \to \infty$; so $\delta_1 + \delta_2 \simeq 2\delta_{2\infty}$. Also $v_u + v_l \simeq 2U_\infty$, and

$C_D = 2\delta_{2\infty}/c$ from equation (2). Thus equation (26) may be written

$$d\Gamma_W = U_\infty c \, C_D \, d\theta. \tag{27}$$

If we now interpret the extended Kutta–Joukowski hypothesis to mean that the dividing streamline turns through an angle approximately equal to the incidence, α, of the aerofoil, we have finally

$$C_{LW} = \rho U_\infty \Gamma_W / \tfrac{1}{2}\rho U_\infty^2 \, c \simeq 2C_D \alpha \simeq (C_D/\pi)C_L. \tag{28}$$

Thus for a normal aerofoil at low incidence for which C_D is of the order of 0·01, the error involved in calculating the circulation and hence the lift by a circuit such as D is, for all practical purposes, negligible.

This is, of course, a crude estimation. Improvements on it have been suggested by Spence and Beasley (1958) following a different line of attack. They argue that the flow past the aerofoil induced by the vorticity in the wake involves a circulation about the aerofoil; in an inviscid approximation, this vorticity is analogous to the jet stream from a jet-flapped aerofoil, the analysis for which is briefly described in Section XII. 3. The factor C_D/π in equation (28) should therefore be replaced by a non-linear variation, a suggested value for which is $0·214(C_D)^{\frac{1}{2}}$.

10. Lift. The first approximation

The first inviscid approximation together with the Kutta–Joukowski hypothesis gives, for the lift coefficient,

$$C_L = 2\pi(1+t/c)\sin(\alpha+\beta). \tag{29}$$

Here $\alpha = -\beta$ is the no-lift angle of incidence and t/c is the thickness-chord ratio. This is an approximate version of the exact relation given in equation (IV. 68) while for an ellipse it is, from (IV. 13), exact.

This formula almost invariably overestimates the lift, the error for unseparated flow usually lying between 10 and 15 per cent. That the lift should be less rather than more than this value given by the first inviscid approximation can be explained by remarking that the boundary layer on the upper, lifting, surface of an aerofoil is thicker than that on the lower; as a result the effective incidence is slightly reduced, or alternatively the effective camber is modified. Stüper (1933) seems to have been the first to consider the problem on these latter lines, but his and later calculations, as typified by column (a) of Table V. 2 in Section 11, show that this simple model of the flow is not adequate for accurate predictions.

A purely empirical correction may be made to equation (29) by inserting on the right-hand side a factor between, say, 0·85 and 0·90;

it is, however, difficult to formulate any general rules for determining this factor in each particular case. A more thorough approach therefore needs to be made.

11. Lift. The second approximation in unseparated flow

Although for the purpose of numerical calculation the distinction is not made, it is useful to consider in turn cusped and wedge-shaped trailing edges, since they emphasize the basic method and a refinement of it.

For a cusped trailing edge the interpretation of the extended Kutta–Joukowski hypothesis is that the streamlines near the trailing edge remain parallel to it. Consequently the pressure may be taken to be constant across the wake at the trailing edge. From this it follows at once that the speed at the edge of the boundary layer at the trailing edge is the same on the two surfaces: in the notation of Section 3, or of Fig. V. 1 (c),

$$U_U = U_L. \tag{30}$$

This condition, it will be recalled, has already been used in the calculation of drag. It now refers to the velocity field of the second inviscid approximation, in which therefore the circulation about the aerofoil is chosen to satisfy the condition.

Now we have already seen, in Fig. V. 3, that experimental values of U_U and U_L satisfy equation (30) only approximately; this implies that there is, usually, a pressure difference across the wake at the trailing edge. This is particularly evident for a wedge-shaped trailing edge, for which the curvature of the streamlines should, if possible, be taken into account. If an estimate of the curvature is made, partly from the aerofoil geometry and partly from the first boundary-layer approximation, the pressure difference $(p_U - p_L)$ can be calculated from equation (19) by an integration along the curve UTL in Fig. V. 1 (c) which is normal to the streamlines. From this a value of $(U_U^2 - U_L^2)$ is obtained and this again is used as the condition to determine the circulation, and hence the lift, in the second inviscid approximation. The suffixes, U and L, here denote the end points of the line in the boundary layer through the trailing edge normal to the streamlines.

In an attempt to justify the importance we are placing on the two values U_U and U_L in the second inviscid approximation, experimental values could be adopted for a calculation, in place of the equality of (30) or of the value of $(U_U^2 - U_L^2)$ of the preceding paragraph. When this is attempted it is in fact found most convenient to work in terms of the ratio U_U/U_L.

These procedures were first suggested and carried out by Preston (1949). Spence (1954) developed the analysis to give an equation for the second approximation to C_L, an improved version of which is

$$\tfrac{1}{2}[1-C_{L1}/C_{L2}](\lambda_U^{-1}+\lambda_L^{-1})\alpha = [\lambda_U/\lambda_L]^{\tau/\pi}-1+\tfrac{1}{2}\alpha(\lambda_U+\lambda_L)+(\Delta u_U-\Delta u_L)$$

(31)

in which C_{L1}, C_{L2} are the values of C_L according to the first and second approximations respectively, τ is the angle of the trailing edge,

$$\lambda = [2-1\cdot3t/c]^{\frac{1}{4}}[\delta_1(H+1)/(H-1)]^{1/(2-\tau/\pi)},$$

and Δu is the increment in the velocity at the edge of the boundary layer due to the source distribution $d\psi^*/ds$. The values of λ and Δu have to be calculated, of course, using a definite value of C_{L2}; thus equation (31) is an implicit equation for C_{L2} and can only be solved by an iteration, full details of which may be found in the original paper.

A summary of some typical results is given in Table V. 2. The tabulated values refer to C_{L2}/C_{L1}, C_{L1} being the Kutta–Joukowski value of the first inviscid approximation. Column (a) gives the result of a simplified method, rather similar to that of Stüper (1933) which has already been quoted, or to that of Pinkerton (1936). Column (b) is the result of applying equation (30) to the second inviscid approximation, while for column (c), the experimental values of U_U/U_L were used in the calculations.

TABLE V. 2

Experimental and theoretical values of C_{L2}/C_{L1}, for two aerofoils each at 6° incidence and Reynolds number $4\cdot2\times10^5$

| | Analytical methods | | | |
Type of symmetrical aerofoil	(a) Camber modification	(b) Equation (30)	(c) Experimental U_U/U_L	Experiment
Joukowski ($t/c = 0\cdot118$)	0·931	0·876	0·900	0·882
Piercy 1240 (with transition wires)	0·759	0·725	0·725	0·695

The results based on equation (30) are very satisfactory, especially in view of the very different character of the trailing edges of the two aerofoils. The Joukowski aerofoil is cusped whereas the Piercy aerofoil has a wedge-shaped trailing edge of total angle 22·15°. The results for the Piercy aerofoil might therefore be improved by taking into account the pressure variation at the trailing edge; the calculations for this, however, have not been done. It is surprising that the experimental values of U_U/U_L do not lead to the best of the predicted values of C_L, and the reason for this is not clear.

In the same paper, Spence has given the results of comprehensive calculations of lift, pressure distribution, pitching moment, and hinge moment for the Joukowski aerofoil of Table V. 2 over a range of Reynolds numbers between about 5×10^5 and 10^8. Only one value, 6°,

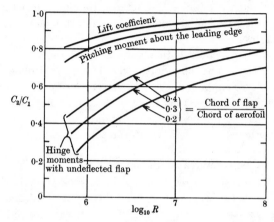

FIG. V. 11. Scale effect on lift and moments for a symmetrical Joukowski aerofoil at 6° incidence, as calculated by Spence (1954).

of the incidence was taken and transition was assumed to occur at the point of least pressure on the upper surface and at 0·4 of the chord on the lower surface. The results are shown in Fig. V. 11, C_2 being the coefficient appropriate to each curve and C_1 being the Kutta–Joukowski value in the first inviscid approximation. The curves for C_L and C_m no doubt represent reliable values. The hinge moments, however, may not be so accurately predicted although these calculations are notable in that they are the first to consider, on a sound basis, hinge moments in viscous flow. The comprehensive and systematic investigations of the characteristics of aerofoil sections which were conducted by Bryant, Halliday, and Batson (1950) are of great practical interest; among many other things, they revealed that if the chord of the flap is of the order of one-fifth of the chord of the aerofoil it is possible for the hinge moment to take values greater than those given by the first inviscid approximation, even if the lift of the whole aerofoil is only, say, four-fifths of its value according to the same approximation. This is a phenomenon which has so far resisted quantitative explanation, but it is probably due to the inadequacies of the assumptions relating to the curvature of the streamlines downstream of the trailing edge, and to the vorticity in the wake as discussed in Section 9.

For most practical purposes, therefore, the problem of calculating the lift and drag of a two-dimensional aerofoil in unseparated flow has been solved. But it is clear that we have by no means uncovered all the hidden mechanisms which determine the flow. In particular, the uncertainties about the detailed character of the flow affect the accuracy of predicted values of hinge and pitching moments more than those of the lift and drag.

So long as we are forced to maintain the distinction between the regions of inviscid and boundary-layer flow, it is probable that the methods we have explained will hold sway. Future developments will almost certainly be concerned more with eliminating this distinction, than with formulating conditions more precise than the Kutta–Joukowski hypothesis or its various interpretations.

12. Drag in well-separated flow

None of the methods or results of the preceding sections is immediately applicable to well-separated flow. The theoretical models of such flow have been discussed in Section III. 9 and it was stressed there that there are no known theoretical methods for predicting the pressure in the wake of a well-separated flow. In other words, the drag of a bluff body cannot be predicted, unless the pressure distribution over its rear part is estimated by some empirical means, or is known from experimental measurements. In the latter case, a theoretical model could be proposed which would yield reasonably good quantitative results for the drag; such a calculation would need, of course, to incorporate a value of the lift and this is discussed in the next section.

It is worth recalling in this context an investigation by Kármán which followed his proposal of a vortex street and which has been described by H. Glauert (1926). The vortex street was shown to involve a drag on the body (with which Glauert identified the form drag). Good agreement with experiment was claimed; it is surprising that the general idea has not been followed up in subsequent years, though it would be limited to the relatively small range of Reynolds number in which a well-formed vortex street appears.

13. Lift in well-separated flow

We consider the flow sketched in Fig. V. 12 and refer to equation (I. 55) which relates the rate of change of circulation round any curve, say AB, to the change of total pressure $[H]_A^B$, and to the rates of convection and diffusion of vorticity, η, across AB. We apply this equation to the closed circuit $TS_L LAUS_U T$ in the steady flow of Fig. V. 12 where S_U and S_L are the two separation points and U and L are at the

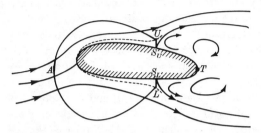

FIG. V. 12. Notation used in the calculation of the lift in well-separated flow.

edges of the boundary layer at those points. Now equation (I. 55) reduces to

$$\int \eta \mathrm{v}_n \, ds - \nu \int (\partial \eta / \partial n) \, ds = 0, \tag{32}$$

the integrals being taken round the closed curve. This equation is further reduced by the following steps:

(i) $\eta \equiv 0$ on LAU in the inviscid region.

(ii) $\mathrm{v}_n \equiv 0$ on $S_U TS_L$ since the aerofoil surface is solid.

(iii) On $S_L L$ and $S_U U$ the second term according to boundary-layer theory equals $\nu \int (\partial^2 u/\partial x \partial z) \, dz$. Using the dimensional arguments of Section I. 11 we find that this term is of order R^{-1} for a laminar layer and so may be ignored. We presume that it is equally valid to ignore it for a turbulent layer.

(iv) On $S_U TS_L$ it is assumed that there is nothing in the nature of a boundary-layer flow, and that therefore $\partial \eta / \partial n$ may be ignored in comparison with its values on $S_L L$ and $S_U U$.

As a result, equation (32) may be written in the form

$$\int_{S_L}^{L} \eta \mathrm{v}_n \, ds = \int_{S_U}^{U} \eta \mathrm{v}_n \, ds. \tag{33}$$

With $\mathrm{v}_n = u$, $\eta = \partial u/\partial z$ and $ds = dz$ according to boundary-layer notation, we find at once that

$$U_U = U_L. \tag{34}$$

It is of great interest that this is of the same form as equation (30) which followed from the extended Kutta–Joukowski hypothesis applied

to unseparated flow. Both results (30) and (34) are embraced by the
single principle (33) which may be expressed by saying that the total
convection of vorticity into the wake, either from the separation points
or from the trailing edge, is zero. This fact has been regarded in the
past by many authors as a self-evident consequence of steady flow. It
is important to realize that this is strictly incorrect—the correct result
follows from equation (I. 55) and equates to zero the sum of the convection and diffusion of vorticity; only in certain special cases is it
permissible to assume that each by itself is approximately zero. It is
important also to recognize that the results (30) and (34) are a consequence only of hypotheses such as (iii) and (iv) above, concerning the
nature of the physical flow; it does not appear to be possible to prove
them as inevitable consequences of the Navier–Stokes equations and
such proofs as have appeared at times are fallacious.

The most important practical application of the theory given here is
to the determination of lift on aerofoils near the stall, for which separation occurs near the leading edge on the upper surface. Theoretical
progress is, however, held up by the difficulty of determining the
pressure distribution to be taken on the streamline representing the
boundary of the wake, in the second inviscid approximation.

Howarth (1935) carried out calculations using the condition (34) for
an elliptic cylinder. These were based not on the second but on the
first inviscid approximation which, for such a well-separated flow, inevitably introduced serious inaccuracies. Piercy, Preston, and Whitehead (1938) considered the same problem more thoroughly and obtained
fair agreement with experiment.

14. Characteristics of flow near the stall

By the stalling characteristics of an aerofoil we mean its behaviour
at or near maximum lift. In this region of C_L there is bound to be
separation of flow from the surface other than near the trailing edge,
and the stall almost always implies, therefore, separation from the front
half of the aerofoil. The state of the boundary layer on the aerofoil
largely determines the stalling characteristics since on it depend the
points of separation and the formation of bubbles. In two-dimensional
flow, it is now thought that a bubble of some sort always results from
separation, with a line of separation on the surface at right angles to the
mainstream. The pressure is roughly constant in the front half of the
bubble and less than that at infinity, and rises towards the rear end
of the bubble. This contrasts with the classical Kirchhoff type of flow,

in which the bubble is of infinite length and width, and at the same static pressure as the mainstream. The position of the separation and the pressure within the bubble are the principal agencies in determining the characteristics of the flow as a whole.

Of the three possibilities mentioned in Section III. 5, two are common: separation of a laminar boundary layer near the nose, and of a turbulent

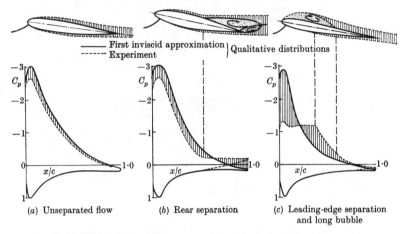

FIG. V. 13. Diagrams illustrating some of the principal effects of the boundary layer on the pressure distribution on aerofoils at incidence.

layer near the trailing edge. The former is usually found on thin aerofoils at incidence, while the latter is perhaps more common for thicker aerofoil sections, say of 12 per cent thickness-chord ratio or more.

The effect of the boundary layer on the pressure distribution round an aerofoil at moderate incidence is sketched in Fig. V. 13 (a). This is the case which can be treated in detail by the methods of the preceding sections. As the lift is increased, the separation point may first appear near the trailing edge and then move forward as the lift increases as a consequence of the increased positive pressure gradients over the rear of the aerofoil. A free boundary or vortex sheet springing from the separation point encloses a bubble of air in which a turbulent circulatory motion is set up by the shear layer along the bubble boundary and by the turbulent mixing at the rear end. An interpretation of the flow pattern in this case, and the effect on the pressure distribution, are illustrated in Fig. V. 13 (b). During each further increment of incidence, ever smaller net amounts of vorticity are cast off into the wake and the lift eventually reaches a maximum value.

The graph of C_L against incidence α normally has a well-rounded peak. This is illustrated in Fig. V. 14 in which curve (a) is for an NACA 63₃–018 aerofoil. This aerofoil is 18 per cent thick and the development of its stall would follow the lines of the preceding paragraph through the stage shown in Fig. V. 13 (b). A maximum value of C_L about 1·4 is typical of such a thick aerofoil.

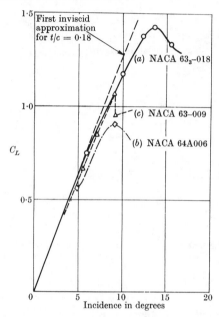

Fig. V. 14. Lift curves illustrating three types of stall.

On thin aerofoils, say those less than 12 per cent thick, an important feature of the flow is the occurrence of separation of the laminar boundary layer near the leading edge as soon as a pronounced minimum of pressure forms there. For moderate incidences, reattachment as a turbulent boundary layer occurs some distance downstream, a bubble thus being formed. Long and short bubbles under these circumstances have already been distinguished in Section III. 5 by the value of R_{δ_2} at separation. It will be recalled that the value of $R_{\delta_2} = 500$ roughly separated the two regimes.

The flow with a long bubble extending from the leading edge is sketched in Fig. V. 13 (c), together with the effect on the pressure distribution. The long bubble is about 2 per cent or 3 per cent of the chord on formation at low incidences but grows rapidly with increasing incidence until the separated layer fails to reattach. In the course of this lengthening of the bubble, the gradient of the lift curve steadily decreases and maximum lift is usually attained when the bubble extends beyond the trailing edge. Under these circumstances the lift curve has a smooth maximum as illustrated by curve (b) in Fig. V. 14. The kink at about 5° incidence is thought to correspond to the change from an initial short bubble to a long bubble.

With short bubbles there is an entirely different train of events. The length of a short bubble is from $\frac{1}{2}$ per cent to 1 per cent of the chord. The bubble causes very little deviation from the pressure distribution given by the first inviscid approximation. As the incidence increases, the pressure decreases in the bubble and this is counteracted by increased curvature which in turn implies a decrease in the size of the bubble. At some critical incidence the short bubble suddenly bursts into a very long one and this is accompanied by a marked loss of lift. The lift curve thus has a sharp maximum as typified in curve (c) of Fig. V. 14 for an NACA 63–009 section. Now the criterion of Owen and Klanfer (1953) does not afford an explanation of this type of stall since it has been found that a short bubble does not always break down into a long one at the same critical value of R_{δ_2} at separation. Crabtree (1957a) has suggested that there is a maximum possible pressure recovery in the turbulent mixing round the edge of the bubble and that the short bubble cannot maintain itself if it is called upon for a greater pressure rise than this. However, Crabtree also shows how Owen and Klanfer's criterion assists an understanding of the differences in behaviour of the two types of bubble and discusses the scale effect on stalling characteristics of aerofoils which experience bubble separations. A valuable review, including a useful bibliography, has been made by Crabtree (1957b). These more recent investigations, however, should not distract attention from one of the earliest and most comprehensive investigations, that of McCullough and Gault (1951) who described most of these effects on the basis of their experimental results.

We are now in a position at least to explain, if not predict, the probable course of events shown in Fig. I. 6, in which the values of C_L near the stall differ for the two cases of increasing and decreasing incidence. At B in that figure there is no reattachment after the separation near the leading edge and decrease of the incidence at first has little effect on the separated region covering the whole surface. From C to D, however, the flow reverts to the short bubble configuration as rapidly as, from A to B, the short bubble had burst. It is quite impossible to predict the difference in the two values of the incidence for which the bubble bursts and reforms: for the NACA 103 aerofoil, the difference is as much as 8°.

The prediction of $C_{L\,max}$ is very difficult and as yet only general trends can be noted. For example, Multhopp (1948) has investigated the

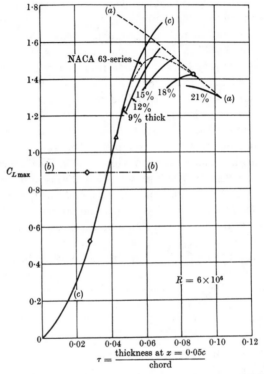

FIG. V. 15. Curves showing the maximum lift of some NACA symmetrical aerofoils.

relation between the maximum C_L of a number of aerofoil sections, and τ, the ratio of their thickness at 0·05 chord to the chord; other investigators have used the leading-edge radius of curvature as an empirical parameter. Typical curves are shown in Fig. V. 15; each aerofoil provides a point in this diagram and envelopes have been drawn marking the highest values of maximum C_L corresponding to the three types of stall, (a), (b), and (c), which were shown in Fig. V. 14.

For the trailing-edge stall of the relatively thick aerofoil, $C_{L\,max}$ is reached when the separation point is at about mid-chord. As curve (a) shows, a thickening of the leading edge increases $C_{L\,max}$ except for the 21 per cent thick aerofoil. For the long-bubble stall-curve (b), the bubble extends over roughly the first half of the thin aerofoil at $C_{L\,max}$. As the figure shows, typical values of $C_{L\,max}$ for this regime are considerably less than those for the trailing-edge stall. Only in case (c)—leading-edge stall—does an abrupt change in flow pattern coincide with maximum lift. Here the short bubble bursts whereupon there is a sudden drop in lift, an increase in drag, and a nose-down change of pitching moment.

Although for any given aerofoil, it is impossible to calculate the complete lift curve or $C_{L\,max}$, we can nevertheless design a section on which laminar separation with a long bubble is avoided, by specifying a suitable pressure distribution; the use of camber is a convenient method of fulfilling such requirements.

Bubbles, and in particular long bubbles, can have significant effects on the drag and pitching moment characteristics of an aerofoil as well as on the lift, and these have been discussed by Küchemann (1953b) and by Crabtree (1957a). The connexion between stalling and spinning of aircraft has been discussed by Young (1952), who also treats the effects of flaps, engine nacelles, and slipstream on the stall.

VI

BOUNDARY-LAYER CONTROL

1. Introduction

WHAT we have called, in previous chapters, the first inviscid approximation to a flow has often been referred to, in the literature of fluid dynamics, as the ideal flow since it refers to the physically impossible state of affairs of a fluid of zero viscosity. As it happens, this description is appropriate also in the sense that the ideal flow, if it were a possibility, would often be preferable to the corresponding real flow. For we have seen already in Chapter V that viscosity is almost wholly disadvantageous: it is responsible for drag and for reductions of lift and it often causes unsteadiness in the flow. Too hasty a wish for real inviscid fluid would, however, be unwise: such a fluid would be unable to generate vorticity, or circulation, or lift, and the flight of the conventional aeroplane would be impossible.

The practical objectives of boundary-layer control are the reduction of drag and the suppression of large wakes, the increase of lift, and the improvement of stalling characteristics generally. We shall also see that, as a by-product of boundary-layer control, configurations of flow may be realized which otherwise are impossible. And the means by which these objectives are gained is almost universal: the creation of conditions under which the energy lost through viscosity is either minimized or restored in an efficient manner. Thus we seek to prevent the separation of the boundary layer in circumstances in which, without some form of control, separation would occur; alternatively, we seek to replace a turbulent boundary layer by a laminar one, or at least to delay transition to a point as far downstream as possible.

One type of boundary-layer control, therefore, can be based on conditions which have already been discussed in earlier chapters. Transition to turbulence has been seen to depend mainly on the roughness of the surface and the pressure gradients on it. Separation, too, depends almost wholly on the latter. Thus the manufacture of very smooth, unwrinkled surfaces, the design of their shape, and in wind-tunnels the production of streams of low turbulence, all come into this category of boundary-layer control. Closely related to this type of control is the slotted wing, considered in Section 2; the shape and position of the slot or flap on such a wing is carefully contrived to minimize the effects of separation.

An important feature of these types of control is that they do not involve the expenditure of any additional power. This is true also of vortex generators which are shown, in Section 3, to offset the lack of energy in a boundary layer by the artificial transfer of energy by turbulent mixing; other methods which exploit this effect of turbulence are mentioned in Sections 4 and 5.

Once, however, we allow the use of auxiliary power in boundary-layer control, great opportunities arise. If, for example, the surface is moved in such a way that the shear stress on it is very small, a boundary layer will never form on it, but the attractions of this are mostly at the academic level as is shown in Section 6. Of far greater practical importance is the removal of the boundary layer into the surface. Much of this chapter is taken up with an account of the various practical methods of achieving this removal in such a way that the power expended on it is more than counterbalanced by the saving in power consequent upon the establishment of thinner boundary layers. Section 19, on the other hand, considers the effects on a boundary layer of air injected into it in a direction roughly parallel to the mean flow; this is a variant of the mechanism of turbulence as an agency transferring energy. We may also mention the use of a porous surface to inject air into the boundary layer so that it is thickened for experimental purposes.

So many different methods of boundary-layer control have been proposed during the last two decades that, until recently, interest in them has been biased towards the academic evaluations of their relative merits, and few have been applied to standard aircraft. Thus most experiments have in the past been made on two-dimensional flow and only lately have some methods of control been tested more widely. To predict widespread use of boundary-layer control on aircraft in the future, however, does not go beyond a sober assessment of its potentialities. But we cannot in this chapter indulge in a discussion of practical applications to future aircraft; and as we are more concerned with the basic principles, we shall consider as a general rule only two-dimensional flow.

2. Slotted wings. Leading-edge slats and trailing-edge flaps

The simplest forms of slotted wing are sketched in Fig. VI. 1. This shows (a) the leading-edge slat and (b) the slotted trailing-edge flap, which are due to Handley Page (1921) and independently to Lachmann

(1921). Handley Page slats and slotted trailing-edge flaps have been greatly developed through the years and their many variants have been perfected for extensive practical applications.

The leading-edge slat amounts to an auxiliary aerofoil at a high lift coefficient; the strong downwash from its trailing edge forces the boundary layer on the main part of the wing to adhere to the surface

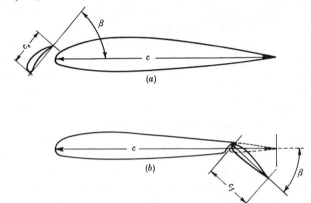

Fig. VI. 1. Sketches of aerofoils with (a) a Handley Page leading-edge slat, and (b) a slotted trailing-edge flap.

instead of separating as it otherwise would, or to reattach quickly if separation does occur. Alternatively, we may explain the action of the slat by saying that the circulation about it decreases the fluid velocity which would otherwise occur over the leading edge of the main wing; the rise in pressure undergone later by the boundary layer is therefore diminished and separation possibly prevented. The flow may well separate from the upper surface of the slat but its wake is discharged into the main stream, where it cannot affect seriously the lift on the main wing. Townend (1929, 1931) was one of the earlier workers in this field and himself produced a similar device, the Townend ring, for axi-symmetric flows such as those past radial engines or nacelles on aircraft. Again, the downwash of the ring prevents the formation of a large wake behind the engine or nacelle, and so diminishes its drag.

The crucial feature of the slotted trailing-edge flap is the slot between the main aerofoil and the flap; the jet of air flowing through this helps to delay the separation of the boundary layer on the upper surface of the flap and so enables a high lift coefficient to be achieved. The efficacy of the arrangement clearly depends to a large extent on the design of the slot.

The simple form of slotted trailing-edge flap shown in Fig. VI. 1 (*b*) has been developed into more complicated geometrical arrangements; in many of these, downstream movement of the flap is achieved by means of a suitable track mechanism. The consequent increase of the chord length itself produces a substantial increase in lift in addition to that arising from the effective camber produced by any hinged flap.

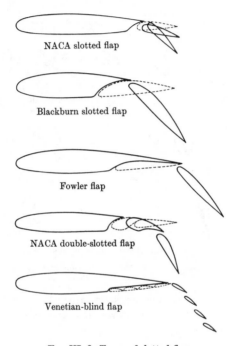

FIG. VI. 2. Types of slotted flap.

Several types of slotted flap using link or track mechanisms are sketched in Fig. VI. 2 and much information is now available on the aerodynamic performance of such devices, including detailed pressure-plotting observations and measurements of the forces on leading-edge slats and of hinge moments on trailing-edge flaps. The results have been analysed by Young (1947) who also gives an extensive bibliography. He too emphasizes the importance of the correct design of the slot.

Typical values of the quantities shown in Fig. VI. 1 (*a*) are: c_s/c between 0·15 and 0·30, and $\beta < 40°$. The increment in maximum lift for such a full-span slat, with $\beta \simeq 40°$, is given roughly by

$$\Delta C_{L\,max} = 3\cdot3c_s/c,\tag{1}$$

and the increase in pitching-moment coefficient at the stall is given roughly by

$$\Delta C_m = 0\cdot9c_s/c.\tag{2}$$

The incidence at which the stall occurs is often increased by between $7°$ and $13°$, and dC_m/dC_L at $C_L = 0\cdot8C_{L\,max}$ may be increased by between $0\cdot075$ and $0\cdot225$.

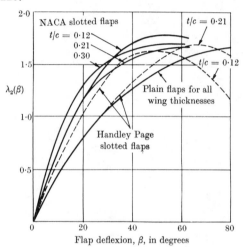

FIG. VI. 3. Comparison between the lift-increment function λ_2 for some plain and slotted flaps.

For full-span trailing-edge flaps on wings of aspect ratio 6, the increment in lift coefficient based on the extended chord was found to be expressible in the form

$$\Delta C'_L = \lambda_1(c_f/c')\cdot\lambda_2(\beta),\tag{3}$$

with the incidence of the wing $10°$ above the zero-lift angle. In this, c_f is the flap chord, c' the extended chord, and β the flap deflexion. The function λ_1 is found to vary very little with the type of flap; the values of λ_2, however, manifest the relative merits of different types, and some typical values are shown in Fig. VI. 3. The important part played by the slot in controlling the boundary layer is indicated by the curves in this figure.

3. Turbulent mixing. Vortex generators

Many methods of boundary-layer control rely for their effect on the re-energizing of a boundary layer which otherwise would separate.

A natural form of this phenomenon is turbulent mixing, which enables a turbulent boundary layer to overcome a pressure rise sufficient to cause a laminar layer to separate. In this and the following two sections we consider artificial means of increasing the transfer, due to turbulent mixing, of energy from the free stream into the boundary layer.

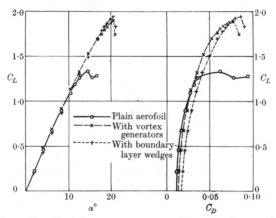

FIG. VI. 4. The effect of vortex generators and boundary-layer wedges on the lift and drag of an NACA 63_3–018 aerofoil.

The best known of such methods is the system of vortex generators which was first proposed at the United Aircraft Corporation and is due largely to H. D. Taylor (1947) and Bruynes (1951). It usually consists of small vanes projecting from the surface and set at an angle of incidence to the local flow direction: the trailing vortices of the vanes are the mechanism of mixing which was established, in some of the earliest experiments, in diffusers and bends in channels. Many applications to wings have been made and we may cite the experiments of McCullough, Nitzberg, and Kelly (1951). In this work the generators were attached to an NACA 63_3–018 aerofoil along a spanwise line at $0.10c$ from the leading edge and were arranged alternately at $\pm 22\frac{1}{2}°$ incidence so as to produce a contra-rotating system of vortices. Their effect on the lift curve is shown in Fig. VI. 4 which includes comparative results for boundary-layer wedges, to be described in Section 4. The vortex generators extend the linear part of the lift curve and raise the stalling incidence from 14° to 20°, with an increase in maximum lift from 1·33 to 1·89. For the lift coefficients above 1·1, the drag with the vortex generators is less than that for the plain aerofoil; at cruising incidences the drag coefficient with generators is greater by about 0·002.

Various basic configurations of vane-type generators are possible. Small lifting surfaces mounted roughly parallel to the surface and off-set from it by a short distance, as shown in Fig. VI. 5, have also been suggested as they are less sensitive to yaw. Tanner, Pearcey, and Tracy (1954) have made extensive wind-tunnel experiments on all these types, paying special attention to the increased pressure rise which they enable

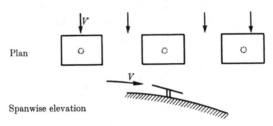

Plan

Spanwise elevation

FIG. VI. 5. A sketch of the finite-wing type of vortex generators.

the boundary layer to surmount before separation takes place. In addition, J. P. Jones (1957) has considered theoretically the paths followed by the shed vortices as they proceed downstream; these and similar studies may make it possible to explain quantitatively the observed effects and to account for the possibilities and limitations of the various alternative arrangements.

4. Turbulent mixing. Wedges and ramps

McCullough, Nitzberg, and Kelly (1951), in experiments already quoted, also considered small wedges attached to the surface, as shown in Fig. VI. 6 (a). By this means it was hoped to combine the triple mechanisms of turbulent mixing (as with vortex generators), boundary-layer attenuation between the wedges (as with the NACA submerged engine inlet), and discharge of the rest of the boundary layer into the general flow well clear of the wing surface. After the basic principle had been explored on a flat plate, tests were made on an NACA 63_3–018 aerofoil and the best arrangement, arrived at empirically, consisted of an array of similarly-handed wedges, $0.033c$ high, spaced one wedge width apart with their leading edges at $0.10c$. As shown in Fig. VI. 4, this array succeeded in increasing the maximum lift from 1.33 to 1.93; it also increased the drag coefficient at low and moderate angles of aerofoil incidence by about 0.006, which would necessitate retraction of the wedges during cruise in a practical application. For lift coefficients above about 1.28 the wedges reduced the drag, since without them the flow would have separated.

Although the wedges resulted, on this aerofoil, in a slightly higher maximum lift coefficient than was obtained with vane-type vortex generators, they produce at low incidences an increase in drag between two and three times that of the vane-type vortex generators. Ramps, as illustrated in Fig. VI. 6 (b), are similar to wedges in their effects and have been discussed by Stephens and Collins (1955).

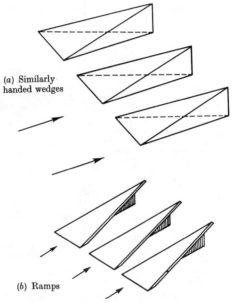

(a) Similarly handed wedges

(b) Ramps

Fig. VI. 6. Sketches of wedges and ramps which encourage turbulent mixing in the boundary layer.

5. Turbulent mixing. Air jets

The underlying intention of this idea, due to Wallis (1952), is to prevent the formation or mitigate the effects of a laminar separation-bubble on the leading edge of a thin aerofoil, by injecting air into the boundary layer through a spanwise row of holes on the lower surface between the front stagnation point and the leading edge. Fig. VI. 7, given by Wallis (1954), shows the influence of the air jets on the pressure distribution round the leading edge of an aerofoil. The effect of the jets is not to induce immediate transition but rather, according to Hurley, Keeler, and Wallis (1955), to induce instability into the laminar layer so that it becomes turbulent as soon as it separates and forthwith reattaches itself. But besides accelerating transition in a separated

laminar layer, jets of air of higher velocity can entrain air from outside
the boundary layer by vortex mixing and thus delay the separation of
a boundary layer which is already turbulent. This use of air jets has
been applied by Cowled and Wallis (1956) to the delay of separation
over the rear of a thick wing, and by Collins (1953) to the improvement
of the flow over a deflected trailing-edge flap.

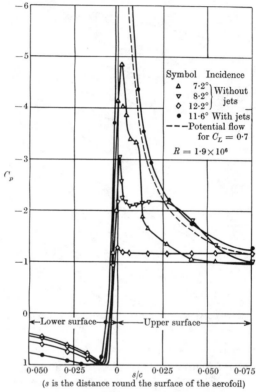

FIG. VI. 7. The effect of air jets on the pressure distribution over
the leading edge of an NACA 64A006 aerofoil.

Hurley, Keeler, and Wallis (1955) have summarized the results of
tests on an NACA 64A006 aerofoil at a Reynolds number of $3 \cdot 2 \times 10^6$.
Without air jets, the bubble at the leading edge began to increase
rapidly in size as the incidence reached a value of $6 \cdot 2^\circ$ at which the
normal force coefficient, C_N, was $0 \cdot 65$. With air jets near the leading edge
on the lower surface, a quantity given by $C_Q = 0 \cdot 00015$, C_Q being defined
in equation (11), enabled an incidence of 8° to be reached without

serious separation, with a corresponding value $C_N = 0.86$. A further C_Q of 0.00016 applied through jets on the upper surface resulted in the values $\alpha = 8.9°$ and $C_N = 0.95$, at which the drag is still moderate, being given by $C_D = 0.02$. Any increase in incidence beyond these values in each case resulted in a very rapid increase in drag.

6. Moving surfaces

The system of air jets differs from the systems described in the earlier sections in that it requires some additional power, the magnitude of which, however, would be very small for most applications. But most other systems of boundary-layer control require power in such quantities that its accurate assessment is as crucial to the practical value of the system as are the aerodynamic effects, and some fundamental considerations of power are given in Section 7. Among such systems, the idea of the moving surface is unique though it is unlikely to be applied at all extensively to aircraft because of the engineering difficulties. Small-scale applications of the rotating-surface principle are, however, very common: the speed of the modern game of tennis, for example, depends almost entirely on the downward force on the heavily top-spun ball. Newton (1671) was well aware of these phenomena, but it was 200 years before Magnus (1853) and Rayleigh (1877) set about systematic experimental and theoretical investigations of them.

That separation of the boundary layer can be prevented if the surface is moved sufficiently fast in the direction of flow was demonstrated by Prandtl (1925) in 1907 with a rotating circular cylinder in a stream of water. Experiments were made by Favre (1936) on an aerofoil whose upper surface formed part of a rotating band and the principle is illustrated in Plate 13 of Goldstein (1938). There is considerable academic interest in this kind of flow and many studies have been made of the flow of a real fluid past a rotating circular cylinder. Notable experiments are recorded by Prandtl and Tietjens (1931) and by Thom (1931); and Flettner (1924) succeeded in demonstrating its application as a replacement for a sail on a boat.

Let us consider a solid cylinder, of diameter d, in a uniform stream of speed U. The configuration of potential flow—or, in other words, of the first inviscid approximation—is shown in Fig. VI. 8 for three values of the circulation about the cylinder; in each case the circulation is, of course, the same for all circuits enclosing the cylinder. In (a), the velocity on the cylinder decreases along CA and along DA; in a real fluid, separation would be expected to occur near C and D, and the consequent large wake would then inhibit the possibility of circulation being either set up or maintained. Clockwise rotation of the cylinder, however, has two consequences for the real flow. First, it moves the

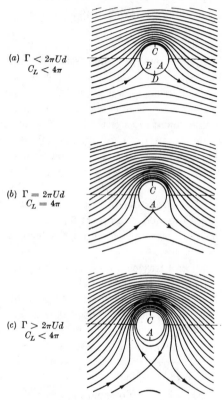

(a) $\Gamma < 2\pi Ud$
$C_L < 4\pi$

(b) $\Gamma = 2\pi Ud$
$C_L = 4\pi$

(c) $\Gamma > 2\pi Ud$
$C_L < 4\pi$

Fig. VI. 8. The potential flow of a uniform stream past a circular cylinder, with various values of the circulation Γ.

separation-point on CA farther towards A; secondly, it induces a circulation about the cylinder. If the peripheral speed is V, then the circulation in a circuit close to the cylinder approximates to πVd. For a larger circuit, the circulation is less than this value owing to the diffusive effect of viscosity, but certainly if V is sufficiently large the circulation in circuits near the cylinder tends to produce patterns of flow similar to those in Fig. VI. 8. The process is further helped by the length of arc BA decreasing with increase of circulation; thus the region in which separation is most likely to occur—in which the surface is moving against the general flow of fluid—is steadily diminished. With, say, $V = 6U$, the peripheral speed is roughly the same as the fluid speed at C in the potential flow of Fig. VI. 8 (c) and at other points on the cylinder is therefore greater, and in the same direction as the fluid speed. Thus we could argue that a real flow similar to that in (c) is possible if the cylinder rotates sufficiently fast, and photographs given as Plate 8 of Prandtl and Tietjens (1931) confirm this. The values of C_L obtained experimentally are rather less than those shown for the potential flow, which presumably overestimates the pressure near D; at the same time, there is a large drag in the real flow. Theoretical work on this flow is meagre, but an investigation by M. B. Glauert (1957) suggests that the lift will increase indefinitely with the rotational speed, in contrast to Prandtl's (1925) prediction that the lift cannot exceed a certain upper limit.

7. The use of auxiliary power. The power required for area and slot suction

In Section 1 we mentioned the possibilities arising from the maintenance of thin boundary layers due to the withdrawal of the fluid into the surface, and they are elaborated in the rest of the chapter. For some applications of boundary-layer suction, the power expended on the suction might not be of first importance—for example, if suction is used to increase the maximum lift of an aircraft's wings for landing, the power required might be covered many times over by the total engine power. In this case there is, of course, the engineering difficulty of converting the engine power from a producer of thrust to a producer of suction; this very difficulty, however, suggests the synthesis of the agencies of thrust and lift, and has led to the suggestion of the jet flap which is considered in Section 20.

But for many applications of boundary-layer suction, it is important to estimate the auxiliary power required, and to begin with we may demonstrate an inherent advantage of the withdrawal of the boundary layer into the surface of a body which is propelled through fluid. For simplicity we consider a two-dimensional flat plate in the stream $(U, 0, 0)$ and let the velocity field near the trailing edge be $(u, 0, w)$. The drag per unit span is, from equation (V. 1), $\int_{-\infty}^{\infty} \rho u(U - u)\, dz$ and so the power required to maintain the flow is

$$P_m = \rho U^3 c \int_{-\infty}^{\infty} (u/U)(1 - u/U)\, d(z/c). \tag{4}$$

Alternatively, the flow may be maintained by withdrawing each element of the boundary layer into the surface at the trailing edge and restoring its total pressure to its free-stream value. If losses in the duct and pump are neglected, the power required is then $\int_{-\infty}^{\infty} \rho u\, dz(\frac{1}{2}U^2 - \frac{1}{2}u^2)$ or

$$P_s = \rho U^3 c \int_{-\infty}^{\infty} (u/U)(1-u/U)\, d(z/c)\{\tfrac{1}{2}(1+u/U)\}, \tag{5}$$

since the static pressure may be assumed constant everywhere. Now $u < U$, so $\frac{1}{2}(1+u/U) < 1$ and $P_s < P_m$. From the practical point of view of an aircraft, this result says that it is more economical to restore the kinetic energy of the fluid in the wake than to overcome its loss of momentum by the creation of momentum elsewhere. The calculation is, of course, highly idealized, no account being taken of the efficiencies of the two systems, nor of the shape of a normal body. Ackeret (1938) seems to have been the first to realize these possibilities of suction.

Much greater gains than are indicated by the comparison between P_m and P_s become feasible if the boundary layer is withdrawn steadily over the whole surface in such a way that laminar flow is maintained where otherwise turbulent flow would occur. This possibility is considered in detail in Section 11.

Whether or not any particular type of boundary-layer control is applicable, on economic grounds, to full-scale aircraft is a question clearly beyond our reach here: but we ought to be able to assess the power required to establish various kinds of flow, so as to form a basis for a designer's more detailed estimates of performance. For this purpose, it is assumed from the start that, unlike the case considered above, the suction system is separate from the main propulsive system of the aircraft, and that the power required for the suction system can be expressed in terms of an equivalent drag coefficient C_{Dp}. The total effective drag coefficient C_{De} is then obtained by adding to C_{Dp} the wake drag coefficient C_{Dw} due to the loss of momentum in those parts of the boundary layers which are not removed by the suction and which pass into the wake. Here induced drag is being ignored as being an additional drag which must inevitably be included at some stage of the calculation of the total drag force. Now it is assumed that the fluid removed by suction is discharged so that its static pressure and velocity are identical to the pressure and velocity at infinity: thus the suction system contributes neither drag nor thrust, and the wake drag is the total drag which has to be overcome by the main propulsive system.

The total power expenditure includes, however, the suction power and so is represented by a drag coefficient $C_{De} = C_{Dp} + C_{Dw}$ which is to be compared with the drag cofficient C_D of the wing without any suction.

For area suction in which the fluid is withdrawn continuously over the whole surface, let H_d be the total pressure of the withdrawn fluid at the input side of the pump in the suction system. If losses in the discharge duct are neglected, then the input power of the pump is

$$P_p = \eta_p^{-1} \int (H_\infty - H_d) w_w \, dS, \tag{6}$$

where H_∞ is the total pressure of the undisturbed stream, w_w is the suction velocity normal to the element dS of wing area, and η_p is the efficiency of the suction pump. If η_a is the efficiency of the main propulsive system of the aircraft, the drag coefficient equivalent to the pump power is

$$C_{Dp} = \eta_a P_p / \tfrac{1}{2} \rho S V_\infty^3. \tag{7}$$

Pankhurst and Gregory (1952) have elaborated the calculation of the total effective drag coefficient, by considering the contributions to it of the loss of energy in the internal duct system and of the porous surface. To take a particular case, let us assume that (i) $\eta_a = \eta_p$, (ii) the duct losses are negligible, and (iii) there is a single internal chamber of pressure p_c into which the sucked fluid flows with negligible kinetic energy. The pump power then becomes

$$P_p = \eta_a^{-1}(H_\infty - p_c) \int w_w \, dS = \eta_a^{-1}(H_\infty - p_c)Q, \tag{8}$$

where Q is the total quantity of fluid sucked in. Thus the total effective drag coefficient, under the above assumptions, is

$$C_{De} = C_{Dw} + C_p C_Q, \tag{9}$$

where $C_p = (H_\infty - p_c) / \tfrac{1}{2} \rho V_\infty^2$ is a pressure coefficient for the internal chamber and C_Q is the quantity coefficient defined, generally, by

$$C_Q = Q / V_\infty S. \tag{10}$$

In two-dimensional flow past aerofoils, Q would stand for the total quantity per unit span, in which case

$$C_Q = Q / V_\infty c, \tag{11}$$

c being the chord of the aerofoil.

When the suction is applied through a slot instead of a porous area, the total effective drag coefficient can again be expressed as the sum of the drag coefficient due to the residual wake and the equivalent drag coefficient of the suction system, as described by Preston, Gregory, and

Rawcliffe (1948). Corresponding to equation (6) we now have

$$P_p = \eta_p^{-1}(H_\infty - H_d)Q. \tag{12}$$

The loss of total pressure $(H_\infty - H_d)$ comprises that in the boundary layer at the slot entry $(H_\infty - H_{BL})$ and the further losses in the slot and the internal ducting. If these latter contributions are neglected and η_a is put equal to η_p, the ideal equivalent pump-drag coefficient may be written in the form

$$C_{Dp} = (H_\infty - H_{BL})C_Q / \tfrac{1}{2}\rho V_\infty^2. \tag{13}$$

The analysis given in this section has considered only the overall effects of suction on the power required. For an analysis of the contributions to the drag made by the various parts of the whole system of aerofoil and ducting, we may refer to Pankhurst and Thwaites (1950). For example, in two-dimensional experiments in wind-tunnels, it often happens that the sucked air is removed from the inside of the model spanwise and out through the tunnel walls. If the forces of the aerofoil are being measured on a balance, the measured drag will include an amount $\rho Q V_\infty$ due to the removal of the air; this quantity should therefore be subtracted to give the drag due to the wake alone. The existence of an effective sink of strength Q in the aerofoil may need to be taken into account in the calculation of the first inviscid approximation; this is also true of the flow past a finite wing in which case, in addition, account may have to be taken of the effect on the inviscid flow of the efflux of the air which has been withdrawn.

8. Area suction

Short of preventing its formation altogether by means of a moving surface, the nearest approach to the elimination of the boundary layer is the continuous convection of vorticity within it through a porous surface which extends from the front stagnation position. In fact, no matter how large the inward suction velocity, w_w, there is always a boundary layer of some thickness: from equation (II. 82), it is simple to show that δ_2 is of order $cR^{-1}(U/w_w)$ and the vorticity of the order $R(U/c)(w_w/U)$. But the same equation shows that, provided the suction velocity is large enough, separation can be prevented and so area suction has been used extensively in experiment as a means of preventing separation near the leading edge of an aerofoil and thus of increasing maximum lift and improving stalling behaviour. It has also been used to establish nearly-inviscid flow past blunt bodies which would normally have substantial wakes, and this possibility was extended by Thwaites (1947a) to a method of controlling circulation, which is discussed in Section 10. Drag may also be reduced by the delay of transition. The following four sections are devoted to a study of the

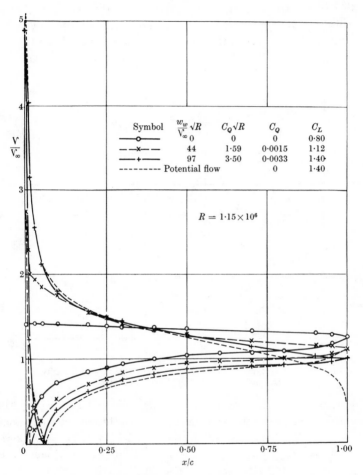

Fig. VI. 9. The chordwise distributions of velocity for an NACA 63A009 aerofoil whose upper surface is porous for $0 \leqslant x/c \leqslant 0.0275$.

various applications of area suction to aerofoils: although applications to three-dimensional wings and to other types of flow past bodies and within ducts are not often mentioned, the extent to which the basic ideas and techniques of area suction could be applied to these other flows will be evident.

9. Area suction near the leading edge of conventional aerofoils. Increase of maximum lift

The possibilities of increasing maximum lift by area suction at the leading edge were pointed out by Thwaites (1946) who showed theoretically that very small suction quantities should suffice to delay the separation which occurs at the nose of a thin aerofoil at high incidence.

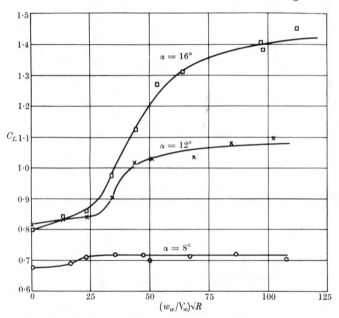

Fig. VI. 10. The experimental variation of lift with suction quantity for an NACA 63A009 aerofoil with porous nose.

Wind-tunnel tests made by Pankhurst, Raymer, and Devereux (1948) provided ample qualitative confirmation of the theoretical predictions, and estimates by Pankhurst and Gregory (1952) indicated that the power requirements in practical applications to the take-off and landing of a high-speed aircraft were likely to be well within practical limits. Since that time, many wind-tunnel investigations on aerofoils with either porous or closely perforated leading edges have fully established the advantages of the system. Flight tests have also been made.

Typical velocity distributions over the surface of a two-dimensional aerofoil at a high incidence are shown in Fig. VI. 9. Without suction, the boundary layer separates near the leading edge and the pressure is roughly constant downstream of the separation point as shown, for a rather different case, in Fig. V. 13; as the suction quantity is increased, the separated region decreases in extent until ultimately it is suppressed entirely and the sharp maximum in velocity is restored.

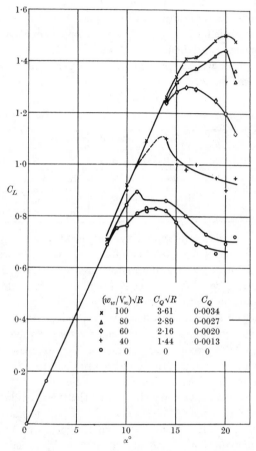

	$(w_w/V_\infty)\sqrt{R}$	$C_Q\sqrt{R}$	C_Q
x	100	3·61	0·0034
▲	80	2·89	0·0027
◇	60	2·16	0·0020
+	40	1·44	0·0013
o	0	0	0

FIG. VI. 11. Experimental lift curves for an NACA 63A009
aerofoil with porous nose.

At the same time, the stagnation point at the nose moves farther round the lower surface, and the pressure at the trailing edge rises. The lift increases rapidly as the suction increases from zero, as is shown in Fig. VI. 10, but once separation has been completely suppressed, little or no further increase in lift can be expected. Fig. VI. 11 indicates the effect of suction on the lift curve.

The suction quantity needed to prevent separation can be minimized by suitably restricting the chordwise extent of the porous area. The results from several experimental investigations are summarized in Table VI. 1. Thwaites (1946) postulated that, at any particular lift coefficient, area suction need only be applied over the region in which the velocity gradients in the first inviscid approximation are greater than the maximum gradient on the aerofoil at maximum lift without suction: this was well confirmed in the experiments for which the comparison was made.

TABLE VI. 1

The optimum extent of area suction at the leading edge

Aerofoil section	Optimum extent of porous area (upper surface)	Reference
NACA 64_1A212 .	$0 < x < 0{\cdot}045c$	Nuber and Needham (1948)
NACA 0010.51 (approx.) .	$0{\cdot}003 < x < 0{\cdot}03c$	Dannenberg and Weiberg (1953)
NACA 63A009 .	$0 < x < 0{\cdot}0275c$	Gregory and Walker (1952)
NACA 0006 .	$0 < x < 0{\cdot}005c$	Weiberg and Dannenberg (1954)

Further economies can be achieved by suitably grading the porous material: for the NACA 0010.51 aerofoil, for instance, chordwise variation of the thickness of the porous material reduced the suction quantity required for a given lift coefficient by more than a third and the pumping power by about a quarter.

Scale effect on the suction quantity required to prevent separation is not easy to determine. Laminar boundary-layer theory leads to a variation $C_Q \propto R^{-\frac{1}{2}}$ provided all other quantities, expressed non-dimensionally, remain unchanged; this proviso is difficult to satisfy in practice since for an aerofoil with a single internal suction compartment, the distribution of suction velocity changes as the stream velocity changes unless the distribution of resistance of the porous material is also changed appropriately. However, when Gregory and Walker (1952) altered the distribution of porosity so that w_w/V_∞ remained approximately constant over the whole of the porous area at each wind-speed, C_Q was found to be proportional to $R^{-\frac{1}{2}}$ for $0{\cdot}6 < R \times 10^{-6} < 1{\cdot}5$. For higher Reynolds numbers C_Q decreased less rapidly than $R^{-\frac{1}{2}}$. This may have been partly due to the effects of Mach number; for the NACA 0006 aerofoil, for example, a maximum velocity of 5·6 times the free-stream velocity was recorded which implied a local Mach number of about 0·7.

All the investigations described so far relate to two-dimensional flow.

Little information has been published on the application of area suction to three-dimensional wings. Poppleton (1951) found that, on a wing of aspect ratio 4·6 and sweep-back 40°, a suction quantity of $C_Q = 0\cdot0013$ increased the maximum lift coefficient from 0·94 to 1·18; this effect is comparable to the two-dimensional effects shown in Fig. VI. 11. Considerable hysteresis was observed, however, in the behaviour of the lift as the incidence varied.

More recently, some remarkable results of flight tests on a North American F-86F Sabre aircraft have been published by Holzhauser and Bray (1956). The aspect ratio of the wing was 4·8, the taper ratio 0·51, and the angle of sweep of the quarter-chord line 35°. The porous nose extended from the wing root (at 0·13 semi-span) nearly to the tip (0·96 semi-span); partial-span extents were also tested, but the re̤ults quoted below all refer to the full-span configuration. In the chordwise direction, the porous area extended from the leading edge to about 0·005 of the streamwise chord at the wing root, to 0·023c at 0·7 semi-span and to 0·020c at the tip. The Reynolds number varied from $6\cdot4\times10^6$ to $9\cdot0\times10^6$ over the corresponding range of lift coefficient of from 1·8 to 0·95. With the flaps and landing gear retracted and $C_Q = 0\cdot0012$ the maximum lift coefficient was 1·60, obtained at an incidence of 26°, compared with 0·95 at 17° with no suction. Table VI. 2 shows the variation with C_Q of the maximum C_L in the important practical condition of flaps and wheels down. In the same paper, the results of full-scale tunnel tests are also described. With suction, the behaviour of the aircraft at the stall was reported to be acceptable to the pilot despite a lack of stall warning, and to be much the same as with the normal wing with slats extended. The power required for the boundary-layer control, assuming a pump efficiency of 0·7, is exemplified by the figure of 138 h.p. for a maximum lift coefficient of 1·82 with C_Q equal to 0·0012.

Table VI. 2
Effect of area suction on Sabre aircraft

	Flight tests		Wind tunnel	
C_Q	Maximum C_L	Stalling incidence	Maximum C_L	Stalling incidence
0	1·08	12°	1·15	12°
0·00035	1·33	16°	..	..
0·00059	1·46	19°	1·28	14°
0·00081	1·59	21°	1·55	18°
0·00107	1·74	23°	1·87	23°
0·00122	1·82	25°	..	..

All these tests were done before Küchemann (1953b) drew attention to the importance of the so-called part-span vortices in the flow near the stall of swept-back wings. These phenomena are discussed in Sections XII. 6 and 8, and knowledge of them brings the possibility of applying area suction rather more effectively to the problem of the stall.

10. The Thwaites flap. Lift independent of incidence

This device, proposed by Thwaites (1947a), makes it possible to produce circulation independently of incidence, about a body with a rounded trailing edge. A thin flap in contact with and roughly perpendicular to the surface fixes the position of the rear dividing streamline, provided some form of boundary-layer control maintains a thin unseparated boundary layer. The circulation and hence the lift are determined by the position of the flap, and the arrangement is an example of the use of boundary-layer control as a means of creating flow patterns which would be physically impossible without it. If the body is an aerofoil with fore-and-aft symmetry, then according to the first inviscid approximation, the centre of pressure is at mid-chord whatever the value of the lift coefficient, provided the incidence is zero; and further, if the aerofoil is uncambered the pitching moment is always zero. The flap itself experiences no resultant force, as it coincides with a streamline.

The first experiments to be carried out used a circular porous cylinder. The inviscid flow can be easily calculated, and has already been illustrated in Fig. VI. 8 (a); the flap, not shown on this figure, would extend from A along the rear dividing streamline for a distance of, say, one-fifth of the radius. If β is the angular deflexion of the flap, the inviscid value of the lift coefficient is $C_L = 4\pi \sin \beta$. Pankhurst and Thwaites (1950) found that a lift coefficient of nearly 9 was attained with a flap angle of 60°, and higher values still would probably have been reached if more suction could have been applied. For small deflexions of the flap, the theoretical values of the lift were almost wholly realized after the measurements had been corrected for the downwash at the mid-span which arose from the separation of the boundary layers on the side walls of the wind tunnel.

Observed pressure distributions over the centre section of the cylinder with suction are shown for various flap angles in Fig. VI. 12. With sufficient suction, the stagnation pressure is recorded at the rear of the cylinder, and a close approximation to the potential flow around the cylinder is achieved.

An unexpected result was obtained, however, in the absence of the flap. Thwaites (1947a) had suggested that, once the flow had been established, the circulation would remain if the flap were withdrawn into the cylinder or—as was tried in the experiments—discarded along a streamline. In fact it did not remain. The flow in these circumstances proved to be unsteady and manifestations of this are shown in the

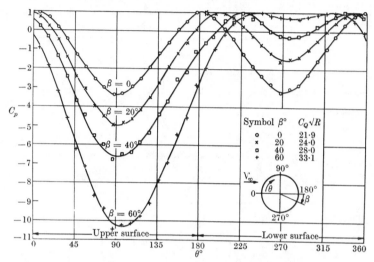

Fig. VI. 12. Experimental pressure distributions on a porous circular cylinder with a Thwaites flap.

observed pressure distributions and the total head distribution across the wake. Figs. VI. 13 and 14 illustrate this very marked behaviour. The latter figure also shows the remarkable capacity of area suction in suppressing the wake entirely even behind such a bluff body as a circular cylinder. The interesting result was found that even a wire whose diameter is less than one-hundredth of that of the cylinder is enough to stabilize the flow, when placed on the cylinder.

The unsteadiness may be due to some form of wind-tunnel inter-ference but, much more likely, to the instability of the flow in the absence of the flap. This phenomenon is not understood but some possible explanations are tentatively suggested by Pankhurst and Thwaites (1950). Similar behaviour was recorded by Gregory, Pank-hurst, and Walker (1950) during a limited investigation on a 33 per cent thick aerofoil in which the area suction was confined to the region of increasing pressure over the rear 20 per cent of the chord.

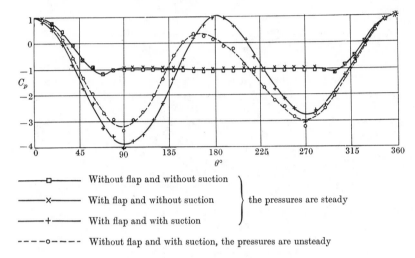

———□——— Without flap and without suction ⎫
———×——— With flap and without suction   ⎬ the pressures are steady
———+——— With flap and with suction   ⎭

— — —○— — — Without flap and with suction, the pressures are unsteady

FIG. VI. 13. Experimental pressure distributions on a porous circular
cylinder with and without a Thwaites flap.

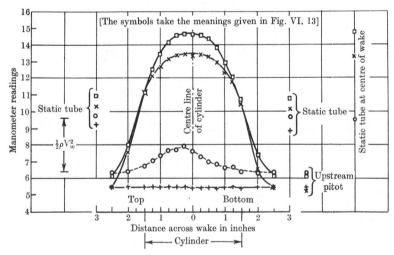

FIG. VI. 14. Pitot traverses of the wake behind a porous circular cylinder
with and without a Thwaites flap.

The extent of the suction was similarly restricted in an extensive
series of two-dimensional tests by Dannenberg and Weiberg (1955) on
an NACA 65₁–012 aerofoil with its trailing edge rounded and made of

perforated sheet backed with felt. It was found that, in common with all other methods of increasing circulation, sharp minima of pressure developed at the leading edge for large values of circulation; these caused separation and so limited the maximum lift. This separation could be prevented by further boundary-layer control over the leading edge. It is preferable, however, to design the aerofoil specifically for the task of producing lift without incidence, and the methods given by Thwaites (1947b) for this purpose have already been mentioned in Section IV. 22.

This method of controlling lift has yet to be investigated thoroughly for three-dimensional flow. The feasibility of varying the spanwise distribution of lift appears to have advantages. In cruising flight, the minimum induced drag could be achieved for a given lift whereas during landing a high ratio of drag to lift could be arranged, as has been suggested by Davidson (1956) in connexion with the jet flap described in Section 20.

The experiments on the porous cylinder were extended by Hurley and Thwaites (1951) to the measurement of the boundary-layer characteristics which were then compared with the results of a theoretical analysis based on the methods of Section II. 17. Fair agreement was obtained for the distribution of momentum thickness, but no conclusive comparison could be made for the velocity profiles or for the separation points.

11. Area suction on conventional aerofoils to obtain low drag

Extensive experimental investigations of area suction as a means of maintaining laminar flow have been made in Great Britain and in America. The British work has consisted mainly of flight tests, first on a model aerofoil carried by an Anson aircraft and subsequently, to obtain higher Reynolds numbers, on a sleeve fitted to the wing of a Vampire fighter; the corresponding American work has been done in a low-turbulence wind-tunnel. The maximum Reynolds number obtainable in the tests was about 30×10^6 and, with suction, laminar flow could be obtained over the whole chord. Drag coefficients, calculated to include the estimated power requirements of the suction, were reduced to about a third or a quarter of the values without suction.

In preparation for the flight tests, Kay (1948) experimented with uniform suction through a porous flat plate of sintered bronze, and succeeded in establishing the asymptotic velocity profile, given in equation (II. 81), for laminar flow. He also showed that the power saved by thus replacing the turbulent by a laminar boundary layer was much greater than that expended on providing the suction.

The first flight tests were made on a wing carried beneath the fuselage of the Anson aircraft and are described by B. M. Jones and Head (1951). The area suction extended from $0 \cdot 11c$ to $0 \cdot 67c$ and when the pressure was constant over the porous part of the surface, laminar flow was achieved with a suction velocity, w_w, less than $0 \cdot 00015 V_\infty$. This is a remarkable confirmation of the two theoretical estimates—$0 \cdot 000143 V_\infty$ and $0 \cdot 000118 V_\infty$, due respectively to Freeman (Chiarulli and Freeman, 1948) and to Ulrich (1944)—of the minimum suction velocity for which stable laminar flow may be maintained under infinitesimal disturbances. The Reynolds number, based on the distance from the leading edge to the rear of the porous area, was 3×10^6. The effect of increasing the Reynolds number is, theoretically, favourable, and it was estimated by B. M. Jones and Head (1951) that the total effective profile drag of a full-scale laminar-flow aircraft could be less than a tenth of the lowest values so far obtained on conventional aircraft. Such a startling result depends, however, on the freedom of all surfaces from dust, flies, and other excrescences; this presents serious difficulties to the realization of a truly low-drag aircraft, especially as the thinness of the boundary layer under conditions of area suction makes the requirements all the more stringent.

The American investigations, described by Braslow, Burrows, Tetervin, and Visconti (1951) and by Schwartzberg and Braslow (1952), succeeded in maintaining laminar flow over the whole chord of the NACA 64A010 aerofoil consistently up to Reynolds numbers of about 20×10^6, at which the total effective drag coefficient was $0 \cdot 0017$, as compared with $C_D = 0 \cdot 0045$ for a smooth solid aerofoil of the same shape. The corresponding suction coefficient was $C_Q = 0 \cdot 00064$. It was also found that the minimum values of C_Q necessary to maintain laminar flow decreased with increase of Reynolds number. A smooth surface finish was essential.

The flight tests on the Vampire aircraft were valuable in extending the previous results up to a Reynolds number of 29×10^6 and were reported by Head, Johnson, and Coxon (1955). Laminar flow over the whole chord was achieved when the porous area extended from $0 \cdot 25c$ to the trailing edge. With the assumption that $C_p = 2$ in equation (9), the total effective profile drag was evaluated from measurements with a pitot comb close to the trailing edge. Fig. VI. 15 illustrates the remarkable saving of power obtainable but again the importance was

found of maintaining a high standard of surface finish, free from roughness and waves.

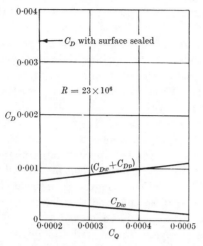

Fig. VI. 15. The variation of C_D with C_Q for the porous
wing on a Vampire aircraft.

12. Suction through perforated surfaces

In most of the experiments on area suction which have been described
so far, as close an approximation as possible has been made to a continuous normal velocity, so that valid comparisons may be made with
theoretical solutions of boundary-layer flow. It has usually been assumed
that, provided the spacing and size of the pores of the surface are small
in comparison with the boundary-layer thickness, the actual structure
of the surface has a negligible effect. No experimental results have
seriously questioned this assumption, though no systematic investigations have been made. From the engineering point of view, however,
it might be argued that this requirement on pore size is unnecessarily
rigorous and that small regular perforations would do just as well and
be very much easier to manufacture.

Raspet (1952), Lachmann (1955), Gregory and Walker (1955), and
Butler (1955) have all studied experimentally the flow over perforated
surfaces, and Raspet's tests show up its general features. Holes were
pricked into the surface of a glider wing from $0.34c$ to $0.9c$, with diameters
of 0.018 in. up to $0.65c$ and 0.010 in. beyond this. They were arranged
in spanwise rows; the spanwise spacing was 0.05 in. and the chordwise
distance between successive rows increased in the downstream direction

from 0·05 in. to 0·25 in. It was found impossible to maintain laminar flow if the chordwise spacing exceeded 0·25 in. Transition was delayed to 0·95c with a total C_Q of 0·0005. The Reynolds number was between 2×10^6 and 4×10^6 and the wing section was NACA 4416. The quantity coefficient was about four times as large as either Ulrich's theoretical estimate for a flat plate or the experimental values found in Section 11; it could probably have been reduced somewhat by varying the distribution of porosity. With reduced porosity towards the rear of the porous area, a value of R_{δ_1} as high as 3150 was achieved without transition occurring; over most of the porous surface a value of about 2·6 for the boundary-layer parameter H was maintained. Even though the perforations were only on the upper surface, the total effective drag coefficient could be reduced by about half at the best value of the suction quantity, this calculation being based on the assumptions that the pump efficiency was 80 per cent and that losses in the ducts, but not through the wing surface, could be ignored.

This investigation again emphasized the importance of reducing surface waviness to an extremely low level. It has also been found, by Carmichael (1954), that too much suction can cause transition to move forward from its far-back position; for then the boundary layer is so thin that it is unsettled by cross-flow at the edges of the perforations and by small roughnesses elsewhere on the surface.

13. Slot suction

In some of the experiments already described the boundary layer was allowed a period of growth before suction was applied, but this feature was incidental to, rather than characteristic of, the systems employed. In many investigations, however, boundary-layer growth upstream of the region of suction has been an essential feature of the system. As early as 1904, Prandtl (1927) showed that separation from the surface of a circular cylinder could be prevented by withdrawing fluid into a single slot; much more recently suction has been used to prevent separation in regions of rapidly increasing pressure, for example on the upper surface of a wing at high incidence, or at the knee of a deflected flap.

The maintenance of laminar flow by suction through a series of spanwise slots also falls in this category: on a wing of conventional section, the growth of the boundary layer may be so controlled that transition does not occur between the slots. Alternatively, according to the original idea of Griffith, the wing section may be designed so that the

pressure decreases everywhere on the surface except at one or more
points at which it increases very rapidly. At these points a suction slot
withdraws the boundary layer and so prevents separation; elsewhere
laminar flow should be guaranteed by the decreasing pressure.

Between 1904 and about 1944 a number of investigations were made
in which suction was applied through a slot or slots at various positions
on aerofoils of conventional design. In most of these, the aim was to
improve the overall performance of the aerofoil rather than specifically
to reduce drag by extending the region of laminar flow or to delay the
stall be preventing the separation near the leading edge. The following
five sections describe more recent work which has been preoccupied
with one or other of the problems of increasing maximum lift or reducing
drag: in both cases research has been pursued on specially-designed
sections as well as on conventional shapes.

14. Slot suction near the leading edge. Increase of maximum lift of conventional aerofoils

Besides thinning or removing the boundary layer, suction through
a slot may also exert on the pressure distribution an appreciable
local influence which reduces the severity of pressure gradients both
up- and down-stream. Like suction through a porous nose, slot suction
postpones separation to higher angles of incidence and so enables higher
lifts to be achieved. The lift-curve slope and the no-lift angle of incidence are hardly affected. Little work on these lines has been done in
this country on conventional aerofoils but in both Germany and America
extensive experimental investigations have been made and we shall
mention some of the more general results which have been found.

There is no reliable theoretical method of determining the best position for the slot but Fig. VI. 16 shows that it must be chosen with
great care. These graphs were obtained by Walz (1946). The best
position varies with the type of flow at the stall and varies widely with
section shape and especially with thickness-chord ratio; Walz also
showed that the radius of curvature at the leading edge is a crucial
parameter.

No definite conclusions can be reached about the best width of slot,
though on the whole narrower slots—say, of width $0 \cdot 01c$ and less—seem
to be more economical in total quantity. Scale effect also is difficult to
predict. Consideration of the boundary layer alone would suggest that
C_Q decreases as R increases. The sink effect of the slot does not, however, vary in the same way and separation, if present, causes further

complication. The possibility of disadvantageous effects of compressibility associated with high lift should also be borne in mind, as has been mentioned already in Section 9.

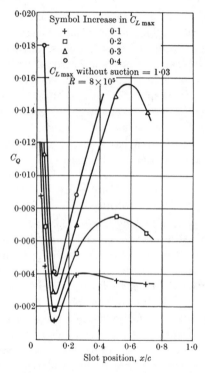

FIG. VI. 16. The experimental variation of suction quantity with slot position, for given lift increments, on an NACA 0012 aerofoil.

The power required for a suction system depends on the suction pressure needed as well as on the rate of flow. For slot suction at the leading edge of a thin aerofoil, the suction which the pump is called on to provide is large because the boundary-layer air has to be withdrawn from regions where the external pressure is low. On an NACA 63_1–012 section McCullough and Gault (1948) found that the suction pump had to operate against pressure reductions up to 22 times the dynamic pressure of the undisturbed stream, but even so the suction power required was surprisingly small. With a flap deflected through 40°, $C_{L\,max}$ was increased from 2·0 to 2·3 at the expense of an equivalent drag coefficient of 0·04. At 100 m.p.h. at sea-level, therefore, the power requirement for a wing of 10 ft. chord would be about 3 h.p. per ft. of span. In applications in which the suction power is provided by the main propulsive system, the boundary-layer control requirements detract from the available thrust for take-off. This consideration also applies to the case of a baulked landing. The permissible suction quantities also may be limited by practical considerations of space available for the ducting.

Relatively little information has been published on applications of suction slots to the leading-edges of swept wings of finite aspect ratio. Some general conclusions may be drawn from the work by Pasamanick and Sellers (1950) on a wing-body combination with $47\frac{1}{2}°$ leading-edge sweep and of aspect ratio 3·4. The Reynolds number of the tests was $6·1 \times 10^6$. Table VI. 3 summarizes the effect of various suction quantities and slot positions on the maximum lift coefficient. In this table, C_Q is based on the area of that part of the wing whose span is covered by the slots. The gains in C_L are much smaller than the corresponding gains for two-dimensional aerofoils; on the other hand, one of the valuable features of the suction is the improvement in longitudinal stability.

TABLE VI. 3

The maximum lift coefficient of a swept wing with leading-edge slots.
Pasamanick and Sellers (1950)

$C_{L\,max}$ without suction	Slot position x/c	C_Q	Maximum C_L	Increase in maximum C_L	Stalling incidence in degrees
	0·005	0·017	1·12	0·09	27
		0·022	1·20	0·17	26
	0·025	0·011	1·13	0·10	23
		0·014	1·20	0·17	22
1·03	0·005 and 0·40	0·011	1·13	0·10	25
		0·017	1·19	0·16	27
	0·025 and 0·40	0·013	1·13	0·10	24
		0·019	1·19	0·16	24

More economical results have been achieved by Poppleton (1951, 1953). The latter tests used a half-wing of aspect ratio 3, constant chord and sweep-back 60°: the thickness of the wing section was only 6·6 per cent of the chord, and the slot was 0·0016c wide and 0·025c from the leading edge. It was found that a value $C_Q = 0·0086$ based on the total area of the wing increased the lift coefficient at which static instability occurred from 0·85 to 1·3 at a Reynolds number of $R = 1·5 \times 10^6$; since these results refer to the case of flaps down, they are useful here only in showing the qualitative effectiveness of suction. The movement of aerodynamic centre was found to be very limited as C_Q varied, and within the small range of Reynolds number of the tests C_Q appeared to be proportional to $R^{-\frac{1}{2}}$.

15. Slot suction near the leading edge. Aerofoils specially designed for high lift

That thin aerofoils might be designed specifically for slot suction was first suggested by Goldstein and Richards, who pointed out that most

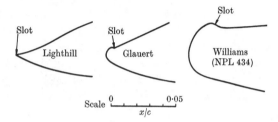

FIG. VI. 17. Leading-edge slots on thin aerofoils designed for high lift.

of the rise in pressure which occurs on the upper surface of a thin aerofoil at high incidence could profitably be concentrated in an abrupt rise at a single chordwise position. With suction through a slot at this position to prevent separation, it should thus be possible to make the adverse gradients over the rest of the aerofoil small enough to avoid separation. Lighthill (1945b), referring now to the velocity distribution, remarked that 'the drop from the summit to the foothills is replaced by a sheer precipice, by a discontinuity in fact where the boundary layer is sucked away, and the remainder of the velocity curve given an even declivity down to the trailing edge'; in a further paper (1945d), he designed such an aerofoil whose shape near the leading edge is shown in Fig. VI. 17. The sharpness of the leading edge is an undesirable feature and M. B. Glauert (1947) designed a section which avoided it. The possibilities of aerofoils of this type were further explored by Williams (1950b), who designed a series of sections for a suction quantity coefficient of 0·003, a value considered at the time to be realistic for a full-scale thin wing. The thickness-chord ratio of all these aerofoils is about 8 per cent. Both Glauert and Williams included the effect of the sink

in their calculations; the latter, however, located the slot somewhat
further aft—at about $0.02c$—in order to reduce the pressure gradient
downstream. At the same time he found it possible to avoid an increasing pressure upstream of the slot by increasing the radius of
curvature of the leading edge.

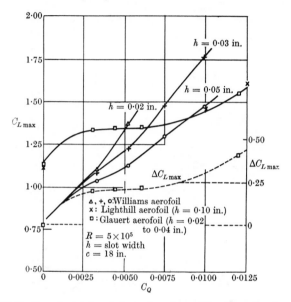

FIG. VI. 18. Experimental variations of maximum lift with suction quantity,
for specially-designed thin aerofoils with slots near the leading edge.

The results of wind-tunnel tests on the three sections shown in Fig.
VI. 17 are compared in Fig. VI. 18. Without suction the maximum
lifts for the Lighthill and the Glauert sections were almost the same
and, in view of their shape, surprisingly high; this may have been due
to the formation of a bubble near the leading edge. Both aerofoils also
gave much the same values of $C_{L \max}$ for suction quantity coefficients of
0.010 and 0.012; comparison for other suction quantities is not possible,
as the Lighthill aerofoil was not tested for C_Q less than 0.01, nor the
Glauert for C_Q more than 0.012. The maximum lift of the Williams
section was much lower without suction, and it was not until C_Q was
considerably greater than the design value of 0.003 that the maximum
lift exceeded that of the two other sections. This behaviour at low
values of C_Q was ascribed partly to the smaller camber of the section,
and partly to separation in the vicinity of the slot; at the low Reynolds

number of the tests, the boundary layer was so thick that not all of it was sucked away. With the narrowest slot tested, however, this section gave the greatest maximum lift for all values of C_Q above 0·005; and for all the slot widths it produced the greatest increment in $C_{L\,\text{max}}$ due to suction for each and every value of C_Q.

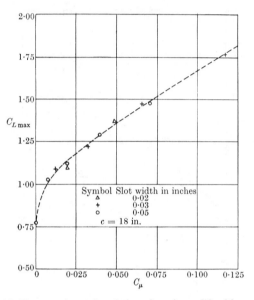

FIG. VI. 19. The experimental variation of maximum lift with momentum coefficient, for an NPL 434 aerofoil.

An effect revealed by the tests on the Williams section is shown in Fig. VI. 19 where the values of the maximum lift are plotted against momentum coefficient, C_μ, defined for incompressible flow by

$$C_\mu = 2(c/h)(C_Q)^2, \tag{14}$$

where h is the width of the slot. It suggests therefore that $C_{L\,\text{max}}$ depends only on C_μ, which is surprising.

There are not sufficient data on which to base reliable estimates of the power required for this type of boundary-layer control. Only in the tests of the Williams section were measurements made of the loss in total pressure from the free stream to the suction ducting; it was very high, of the order of thirty times the free-stream dynamic pressure, though it could probably have been reduced by improvements in the shape of the slot. It increased as the width was reduced, so that although the suction quantity required to achieve a given maximum lift was least for the narrowest slot, there was little change in the power required. In any case, all three sections were tested at the low Reynolds number of about 0.5×10^6 and no information has been obtained on scale effect. Few data are available on pitching moments, although these would be expected to be normal with any form of boundary-layer control at the aerofoil nose; and no investigations have been made on the performance of these aerofoils with the addition of trailing-edge flaps. Again, all the work has been done in two-dimensional conditions, and nothing is known about the effects of finite aspect ratio, taper, or sweep. Research on sections of this type has now been discontinued in Great Britain since their performance at high speed is likely to be poor in comparison with more conventional shapes.

16. Slot suction on conventional aerofoils to obtain low drag

In Section 11 it was seen that area suction could be used to achieve laminar flow up to high Reynolds numbers and in Section 12 perforations were discussed as a practical approximation to a continuously porous surface. The growth of the boundary layer may equally well be controlled by suction through a series of spanwise slots or porous strips positioned on the surface in such a way that the thickness of the boundary layer is kept below a certain value between successive slots. Such slots have the further effect of producing favourable pressure gradients in their immediate vicinity. On the other hand, the shear stress at the surface immediately downstream of each slot is greater than it would be for a solid surface; it has been found by Gregory and Curtis (1950) that in general the minimum total effective drag is obtained by using the least number of slots needed just to maintain laminar flow. The inherent advantage of suction mentioned in Section 7 gives an exception to this rule, however, if a further slot is placed very near the trailing edge.

Prominent investigators in the achievement of low drag by suction through slots have been Holstein (1940), Loftin and Burrows (1949), and Pfenninger (1946, 1949). The latter tested three aerofoils: section A was a symmetrical section, 3·35 per cent thick with 8 slots on one surface only; for section B, the camber was $0.019c$, the thickness $0.105c$, and it had 14 slots on the upper surface and 10 on the lower; while for section C, the camber was $0.01c$, the thickness $0.17c$, and it had 24 slots on the upper surface and 16 on the lower. The results are summarized in Figs. VI. 20 and 21, in which the

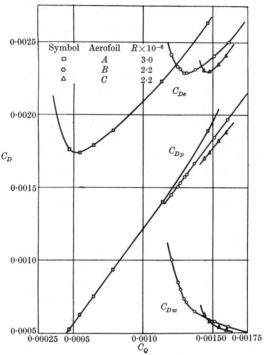

Fig. VI. 20. The experimental variation of wake drag, equivalent pump drag, and total effective drag with suction quantity on Pfenninger's multi-slot aerofoils.

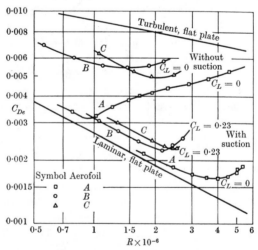

Fig. VI. 21. Scale effect on the optimum total effective drag coefficients of Pfenninger's multi-slot aerofoils.

total effective drag—that is, wake drag plus equivalent pump drag—is shown together with curves for laminar and turbulent flow on a flat plate. The minimum total effective drag coefficients attained for the three sections are given in Table VI. 4; the figures given for aerofoil A are those which would have been obtained if slots had been placed on both surfaces. From Fig. VI. 21, we see that C_{De} tended to increase with Reynolds number at the highest values of R and this was ascribed to the turbulence in the wind tunnel; at these Reynolds numbers in full-scale flight in the atmosphere, therefore, values of C_{De} less than those given in the table might well be achieved.

TABLE VI. 4

Multi-slot laminar flow aerofoils tested by Pfenninger (1946, 1949)

Section	Minimum C_{De}	C_Q	$R \times 10^{-6}$
A	0·0017	0·0007	4·0
B	0·0023	0·0013	2·2
C	0·0023	0·0015	2·4

By maintaining full-chord laminar flow on both surfaces over a considerable range of lift coefficient, the suction more than doubled the low-drag range of the 17 per cent thick aerofoil. The values of R_{δ_2} at transition were between 850 and 900 for section A both with and without suction. The tests on section B included the effects of incidence and showed a reduction of R_{δ_2} at transition due to the positive pressure gradient on the upper surface. For section C the value was 750 to 800 over the forward two-thirds of the chord and 400 to 600 in the region of adverse gradient. Over the forward part of the aerofoil the suction quantity required at each slot was extremely small but it was increased just upstream of the pressure minimum so as to prepare the boundary layer for the rise in pressure; it then had to be progressively increased to maintain R_{δ_2} below its critical value.

These figures suggest criteria on which to base the choice of the spacing between successive slots. The maximum allowable value of R_{δ_2} depends, of course, on the pressure gradient, as is suggested by Fig. I. 16. On the other hand, the maintenance of values of R_{δ_2} very much lower than about 1,000 is not recommended, because it necessitates either the engineering complication of many slots, or the loss of power involved in higher velocities in the slots; furthermore, it runs the risk of the surface roughnesses being too large in comparison with the reduced thickness of the boundary layer.

These and the other experimental investigations mentioned earlier have stressed the imperative need for a very high standard of surface finish if laminar flow is to be achieved for Reynolds numbers of the order of 10×10^6. Yet at this high Reynolds number on a 10 per cent thick aerofoil with forty-one slots, Burrows and Schwartzberg (1952) succeeded in obtaining a total effective drag of about half that of the plain aerofoil, with an equivalent pump drag coefficient of 0·0006. It should also be noted that model tests at high Reynolds numbers are likely to give pessimistic predictions for full-scale applications since a given size of surface imperfection is disproportionately large in relation to the thickness of the boundary layer.

Success in maintaining laminar flow in unfavourable pressure gradients and up to very high Reynolds numbers has also been achieved by Pfenninger (1952) in some interesting experiments in the entry length of a circular pipe. The suction was applied through eight circumferential slots on the wall and, by reducing the mass flow in the pipe, was also the means of producing the positive pressure gradient. At Reynolds numbers of 8, 11, 13, and 30×10^6, the pressure rise for laminar flow expressed as a fraction of the pressure difference between stagnation conditions and minimum pressure was respectively 0·995, 0·81, 0·76, and 0·41.

Reference has already been made to the aerodynamic advantage of a minimum number of slots, which from the engineering point of view also happens to be desirable. Most investigators have recognized that detailed design of the slot is no less important if significant gains in economy are to be achieved, and we may refer, for example, to Loftin and Burrows (1949), and to the earlier work of Fage and Sargent (1944). Rawcliffe (1947) has considered the internal design of a duct, and A. M. O. Smith and Roberts (1947) the stability of flow into a slot.

Mainly on account of the difficulties of manufacturing multi-slotted aerofoils and of maintaining them in actual operating conditions, Lachmann (1955) proposed in 1949 that porous strips, fitted flush with the surface, should replace slots. In an experiment on a model of 8 ft. chord, fitted with fourteen porous strips, laminar flow almost to the trailing edge was achieved at a full-chord Reynolds number of 15×10^6, provided the surface was sufficiently smooth. The result is exemplified in Fig. VI. 22, which corresponds to the lower Reynolds number of 9×10^6; the china-clay technique of visualization indicates that with

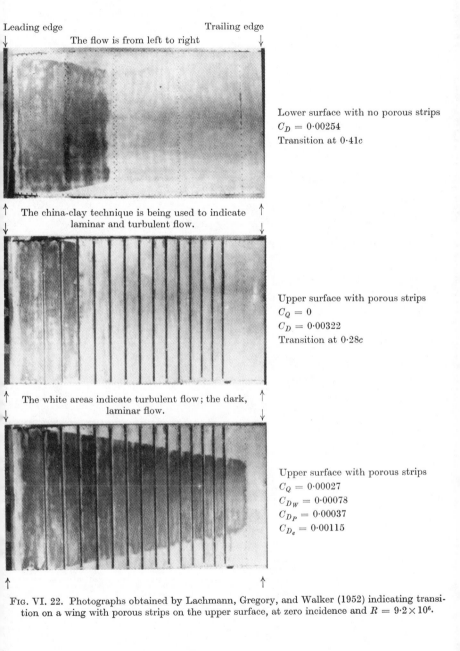

Leading edge   Trailing edge
↓   The flow is from left to right   ↓

Lower surface with no porous strips
$C_D = 0.00254$
Transition at $0.41c$

↑   The china-clay technique is being used to indicate   ↑
laminar and turbulent flow.
↓   ↓

Upper surface with porous strips
$C_Q = 0$
$C_D = 0.00322$
Transition at $0.28c$

↑   The white areas indicate turbulent flow; the dark,   ↑
laminar flow.
↓   ↓

Upper surface with porous strips
$C_Q = 0.00027$
$C_{D_W} = 0.00078$
$C_{D_P} = 0.00037$
$C_{D_e} = 0.00115$

↑   ↑

FIG. VI. 22. Photographs obtained by Lachmann, Gregory, and Walker (1952) indicating transition on a wing with porous strips on the upper surface, at zero incidence and $R = 9.2 \times 10^6$.

suction through the porous strips, transition is delayed to 0·93c. The total effective drag was reduced to about half the value for a smooth wing without slots. This work has been followed up by flight tests in which one wing of a Vampire aircraft was fitted with a glove with thirty-nine suction strips on the test surface. Laminar flow over the whole chord was achieved and the skin-friction drag, after allowing for equivalent pump drag, was reduced to less than one-fifth of its normal value. Perforations in the skin could be substituted for strips of porous material; they would avoid the structural difficulties of butt joints and lessen the risk of the surface being clogged by dirt.

17. Slot suction on aerofoils specially designed for very low drag

The work on aerofoils which were specially designed with suction slots for laminar flow was intimately linked with the evolution of methods, described in Chapter IV, for calculating the shape of an aerofoil on which the inviscid velocity distribution is specified. Thus by about 1943, it became possible to design aerofoils with near-discontinuities in velocity and so to realize the suggestion of Griffith already mentioned in Section 13. A strict discontinuity is, of course, a mathematical fiction peculiar to the first inviscid approximation; in a real fluid the boundary layer at such a point would be withdrawn through a slot and the discontinuity would manifest itself as a rapid increase in pressure across the region of the slot. A boundary layer, laminar over the whole chord, was confidently predicted to be a possibility.

First experiments by Richards, Walker, and Greening (1944) on a specially designed 16 per cent thick aerofoil confirmed the effectiveness of the suction slot in preventing separation and the observed pressure distribution was satisfactorily close to the theoretical. Only at the lower Reynolds numbers of the test, however, could the boundary layer be kept laminar downstream of the slot. It was soon realized that this was inevitable and due to the dynamic instability of a boundary layer on a concave surface. Thus the total effective drag of this aerofoil could be no less than that of conventional laminar-flow aerofoils of normal thickness. The thickness of the suction wing could, however, be increased without a disproportionate increase in drag; at the time, this possibility of thick wings was favoured in view of the attendant advantages of increased stowage space, simplification of structural problems, and suitability for all-wing aircraft, as well as the increased range of C_L in which low drag was possible.

The next aerofoil, then, was 30 per cent thick; it was symmetrical and was designed to have an increasing velocity over most of the surface in the range $-0.6 < C_L < +0.6$. Fig. VI. 23 (a) shows the shape and

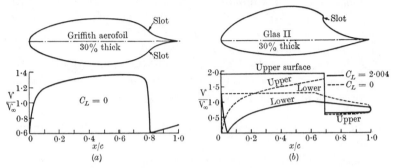

FIG. VI. 23. Thick low-drag aerofoils with suction slots.

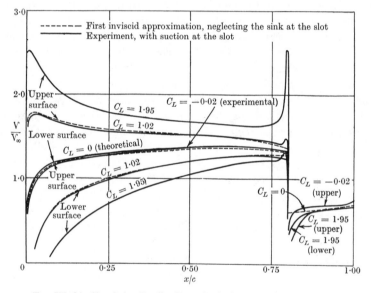

FIG. VI. 24. Chordwise distributions of velocity on a 30 per cent thick symmetrical Griffith aerofoil.

the designed velocity distribution at $C_L = 0$. Fig. VI. 24 shows the velocity distribution observed by Richards, Walker, and Taylor (1945) for three values of C_L; apart from the sink effect in the immediate vicinity of the slot this agrees well with that of the inviscid approximation. It was found that the measured lift curve was linear at least up to 15° incidence and, after corrections had been made to allow for the effects of the finite aspect ratio of the test section, the lift-curve slope was found to be 7·3 per radian; this compares well with the theoretical value of 7·9. A lift coefficient of 2·47 was measured at 18° incidence, at which there was still no sign of separation and stall. This aerofoil was also tested by Gregory and Walker (1946), with the part behind the slot used as a trailing-edge flap.

To calculate the proportion of a boundary layer which should be sucked away to avoid separation during a rapid increase of pressure, G. I. Taylor put forward a criterion which was examined experimentally by Gregory (1947). Suppose Δp is the increase of static pressure across the region of the slot; then if the effect of the viscous shear stresses is considered negligible, those stream tubes whose dynamic pressure just upstream is less than Δp cannot withstand the increase of static pressure. It is these stream tubes which therefore should be sucked away; those lying farther from the surface upstream and having a dynamic pressure greater than Δp are able to overcome the increase of static pressure. This criterion was found to predict with fair accuracy the minimum suction quantities on the 30 per cent thick aerofoil. For this aerofoil, it was found necessary to suck away about 0·4 and 0·25 of the flux in the boundary layer, respectively, in the two cases of a laminar and a turbulent boundary layer at the slot. For most practical purposes the variations in pressure near the slot arising from the large curvature of the streamlines may be ignored in the application of the criterion.

We notice in Fig. VI. 23 (a) that the design has not fully succeeded in producing an increasing velocity and a more accurate design, GLAS II, was made by M. B. Glauert (1947) and tested by M. B. Glauert, Walker, and Gregory (1948). Now, a strict discontinuity of velocity is only obtained in potential flow by a logarithmic spiral in the surface, and the design of the second aerofoil, shown in Fig. VI. 23 (b), included this feature; of course, this cannot be reproduced in practice but the curvature near the slot of the manufactured wing was certainly large. Experiment on this second aerofoil then revealed an unexpected phenomenon: the flow was often found to be unsteady and to separate from the surface near the slot in a haphazard fashion. Separation could be suppressed, but only by a much larger suction quantity than for the first aerofoil, and it was often necessary to suck away more than the whole boundary layer.

None of these effects is at all fully understood, and they raise interesting questions about the validity of the first inviscid approximation, or rather about the theoretical model which should be chosen to represent a very rapid increase in pressure. If we wish to design an arrangement which enables the fluid to sustain, without separation, a very rapid increase in pressure on the surface, what theoretical models of the flow should be chosen on which a design could be based? First, it appears from the tests on GLAS II that a discontinuous change of velocity in the first inviscid approximation is not satisfactory though more detailed consideration of the pressure gradients, which would occur if, in fact, the boundary layer were not to separate, does not indicate which feature of this theoretical model is at fault. It would naturally be an improvement to take into account, in the theoretical model, the sink effect of the slot; and in this it would be preferable to assume the slot to be of non-zero width, or in other words for the sink not to be concentrated. Williams (1950b) incorporated the design of the slot shape into his calculations and at the same time spread the pressure rise over the surface to some extent.

Tests by Keeble and Atkins (1951) showed that these considerations may certainly improve the design but even so they found that suction quantities were still considerably greater than those predicted by Taylor's criterion. Further significant improvements were obtained empirically, on the aerofoil tested, by paring away the surface upstream of the slot or by partially filling in the cavity downstream of it. As a result of these modifications, a surface is obtained for which the velocity distribution according to the inviscid approximation is similar to that shown in Fig. VI. 23 (a). The slight pressure rise just upstream of the slot seems to have the desirable effect of causing transition, the turbulent boundary layer then having less inclination to separate.

Fig. VI. 25 shows the minimum total effective drag coefficient as a function of C_L for a modified GLAS II aerofoil, as found in the flight tests on a glider reported by Keeble (1951). The values of C_D are roughly the same as for a conventional 16 per cent thick section with transition at $0\cdot4c$. The Reynolds number of these tests was between 6 and 11×10^6, and much lower values of C_D may be expected at higher values of R. Fig. VI. 26 shows some theoretical predictions by Preston, Gregory, and Rawcliffe (1948) for the aerofoil shown in Fig. VI. 23 (a). These indicate the very low values of C_D which may be realized on a very large aircraft, and also the importance of ensuring that transition occurs as far back as is consistent with the requirements, discussed in the

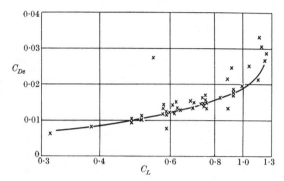

Fig. VI. 25. The variation of the minimum total effective drag with lift for the GLAS II section as tested on a glider by Keeble (1951).

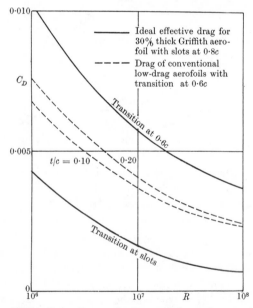

Fig. VI. 26. Scale effect on the drag coefficients of conventional and suction aerofoils.

previous paragraph, in the region of the slot. The highest value of R_{δ_1} at transition in the flight tests on the modified GLAS II aerofoil was 3210, and is almost the same as that found in the tests on a perforated aerofoil mentioned in Section 12.

An interesting phenomenon associated with these aerofoils occurs if the suction quantity is decreased below the minimum necessary to

prevent separation: very much larger quantities then need to be sucked
to re-establish the unseparated flow. This is not to be wondered at,
since in the separated flow the slot has a more or less unlimited wake
from which to draw its supply of air; it is, however, one of the obstacles
facing the practical application in full scale of Griffith's idea. The
phenomenon is highly reminiscent of the collapse and re-establishment

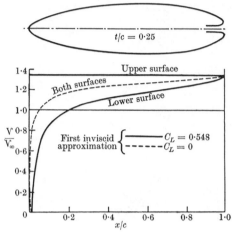

Fig. VI. 27. A symmetrical aerofoil with a slot at the trailing edge.

of a bubble on an aerofoil as the incidence is varied, which was discussed
in Section V. 14 in conjunction with Fig. I. 6. Since, also, applications
of thick wings are restricted by the effects of Mach number to relatively
low speeds, there is little enthusiasm at present to design an aeroplane
using these wings and research on them has more or less come to a
stop.

We may mention a kind of limiting Griffith aerofoil in which the
velocity gradients are favourable over the whole surface and the suction
slot is at the trailing edge. This was the idea of M. B. Glauert (1947) who
designed the shape shown in Fig. VI. 27. Heughan (1953) tested this
in a wind-tunnel and showed that, with sufficient suction, a decreasing
pressure is in fact obtained and that the wake could be suppressed
entirely. To do so, however, it was necessary to provide a small flap
at the rear of the aerofoil, without which flap the flow was violently
unstable. This is analogous to the unsteadiness of the flow about the
porous cylinder without a flap, which was discussed in Section 10; the
instability in the present case was ascribed to the existence of the rear

stagnation point away from the solid surface and it was confirmed that, to be effective, the flap needed to extend beyond the enclosing stream-line at the rear of the aerofoil. Such an aerofoil, with the flow stabilized by means of a flap, has been used as a means of introducing, without disturbance, smoke into a stream for air-flow visualization.

18. Suction on trailing-edge flaps. High lift

In the first inviscid approximation, the velocity over the upper surface of an aerofoil with a deflected trailing-edge flap reaches a maximum near the hinge and decreases rapidly over the top surface of the flap. Many kinds of boundary-layer control have been tried in this region of a flap, and in Section 2 we reviewed the effect of a slot through which air passes naturally; alternatively, significant effects can be obtained by withdrawing air into a slot placed near the hinge.

Just as slot or area suction near the leading edge of an aerofoil at high incidence prevents separation at the leading edge, so suction at a flap hinge prevents separation there when the effective camber and incidence of the aerofoil are changed by the deflexion of the flap. In the latter case, lift coefficients up to $C_L = 5$ or more are obtainable in two-dimensional flow without necessarily increasing the incidence of the main part of the wing, but at the expense of the large pitching moment associated with the effective camber.

Suction through a slot at the hinge was tested many years ago by Schrenk (1935) and by Freeman (1946). This work was followed by extensive German studies which have been described in a series of papers by Regenscheit (1946), by Regenscheit and Schrenk (1947), and by Walz and Ehlers (1947); but although these investigations covered systematically a range of thickness-chord ratio, camber, flap chord, and slot configuration, the results were presented in such a way that it is difficult to formulate general conclusions. Further, the suction quanti-ties were so high, with typical values of C_Q between 0·01 and 0·03, that they are now of only limited interest; the thickness-chord ratios also were rather large, mostly 0·15 and 0·18. A valuable review of published data has been given by Williams (1949).

Area suction near the hinge has also been investigated, and results have been published from investigations on a 35° swept-back wing by Cook, Holzhauser, and Kelly (1953), and on a delta wing of aspect ratio 2 by M. W. Kelly and Tolhurst (1954). Both models incorporated a fuselage and the tests were made at Reynolds numbers of the order of 10×10^6. On the swept wing a lift increment very close to the inviscid-flow value was obtained at 55° flap deflexion, with $C_Q = 0.0005$; with 70° flap deflexion, the lift increment reached about 90 per cent of the theoretical value, when C_Q was equal to 0.0009. In both cases there was little further increase in lift for higher suction rates. Similar suction rates gave substantial lift increments on the delta wing as well, but the effects in this case were complicated by an area of separated flow at each end of the flap, unless special preventive measures were taken. This applied especially to the inboard end of the flap, where the separation appeared to be induced by separation from the neighbouring surface of the fuselage. Another interesting observation made on the delta model was that separation from the nose did not seriously affect the lift increment, provided the flow reattached forward of the $0.3c$ line. On the swept wing there was little nose separation at any incidence below that for maximum lift.

19. Blowing on trailing-edge flaps. High lift

To mitigate the effects of separation over a trailing-edge flap by blowing, rather than by sucking, is attractive to the aircraft engineer since, on most modern aircraft, large supplies of gas at pressure are now available. Much work has been done on this particular application of boundary-layer control, which is likely to be used increasingly to reduce the landing speeds of certain types of aircraft. Available data have been reviewed and analysed by Williams (1955, 1958) and by Riebe (1955), and a very detailed investigation has been made on a thin aerofoil, NACA 0006, by Dods and Watson (1956).

In this method of boundary-layer control, a slot is arranged so that air is discharged through it at high speed over the top surface of the flap; the energy in this jet induces the flow to overcome, without separating, the increases of pressure towards the trailing edge. Details of the configuration in the vicinity of the slot are of considerable importance, particularly the vertical location of the blowing slot in relation to the nose of the flap.

As the rate of discharge is increased, the lift coefficient rises rapidly at first until the flow over the deflected flap has become fully attached; suction peaks develop on the knee of the flap and on the nose of the wing, and the static pressure at the trailing edge increases. A still greater discharge is needed to achieve the values of lift given by linearized theory; this is consistent with the fact that that theory appreciably overestimates the lift increment for large flap deflexions. After separation has been suppressed, the lift continues to rise, though less rapidly.

This continued steady increase is mainly due to the additional circulation induced by the jet, though there may be a small contribution from the downward thrust of the jet.

As typical of this system as of suction at the hinge of a flap is the large nose-down pitching moment which accompanies the increase in lift; if this has to be trimmed out by a tailplane, much of the gain in lift may be forfeited. Again as in other methods which achieve large circulation, high suction peaks develop near the leading edge and are liable to cause boundary-layer separation there unless suitable preventive measures are taken, such as the use of a nose flap, area suction, or some other method of boundary-layer control.

The important part played by turbulent mixing is reflected in the fact that the increase in C_L may be best expressed as a function of the momentum coefficient C_μ, defined for incompressible flow in equation (14), rather than the quantity coefficient C_Q. As the governing parameter is C_μ, the flow quantities required, and hence the space needed to accommodate the ducting within the wing, can be reduced by reducing the slot width and increasing the blowing pressure. Indeed, interest in blown flaps received a great stimulus from a proposal made by Attinello to discharge high-pressure air from the engine compressor through the slot without prior expansion, so that the slot runs choked. Full-scale wind-tunnel tests by M. W. Kelly and Tucker (1956) have established the validity of correlation on the basis of C_μ over a wide range of jet pressure-ratio, from subcritical to the highest value, of 9·5, that their apparatus was able to employ.

There have been a considerable number of applications of blowing over trailing-edge flaps to specific aircraft. During the Second World War experiments were made on the German Dornier 24 flying boat and the Arado 232 troop transport. Wagner (1943) has reported the work on the latter aircraft, while Attinello (1955) and Flatt (1955) have described later developments in America. In these investigations a suction slot covered the inboard part of the span and the air was then discharged through a slot covering the outer part. Another scheme in which the same air was used to double effect has been described by Poisson-Quinton (1948), who conducted full-scale tunnel tests on a swept wing fitted with a full-span double flap with suction at the first slot and with blowing at the second. More recent applications of blowing over simple trailing-edge flaps on production aircraft have been described by Williams (1958) and by Anderson, Quigley, and Innis (1956). The discharge rates needed in order to achieve valuable lift increments in such applications are modest, and well within the engine bleed which designers are prepared to allow.

20. The jet flap. Lift independent of incidence

The jet flap consists of the discharge of a high-velocity jet, in the form of a thin full-span sheet, from the trailing edge at an angle to the direction of the undisturbed stream. Although not primarily a form of boundary-layer control, it is closely related to blowing over trailing-edge flaps, especially in its 'shrouded' form in which a small hinged flap at the trailing edge is used to control the jet angle; the inclination of the jet may alternatively be obtained by an inclined jet exit. The lift on the wing is considerably greater than the component of the reaction of the inclined jet, for the jet at the same time induces a circulation about the wing. In England, the early experimental contributions in this field were made by Davidson (1956) and his collaborators. It is interesting to note that Davidson's conception of the scheme stemmed from a remark made by Constant, in 1952, to the effect that the propulsive system of an aircraft should be completely integrated with its lift-producing mechanism; this thought suggested the use of the whole efflux of the propulsive jets in some form of lift-producing device. What is remarkable, in the event, is that the gross thrust available seems not to be seriously affected by moderate deflexions of the jet.

Although the early literature on the jet flap contains much theoretical speculation on the origins of the lift, only recently have the foundations of a satisfactory theory been laid and these are described in Sections XII. 2–5; one of the principal difficulties had been the choice of the theoretical model for the first inviscid approximation.

The mechanism by which the jet mixes with the stream is also of great importance to a theoretical investigation and has been considered by Stratford (1956a, b).

The experiments described by Davidson (1956) relate mainly to the flow past a two-dimensional ellipse, $12\frac{1}{2}$ per cent thick, with jet angles, τ, of approximately 30°, 60°, and 90°. Fig. VI. 28 shows the measured lift for $\tau = 60°$, with the aerofoil at zero incidence. The jet coefficient, C_J, is defined as

$$C_J = J/\tfrac{1}{2}\rho v_\infty^2 c, \tag{15}$$

where J is the total jet reaction per unit span. The total lift comprises the component of the jet, $J \sin \tau$, together with the contribution, L_p, provided by the pressure distribution over the external surface. The remarkable effect of the jet flap lies in the fact that L_p is much the greater part of the total lift.

A particularly interesting feature of the jet flap is that it appears likely that the lift increases indefinitely as C_J increases, at least for practicable values of C_J. Even though separation occurs near the leading edge at a sufficiently high value of C_L, the effect of the jet is to form

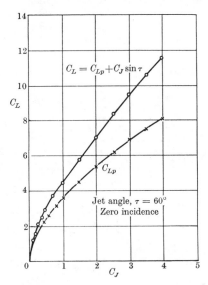

FIG. VI. 28. The experimental variation of lift coefficient with jet coefficient, for a $12\frac{1}{2}$ per cent thick elliptic cylinder fitted with a jet flap.

a bubble over the whole of the upper surface; the width of the bubble thereafter increases with C_J but, unlike the case of a conventional aerofoil at high incidence, the bubble sustains an ever-decreasing pressure and so the lift continues to increase. This again creates difficulty in the choice of a theoretical model of the flow for large values of C_J.

Some relationships between C_L and α, the incidence of the elliptic cylinder, are shown in Fig. VI. 29. At zero incidence, with $\tau = 30°$ and $C_J = 4\cdot0$, a lift coefficient of about 6 is obtained, which may be increased to about 8 by applying an incidence of about $8°$. It is interesting to note that the lift-curve slope, at $\alpha = 0$, increases with C_J and for $C_J = 4$ is very much greater than 2π which is the typical value for a thin body. Increase of incidence is not necessarily accompanied, however, by increase of lift. If, for example, the jet angle is 60°, we see that for $C_J = 4$, the maximum lift is experienced at $\alpha = 0$, though for smaller values of C_J, $(\partial C_L/\partial \alpha)_{\alpha=0} > 0$.

For a doubly-symmetrical aerofoil at zero incidence, the centre of lift may be expected to be near the mid-chord position by analogy with the property, mentioned in Section IV. 22, of aerofoils fitted with a

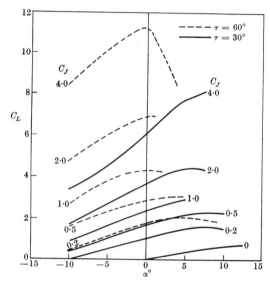

FIG. VI. 29. The experimental variation of lift coefficient with incidence, for a $12\frac{1}{2}$ per cent thick elliptic cylinder fitted with a jet flap.

Thwaites flap. This expectation is borne out fairly well by the experiment on the $12\frac{1}{2}$ per cent thick elliptic aerofoil: the centre of lift moved steadily rearwards from $0.5c$ at $C_J = 0$ to about $0.65c$ at $C_J = 4$. The jet angle seemed barely to affect this position.

The effects of finite aspect ratio on the performance of a wing fitted with a jet flap are not yet fully investigated. The existing theory is briefly described in Sections XII. 4–5. So far, there have not been enough experiments for any general conclusions to be reached, although some exploratory wind-tunnel tests have been reported by Williams and Alexander (1957).

VII

THE DISPLACEMENT EFFECT OF WINGS IN UNIFORM FLOW

1. Technical terms, notation, and geometrical properties of wings.
Now that we come to consider three-dimensional flows, there is such
a vast variety of possible configurations of surface, even of closed
bodies, that it is necessary to be quite precise in defining the classes of
shapes to be studied. This and the next chapter are devoted to wings
and Chapter IX to bodies of revolution. The latter are sufficiently well
defined as to their shape, but there are still ambiguities in the literature
as to some of the definitions relating to wings. It is best, therefore, to
start this chapter with a statement of the terminology adopted throughout the book.

A wing is a body in which may be fixed a direction such that planes
perpendicular to it cut the body in sections of aerofoil shape. This
direction is usually associated, in addition, with the properties of symmetry of the body and is called the spanwise direction. Any plane
perpendicular to the spanwise direction will be said to cut the wing in,
simply, a section; the greatest distance between two sections is the span,
denoted by $2s$, and the two sections which determine the span are the
tip sections or simply the tips. The thickness of the wing at any point
is measured along the line in the section which goes through the point
and is perpendicular to the chord of that section.

The distinctive aerodynamic feature of a wing, as compared with a
general three-dimensional body, is that when it is suitably placed in
a uniform stream, its lift is far greater than its drag. By suitably
placed, we mean that, in the normal attitude for a wing in a uniform
stream, its spanwise direction is perpendicular to the stream direction.
For this feature of a wing to be realized, it is not usually enough that
its sections should be of aerofoil shape; in addition, wings are generally
thought of as being thin, that is, the maximum thickness is usually
much smaller than not only the greatest chord but also the span.
A body of revolution, for example, would not normally be described as
a wing even if its sections were of aerofoil shape. Further common
usages may be listed:

Cartesian coordinate axes. Most wings are symmetrical about a certain plane perpendicular to the span. This plane is taken as $y = 0$ and the section of the wing at $y = 0$ is the centre section whose chord is c_0. The x-axis is usually taken as the chord of the centre section, positive in the downstream direction. The origin is at the leading edge of the centre section. The z-axis is therefore roughly perpendicular to the surface of the wing.

Leading edge. This, applied to a wing, is the line of the leading edges of the sections and on it, $x = x_L(y)$. The trailing edge is similarly defined, with $x = x_T(y)$.

Mid-chord line. This is the line joining the mid-points of the chords of the sections. It extends from tip to tip. One refers in a similar way to the three-quarter-chord line, and so on.

Straight wings. If the mid-chord line lies in a plane $x = $ constant, the wing is said to be straight.

Swept wing. A swept wing is any wing which is not straight.

Sweep. The term sweep may be applied to any characteristic span-wise line such as the leading edge; or to any segment of such a line—in which case one refers to the local sweep.

Tapered wings. Wings are tapered in chord if the lengths of the chords vary along the span. Similarly, wings may be tapered in thickness.

Rectangular wings. These are straight wings which have no taper in chord.

Twist. A wing is twisted whose chords vary in direction along the span. There is no commonly accepted definition of the reference direction from which the angle of twist is measured.

Symmetrical wing. This is a wing which is, in addition, symmetrical about $z = 0$.

Crank. A crank, and a crank section, refer to a discontinuity in the tangent of the leading or of the trailing edge.

Kink. A kink, or a kink section, refers to a crank section about which the wing is symmetrical at any rate in the neighbourhood of the kink. The centre section is the most common example of a kink section.

Plan area, S. This is the projected area of the wing on the plane $z = 0$.

Aspect ratio, A. $A = 4s^2/S$.

Mean chord, $\bar{c}$. $\bar{c} = 2s/A = S/2s$.

2. Introduction

In Chapter V we saw that even for two-dimensional flow it is impossible, in the present state of knowledge, to progress beyond the representation of a real flow at a large Reynolds number by the two regions of inviscid and boundary-layer flow. The complexity of the three-dimensional flow past wings is such that theoretical predictions are still largely confined to the first inviscid approximation. Now the accuracy of this approximation in predicting the pressure distribution on a body in uniform flow depends principally on the flow being unseparated and of large Reynolds number. Thus the theory of Chapters VII and VIII is applicable to the unseparated flow past wings at high Reynolds number.

Calculations of the boundary layer are not displayed in any of the following sections, it being assumed that the methods of Chapter II can be adapted to each section of a wing. This is equivalent to assuming that there is negligible interference, in the boundary layer, between one section of the wing and the next. For straight wings of large aspect ratio, the consequent errors of this assumption are probably no greater than those of the boundary-layer approximation itself; but for wings of large sweep or of small aspect ratio, the errors may be large.

Even in the first inviscid approximation itself, further simplifying approximations have to be made. By far the most important one concerns the separation of the effects of thickness on the one hand, and of camber and incidence on the other. We saw in Section IV. 8 how these two effects may, according to a linearized theory, be distinguished for two-dimensional aerofoils; there the necessity for it arose mainly from the problem of design. Here it is necessary from the outset; thus this chapter deals with the effects of the thickness of wings, while the next deals with the effects of camber and incidence. For any given wing, the results of the analyses of the two chapters are regarded as additive.

The flows considered in this chapter may be deemed to be those past wings all of whose sections are symmetrical and at zero incidence. There is therefore no lift on, or circulation about, any section, and hence no trailing vorticity. Thus source distributions will be characteristic of the analysis of this chapter, while the following chapter will be concerned mainly with distributions of vorticity.

3. Displacement flows

Our mental picture of physical mechanisms often reflects the nature of the theoretical models we find useful. In the calculation of two-

dimensional irrotational flow, it happens that the physical nature
of the flow can be absorbed almost completely in the very existence
of the complex velocity potential. As a result, the theory of two-dimensional flow reduces to the specialized mathematical technique of conformal transformation and it is not necessary to think in terms of further
physical effects. But for three-dimensional flow, there is nothing analogous to the complex velocity potential and we need to be guided in the
theoretical problem by various physical conceptions.

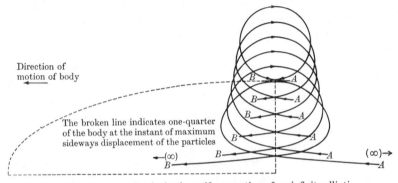

Direction of
motion of body

The broken line indicates one-quarter
of the body at the instant of maximum
sideways displacement of the particles

FIG. VII. 1. Particle paths in the uniform motion of an infinite elliptic
cylinder through fluid otherwise at rest.

One useful concept is that of the displacement flow and we consider
a body moving with constant velocity, in a stationary incompressible inviscid fluid, in such a way that it experiences no lift force. A
fluid element in the track of the body and ahead of it will first be
displaced forwards, that is in the direction of the body's motion; later it
will be displaced sideways to allow the passage of the body and then will
be drawn in behind the body when it has passed. Fig. VII. 1 illustrates
the paths of such fluid elements during the passage of a two-dimensional
elliptic cylinder: the letter A denotes the initial positions of the particles
and B the final positions. The innermost line is the trace of a particle
moving along the surface of the body; the centre-line of the motion is
an asymptote of this particular trace.

The velocity of a fluid element relative to the body is smaller than
the velocity of the body when the element moves roughly in the same
direction as the body, and is greater when the element moves in the
opposite direction. Thus a general characteristic of such displacement
flows is that the relative velocities ahead and behind the body are low,
and at the sides are high. The pressure may be deduced from the

velocity by Bernoulli's equation and is thus higher than the pressure at infinity at the front and rear ends of the body, and lower at the sides.

Considerable differences in the magnitudes of these effects must be expected between the flows past two- and three-dimensional bodies. In the former case, the fluid can escape only to the two sides and the velocity relative to the body at its sides will be higher than in the case of a three-dimensional body when the fluid can escape in all directions. Morton (1913) has calculated the paths of fluid elements for the motion

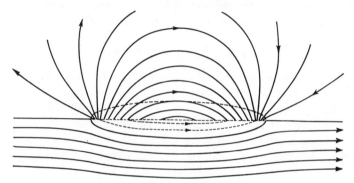

FIG. VII. 2. Two-dimensional flows relating to an ellipse. Top half: some streamlines of a source-sink type of flow. Bottom half: streamlines with a uniform stream superposed. Note that the flux between adjacent streamlines in the upper half of the figure is one-fifth of that in the lower half.

of a circular cylinder, and it is interesting to compare these with those for the motion of a sphere, as calculated by Riecke (1888) and reproduced as Fig. 65 of Prandtl and Tietjens (1931). Darwin (1953) and Lighthill (1956a) have also given illuminating examples.

Consider now the same flow as it appears relative to an observer fixed in the body. The flow appears to him to be steady, paths of fluid elements are now identical with streamlines and we obtain the familiar pattern shown in the lower part of Fig. VII. 2. If the constant velocity of the stream is subtracted from this velocity field, we obtain a flow for which typical streamlines are shown in the upper part of the figure. This velocity field constitutes what is called the displacement flow and the main object of this chapter is to find the variations, or increments, in velocity and pressure on the surface of a given body which are associated with the displacement flow.

The streamlines of the typical displacement flow shown in the upper half of Fig. VII. 2 are suggestive of a distribution of sources over the front half of the chord of the body and of sinks over the rear part.

This representation of a flow was discussed in Sections I. 22 and 23, and in Section IV. 9. The pattern of Fig. VII. 2 cannot, of course, be regarded as a proof that the body may be replaced by a source distribution confined to the chord. Nevertheless, we shall assume in this chapter that a wing may be represented by a source distribution in the plane $z = 0$; thus the problem of finding a solution of Laplace's equation is transferred to the determination of an appropriate source distribution.

In general, we shall take $\mathbf{V}_\infty \equiv (U_\infty, 0, 0)$ to be the mainstream velocity and $\mathbf{v} \equiv (u, v, w)$ as the velocity field of the displacement flow; the condition that the body is a stream surface is

$$\frac{dx}{u+U_\infty} = \frac{dy}{v} = \frac{dz}{w} \quad \text{on the body.} \tag{1}$$

If $\mathbf{v}$ is now regarded as the induced velocity of the source distribution $Q(x, y, z)$ per unit volume, $\mathbf{v}$ may be put in terms of Q and equation (1) represents an integral equation for Q. It is impossible, however, to solve this integral equation generally. Different types of approximation, appropriate to various types of wing, therefore have to be made which enable $Q(x, y, z)$ to be found without too much difficulty.

It is convenient now to recall equation (I. 73), that

$$\mathbf{v} = (Q/4\pi)|\mathbf{r}-\mathbf{a}|^{-3}(\mathbf{r}-\mathbf{a}) \tag{2}$$

is a velocity field satisfying Laplace's equation and generated by a source at $\mathbf{a}$ of flux Q. If $\mathbf{r} \equiv (x, y, z)$ and $\mathbf{a} \equiv (x', y', z')$, then

$$|\mathbf{r}-\mathbf{a}| = [(x-x')^2+(y-y')^2+(z-z')^2]^{\frac{1}{2}}.$$

For the two-dimensional flow due to a line source of strength q per unit length, the corresponding result is

$$\mathbf{v} = (q/2\pi)|\mathbf{r}-\mathbf{a}|^{-2}(\mathbf{r}-\mathbf{a}). \tag{3}$$

It is characteristic of such flows that the displacement velocity at large distances from a body decreases like $1/r^2$ in three-dimensional flow and like $1/r$ in two-dimensional flow.

4. Linearized theory

To replace the volume distribution $Q(x, y, z)$ by a surface distribution $q(x, y)$ in the plane $z = 0$ leads to an important simplification. $\mathbf{v}$ is then analytic everywhere except on $z = 0$ and so the value of w on the aerofoil surface differs from its value on $z = 0$ by an amount which depends primarily on the thickness of the wing. Now on $z = \pm 0$, $w = \pm \frac{1}{2}q$ and in the linearized theory this value of w is inserted into equation (1) which, strictly, refers to the surface of the wing. Similarly,

u is neglected in comparison with U_∞. Equation (1) may then be written, approximately, as

$$q(x,y) = 2U_\infty(\partial z(x,y)/\partial x), \tag{4}$$

where $2z(x,y)$ is the thickness of the wing. Thus the wing shape determines the source distribution from which the flow can be calculated. The value of u on the body may be taken, by a consistent approximation, as the value of u calculated on $z = 0$.

What is the validity of these approximations? First, if by chance the given body can be represented exactly by two or more concentrated source lines—as, for example, the bodies shown in Fig. I. 9—equation (4) is severely in error since it gives instead a continuous source distribution. This error may be less serious for bodies whose exact representation is a continuous source distribution. A two-dimensional ellipse, for example, may be represented exactly by a source distribution extending over a distance $c[1-(t/c)^2]^{\frac{1}{2}}$, c being the chord and t the maximum thickness, and this distance is not much less than the chord if the ellipse is thin. For thin ellipses, therefore, the distribution given in equation (4) may be reasonably good; however, since it gives a constant value of u along the whole chord, it fails near the rounded ends of the ellipse. This failure at the two stagnation points is typical of linearized theories, for at such points u must equal $(-U_\infty)$, which is not in accordance with one of the principal approximations of the theory.

Now it so happens that the exact distribution of speed on a two-dimensional ellipse can be expressed as a product of two terms, one being the result of linearized theory and the other being related solely to the geometry of the section: it may easily be verified that on the surface of the ellipse, the speed is correctly given as

$$V(x,z) = \frac{U_\infty+u(x,0)}{[1+(z'(x))^2]^{\frac{1}{2}}} = \frac{U_\infty+u(\frac{1}{2}c,z)}{[1+(z'(x))^2]^{\frac{1}{2}}} = \frac{U_\infty(1+t/c)}{[1+(z'(x))^2]^{\frac{1}{2}}}, \tag{5}$$

u here referring to the linearized value of the perturbation. It can be argued that to modify the result of linearized theory by the factor $[1+(z'(x))^2]^{-\frac{1}{2}}$ improves the result in more general cases, for the first relationship in equation (5) may be written in the form

$$\int V(x,z)[dx^2+dz^2]^{\frac{1}{2}} = \int [U_\infty+u(x,0)]\,dx,$$

both integrals being taken round the wing contour. This equation as a general statement is correct since the left-hand side, being the circulation round the section contour, and the right-hand side, being the circulation round the sources on the chord, are both zero. This modification is frequently used not only for aerofoils—it is the principal feature of Goldstein's second approximation of Section IV. 13—but also for wings provided that their span is sufficiently large, and it is especially valuable in overcoming the inaccuracy of the linearized theory near stagnation points. That the modification is useful in the three-dimensional case also is supported by a relation similar to equation (5) which holds for ellipsoids; Dyke (1954) discusses this point and shows that, on the surface of an ellipsoid,

$$V(x,y,z) = [U_\infty + u(\tfrac{1}{2}c, 0, z)][1 + \{r'(x)\}^2]^{-\frac{1}{2}}, \tag{6}$$

where $r = [(y(x))^2 + (z(x))^2]^{\frac{1}{2}}$ is the radial distance in the plane $y/z = $ constant through the point under consideration. This implies that equation (5) holds in all planes through the x-axis.

Although, in general, the value of u given by linearized theory differs from the exact value by a term proportional to $(t/c)^2$, the discrepancy between linearized and exact theory becomes more serious as the aspect ratio of the body is decreased. In the extreme case of a body of revolution represented by a source distribution on the axis, the velocity increment u on the axis is logarithmically infinite; in fact, the velocity must be determined on the surface anyway, as will be shown in Chapter IX. A similar difficulty is likely to arise for wings of small aspect ratio. For such a wing of given span, the chord is so large that, in any plane $x = $ constant normal to the main stream, the effect of the source distribution can be taken as that of an infinitely long one in the streamwise direction. The streamlines and induced velocity components of a uniform source distribution on such a strip are shown in Fig. VII. 3. Whereas $w = \pm\tfrac{1}{2}q$ in the chordal plane $z = \pm 0$ as before, w becomes much smaller than that at some places outside the chordal plane where the surface of a wing of non-zero thickness would be, even if t/c were very small. Further, v, the cross-flow component, tends to infinity logarithmically at either tip: this is the singularity which remains when, in the case of bodies of revolution, the source strip is contracted into a line on the axis. Thus the assumptions of linearized theory are of doubtful validity in the tip regions of wings even if the aspect ratio is large, since the flow conditions in the immediate neighbourhood of the tip must be similar to those prevailing over the whole surface of wings of very small aspect ratio.

The pressure distribution on the surface is obtained from the velocity by means of Bernoulli's theorem:

$$C_p = (p - p_\infty)/\tfrac{1}{2}\rho U_\infty^2 = 1 - (v/U_\infty)^2 = 1 - (1 + u/U_\infty)^2 - (v/U_\infty)^2 - (w/U_\infty)^2.$$

According to the assumptions of linearized theory, the quadratic terms may be ignored so that $C_p = -2u/U_\infty$ is an approximation consistent with the general theory.

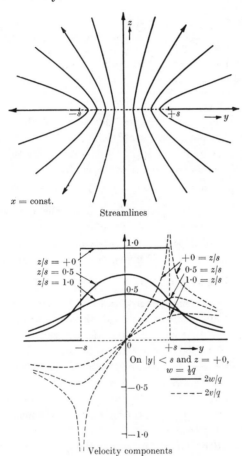

FIG. VII. 3. Streamlines and velocity components for a source distribution uniform on the strip $-\infty \leqslant x \leqslant +\infty$; $-s \leqslant y \leqslant +s$; $z = 0$.

5. Straight wings

Such wings, of finite span, represent the first stage of complication after the two-dimensional aerofoil. The main interest in the study of them is the effect of the aspect ratio and for this reason we shall consider first wings of constant section. Equation (4) then shows that, according to linearized theory, the source distribution is a function of x only and so the flow is represented by a distribution of source lines of constant strength along the span in $-s \leqslant y \leqslant s$. The streamwise velocity increment is, from equations (2) and (4),

$$\frac{u(x,y,0)}{U_\infty} = \frac{1}{2\pi} \int_0^c \int_{-s}^{+s} \frac{dz(x')}{dx'} \frac{x-x'}{[(x-x')^2+(y-y')^2]^{\frac{3}{2}}} \, dx'dy'. \qquad (7)$$

The integrations can be performed explicitly for certain section shapes. For the biconvex section formed by parabolic arcs,

$$z(x) = 2(t/c^2)x(c-x),$$

and the solution has been given by Ludwieg (1945), Neumark and Collingbourne (1949), and Holme and Hjelte (1953). Another simple case is the elliptic section, $z(x) = \frac{1}{2}(t/c)[c^2-(c-2x)^2]^{\frac{1}{2}}$; for this, the velocity increment at the mid-chord point of the centre section is given by

$$u(\tfrac{1}{2}c, 0, 0)/U_\infty = (2/\pi)(t/c)A(1+A^2)^{-\frac{1}{2}}\mathbf{K}(k^2), \qquad (8)$$

where $\mathbf{K}$ is the complete elliptic integral of the first kind with the modulus $k^2 = (1+A^2)^{-1}$, and A is the aspect ratio of the wing. For wings of very small aspect ratio $A \ll 1$ and so $(1-k^2) \ll 1$; the first term in the expansion of $\mathbf{K}(k^2)$ gives, as a good approximation,

$$u(\tfrac{1}{2}c, 0, 0)/U_\infty = (2/\pi)A(t/c)\log(4/A). \qquad (9)$$

That the velocity increment decreases with the aspect ratio of the wing is possibly the main result of these calculations and may be explained by the observation that conditions at the centre section become more three-dimensional as the aspect ratio decreases. Fig. VII. 4 illustrates this and it is seen that equation (9), derived for small values of A, is reasonably accurate for values of A even as high as 2.

We may mention here that the main practical interest in wings of very small aspect ratio rests on the extension of the incompressible-flow theory to the subcritical flow of compressible fluid by means of the well-known Prandtl–Glauert analogy in the form proposed by Göthert (1941). This states that the velocity increment, u_c, in compressible flow is $1/\beta^2$ times the velocity increment in incompressible flow on a derived wing obtained by reducing the lateral dimensions of the given wing in the ratio $\beta:1$, where $\beta^2 = (1-M_\infty^2)$ and M_∞ is the free-stream Mach number. Taking equation (9) for the velocity increment of the derived wing in incompressible flow, we find for the velocity increment in subsonic compressible flow, at mid-chord of the centre section,

$$u_c/U_\infty = (1/\beta^2)(2/\pi)\beta A(\beta t/c)\log(4/\beta A) = (2At/\pi c)\log(4/\beta A). \qquad (10)$$

This indicates that the velocity increases more slowly with Mach number on wings of small aspect ratio than on the corresponding two-dimensional aerofoil on which u_c is proportional to $1/\beta$ according to the Prandtl–Glauert rule. This general tendency is well supported by experimental evidence.

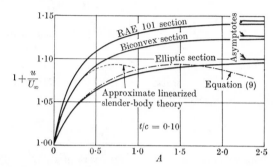

FIG. VII. 4. The velocity at the position of maximum thickness of the centre section of some straight wings, according to linearized theory.

For more general section shapes, an explicit solution of equation (7) is not likely to be obtained and the following method due to Weber (1954a) may be used. Performing the integration in the spanwise direction and taking here and elsewhere the Cauchy value of any singular integral, we find

$$\frac{u(x,y,0)}{U_\infty} = \frac{1}{2\pi} \int_0^c \frac{dz(x')}{dx'} \left[\frac{s-y}{[(x-x')^2+(s-y)^2]^{\frac{1}{2}}} + \frac{s+y}{[(x-x')^2+(s+y)^2]^{\frac{1}{2}}} \right] \frac{dx'}{x-x'},$$

which can be written as

$$\frac{u(x,y,0)}{U_\infty} = \frac{1}{\pi} \int_0^c \frac{dz(x')}{dx'} \frac{dx'}{x-x'} - \frac{1}{2\pi} \int_0^c \frac{dz(x')}{dx'} \times$$

$$\times \left\{ \frac{[(x-x')^2+(s-y)^2]^{\frac{1}{2}}-(s-y)}{[(x-x')^2+(s-y)^2]^{\frac{1}{2}}} + \frac{[(x-x')^2+(s+y)^2]^{\frac{1}{2}}-(s+y)}{[(x-x')^2+(s+y)^2]^{\frac{1}{2}}} \right\} \frac{dx'}{x-x'}.$$

(11)

Recalling equation (IV. 37), we see that the first integral in this equation represents the velocity increment for the corresponding two-dimensional aerofoil and therefore the second integral is the allowance which has to be made for the finite aspect ratio of the wing.

In practice, it is not usually possible to perform these integrations analytically and in any case $z(x)$ is usually specified only numerically.

Thus numerical approximations to the integrals have to be made and the usual procedure follows the lines already laid down in Section IV. 15. For the evaluation of u in equation (11), it is sufficient to consider integrals of the form

$$S(x) = \frac{1}{2\pi} \int_0^1 \frac{dz(x')}{dx'} \frac{f(x/c, x'/c)}{x/c - x'/c} \, d\left(\frac{x'}{c}\right). \tag{12}$$

In the method given by Weber (1954a), the section ordinates are specified at points $x = cx_\mu = (\frac{1}{2}c)[1+\cos(\mu\pi/N)]$, $\mu = 0, 1,..., N$. $z(x)$ is then replaced by an interpolating function which takes the correct values cz_μ at these $(N+1)$ points. In this way, we obtain the following sum formula for the integral in equation (12):

$$S(cx_\nu) = \sum_{\mu=1}^{N-1} s_{\mu\nu}^{(1)}[f(x_\nu, x_\mu) + (x_\nu - x_\mu)[\partial f(x_\nu, t)/\partial t]_{t=x_\mu}]z_\mu, \tag{13}$$

in which the coefficients $s_{\mu\nu}^{(1)}$ are obtained by taking $f \equiv 1$. Thus

$$S^{(1)}(cx_\nu) = \frac{1}{\pi} \int_0^1 \frac{dz(x')}{dx'} \frac{d(x'/c)}{x_\nu - x'/c} = \sum_{\mu=1}^{N-1} s_{\mu\nu}^{(1)} z_\mu, \tag{14}$$

which is valid for $0 < \nu < N$, as may be seen from equations (IV. 89 and 91). The numerical values of $s_{\mu\nu}^{(1)}$ for $N = 16$ are given in Table IV. 2; the coefficients of z_μ in equation (13), relevant to the second integral in (11), are given in the original paper by Weber.

The final form of equation (11) is $u(cx_\nu) = U_\infty \sum_{\mu=1}^{N-1} s_{\mu\nu} z_\mu$, the coefficients $s_{\mu\nu}$ being independent of the wing section. This method is suitable for routine applications, and the time needed to calculate the velocity distribution for each section of a given wing is about the same as that needed for a two-dimensional aerofoil. An example is given in Fig. VII. 5 for wings with the RAE 101 section; the effect of aspect ratio and the need for the correction in equation (5) are both illustrated.

Equations (11) to (14) are valid only if the surface slope is finite and continuous over the wing, and this condition is not always fulfilled. A modified procedure is then necessary, and it may be illustrated in the case of a wing tapered in thickness such that $z(x,y) = z(x,0)(1-\delta|y|)$, in which $\delta = (t_C - t_T)/st_C$, the suffix C denoting the centre section and the suffix T the tip section. The source distribution is, from equation (4), $q(x,y) = 2U_\infty(dz/dx)_{y=0}(1-\delta|y|)$ and depends on the spanwise coordinate, y. The factor $(1-\delta|y|)$ occurs inside the integral of equation (7). The y-integration can be performed and results in the following expression for the velocity distribution on the centre section:

$$\frac{u(x,0,0)}{U_\infty} = \left[\frac{u(x,0,0)}{U_\infty}\right]_{\delta=0} -$$

$$-\delta\left[\int_0^c \frac{dz}{dx'}\frac{|x-x'|}{(x-x')}\,dx - \frac{1}{\pi}\int_0^c \frac{dz}{dx'}\frac{(x-x')^2}{[(x-x')^2+s^2]^{\frac{3}{2}}}\frac{dx'}{x-x'}\right]. \quad (15)$$

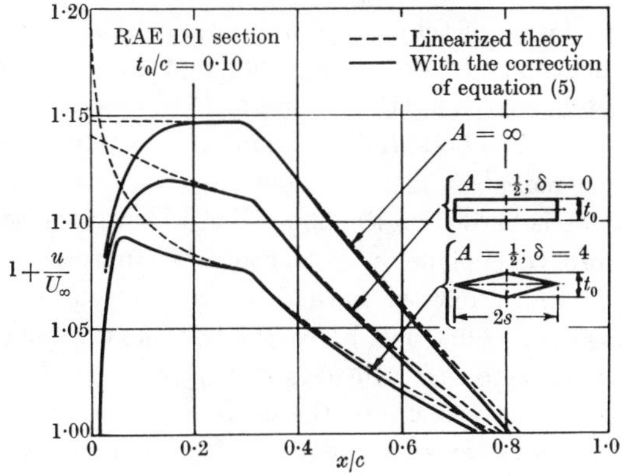

Fig. VII. 5. The velocity distributions at the centre sections of some straight wings.

The last integral, being of the type given in equation (12), can be calculated as in equation (13) but the first integral is

$$\int_0^c \frac{dz}{dx'}\frac{|x-x'|}{(x-x')}\,dx' = 2z(x).$$

This method of dealing with wings which are tapered in thickness is described in the paper by Weber (1954a) and an example of its use is included in Fig. VII. 5. The figure shows that thickness taper has a distinctly beneficial effect in reducing the velocity along the centre section and this is due to the three-dimensional nature of such wings being more pronounced than for untapered wings.

6. Slender-body theory

It was seen in Section 4 that the linearized theory might be seriously in error for wings of very small aspect ratio. Such wings are commonly called slender as they can alternatively be regarded as being very long, in the x-direction, in comparison with their span. This suggests that an approximation at least worth considering for a slender body is the neglect of x-derivatives in comparison with derivatives in the other two directions, the approximation presumably being better for the region near the body than for elsewhere. Laplace's equation for the displacement flow thus reduces to

$$\partial^2\phi/\partial y^2 + \partial^2\phi/\partial z^2 = 0. \tag{16}$$

For flows with lift, this equation is the basis of methods derived by Munk (1924) and by R. T. Jones (1946) which are described in Section VIII. 12; a variation of these applicable to non-lifting bodies has been proposed by Keune and Oswatitsch (1953), and Adams and Sears (1953) have reviewed and extended the general method based on equation (16).

Equation (16) is the potential equation for a two-dimensional flow in a transverse plane $x = $ constant. This may be solved if the normal derivative $\partial\phi/\partial n$ is known on the boundary, which is the section of the wing in the transverse plane. n is the coordinate normal to the contour of this section and is not the normal to the wing surface. Except in the trivial case of a cylindrical body, the boundary value of $\partial\phi/\partial n$ will be different from zero and will usually vary with x. Its exact value depends on the velocity vector on the surface and so on prior knowledge of the solution; however, if we neglect u in comparison with U_∞ as in the linearized theory, we find that on the boundary

$$\partial\phi/\partial n = \mathrm{v}_n = U_\infty(\partial z/\partial x)[1 + (\partial z/\partial y)^2]^{-\frac{1}{2}}, \tag{17}$$

the form of which equation is suitable if the shape of the body is given as $z = z(x, y)$. With this easily calculated value of $(\partial\phi/\partial n)$ at the boundary, equation (16) may be solved.

The three-dimensional problem has therefore been reduced to what amounts to a two-dimensional problem and the potential for the displacement flow is taken in the form

$$\phi(x, y, z) = \phi_1(y, z; x) + \phi_2(x), \tag{18}$$

ϕ_1 being the solution of (16) with x as a parameter. Nothing in the argument so far enables $\phi_2(x)$ to be determined, and this is a consequence of the approximation that the dependence of one transverse section on the next is ignored. Some further boundary condition therefore must be formulated for the calculation of $\phi_2(x)$, and this will be considered later when the solution of ϕ_1 has been completed.

The section of the wing in the transverse plane $\zeta = y + iz$ is first transformed into the circle $|\zeta_1| = r$ in the plane $\zeta_1 = y_1 + iz_1$. In this latter plane, the normal velocity, v_{n1}, is given by

$$\mathrm{v}_{n1} = \mathrm{v}_n |d\zeta/d\zeta_1|. \tag{19}$$

The total flux through the circle is $\int\limits_0^{2\pi} v_{n1} r \, d\theta$: this suggests a concentrated source at $\zeta_1 = 0$ of strength

$$Q(x) = r \int\limits_0^{2\pi} v_{n1} \, d\theta = 2\pi r \bar{v}_{n1} \qquad (20)$$

which induces a normal velocity $\bar{v}_{n1}$ at the circle. The residual normal velocity is $(v_{n1} - \bar{v}_{n1})$ which, since its total flux is zero, can be represented by a source distribution $q(\theta)$ on the circle given by

$$q(\theta) = 2(v_{n1} - \bar{v}_{n1}), \qquad (21)$$

as shown by Betz (1948). The complete solution for the potential, due to both $Q(x)$ and $q(\theta)$, is therefore

$$\phi_1(\zeta_1) = [Q(x)/2\pi]\log|\zeta_1| + (r/2\pi)\int\limits_0^{2\pi} q(\theta')\log|\zeta_1 - \zeta_1'| \, d\theta'. \qquad (22)$$

If we substitute the values of Q and q from (20) and (21) and take values on the circle, (22) becomes

$$\phi_1(\zeta_1) = (r/\pi)\int\limits_0^{2\pi} v_{n1}(\theta')[\log|\zeta_1 - \zeta_1'| - \tfrac{1}{2}\log r] \, d\theta'.$$

For the particular case of a symmetrical wing, $v_{n1}(\theta') = v_{n1}(-\theta')$ and so

$$\phi_1(\zeta) = (r/\pi)\int\limits_0^{\pi} v_{n1}(\theta')\log 2|y_1 - y_1'| \, d\theta', \qquad (23)$$

in which v_{n1} is given by equation (19).

The most laborious part of the calculation of ϕ_1 is the determination of the conformal transformation. The subsequent algebra in finding first y_1 as a function of y and then $|d\zeta/d\zeta_1|$ which is needed to determine v_{n1} from equation (19), may be slightly simplified by working in terms of the new variable ζ_2 given by $\zeta_2 = y_2 + iz_2 = \zeta_1 + r^2/\zeta_1$. By this the circle is transformed into a cut of length $4r$ along the y_2-axis. It may be shown that equation (23) is equivalent to

$$\phi_1(y, z; x) = (1/\pi)\int\limits_{-s(x)}^{+s(x)} [\partial z(y')/\partial x]\log|y_2(y) - y_2(y')| \, dy', \qquad (24)$$

where s is the length of arc of the contour of the section in the physical plane.

The analysis given so far has depended only on the shape of each transverse cross-section of the wing: the relative sizes of these cross-sections should therefore be taken into account by $\phi_2(x)$ of equation

(18) and should provide the further condition which we have already noted to be necessary. This is not a simple matter and for a satisfactory treatment solutions of the full Laplace equation must be considered. In a similar way, Ward (1949) and Adams and Sears (1953) have developed an expression for ϕ_2. Here, we consider a body of revolution whose distribution, $S(x)$, of cross-sectional area is the same as that of the given wing. For such a slender body of revolution, the total potential $\phi(x, r)$ and the partial potential $\phi_1(r; x)$ are both known, and $\phi_2(x)$ is obtained as the difference between them. Now, for a body of revolution, $\mathrm{v}_n = U_\infty(dr/dx)$ to the usual approximation: this may be induced by a source distribution, $Q(x)$, along the x-axis given by

$$Q(x) = 2\pi r \mathrm{v}_n = 2\pi r U_\infty(dr/dx) = U_\infty(dS(x)/dx),$$

where $r^2 = y^2 + z^2$. Thus

$$\phi(x, r) = -\frac{1}{4\pi} \int_0^c \frac{Q(x')\, dx'}{[(x-x')^2 + r^2]^{\frac{1}{2}}} = -\frac{U_\infty}{4\pi} \int_0^c \frac{dS(x')}{dx'} \frac{dx'}{[(x-x')^2 + r^2]^{\frac{1}{2}}}$$

and, from equation (22),

$$\phi_1(r; x) = (U_\infty/2\pi)[dS(x)/dx]\log r(x).$$

The difference of these two expressions is $\phi_2(x)$; thus, after some integrations by parts, we obtain

$$-(2\pi/U_\infty)\phi_2(x)$$

$$= \frac{dS(x)}{dx}\log 2 + \frac{1}{2}\left[\frac{dS(x)}{dx}\right]_{x=0}\log x + \frac{1}{2}\left[\frac{dS(x)}{dx}\right]_{x=c}\log(c-x) +$$

$$+ \frac{1}{2}\int_0^x \frac{d^2 S(x')}{dx'^2}\log(x-x')\, dx' - \frac{1}{2}\int_x^c \frac{d^2 S(x')}{dx'^2}\log(x'-x)\, dx', \quad (25)$$

in the derivation of which the assumption of slender-body theory has been used again. This is the expression obtained by Adams and Sears (1953), and in the present theory is taken to be the value of $\phi_2(x)$ for a body of any shape whose distribution of cross-sectional area is $S(x)$.

The full solution for the displacement flow, as given by slender-body theory, is thus obtained as the sum of the two partial potentials, ϕ_1 and ϕ_2, given in equations (24) and (25). The pressure field may be obtained from Bernoulli's equation: the approximation, $C_p = -2u/U_\infty$, of linearized theory is not consistent with the assumptions of slender-body theory since it neglects terms containing $\partial\phi/\partial y$ and $\partial\phi/\partial z$. The appropriate approximation is $C_p = -2u/U_\infty - [(v/U_\infty)^2 + (w/U_\infty)^2]$.

Let us apply the slender-body theory to the simple case of flow past ellipsoids, considered by Weber (1954a). For an ellipsoid whose semi-axes are (i) $\frac{1}{2}t$, half the maximum thickness of the centre section, (ii) s, the semi-span, (iii) $\frac{1}{2}c$, half the centre chord, the distribution of thickness is given by

$$z(x,y) = (t/2c)[c^2-(c-2x)^2-(cy/s)^2]^{\frac{1}{2}}. \tag{26}$$

If $16c^2R^2 = (4s^2-t^2)(c^2-(c-2x)^2)$, the transformation $\zeta = \zeta_1+R^2/\zeta_1$ transforms a cross-section in the plane $x = $ constant into a circle of radius $r = [(2s+t)/4c][c^2-(c-2x)^2]^{\frac{1}{2}}$. Equations (17), (20), and (21) lead to

$$v_{n1} = U_\infty[4st/(2s+t)c](c-2x)[c^2-(c-2x)^2]^{-\frac{1}{2}} = \bar{v}_{n1} = Q(x)/2\pi r. \tag{27}$$

In this case, there is no source distribution on the circle since $q(\theta) = 0$ by equation (23). The partial potential ϕ_1 is then, by equation (22),

$$\phi_1(y,z;x) = U_\infty ts(c-2x)[\log\{(2s+t)/4c\}+\tfrac{1}{2}\log\{4x(c-x)/c^2\}]/c^2,$$

and from equation (25),

$$\phi_2(x) = U_\infty ts(c-2x)[1-\tfrac{1}{2}\log\{4x(c-x)/c^2\}]/c^2.$$

The complete potential for the displacement flow is therefore

$$\phi(x,y,z) = U_\infty ts(c-2x)[1+\log\{(2s+t)/4c\}]/c^2 \tag{28}$$

and the streamwise velocity increment is given by

$$u/U_\infty = (t/b)(\pi A/4)^2[-1-\log\{\pi A(1+t/b)/16\}], \tag{29}$$

in which the aspect ratio, $A = 8s/\pi c$, and the span, $b = 2s$, of the wing are introduced.

According to this theory the velocity increment on an ellipsoid is constant over the whole surface and depends only on the aspect ratio and the thickness-span ratio. A more accurate result, especially near the leading and trailing edges of the ellipsoid, can be obtained by introducing the factor in equation (6). In comparison with the result (9) for the untapered wing of elliptic section, the ellipsoidal wing has a slightly smaller velocity increment than the untapered wing, for the same aspect ratio and thickness. Some numerical values from equation (29) are shown in Fig. VII. 6 and compared with the exact values, taken from Maruhn (1941). The expectation is confirmed that the accuracy of the theory improves with decrease of thickness and aspect ratio: for sufficiently small values of these two properties, the slender-body theory is appreciably superior to the linearized theory.

Both these theories are of practical importance owing to their relevance to compressible flow. Applying to equation (29) the argument resulting in equation (10), we have for subsonic compressible flow past an ellipsoid

$$u_c/U_\infty = (t/b)(\pi A/4)^2[-1-\log\{\pi A\beta(1+t/b)/16\}] \qquad (30)$$

which includes the ellipsoid of revolution as the special case $t/b = 1$. This result agrees with the exact solution, or with experimental results,

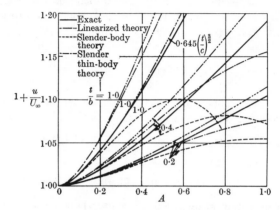

FIG. VII. 6. A comparison between the values, obtained by various theories, of the velocity at the mid-chord points of the centre sections of ellipsoids.

only if βA is small; thus either the ratio $(4/\pi A)$ must be large or the Mach number of the stream close to unity. A better result is obtained, as shown in Fig. VII. 6, if the incompressible velocity increment u_i is taken empirically as $0\cdot645U_\infty(t/c)^{\frac{3}{2}}$: this leads to $u_c/u_i = \beta^{\frac{3}{2}}$.

The application of slender-body theory is difficult in a general case largely because of the transformation of the cross-section of the wing into circles. Keune (1952) overcame much of this difficulty by replacing the term $[y_2(y)-y_2(y')]$ in equation (24) by $(y-y')$. This amounts to placing the source distribution $q(y,z)$ in the chordal plane $z = 0$ instead of on the boundary of the cross-section, and to determining its strength according to linearized theory in analogy with equation (4). In the calculation of u, a similar simplification is made by taking values in $z = 0$ rather than on the surface of the wing. This version of the theory may be called slender thin-body theory. In the case of ellipsoids, it leads to the omission of t/b in the logarithmic term of equation (30) and to numerical results which, as may be seen in Fig. VII. 6, are rather closer to the exact results than to those of the unapproximated slender-body theory. This latter consequence could hardly have been foretold and must be regarded, in the present state of knowledge, as coincidental.

It remains to determine how the results from slender-body theory compare with those of the standard linearized theory for thin wings. As shown by Weber (1954a), the main results of the two theories do not agree and the values of u tend to zero in a different manner as A tends to zero: while u from slender-body theory behaves like the exact solution, u from linearized theory for thin wings behaves like the solution from slender thin-body theory. Some numerical results for ellipsoids are shown in Fig. VII. 6 and indicate the scope for improvement of the theories. Keune (1953) has extended his slender thin-body theory to bring its results practically in line with those from ordinary slender-body theory; Adams and Sears (1953) have proposed an extension of slender-body theory to not-so-slender bodies. But both extensions are necessarily rather complicated.

7. Infinite sheared wings

It will have been noticed that, in the previous sections, the flow past unswept wings was considered from a distinctly two-dimensional standpoint which is seriously at fault only near the tips of a wing and in cases of very small aspect ratio. Such a conception, however, is found to fail altogether when we come to consider swept wings for which the displacement flow is of a different kind from those already considered. Fig. VII. 7 illustrates the streamlines in the flow past a typical swept-back wing. The flow near the centre section is dominated by the kink, and similarly the tips strongly affect the flow near them. But provided the aspect ratio is sufficiently large, there will be a region between the centre section and the tips in which the flow is largely unaffected by either and in which the dominant effect is the sweep itself. It is this primary effect of sweep which is studied in this section.

It is instructive to consider an infinite sheared wing derived from a straight wing of infinite aspect ratio so that the sections of the two wings at corresponding points are the same. Thus if $z(x) = 0$ represents the straight wing, $z(x - y \tan \varphi) = 0$ is the sheared wing, swept-back through $\varphi°$. Study of the flow past this wing will not only bring out the inherent properties of sweep but will also enable numerical estimates to be made of the effect of variations in φ. The coordinate system for this wing is shown in Fig. VII. 8. The sweep may be taken into account by resolving the stream velocity into the two components U_∞ and V_∞ perpendicular and parallel to the leading edge. The uniform velocity field $(0, V_\infty, 0)$, since it does not violate the boundary condition on the wing, may be added to the velocity field $(U_\infty + u, 0, w)$ due solely to a stream $(U_\infty; 0, 0)$ at infinity. The complete field is therefore given by

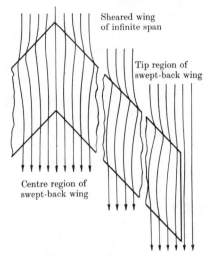

Fig. VII. 7. A sketch of the pattern of streamlines over the various parts of a swept-back wing, in the absence of separation.

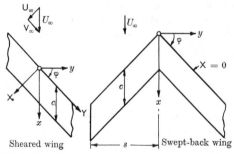

Fig. VII. 8. Coordinate systems for sheared and swept wings.

$(U_\infty + u, V_\infty, w)$. Now u at any point is proportional to $U_\infty = U_\infty \cos\varphi$. Also $V_\infty = U_\infty \sin\varphi$. Thus if $u < 0$, the streamline is deflected towards the downstream tip, while if $u > 0$, it is deflected in the opposite direction.

If we now recall from our knowledge of two-dimensional flows the distribution of u, the pattern of the streamline traces in $z = 0$ shown in Fig. VII. 7 is understood: the maximum deflexion of the streamlines in the outward direction occurs at the leading edge where u equals $-U_\infty$, while the maximum deflexion in the opposite direction occurs when u is maximum, that is on the line of minimum pressure. This phenomenon, that any one streamline for the uniform flow $(U_\infty, 0, 0)$ does not lie in a plane $y = $ constant, is an important characteristic of the flow past an infinite sheared wing, or past a finite swept wing in a region away from both the centre section and the tips.

If a finite swept wing is symmetrical about the plane $y = 0$, this plane is, presumably, a plane of symmetry for the flow field and contains completely the streamlines which are in it at infinity upstream; the flow in this centre section therefore differs radically from the flow which occurs some way from the centre section.

It may be mentioned that swept wings are of practical importance primarily on account of their properties at high speeds, as suggested originally by Busemann (1928) and Betz (1940). The beneficial properties are directly connected with the flow pattern found on an infinite sheared wing, while the distortions of the flow introduced by the central kink have a detrimental effect.

The linearized theory of Section 4 may be applied to the partial field $(u, 0, w)$ due to the oncoming stream $(U_\infty, 0, 0)$. The appropriate source distribution will consist of a continuous distribution of source lines, $Q(X)$, in $z = 0$ parallel to the leading edge, given by $Q(X) = 2U_\infty(\partial z/\partial X)$. But $U_\infty = U_\infty \cos\varphi$ and $\partial X/\partial x = \cos\varphi$. Thus $Q(X) = 2U_\infty(\partial z/\partial x)$, which is the source distribution for the straight wing of the same section. u is then given by

$$u/U_\infty = (1/2\pi U_\infty) \int_0^{c\cos\varphi} Q(X')\, dX'/(X - X')$$

$$= (1/\pi) \int_0^c [dz(x')/dx']\, dx'/(x - x'). \tag{31}$$

This interesting result says that the increment of speed on the sheared wing perpendicular to the sweep is the same as that on the corresponding two-dimensional wing. Since the velocity vector of the displacement flow is not parallel to the stream, the fluid speed at any point on the sheared wing is less than that on the straight wing. In particular, this analysis gives $u = u_{\varphi=0} \cos\varphi$ and $C_p = (C_p)_{\varphi=0} \cos\varphi$. It must be understood that these widely-quoted 'cosφ-rules' or 'simple sweep theories' are the result of a linearized theory and are not exact even for an infinite sheared wing of constant section.

The results so far obtained require some improvement, especially near the edges, according to the ideas of equation (5). Thus the speed in the X-direction is best given by

$$\frac{U_\infty \cos\varphi + u(x,0)}{[1+\{dz(x)/dx\}^2]^{\frac{1}{2}}} = \frac{U_\infty[\cos\varphi + S^{(1)}(x)]}{[1+\{\sec\varphi\, S^{(2)}(x)\}^2]^{\frac{1}{2}}}, \qquad (32)$$

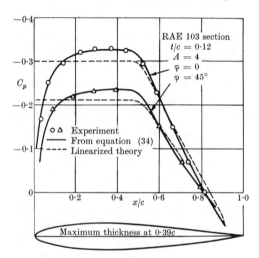

Fig. VII. 9. A comparison between the chordwise pressure distributions of an unswept wing and a sheared wing of 45° sweep-back.

in which the functions $S^{(1)}(x)$ from equation (14) and

$$S^{(2)}(cx_\nu) = [dz(t)/dt]_{t=cx_\nu} = \sum_{\mu=1}^{N-1} s^{(2)}_{\mu\nu} z_\mu \qquad (33)$$

of Weber (1953) have been introduced; the form of these equations enables a standardized numerical procedure to be adopted and the coefficients $s^{(1)}_{\mu\nu}$ in the expression for $S^{(1)}$, and $s^{(2)}_{\mu\nu}$ have been given in Table IV. 2 for $N = 20$. The suffix μ refers, here, to the point

$$x = cx_\mu = (\tfrac{1}{2}c)\{1 + \cos(\mu\pi/N)\}.$$

Remembering the speed at infinity in the Y-direction is $V_\infty = U_\infty \sin\varphi$, we may use equation (32) to obtain the speed on the surface: the pressure coefficient, C_p, may then be calculated from Bernoulli's equation as

$$C_p = [-2\cos\varphi S^{(1)}(x) - \{S^{(1)}(x)\}^2 + \{S^{(2)}(x)\}^2][1+\{\sec\varphi S^{(2)}(x)\}^2]^{-1}. \quad (34)$$

If this relation is linearized by omitting quadratic terms in the functions $S^{(1)}$ and $S^{(2)}$, which contain the thickness-chord ratio t/c as a factor, the form for the pressure coefficient already quoted is obtained:

$$C_p(x) = -2\cos\varphi \, S^{(1)}(x) = \cos\varphi [C_p(x)]_{\varphi=0}.$$

The fact that this formula does not hold with the same accuracy over the whole chord is indicated in Fig. VII. 9, where results from equation (34) are given; furthermore, as the angle of sweep increases it becomes more important to include the correction term of equation (5) and to calculate C_p from equation (34).

8. The centre section of swept wings

The physical flow is now becoming more complicated, and so little hesitation is felt in adopting the simplest analytical devices. Thus we

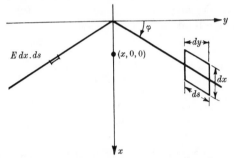

Fig. VII. 10. Notation for a kinked source line of strength $E\,dx$ per unit length.

shall investigate the flow near the centre section $y = 0$ of an infinite swept-back wing, as shown in Fig. VII. 8, from the first by a technique of linearization based on a source distribution in $z = 0$. To achieve analytical simplicity we even postulate that the source distribution consists of kinked source lines of constant spanwise strength as sketched in Fig. VII. 10. Further, at any rate to begin with, advantage will be taken of the symmetry of the wing and values will be calculated only in the centre section $y = 0$.

The source distribution for the wing, according to linearized theory, is given by equation (4) and is $2U_\infty(\partial z/\partial x)$ per unit area. If this is represented by a distribution of kinked source lines of strength $E(x)\,dx$ per unit length, consideration of the parallelogram element of area in Fig. VII. 10 leads to

$$2U_\infty(\partial z/\partial x)\,dxdy = E\,dxds = E\,dxdy \sec\varphi.$$

Thus
$$E(x) = 2U_\infty \cos\varphi(\partial z/\partial x). \tag{35}$$

The double integrals for the velocity component $u(x, 0, z)$ are simple to formulate. Küchemann and Weber (1953*b*) obtained the following equation by integrating along the span first:

$$u(x, 0, z) = \cos\varphi[I_1(x, 0, z) + I_2(x, 0, z)], \tag{36}$$

where
$$I_1(x, 0, z) = \frac{U_\infty}{\pi} \int_0^c \frac{\partial z(x')}{\partial x'} \frac{x - x'}{(x - x')^2 + z^2 \sec^2\varphi} \, dx'$$

and

$$I_2(x, 0, z) = -\frac{U_\infty \sin\varphi}{\pi} \int_0^c \frac{\partial z(x')}{\partial x'} \frac{z^2 \sec^2\varphi}{[(x - x')^2 + z^2 \sec^2\varphi][(x - x')^2 + z^2]^{\frac{1}{2}}} \, dx'.$$

This calculation has been made for the point $(x, 0, z)$ rather than for $(x, 0, 0)$ to avoid the singular behaviour of the velocity field in $z = 0$. Now, however, the limit as $z \to 0$ can be taken. The first integral then becomes

$$I_1(x, 0, 0) = \frac{U_\infty}{\pi} \int_0^c \frac{\partial z(x')}{\partial x'} \frac{dx'}{(x - x')} = [u(x, 0)]_{\varphi=0} = S^{(1)}(x) \tag{37}$$

and, from (36), contributes a term $u_{\varphi=0} \cos\varphi$ to $u(x, 0, 0)$. This is the contribution to the velocity which is due only to the sweep and was obtained, for an infinite sheared wing, in Section 7. The effect of the kink is therefore contained in I_2 and in the limit as $z \to 0$ it may be shown that

$$I_2(x, 0, 0) = -U_\infty(\partial z/\partial x)f(\varphi) = -(U_\infty/\pi)(\partial z/\partial x)\log[(1 + \sin\varphi)/(1 - \sin\varphi)]. \tag{38}$$

Using equations (36), (37), and (38), we may write the displacement velocity on the centre section in the form

$$u(x, 0, 0) = u_{\varphi=0} \cos\varphi - \cos\varphi(\partial z/\partial x)f(\varphi). \tag{39}$$

TABLE VII. 1

Values of the function $f(\phi)$

$36\varphi^c/\pi$	$f(\varphi)$	$36\varphi^c/\pi$	$f(\varphi)$
0	0		
1	0·056	10	0·643
2	0·112	11	0·735
3	0·169	12	0·838
4	0·227	13	0·959
5	0·287	14	1·105
6	0·350	15	1·291
7	0·316	16	1·551
8	0·486	17	1·993
9	0·561	18	∞

Some numerical values of $f(\varphi)$ are given in Table VII. 1. For values of φ up to about $\frac{1}{6}\pi$, the first two terms $(2\varphi+\frac{1}{3}\varphi^3)/\pi$ in the Taylor expansion give a good approximation to $f(\varphi)$. Equation (39) can be put in terms of the functions $S^{(1)}(x)$ and $S^{(2)}(x)$ which, from equations (14) and (33), represent approximately the shape of the wing; the displacement velocity can then be written

$$u(x,0,0)/U_\infty = \cos\varphi[S^{(1)}(x)-f(\varphi)S^{(2)}(x)]. \qquad (40)$$

This result will be seriously inaccurate near the leading and trailing edges and, as in previous cases, can be improved so that finally

$$1+u/U_\infty = [1+\cos\varphi S^{(1)}(x)-\cos\varphi f(\varphi)S^{(2)}(x)][1+\{S^{(2)}(x)\}^2]^{-\frac{1}{2}}. \qquad (41)$$

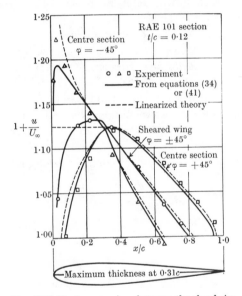

FIG. VII. 11. A comparison between the chordwise velocity distributions at centre sections of swept wings and sheared wings.

Numerical results are illustrated in Fig. VII. 11 in which sweep-back and sweep-forward of 45° are compared with shear of 45°. It will be seen that the velocity distribution at the kink section is very different from that far away from it and also that equation (41) seems to give a satisfactory approximation. It is interesting to note that, in the case of the RAE 101 section, the maximum speed on the swept-back wing is less than that on a sheared wing; this is by no means so for all section shapes. Further, in the former case, it is not correct to infer that the critical Mach number of the centre section is greater than that elsewhere on the wing or on the corresponding infinite sheared wing, since this Mach number depends also on the configuration of isobars.

The effects of the kink section on the flow past a swept wing were first pointed out by Göthert (1942) for swept-forward wings and by Krüger (1946) for swept-back wings. Calculations for the biconvex parabolic and other related aerofoil sections have been made by R. T. Jones (1947), Neumark (1947), and Ursell (1949) on the basis of linearized theory, and by Küchemann (1947) and Küchemann and Weber (1953b) for general section shapes. A detailed account of the theory together with further refinements has been given by Weber (1953).

The inverse problem, that of determining the shape for a given velocity distribution at the centre section, may be treated with some success on the basis of linearized theory. One approach would state equation (40) at, say, the $(N-1)$ points $x = cx_\nu$: the $(N-1)$ values of $z(cx_\nu)$ which occur in the S-functions could then be calculated by solving the $(N-1)$ simultaneous linear equations. There is much in this which is similar to the work involved in the two-dimensional inverse problem. A more elegant approach which avoids the solution of a system of linear equations is due to Ursell (1949). He puts equation (39) in the form

$$\frac{dz(x)}{dx} = \frac{1}{\pi f(\varphi)} \int_0^c \frac{dz(x')}{dx'} \frac{dx'}{x-x'} - \frac{u(x)}{\cos\varphi f(\varphi)},$$

the values of z being those for the centre section, and shows that its solution is

$$\frac{dz}{dx} = -\frac{u}{U_\infty} \frac{\sec\varphi f(\varphi)}{[1+\{f(\varphi)\}^2]} - \frac{\sec\varphi}{\pi[1+\{f(\varphi)\}^2]} \left(\frac{x}{c-x}\right)^\Theta \int_0^c \left(\frac{c-x'}{x'}\right)^\Theta \frac{x'}{x} \frac{u(x')}{U_\infty} \frac{dx'}{x-x'},$$

(42)

in which $\Theta = \frac{1}{2}-(1/\pi)\tan^{-1}f(\varphi)$. This solution fulfils the closing condition $\int_0^c (dz/dx)\, dx = 0$. The integral in equation (42) is of the type $(1/\pi)\int_0^c F(x'/c)\, dx'/(x-x')$ where $F(0) = F(c) = 0$, and can be approximated in the form

$$\frac{1}{\pi} \int_0^1 \frac{F(x'/c)d(x'/c)}{x_\nu-x'/c} = \sum_{\mu=1}^{N-1} (x_\mu-x_\nu)s_{\mu\nu}^{(1)}F(x_\mu).$$

(43)

Equation (42) may then be written approximately as a sum, and its integral similarly; this procedure finally gives

$$z(cx_\nu) = c \sum_{\mu=1}^{N-1} s_{\mu\nu}^{(19)} u(cx_\mu)/U_\infty. \qquad (44)$$

The coefficients $s_{\mu\nu}^{(19)}$ have been tabulated by Weber (1955), so that the calculation of the section shape for a given velocity distribution at the kink presents no difficulties. The values of $s_{\mu\nu}^{(19)}$ depend, of course, on the angle of sweep.

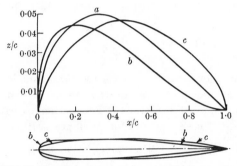

FIG. VII. 12. The same chordwise velocity distribution is given
by the following wings of 45° sweep:

section (a) RAE 101 section, $t/c = 0.1$, on sheared part of the wing;
section (b) at centre section of swept-back wing;
section (c) at centre section of swept-forward wing.

If the velocity distribution at the centre of a swept wing is chosen to be the same as that of a given infinite sheared wing, the general tendency is for the position of maximum thickness on the swept wing to be forward, in the case of sweep-back, of its position on the sheared wing and to be rearward, in the case of sweep-forward. A typical comparison is shown in Fig. VII. 12. There is also a marked inflexion at the rear of the section for the swept-back wing and a considerable reduction of the nose thickness of the section of the swept-forward wing. The differences in thickness-chord ratio are usually less significant than the change $\Delta x/c$ in the position of maximum thickness. As a rough rule, $\Delta x/c = \varphi^c/2\pi$ as shown by Küchemann and Weber (1953b).

In contrast to the two-dimensional flow past an aerofoil and to the flow past an infinite sheared wing, the three-dimensional flow past an infinite swept wing results in a drag force even if it experiences no lift, as we shall see again in Section 9. The drag, being a result of the normal pressures over the surface of the wing, may be calculated; $C_D(y)$, the drag coefficient for each section, is given by $C_D(y) = \int C_p\,dz$. Alternatively, a theorem given by Betz (1932) says that

$$C_D(y) = -2\int_0^c \frac{U(x)}{U_\infty}\frac{q(x)}{U_\infty}\frac{dx}{c} = -2\int_0^c \frac{u(x)}{U_\infty}\frac{q(x)}{U_\infty}\frac{dx}{c}, \qquad (45)$$

the calculation being made at $y = 0$ for simplicity. Now u is given in equation (39) and the contribution to C_D of the term $u_{\varphi=0}\cos\varphi$ is zero, since that term refers to a two-dimensional wing. Thus (45) becomes

$$C_D(0) = 4\cos\varphi f(\varphi)\int_0^c \frac{\partial z}{\partial x}\frac{1}{c}\frac{dx}{\left[1-(\partial z/\partial x)^2\right]} \qquad (46)$$

if the approximations of equations (4) and (5) are made.

The sectional drag coefficient can be calculated easily for the two particular wings quoted in Section 5. For a biconvex parabolic section $C_D(0) = (16/3)(t/c)^2\cos\varphi f(\varphi)$, and for an elliptic section

$$C_D(0) = 4(t/c)^2\cos\varphi f(\varphi)[\mathbf{K}(k)-\mathbf{E}(k)]/k^2.$$

Here $k^2 = 1-(t/c)^2$, and $\mathbf{K}(k)$ and $\mathbf{E}(k)$ are the complete elliptic integrals of the first and second kind respectively. Although proportional only to the square of the thickness-chord ratio, the drag force can nevertheless be considerably greater than the skin-friction drag. For example, a 10 per cent thick elliptic section, swept-back through $45°$, has a drag coefficient of 0.043: the same degree of sweep-forward results in a thrust of the same magnitude.

An exception to the general result that the kink section experiences a drag has been noted by Weber (1955) who produced an exact solution to equation (42). She assumed a constant velocity distribution, $u(x) = CU_\infty$ (which leads to an ellipse in the two-dimensional case), and found that

$$dz/dx = -C\sec\varphi[1+\{f(\varphi)\}^2]^{-\frac{1}{2}}[x/(c-x)]^\Theta(1-\Theta c/x),$$

Θ having the same value as in equation (42). This gives a reasonable section shape in that it does not cross itself. Since $q(x) = 2U_\infty(dz/dx)$ and $u(x)$ is constant, equation (45) gives

$$C_D(0) = -(2/c)\int_0^c \{u(x)/U_\infty\}(dz/dx)\,dx = -(2C/c)\int_0^c dz = 0.$$

The determination of the velocity increment at sections other than the centre section leads to cumbersome formulae even with the simplest analysis of linearized theory, but they are given in the paper by Küchemann and Weber (1953*b*). Calculations for wings of biconvex parabolic section have been made by Neumark (1947) and his result for $C_D(y)$ for a certain wing is shown in Fig. VII. 13. For other section shapes the effect of the kink can also be expected to decrease fairly

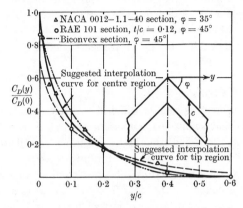

Fig. VII. 13. The spanwise variation of the local drag coefficient on certain swept wings.

rapidly in the spanwise direction and may be estimated by interpolation between conditions for a sheared wing and those at a kink. Since the velocity distribution for the sheared wing is represented by the first two terms in equation (41), a reasonable approximation for the velocity on the swept wing should therefore be obtained by multiplying the second term by a factor, depending on y, which is unity at the centre and approaches zero for large y. This factor may be conveniently taken as $C_D(y)/C_D(0)$. In Fig. VII. 13 measured values of this ratio for two other wings are compared with those calculated by Neumark for the biconvex parabolic section and are seen not to differ greatly: a mean curve may be taken for the purposes of interpolation.

It is noticeable that the influence of the kink, at any rate for moderate angles of sweep, does not reach farther than about half-a-chord's length from the centre section.

The flow near a centre section is closely related to that near a crank at which the angle of sweep changes abruptly. It can be seen intuitively that conditions at a crank, where the sweep is greater on the inboard side than on the outboard, bear some resemblance to conditions at the centre of a swept-forward wing; working on this line of thought, Brebner (1953) investigated the flow in the region of a crank and found that the velocity at the crank section may be expressed approximately by

$$1 + \frac{u}{U_\infty} = \frac{1 + \frac{1}{2}(\cos\varphi_1 + \cos\varphi_2)S^{(1)}(x) - \cos\frac{1}{2}(\varphi_1 + \varphi_2)f(\varphi^*)S^{(2)}(x)}{[1 + \{S^{(2)}(x)\sec\frac{1}{2}(\varphi_1 + \varphi_2)\}^2]^{\frac{1}{4}}},$$

where φ_1 is the angle of sweep on the inboard side of the crank, φ_2 that on the outboard, and φ^* is defined by $\tan\varphi^* = \frac{1}{2}(\tan\varphi_2 - \tan\varphi_1)$. We notice the resemblance to equation (41). The effect of a crank may be expected to be similar to the centre-section effect in the manner of spanwise decay of influence.

9. The tips of a wing

One of the interesting results which have come out of our study of swept wings is that such wings experience a drag force. This appears to be a contradiction of d'Alembert's hypothesis until we recall that we have so far been studying wings of infinite extent; the disturbance at infinity due to the wing produces changes in momentum and pressure which exactly account for the drag force on the wing as a whole. A finite wing, however, must be free of any such total drag force and since we have seen in Section 8 that, for swept-back wings, there is a drag in the centre region, there is presumably an equal thrust exerted on the tip regions.

A serious difficulty arises as soon as we try to apply the simple linearized theory to the flow near the tips of a finite wing. Consider a finite sheared wing, in $-s \leqslant y \leqslant s$, represented by a source distribution whose strength is given by equation (4) and which, so far in our analysis, has proved more or less adequate. At the tips, the spanwise velocity component tends logarithmically to infinity and the velocity component normal to the surface, taken in $z = 0$, jumps discontinuously from $\frac{1}{2}q$ in $-s < y < s$ to 0 for $|y| > s$. The streamwise velocity increment at the tips is also only half that of a two-dimensional distribution. This singular behaviour has, of course, already been found at the leading and trailing edges of the wing and is a feature of linearized theory: it is not inherent in the idea of representation by a source distribution and may be overcome, in principle, by ensuring that the source distribution is completely enclosed by the contour of the body and by calculating the velocity components in space, outside the source layer, where they are finite and continuous. We have seen nevertheless that, even if the source distribution does extend to the leading and trailing edges, it is possible to deal in a simple manner with the singularities there on two-dimensional aerofoils and on certain three-dimensional wings. This is the linearized theory with correction terms according to equations (5) and (6). No such simple correction has yet been found for the tips of wings with finite tip chord and, in the absence of any exact solution, we have to be content with some crude approximation. The strength of the source distribution as given by linearized theory is obviously seriously incorrect: this theory suggests source lines of constant strength along the span to represent a wing of constant thickness but the actual wing produced by these finite source lines grows thinner towards the tips and also extends beyond the source distribution. Therefore, a wing of constant thickness must be represented by a source distribution whose strength increases towards the tips, and so the normal and streamwise velocity increments are each greater than half their value for the two-dimensional aerofoil. We may expect the value of the streamwise velocity increment to lie between that for a wing of infinite span and half this value; and it appears reasonable to apply a factor, constant over the chord, with a value between 1·0 and 0·5, to the chordwise velocity distribution obtained for infinite span. At present, this factor must be chosen from experimental results and they suggest a value of about 0·7.

A very simplified conception arises from the consideration of sweep, as it affects the preceding argument. The striking characteristic of the flow past swept wings, namely the curved streamlines shown in Fig. VII. 7, may be expected to weaken as the tips are approached and to disappear at quite a short distance outboard of the tips. $v = 0$ may therefore be an acceptable approximation on $y = \pm s$ and this also holds at the centre or kink section of a swept wing. We are thus led to liken the tip region of a swept-back wing to the centre region of a swept-forward wing of the same angle of sweep. Hence we could write, using equation (41),

$$1 + \frac{u}{U_\infty} = \frac{1 + 0 \cdot 7 \cos \varphi \left[S^{(1)}(x) - f(-\varphi) S^{(2)}(x) \right]}{\left[1 + \{ S^{(2)}(x) \}^2 \right]^{\frac{1}{2}}} \tag{47}$$

for the tip section of a semi-infinite sheared, or swept, wing. Further refinements are discussed by Küchemann and Weber (1953b). Fig. VII. 14 shows that this theory gives fair agreement with the experimentally observed features. It also shows that conditions at the centre and at the tips are not affected much by the value of the aspect ratio, even for values of A as low as unity; our argument indeed applies so long as

the aspect ratio is large enough to prevent interaction between the tip
and centre sections.

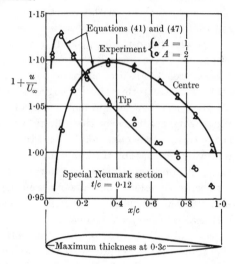

Fig. VII. 14. The chordwise distributions of velocity at the centre
and tip sections of two untapered wings of 53° sweep-back.

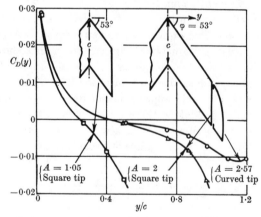

Fig. VII. 15. The spanwise variation of the local drag coefficient
of some untapered wings of 53° sweep-back.

The suggestion that the tip region of a swept-back wing is similar to
the centre region of a swept-forward wing leads to a thrust near the tips
just as a drag occurs at the centre; in this way we see how the drag for
the whole wing is zero. Fig. VII. 15 shows the measured spanwise

distribution of drag for three wings of different aspect ratios but of the same sweep.

The velocity distribution on sections near the tips may be estimated by an interpolation between the conditions at the tip and those on the sheared wing. The interpolation function may be constructed according to ideas analogous to those used in Section 8 for sections near the centre of a wing. The function proposed for the tip region is illustrated in Fig. VII. 13, in which y is now measured from the tip.

10. Wings of general planform

It might at first be thought that none of the specialized flows so far considered is relevant to the flow past a wing of general shape, a wing which is tapered in both chord and thickness. The basic equations of the two theories—the linearized and the slender-body theories—are, of course, just as applicable to the general case as to the specialized ones; but the numerical work is enormously greater and to undertake it as a general routine would not be advisable without the use of an electronic computer.

Yet it has been found that quite drastic simplifications may be made in the application of the linearized theory to general wings without serious loss of accuracy, and these will briefly be explained. It must, however, be remembered that, as the error of the linearized theory cannot be estimated, still less can that of some arbitrarily simplified version of it. Indeed it is one of the weaknesses of both the theories of this chapter that neither their errors, nor any limits to them, can be expressed analytically, and that neither theory is exact as a limiting case.

The slender-body theory is readily applicable to wings of general shape provided that their aspect ratio is sufficiently small. The main difficulty in this theory is the conformal transformation. We have seen further that the theory gives, at any rate in favourable circumstances, reasonably good results for values of the aspect ratio even as high as 2. Fig. VII. 16 shows an example given by Keune (1952); since there is virtually no sweep of the isobars on the rear part of the wing the critical Mach number could be expected to be roughly the same as that on an unswept wing with the same maximum velocity. It is interesting to compare the maximum velocities of associated wings: a straight wing of the same section and aspect ratio has a maximum velocity of $1\cdot070U_\infty$ (which may be deduced from Fig. VII. 4) and this can be reduced to $1\cdot046U_\infty$, which is below the value for the original delta wing, by tapering in thickness equally with the delta wing. On the other hand, a wing of constant chord and constant sweep-back of 57°, which is the mean sweep of the delta wing, has a maximum velocity of $1 \cdot 056 U_\infty$ which again may be reduced to $1 \cdot 040 U_\infty$ by the appropriate taper in thickness.

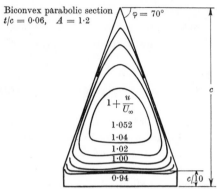

Biconvex parabolic section
$t/c = 0 \cdot 06$, $A = 1 \cdot 2$

FIG. VII. 16. Lines of constant velocity on a cropped delta wing.

For wings of large aspect ratio, which are tapered both in chord and thickness, the following procedure has been found practicable for finding the velocity at a particular point (x_0, y_0, z_0). First the local sweep at that point is determined, that is the sweep, φ_0, at the point of the line $(x - x_L)/c(y) = \text{constant} = \{x_0 - x_L(y_0)\}/c(y_0)$. A fictitious wing is then considered, of constant sweep $\varphi = \varphi_0$, whose constant section is the same as that of the original at $y = y_0$, and whose span is the same as that of the original wing. The velocity at the point on the fictitious wing corresponding to (x_0, y_0, z_0) can then be calculated by the methods of Sections 2–6 and is taken to be the velocity at that point on the original wing.

It is not feasible to summarize the ramifications of this kind of approach and we should refer to the work of Weber (1954a), of Neumark and Collingbourne (1949, 1951), and of Neumark, Collingbourne, and York (1955) for further details. One or two general characteristics of flow past general shapes of wing are, however, worth a mention. The effect of thickness taper in decreasing the velocity at the centre section has been noted before: this effect is intensified when the chord is untapered and the comparisons given in Fig. VII. 17 illustrate this. The figure includes wings whose thickness varies parabolically along the half-span; they are interesting in that they can be calculated with comparative ease. The work of Newby (1955) and of Holme and Hjelte (1953) may also be consulted. We might expect, from general considerations, that the effects of aspect ratio would decrease as sweep-back increases

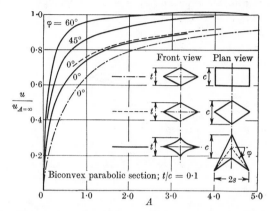

FIG. VII. 17. The effect of aspect ratio on the velocity increment at the position of maximum thickness of the centre section of various wings.

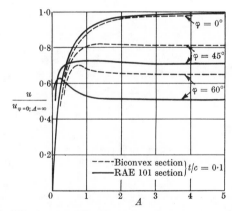

FIG. VII. 18. The effect of sweep and aspect ratio on the maximum velocity increment on the centre section of various untapered swept-back wings

and Fig. VII. 18 gives substance to this for two particular section shapes; this explains why the theory for swept wings of infinite span is often applicable to aspect ratios as low as unity, as has previously been noted in Fig. VII. 14.

It therefore appears that, at any rate for wings of substantial sweep, the ranges of applicability of the linearized theory and its simplified versions, and of the slender-body theory overlap over the range $1 < A < 2$ and that only unusual shapes fall outside the scope of the standardized methods we have described.

VIII

THE LIFTING EFFECT OF WINGS IN UNIFORM FLOW

1. Physical characteristics. Lift and vorticity. Theoretical models

THE peculiar characteristic of uniform flow past a finite lifting wing, as has already been noted in Section III. 4, is the existence in the wake of vorticity whose dominant component lies in the stream direction; further, the distribution of this component of vorticity is closely related to the lift on the wing. To find the relations between this trailing vorticity and the shape of the wing on whose surface the vorticity is at first generated, is the fundamental problem of the theory of three-dimensional lifting surfaces.

The classical theory, the most recent developments of which are studied in this chapter, refers principally to unseparated flow and rests on simple geometrical models for the region in which the trailing vorticity is of significant magnitude. Separated flow, however, seems to be inevitable with the shapes of wing now being considered for future aircraft and other winged bodies, and for them it is important to know the lines of separation on the surface, from which vorticity is shed into the wake, and the resulting shape of the surface of separation. In this, there are two principal difficulties. First comes the consideration of the nature of separation in three dimensions, which has been described by Maskell (1955); then there is the choice of a theoretical model. As non-linear theories, these matters are reviewed briefly in Sections XII. 6–10.

Insight into the physical nature of three-dimensional flow past a lifting wing may be gained by reference to the flow past a circular flat plate set perpendicularly to the stream. This flow separates along the whole of the circumference; it forms a bubble, containing viscous eddies, which is bounded by shear layers of high vorticity. The mean flow is shown diagrammatically in Fig. VIII. 1. By analogy with the corresponding two-dimensional flow past a plate which has been discussed in Chapters III and IV, the first inviscid approximation would assume a steady mean flow with an axi-symmetric boundary of the wake along which the pressure is taken either to be constant, according to Kirchhoff's hypothesis, or to increase steadily from the typical under-pressure at the back of the plate to the static pressure of the uniform flow far downstream.

The inviscid model of this flow may thus be considered as a type of displacement flow in which there are evidently no lift forces: the methods of the previous chapter, however, are not immediately applicable owing to the mixed nature of the boundary conditions. Now

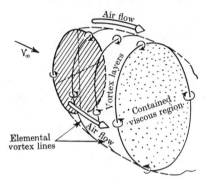

FIG. VIII. 1. An idealization of the flow past a circular
plate normal to a uniform stream.

mixed boundary conditions in two-dimensional flow can often be treated by conformal transformation, but in three-dimensional flow this powerful analytical device is not available. Therefore, for the purpose of calculating the external flow of Fig. VIII. 1, we might choose to represent the boundary of the wake by a vortex sheet in which the vortex lines are circles about the axis of symmetry of the whole flow. One vortex line coincides with the edge of the disk which itself may be thought of as being composed of, or represented by, so-called bound ring vortices. The boundary conditions on the vortex sheet would be determined by whatever assumptions are made about the viscous region, but no complete solution for the whole flow has yet been attempted on these lines.

Consider now the effect of decreasing the incidence of the plate. Conditions are no longer axi-symmetric and the elemental vortex lines on the boundary of the separated wake, which constitute the model of the steady mean flow, are distorted into the patterns sketched in Fig. VIII. 2. The plate now experiences a lift force. Features to notice particularly are the upward flow which is induced along the sides of the wake, and the tendency for a downward flow along the top of the wake. These two features are emphasized still more at a smaller angle of incidence as illustrated in Fig. VIII. 3. Here, although the flow still separates at all points of the plate's edge, the wake downstream rapidly forms itself into two cores, round each of which the fluid flows in a spiralling fashion. The flows observed by Hansen (1939) conform closely to these descriptions, and from Fig. VIII. 3 it will be possible to deduce a number of specialized types of inviscid flow.

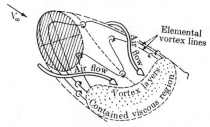

Fig. VIII. 2. An idealization of the flow past a circular plate at a large incidence to a uniform stream.

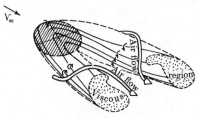

Fig. VIII. 3. An idealization of the flow past a circular plate at a small incidence to a uniform stream.

Types of flow in which the viscous regions may be adequately represented by vortex sheets not only are more amenable to analytical treatment than are bubble flows with mixed boundary conditions, but also are of greater practical application. Such a flow can be derived from Fig. VIII. 3 if it is supposed that the circular plate is lengthened in the spanwise direction and provided with a rounded leading edge; with now the incidence so small that separation occurs near the trailing edge only, there results a wake of negligible width which may then be thought of as a vortex sheet. The classical mathematical model for flow past a thin straight wing of large aspect ratio is thus derived and it is illustrated in Fig. VIII. 4. The vortex lines which now lie on the surface of the wing are in a predominantly spanwise direction and are called bound vortices while those lying in the vortex sheet which extends downstream from the trailing edge are called trailing vortices.

Lanchester (1908) introduced the concept of a single trailing vortex line which evidently bears an affinity to the idea of a fully rolled-up trailing vortex sheet, and Prandtl (1918) postulated a continuous sheet of trailing vortices; they were thus the originators of the ideas on which all later theories are based, and this chapter is devoted to the many analytical developments of them. Betz (1950) has pointed out that the flow near the centre of the spiral-shaped edges of the trailing sheet resembles that of discrete vortex lines, so that far behind the wing,

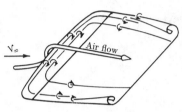

where the rolling-up process has fully developed, the trailing vortex sheet has the appearance of two concentrated line vortices. In this way Lanchester's concept, appropriate for the flow at greater distances, can be reconciled with Prandtl's, which is more appropriate for the flow closer to the trailing edge and over the wing itself.

FIG. VIII. 4. The classical conception of the vortex lines in the flow past a thin wing of large aspect ratio.

In the well-behaved flow of Fig. VIII. 4, the circulation about any section of the wing equals the sum of the strengths of the vortex lines passing through that section. The lift is related to this circulation which, in the first inviscid approximation, is determined by the Kutta–Joukowski condition: the distribution of vorticity must ensure zero load at the trailing edge which is assumed to be the line of separation.

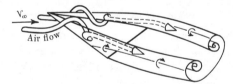

FIG. VIII. 5. The present conception of the flow past a thin delta wing of small aspect ratio.

We may take next the case of a thin delta wing of small aspect ratio, as shown in Fig. VIII. 5. It is assumed that separation occurs from all edges; but, unlike the case of Fig. VIII. 3, the large angle of sweep of the leading edge now results in a flow in which the bubble disappears or can be ignored, so that a vortex sheet, which springs from all edges, alone remains. A photograph of this type of flow has already been given in Fig. III. 4. The free edges of this sheet above and behind the wing necessarily begin to roll up and fluid is drawn over the tops of the sheet and then into the centres of the spirals. This model of the flow past a slender delta wing was introduced by Roy (1952). Compared with the classical model for the same wing which would assume separation only at the trailing edge, Roy's model implies that more fluid is accelerated downwards and that more vorticity is being shed, and hence the lift force on the wing at a given angle of incidence is greater. The analytical details of this model are necessarily complicated and have not yet been fully developed.

2. Physical characteristics. Displacement effects. Drag

In the preceding section, the discussion presupposed wings of zero thickness to enable the phenomena associated with lift to be studied most easily. The thickness of a real wing has, of course, an effect on the lift generated by it, and one approach to a complete theory of the first inviscid approximation would necessitate distributions of both sources and vortices. These singularities would lie within the wing surface, except for the trailing vorticity. The boundary condition is that the wing is a stream surface; further, if the trailing vorticity is assumed, as is almost universally done, to lie in a sheet, this sheet must also be a stream surface and cannot sustain any resultant forces.

These boundary conditions are usually simplified by referring them to the chord line on which all boundary values are calculated and in which all singularities lie. This is the typical technique of linearization and it makes the effects of thickness and of lift additive. Thus it is assumed that the displacement effect of the thickness of the wing may be calculated according to the methods of Chapter VII and independently of the lift. This assumption was considered more fully in Section VII. 2. Greater accuracy might be achieved through an iterative procedure characteristic of the technique of deformed boundaries, but in the absence of any exact solutions which could be used for comparison, there seems little point in complicating the analysis further.

It will be found that, even in inviscid flow, there is a non-zero drag, called the induced drag, on a finite wing. The induced drag is a corollary of the lift force; it corresponds to the work which is done on the fluid and is manifested in the kinetic energy of the velocity field due to the trailing vorticity. (In a two-dimensional flow, there is no trailing vorticity and no increase of kinetic energy in the fluid field.) The value of the induced drag thus depends on, among other things, the shape of the trailing vortex sheet: it will differ, for example, in the two cases of Figs. VIII. 4 and 5 even if the lift is the same. The induced drag is an overall force and does not necessarily imply a drag force on all sections of the wing. The contribution to the total drag due to the

stresses, both normal and shear, at the surface of the wing may, however, be calculated according to the principles already laid down for
the first boundary-layer approximation. Such is the doubt about the
validity of all the mathematical models of three-dimensional flow and
such also is the difficulty of their computation that it is not realistic
to attempt the second approximation to the inviscid flow, as defined
in Section III. 7.

3. Some properties of vortex sheets. Applications to lift curves

The basic analytical description of vortex sheets has been laid down
already in Section I. 19. In this chapter, flows past wings will be
described largely in terms of vortex sheets
or of the vortex lines comprising the sheets.
For inviscid flow, the main theorems concerning vortex lines were established by
Helmholtz (1858) and Kelvin (1869). The
bound vortex lines by which we represent
solid surfaces are hypothetical to the extent that they are regarded as capable of
sustaining a pressure, and as not moving
with the fluid.

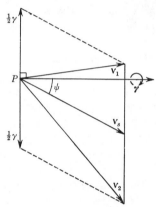

The velocity field of an element of vortex
line is given by equation (I. 56) and to
represent a flow by the sum of the induced
velocities of a number of such elements
automatically ensures that the equations
of inviscid flow are satisfied.

FIG. VIII. 6. The conditions at a
point P of a vortex sheet, the tangent plane at P coinciding with the
plane of the paper. All vectors are
in the plane of the paper.

In Fig. VIII. 6 are sketched the conditions at a point P of a three-dimensional
vortex sheet, the tangent plane at P coinciding with the plane of
the paper. $\mathbf{v}_1$ and $\mathbf{v}_2$ are the velocities on either side of the sheet.
$\mathbf{v}_s = \frac{1}{2}(\mathbf{v}_1 + \mathbf{v}_2)$ is the so-called mean velocity, and $\boldsymbol{\gamma}$ is the vorticity
vector which is perpendicular to the velocities it induces on either
side of the sheet. We recall from equation (I. 58) the general result for
any vortex sheet that the induced velocity increments are $\pm\frac{1}{2}\gamma$ and
that $\boldsymbol{\gamma}$, $\mathbf{v}_1$, and $\mathbf{v}_2$ are coplanar. γ has dimensions of speed and represents
the vortex strength per unit length of a vortex line.

If the suffixes 1 and 2 refer to the two sides of the sheet, Bernoulli's
equation may be written

$$H_1 = p_1 + \tfrac{1}{2}\rho v_1^2; \qquad H_2 = p_2 + \tfrac{1}{2}\rho v_2^2. \tag{1}$$

Thus the pressure difference, Δp, across the sheet is

$$\Delta p = p_2 - p_1 = H_2 - H_1 + \tfrac{1}{2}\rho(v_1^2 - v_2^2) = \Delta H + \tfrac{1}{2}\rho(v_1^2 - v_2^2), \qquad (2)$$

ΔH being the difference in total pressure. Elementary trigonometry, applied to Fig. VIII. 6, puts equation (2) in the form

$$\Delta p = \Delta H + \rho v_s \gamma \sin \psi. \qquad (3)$$

This equation has obvious importance in dynamical problems and some particular cases are now taken.

(i) For a vortex sheet separating regions of equal total pressure—for example, a trailing vortex sheet—both Δp and ΔH are zero, and so ψ is zero also. The velocities on either side of the sheet are then equal in magnitude and equally inclined to the vorticity or mean velocity vectors which are in the same direction. We may note, incidentally, that the fact that a trailing vortex sheet cannot sustain a pressure difference across it is consistent with the generalized Kutta–Joukowski condition given in Section V. 2; in the jargon of wing theory, there can be no load across the separation line from which the trailing vorticity springs.

(ii) If ΔH is not zero—as for the surface of a bubble—then ψ is also not zero if the vortex sheet is such that Δp is necessarily zero.

(iii) In the case of a bound vortex sheet—such as that which represents a solid boundary—Δp is not zero. If the total pressure is constant on either side, as is usual with a thin wing,

$$\Delta p = \rho v_s \gamma \sin \psi \qquad (4)$$

and the solid boundary must sustain this pressure difference. As an example, consider a thin unswept wing of large aspect ratio. Except near the tips, the vorticity vector is almost at right angles to the mainstream; thus $\psi \simeq \tfrac{1}{2}\pi$. Further, v_s may be taken as V_∞, the speed of the stream at infinity. Thus

$$\Delta p = \rho V_\infty \gamma, \qquad (5)$$

which is commonly called the Kutta–Joukowski theorem for the lift force. It holds for the local force from the vortex element; it is equally true for a whole wing in the form of equation (I. 72), which connects the overall lift force with the overall circulation $\Gamma = \int_0^c \gamma(x)\, dx$. Integration of the pressure difference Δp along the chord leads to the sectional lift coefficient, C_L. For a flat wing at a small angle of incidence, α, to the mainstream,

$$C_L/\alpha = 2\pi \qquad (6)$$

which follows from the appropriate function $\gamma(x)$ which will be found in Section 4. This is, of course, the two-dimensional value of C_L as found in Section IV. 4.

(iv) For a sheared wing of large aspect ratio the vorticity vector lies along the generators of the wing whereas the mean velocity at the boundary may be taken to be the stream velocity $\mathbf{V}_\infty$. The angle between

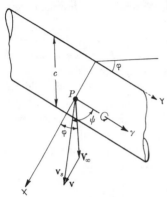

the mean velocity and the vorticity vector is thus $(\tfrac{1}{2}\pi-\varphi)$, where φ is the angle of sweep, and equation (3) gives

$$\Delta p = \rho V_\infty \gamma \cos\varphi. \qquad (7)$$

Since the chordwise distribution $\gamma(x)$ is given by the same equation whether the wing is sheared or not, integration of the pressure difference Δp in the stream-wise direction along the chord leads to the so-called sectional lift slope given by

$$C_L/\alpha = 2\pi\cos\varphi \qquad (8)$$

for the sheared wing.

Fig. VIII. 7. A sketch illustrating the vorticity vector and mean velocity vector on a sheared wing of infinite span.

(v) More complicated interpretations of equation (3) arise when the mean velocity $\mathbf{v}_s$ is no longer adequately given by the stream velocity $\mathbf{V}_\infty$. For example,

on an unswept thick wing of infinite span the displacement velocity $\mathbf{v}$ should be taken into account so that

$$\Delta p = \rho(V_\infty+v)\gamma. \qquad (9)$$

To a first approximation, $\gamma(x)$ takes the same value as for the wing of zero thickness and the linearized result for an elliptic section is $v = V_\infty(t/c)$; the lift slope then becomes

$$C_L/\alpha = 2\pi(1+t/c). \qquad (10)$$

It so happens that this particular result is correct for the two-dimensional flow, having been given in equation (IV. 13).

(vi) As a last case, consider the sheared elliptic wing shown in Fig. VIII. 7. The displacement velocity $\mathbf{v}$ is in the X-direction and of magnitude

$$v = V_\infty t/c, \qquad (11)$$

as given from Section VII. 7. Here, c is the chord of the streamwise section. Then

$$v_s\sin\psi = V_\infty\cos\varphi+v = V_\infty[1+(t/c)\sec\varphi]\cos\varphi \qquad (12)$$

and equation (3) leads to

$$C_L/\alpha = 2\pi(\cos\varphi + t/c), \tag{13}$$

which is seen as a kind of combination of equations (8) and (10). This again is an exact solution as has been shown by Weber (1953). For real aerofoils with sharp trailing edges, the insertion of the coefficient 0·8 before the term (t/c) makes equations (10) and (13) fit experimental results reasonably well; equation (13) shows that although sweep generally reduces the lift-curve slope, the effect of thickness on the lift becomes more important as the sweep increases.

4. Bound vorticity for a two-dimensional flat plate

The distributions of vorticity, considered in Section IV. 10 for two-dimensional aerofoils, would now be described as bound vorticity, and a few particular results are of interest later on.

The integral equation for the bound vorticity, $\gamma(x)$, on a flat plate is equation (IV. 43) with $w = -\alpha$; $-w$ is called the downwash induced by the vorticity. The two distributions of $\gamma(x)$,

$$\left.\begin{array}{l} \gamma_1(x) = k_1 V_\infty (c-2x)[x(c-x)]^{-\frac{1}{2}} \\ \gamma_2(x) = k_2 V_\infty c[x(c-x)]^{-\frac{1}{2}} \end{array}\right\}, \tag{14}$$

induce constant downwashes given by

$$-w_1 = k_1 V_\infty \quad \text{and} \quad -w_2 = 0, \tag{15}$$

while the respective circulations, $\Gamma = \int_0^c \gamma(x)\, dx$, are

$$\Gamma_1 = 0 \quad \text{and} \quad \Gamma_2 = \pi V_\infty c k_2. \tag{16}$$

Thus the flow past a flat plate at any incidence and with any circulation may be obtained by adding γ_1 and γ_2 and by taking suitable values for k_1 and k_2.

For a plate at incidence α, we may think of the downwash equalling the upwash, $V_\infty \alpha$, of the stream: thus from (15)

$$k_1 = \alpha. \tag{17}$$

Each of these distributions has a load, $\Delta p = \rho V_\infty \gamma$, which becomes infinite at the leading and trailing edges; but they may be combined so as to satisfy the Kutta–Joukowski condition, that Δp is zero at the trailing edge. This requires $k_1 = k_2$; the infinite load remains at the leading edge and we have finally, with (17),

$$l(x) \equiv \Delta p/\tfrac{1}{2}\rho V_\infty^2 = 4\alpha[(c-x)/x]^{\frac{1}{2}}. \tag{18}$$

This result is equivalent to (IV. 14) which expresses the speed on the two surfaces of the plate; much of wing theory, however, is put in terms of the local load, or of the local coefficient defined in (23), and the form (18) will often recur in various guises.

5. Equations for the representation of a lifting wing by a vortex sheet

Suppose that the wing and wake have been replaced, according to the general ideas of Section 1, by a vortex sheet of strength γ. The velocity induced at the point $\mathbf{r}$ of the sheet is then given by

$$\mathbf{v}(\mathbf{r}) = -\tfrac{1}{4}\pi \int \mathbf{\gamma}' \times (\mathbf{r}' - \mathbf{r}) |\mathbf{r}' - \mathbf{r}|^{-3} \, dS', \qquad (19)$$

a prime denoting a general value on the vortex sheet. The vector $(\mathbf{r}' - \mathbf{r})$ depends on the geometry of the vortex sheet. In principle, both the shape of the free part of the vortex sheet and the distribution of vorticity on the free and bound parts may be determined by the three following conditions:

(i) The velocity normal to the sheet is zero. This is made up of the components of $\mathbf{v}$ from equation (19) and of the free stream velocity $\mathbf{V}_\infty$.

(ii) Δp is zero on the free part of the sheet. This condition is obtained from equation (3) where $\mathbf{v}_s$ is the sum of the components in the tangential plane of $\mathbf{v}$ from (19) and $\mathbf{V}_\infty$. On the bound part of the sheet, the same equation enables Δp and hence the force on the wing to be calculated.

(iii) The Kutta–Joukowski condition requires that $\Delta p = 0$ at the trailing edge.

The possibility of general solutions along these lines is obviously remote. The approximation due to Prandtl assumes that the induced velocity $\mathbf{v}$ is small in comparison with $\mathbf{V}_\infty$. Both the wing and trailing vortex sheet are then assumed to lie in a plane parallel to the free stream. According to this approximation, condition (i) is then satisfied on the free vortex sheet; on the bound vortex sheet it is assumed that the induced normal velocity equals αV_∞, α being the angle between the tangent to the camber line of the section of the wing and the main-stream velocity. Condition (ii) is also satisfied in the same way when, on the free sheet as well as on the bound sheet, $\mathbf{v}_s$ is taken to equal $\mathbf{V}_\infty$; thus, with ΔH also equal to zero, Δp can be calculated on the bound sheet. Condition (iii) is interpreted in various ways by different methods; with $\mathbf{v}_s = \mathbf{V}_\infty$ the vorticity vector must either be zero or directed along the mainstream at the trailing edge.

The system of Cartesian coordinates which is customarily used is left-handed. The x-axis is in the stream direction and the vortex sheet lies in $z = 0$. z is taken positively downwards. The stream velocity is $(U_\infty, 0, 0)$ and (u, v, w) is the perturbation velocity.

Fig. VIII. 8 is a view of the vortex sheet $z = 0$ in the positive z-direction; it also shows a so-called horseshoe vortex the use of which simplifies considerably the analysis of the linearized equations. Each element of area of the wing surface, $dx'dy'$, is assumed to contribute to the total sum of vorticity a vortex line, of strength $\gamma\, dx'$, which stretches to infinity and is shaped and placed as the figure shows. The load per unit area on the wing surface due to this element is obtained from equation (5) and is usually put in terms of the non-dimensional pressure coefficient, commonly called the load function, defined by

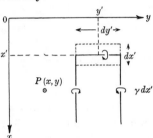

Fig. VIII. 8. Horseshoe-vortex element in a plane vortex sheet.

$$l(x,y) = \Delta p / \tfrac{1}{2}\rho U_\infty^2 = 2\gamma(x,y)/U_\infty. \tag{20}$$

Equation (19) may be used, then, to derive the downwash at the point $P \equiv (x, y, 0)$ in the form

$$\frac{w(x,y)}{U_\infty} = \frac{w}{U_\infty} = -\frac{1}{8\pi} \iint\limits_S \frac{l(x',y')}{(y-y')^2}\left[1 + \frac{x-x'}{\{(x-x')^2+(y-y')^2\}^{\frac{1}{2}}}\right] dx'dy', \tag{21}$$

where the integration is over the wing surface S. The elementary vortex line shown in the figure is commonly called a horseshoe vortex and it should be noted that, since it extends downstream to infinity, its use enables the integral of the downwash equation (21) to be taken over the surface of the wing only. But elementary horseshoe vortices are only a convenient form of representing the continuous distribution of vorticity over wing and wake, and equation (21) is valid quite generally.

This equation may be derived by alternative arguments to those we have used: Prandtl (1936), Reissner (1944), and Flax and Lawrence (1951) have all used different methods, the latter authors deriving the equivalent form

$$\frac{w(x,y)}{U_\infty} = \frac{w}{U_\infty} = \frac{1}{8\pi}\frac{\partial}{\partial y}\iint\limits_S \frac{l(x',y')}{y-y'}\left[1 + \frac{\{(x-x')^2+(y-y')^2\}^{\frac{1}{2}}}{x-x'}\right] dx'dy'. \tag{22}$$

This is preferable to (21) since the integral involves only a Cauchy principal value: the higher-order singularity in (21) is more difficult to handle though Multhopp (1950) has defined a principal value to be taken at the singularity $y = y'$.

Equation (22) is called the downwash integral equation and is the fundamental equation of the linearized theory. Its derivation is based on elementary horseshoe-vortex lines; it is not immediately applicable to cases in which any bound vortex line has a discontinuity in direction, such as a swept wing whose leading edge, which is a bound vortex line, has a kink at the centre section.

Before we attempt to solve equation (22) in particular cases, there are a number of concepts which may usefully be established and which are common to most, if not all, theories. These we now describe.

6. Lift, and drag due to lift

Although the fundamental downwash equation (22) is put in terms of the load function $l(x, y)$, much of the later analysis is in terms of the lift coefficient, C_L, of streamwise sections at given spanwise stations. This is defined as

$$C_L(y) = C_L = [1/c(y)] \int_{x_L(y)}^{x_T(y)} l(x, y) \, dx, \tag{23}$$

in which the suffixes L and T refer to the leading and trailing edges. $C_L(y)$ is called the local, or sectional, lift coefficient, and the quantity $C_L(y)c(y)$ is called the spanwise distribution of chord load or, more briefly, the spanwise loading. The lift force, L, as found by integration over the chord of the section considered, is related to the circulation, Γ, round the section and to the spanwise loading by

$$L(y) = L = \tfrac{1}{2}\rho U_\infty^2 \, c(y) C_L(y) = \rho U_\infty \Gamma. \tag{24}$$

The overall lift coefficient for the whole wing, $\bar{C}_L$, is given by

$$\bar{C}_L = \bar{L}/\tfrac{1}{2}\rho U_\infty^2 S = [1/2\bar{c}s] \int_{-s}^{+s} C_L(y)c(y) \, dy = (A/4s) \int_{-1}^{+1} C_L(y)c(y) \, d(y/s), \tag{25}$$

where $\bar{c}$, s, and A are the geometric mean chord, semi-span, and aspect ratio respectively, as defined in Section VII. 1, and $S = 2\bar{c}s$ is the area of the wing plan.

According to the concept of a continuous vortex sheet replacing wing and wake, any change in $\Gamma(y)$ along the span must be accompanied by the shedding of some vorticity from the trailing edge. The strength of this trailing vorticity, $\gamma_t(y)$, is given by

$$\gamma_t(y) = d\Gamma(y)/dy = \tfrac{1}{2} U_\infty d(C_L c)/dy. \tag{26}$$

The contribution of this trailing vorticity to the downwash over the wing is, of course, included in equation (22).

Since the trailing vortices extend to infinity, they produce a downwash, w_∞, on the sheet at infinity which may be calculated on the assumption that the vortex lines are straight and infinite in extent. Thus $w_\infty = (1/2\pi) \int_{-s}^{s} \gamma_t(y')dy'/(y-y')$. But $\gamma_t(y)$ is related to the spanwise distribution of the trailing vorticity and to the spanwise loading by equation (26); therefore

$$w_\infty = \frac{U_\infty}{4\pi} \int_{-s}^{s} \frac{d(C_L c)}{dy'} \frac{dy'}{y-y'}, \tag{27}$$

where the Cauchy principal value of the integral is to be taken. The downward momentum of the air surrounding the sheet, which is associated with this downwash, is directly related to the overall lift force on the wing which created the sheet. On the other hand, the kinetic energy associated with this downwash has to be supplied by the wing in the form of work on the air, and this implies a drag force, D_i, on the wing. This has usually been called the induced drag though the terms vortex drag, or drag due to lift, have begun to be used in an attempt to distinguish more clearly between the various components of the total drag on a wing. The existence of a lift force on the wing, due to circulation, is therefore necessarily linked with the shedding of vorticity from the trailing edge and the occurrence of a drag force.

Munk (1919) showed that there is a minimum induced drag for a wing of given lift and span, and that this occurs when the downwash w_∞ is constant across the span. It follows from (27) that $C_L c$ is proportional to $[1-(y/s)^2]^{\frac{1}{2}}$; using equation (25), we then find the spanwise loading in the form

$$C_L c = (8s/\pi A)\bar{C}_L[1-(y/s)^2]^{\frac{1}{2}}, \tag{28}$$

corresponding to which, we have, from (27),

$$w_\infty/U_\infty = (2/\pi A)\bar{C}_L. \tag{29}$$

This implies that the wing must be so shaped that it sheds trailing vorticity which corresponds to elliptic spanwise loading. We shall see later what the shapes of such wings are, in some simple cases.

We can now establish a general relation between the lift and the minimum induced drag by introducing a fictitious mass of air, $\rho U_\infty S' \delta t$, whose rate of change of downward momentum far behind the wing is equal to the lift force

$$\bar{L} = \rho U_\infty S' w_\infty.$$ (30)

The rate at which kinetic energy is given to the air equals the rate at which work is done in overcoming the induced drag; thus

$$\bar{D}_i U_\infty = \tfrac{1}{2} \rho U_\infty S' w_\infty^2.$$ (31)

The result is attributed to Pohlhausen that S' in equations (30) and (31) is the same quantity and that it has the value πs^2. However, S' can be eliminated to obtain

$$\bar{D}_i = \tfrac{1}{2}(w_\infty/U_\infty)\bar{L}, \quad \text{or} \quad \bar{C}_{Di} = \tfrac{1}{2}(w_\infty/U_\infty)\bar{C}_L.$$ (32)

Hence, with equation (29),

$$\bar{C}_{Di} = (\bar{C}_L)^2/\pi A;$$ (33)

thus, the minimum induced drag increases with the square of the lift and is the smaller the larger the aspect ratio of the wing. Equation (33) is valid for wings of any aspect ratio, from zero to infinity, provided a planar vortex sheet is shed. The value from equation (33) is often used as a standard of comparision for the induced drag of a wing which is not so shaped as to give minimum induced drag; the drag factor K is defined by

$$\bar{C}_{Di} = K(\bar{C}_L)^2/\pi A,$$ (34)

and unity is the minimum value of K for wings which shed planar vortex sheets. General relations for the forces and moments under certain other minimum conditions have been derived by Nickel (1952).

These are the only general relations that can be derived from the model of the flow alone. Any more detailed information which might be required depends on solving the general equation (21), or (22).

7. Formulation of the main problems

A relatively simple design problem is obtained when the planform of the wing as well as the loading on it are given and the shape of the, in general, warped surface $z(x, y)$ of the wing is to be determined. This is solved by performing the integration in equation (22) for $w(x, y)$ and obtaining the shape from the condition that the surface is a stream-surface. This condition can be linearized to give

$$\partial z(x, y)/\partial x = w(x, y)/U_\infty,$$ (35)

so that the shape is found by another integration at each spanwise station. The approximation (35) implies that the downwash w is evaluated in the chordal plane $z = 0$ and not on the surface of the real, thick, wing. This is in general, but not always, justified and we shall later meet some exceptions.

More common, and more difficult, is the problem of finding the aero-dynamic coefficients relating to a wing of given shape. In other words, $c(y)$ and $z(x, y)$ are given and it is required to find $l(x, y)$, $C_L(y)$, $\bar{C}_L$, $\bar{C}_{Di}$, and so on. Uncambered wings present a simplified problem because the shape of the wing is then defined by the spanwise distribution of the angle of incidence so that the stream-surface condition (35) reads

$$\alpha(y) = w(x, y)/U_\infty. \tag{36}$$

For uncambered, untwisted wings, α is constant. With modern computational aids, one might consider solving equation (21) numerically without further ado. This has not yet been seriously attempted in full, however, and the available theories constitute attempts to obtain analytical solutions in simple cases or to simplify the numerical evaluation. This has the advantage that it exposes many fundamental and simple interrelations and concepts. As a rule, these are not only instructive but also of considerable help in practical applications and design. The remainder of the chapter is, therefore, primarily concerned with the discussion of such methods.

It has been customary to regard as the third fundamental problem of aerofoil theory that of determining the shape of the wing to give the smallest induced drag under given conditions. The main aspects of this problem have already been discussed in the preceding section.

8. The general solution for unswept wings of large aspect ratio

Consider an unswept wing whose aspect ratio is so large that we may assume, in equation (22), that

$$(x - x')^2 \ll (y - y')^2. \tag{37}$$

This clearly cannot hold for the region around $y = y'$, but it can be shown that the error will not be serious even near $y = y'$ provided $s\,dC_L/dy$ is much less than unity there. Errors are therefore likely to be greatest near the wing tips; but again the fact that C_L tends to zero towards the tips has a mitigating effect. In any case, too rigorous an approach to the equation (22) may be useless for, since a separation line normally extends along the tip edge as well as along the trailing edge, the underlying conceptions of Section 5 may be invalid near the tips.

Following an analysis similar to that of Lawrence (1951), we write equation (22) as

$$w(x,y)/U_\infty = (1/8\pi)(\partial/\partial y) \iint\limits_S [1+|y-y'|/(x-x')]l(x',y')\,dx'dy'/(y-y'),$$

which becomes

$$\frac{w(x,y)}{U_\infty} = \frac{1}{8\pi}\frac{\partial}{\partial y}\iint\limits_S \frac{l(x',y')}{y-y'}\,dx'dy' + \frac{1}{4\pi}\int\limits_{x_L(y)}^{x_T(y)} \frac{l(x',y)}{x-x'}\,dx'. \tag{38}$$

Consider now the case of an uncambered, but possibly twisted, wing such that the local angle of incidence is $\alpha(y)$ and the stream-surface condition is given by equation (36). Since the first integral in equation (38) is a function of y only, the second integral also must be a function of y only: thus

$$\int\limits_{x_L(y)}^{x_T(y)} l(x',y)(x-x')^{-1}\,dx' = F(y). \tag{39}$$

This is an integral equation from which the dependence on x of the load function $l(x,y)$ can be determined without a knowledge of the spanwise distribution. l must further satisfy the Kutta–Joukowski condition

$$l(x_T,y) = 0. \tag{40}$$

Now equation (39) with the condition (40) is analogous to equation (IV. 44) whose solution (18) has already been discussed. Thus

$$l(x,y) = \{F(y)/\pi\}[(x_T(y)-x)/(x-x_L(y))]^{\frac12},$$

and, from equation (23), $F(y) = 2C_L(y)$. Thus it follows that

$$l(x,y) = \frac{2}{\pi}C_L(y)\left[\frac{x_T(y)-x}{x-x_L(y)}\right]^{\frac12}. \tag{41}$$

Hence, we find the important result that wings of finite span but of large aspect ratio have the same chordwise loading as the two-dimensional flat plate at an angle of incidence as yet unknown.

It remains to find the spanwise loading. Insertion of $l(x,y)$ from equation (41) into equation (37), and the use of equation (36), gives

$$\alpha(y) = C_L(y)/2\pi - (1/8\pi)\int\limits_{-s}^{+s} C_L(y')c(y')(y-y')^{-2}\,dy'.$$

Integrating by parts and demanding that $c(y)C_L(y)$ vanishes at the tips $y = \pm s$, we find

$$C_L(y)/2\pi = \alpha(y) - \frac{1}{8\pi}\int\limits_{-s}^{+s} \frac{d(C_L c)}{dy'}\frac{dy'}{y-y'}. \tag{42}$$

This is Prandtl's classical aerofoil equation. For an uncambered wing, it connects $\alpha(y)$, $c(y)$, and $C_L(y)$, and it is normally regarded as an integral equation for $C_L(y)$. The complete solution for the loading over the whole lifting surface is obtained by combining $C_L(y)$ from equation (42) with the chordwise loading from equation (41).

The analysis can be repeated for cambered wings where α may be regarded as being also a function of x. The resulting loading $l(x, y)$ is then again of a form similar to that in equation (41), with the function of x replaced by the function which corresponds to the chordwise loading of the two-dimensional cambered section. The spanwise loading is again determined by equation (42), where it is possible to replace α by a function of y alone; but $\alpha(y)$ must then be measured from the direction along which the mainstream does not produce a lift force on the two-dimensional cambered section, that is, from the no-lift angle. This is discussed in more detail in Section 22.

The solutions (41) and (42) allow the sectional pitching moment of these wings to be determined once for all. The pitching-moment coefficient in the direction of increasing incidence, referred to the leading edge $x = x_L(y)$, is found to be

$$C_m(y) = -(1/c^2) \int_{x_L}^{x_T} l(x, y)(x - x_L)\, dx \qquad (43)$$

for each section, which gives, for the particular loading of equation (41),

$$C_m(y) = -\tfrac{1}{4} C_L(y). \qquad (44)$$

C_m is negative, and so is referred to as a nose-down moment. Equation (44) implies that the same sectional pitching moment can be obtained from the resultant sectional lift force put at the distance of a quarter of the local chord from the leading edge; that is, the position of the centre of pressure is $x_{cp}/c = -C_m/C_L = \tfrac{1}{4}$ at all spanwise stations.

9. Discussion of the classical solution

The particular form, in which the solution for the loading over unswept wings of large aspect ratio emerges, allows the introduction of some potent concepts. In the first place, the fact that the chordwise loading is always the same as that of the corresponding two-dimensional aerofoil puts all the results obtained for two-dimensional aerofoils as well as those of the theory of two-dimensional boundary layers at the disposal of three-dimensional wing theory. Thus refinements to the

thin-wing concept can be made in order to take account of wing thickness and viscosity effects from data for the two-dimensional aerofoil.
Since the flow past the classical aerofoil with a thin boundary layer
represents an extremely useful engineering type of flow, the dichotomy
between classical wing theory and boundary-layer theory has dominated
aircraft engineering for about half a century.

In the second place, the term $C_L/2\pi$ and the integral on the right-
hand side of equation (42) can be interpreted as certain well-defined
angles of incidence. $C_L/2\pi$ can be interpreted as the effective incidence,
α_e, of the aerofoil in the absence of trailing vortices. It depends entirely
on the distribution of the bound vortices and is equal to the geometric
angle of incidence of the aerofoil in two-dimensional flow. The value
2π, being the sectional lift slope of the two-dimensional thin aerofoil,
may be replaced by the more general value $a_0 = C_L/\alpha_e$, which takes
thickness and viscosity into account, as for instance in equation (10).
The integral in equation (42) can be interpreted as the induced incidence,
α_{i0}, which is entirely due to the presence of streamwise trailing vortices.
The concept of an angle of incidence is justified because equation (42)
implies that the downwash induced by the trailing vortices is constant
along the wing chord, and so independent of x. That this result is also
plausible follows from the sketch in Fig. VIII. 9 (a), in which the wing
chord is assumed to be small as compared with the span. $\alpha_i = \alpha_{i0}$ is
exactly half the value w_∞/U_∞ of the downwash induced at the trailing
vortex sheet far behind the wing, as given by equation (27):

$$\alpha_{i0} = \tfrac{1}{2}w_\infty/U_\infty. \tag{45}$$

The classical aerofoil equation (42) thus reads

$$\alpha_e = \alpha - \alpha_{i0}, \tag{46}$$

which is illustrated in Fig. VIII. 10. The separation of the given angle
of incidence into two contributions, from the bound and from the
trailing vortices, is a powerful tool, which will be used later on as an
approximation in more complicated cases.

The classical aerofoil theory of Prandtl has often been described as
a 'lifting-line' theory in contrast to other 'lifting-surface' theories.
This is a mistake. The concept of a single lifting line on which all the
circulation is concentrated could be used to derive the relation for α_{i0};
but it cannot lead to a value for the sectional lift slope a_0, for this
requires a knowledge of the chordwise distribution of vortices. Prandtl's
theory is, therefore, a lifting-surface theory for wings of small but not

vanishing chord, the fundamental equations being (41) and (42). The theory has been used extensively and detailed accounts have been given among others by H. Glauert (1926), Betz (1935), and by Kármán

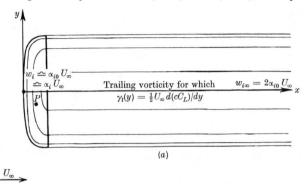

(a)

U_∞

(b)

Fig. VIII. 9. Sketches illustrating the physical distinction between wings of large and of small aspect ratio.

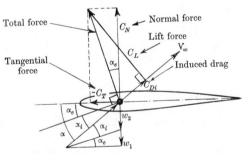

Fig. VIII. 10. Notation for the flow at a section of a wing.

and Burgers (1935). Exact solutions have been treated by Schmidt (1937, 1938) and his collaborators, while Muskhelishvili (1946) has treated the integro-differential equation (42) from a formal mathematical standpoint.

For a rectangular wing, we may take $x_L = 0$ and $x_T = c$, so that the complete loading reduces to

$$l(x, y) = \{2C_L(y)/\pi\}[(c-x)/x]^{\frac{1}{2}}. \tag{47}$$

10. The elliptic wing of large aspect ratio

A simple but important solution of equation (42) is that for an untwisted, uncambered wing of elliptic planform. The following results are obtained:

the chord: $c(y) = (8s/\pi A)[1-(y/s)^2]^{\frac{1}{2}} = (4\bar{c}/\pi)[1-(y/s)^2]^{\frac{1}{2}}$ (48)

the local lift: $C_L(y) = \bar{C}_L$ (49)

the induced incidence: $\alpha_i = \alpha_{i0} = \bar{C}_L/\pi A$ (50)

the overall lift coefficient: $\bar{C}_L = 2\pi\alpha[A/(A+2)]$ (51)

the distribution of load:

$$l(x,y) = 4\alpha[1+2/A]^{-1}[(x_T(y)-x)/(x-x_L(y))]^{\frac{1}{2}}$$ (52)

the induced drag: $C_{Di}(y) = \bar{C}_{Di} = \alpha_{i0}C_L = \bar{C}_L^2/\pi A.$ (53)

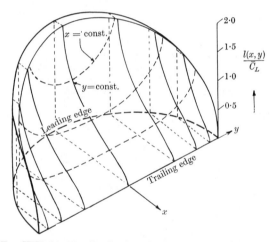

FIG. VIII. 11. The distribution of load on a thin wing of large aspect ratio in Prandtl's type of flow.

The spanwise loading $C_L(y)c(y)$ is elliptic. The complete loading is illustrated in Fig. VIII. 11 which indicates the infinite load along the leading edge predicted by this linearized theory, and the zero load along the trailing edge as a result of the Kutta–Joukowski hypothesis. The result of equation (51), that the overall lift-curve slope is proportional to $A/(A+2)$ for wings otherwise similar, is often used to deduce the lift-curve slope for a range of wings from the experimental results for a single wing. In particular, the two-dimensional lift slope, a_0, for the wing section may be deduced from an experiment on a finite wing.

Elliptic wings of large aspect ratio are further distinguished by the fact that the drag factor K from equation (34) has the minimum value of unity; in other words, for flat wings of large aspect ratio, an elliptic chord distribution is needed to give elliptic spanwise loading, which is required for minimum induced drag.

Particularly simple relations are obtained in this case for the force components tangential and normal to the chord. With the notation of Fig. VIII. 10, we have, to the first order in the angles shown,

$$C_T = -\alpha_e C_N = -\alpha C_L + C_D \Big\} , \qquad (54)$$
$$C_N = C_L + \alpha C_D$$

for an aerofoil section at some spanwise station as well as for the overall values. Lift, L, and normal force, N, are positive if directed upwards; drag, D, and tangential force, T, are positive if directed backwards. For elliptic spanwise loading, equations (51) and (53) lead to

$$\bar{C}_T = -(1/2\pi)(\bar{C}_N)^2$$

or, more generally, as shown by Küchemann (1940a),

$$\bar{C}_T = -(1/2\pi)(\bar{C}_N)^2 + \beta \bar{C}_N + \bar{C}_{D0}, \qquad (55)$$

where $(-\beta)$ is the no-lift angle if the wing is cambered and $\bar{C}_{D0}$ is the profile drag. We note that equation (55) does not contain the aspect ratio of the wing whereas the corresponding relation (53) between $\bar{C}_L$ and $\bar{C}_{Di}$ does. This is another consequence of the two-dimensional chordwise loading, C_N and C_T being essentially sectional characteristics. Experimental results confirm equation (55) for wings of large aspect ratio but deviations become apparent if the aspect ratio is about 4 or less. Thus deviations from the two-dimensional chordwise loading are an indication of small-aspect-ratio effects.

11. The Trefftz plane

An interpretation of the theory of Section 9 which has special importance was developed by Trefftz (1921). This depends on the idea that the flow far behind the wing in the vicinity of the plane sheet of trailing vortices does not depend on the streamwise coordinate and may therefore be regarded as two-dimensional in planes normal to the mainstream. The problem is thus to find a velocity potential, $\phi(y, z)$, satisfying certain boundary conditions in the region outside the slit—the trace of the vortex sheet—shown in Fig. VIII. 12. The velocity component on the upper surface (suffix u), which is tangential to the slit, is equal to $\frac{1}{2}\gamma_l$, which in turn is equal to $\partial\phi_u/\partial y$; thus $\partial\phi_u/\partial y = \frac{1}{2}\gamma_l$;

similarly, on the lower surface (suffix l) $\partial\phi_l/\partial y = -\frac{1}{2}\gamma_t$, the mean velocity being zero in the absence of other bodies. Thus the vorticity in the sheet corresponds to a discontinuity in the potential function:

$$\gamma_t = \partial(\phi_u-\phi_l)/\partial y = \partial(\Delta\phi)/\partial y. \tag{56}$$

On the other hand, the vorticity in the sheet is related to the spanwise change of the wing loading by equation (26). Hence

$$2\Delta\phi(y)/U_\infty = 4\phi_u(y)/U_\infty = C_L(y)c(y), \tag{57}$$

if we put $\phi_l(y) = -\phi_u(y)$.

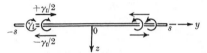

FIG. VIII. 12. Trace of the trailing vortex sheet in the Trefftz plane.

The velocity component normal to the slit is $(\partial\phi/\partial z)_u$ and equal to the downwash velocity $2\alpha_{i0} U_\infty$ at infinity downstream. Hence

$$\alpha_{i0} = (\partial\phi/\partial z)_u/2U_\infty. \tag{58}$$

Equation (42) may now be put in terms of $\phi_u(y)$ and $(\partial\phi/\partial z)_u$ by substitution from equations (57) and (58), and with the result (45) for Prandtl's type of flow. Thus

$$4\phi_u(y) = 2\pi c(y)[U_\infty\,\alpha(y)-\tfrac{1}{2}(\partial\phi/\partial z)_u]. \tag{59}$$

Further, $\partial\phi/\partial y = \partial\phi/\partial z = 0$ for $y \to \infty$ and $z \to \infty$, and so the problem reduces to that of finding a solution $\phi(y,z)$ of Laplace's equation where the value of $\partial\phi/\partial z$ on the boundary is given by equation (59).

We note that, although α_{i0} and $\partial\phi/\partial z$ may vary with y, the vortex sheet and thus the slit are assumed to be straight. Only in the case of minimum induced drag is $\partial\phi/\partial z$ constant, when it is given by

$$(\partial\phi/\partial z)_u = 2\alpha_{i0} U_\infty = 2\bar{C}_L U_\infty/\pi A.$$

For this particular case, we may use the complex variable $\zeta = z+iy$ and the conformal transformation of the slit into a circle, and find for the complex potential function:

$$\phi+i\psi = -(2\bar{C}_L/\pi A)[(\zeta^2+s^2)^{\frac{1}{2}}-\zeta], \tag{60}$$

so that $\qquad \Delta\phi/U_\infty s = (4/\pi A)\bar{C}_L[1-(y/s)^2]^{\frac{1}{2}}. \tag{61}$

These are, in fact, equivalent to equations (51) and (52) derived previously. As this form of the theory is due to Trefftz, the transverse plane far behind the wing is called the Trefftz plane. The flow in the Trefftz plane is illustrated in Fig. VIII. 13.

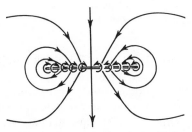

Fig. VIII. 13. Typical streamlines in the Trefftz plane.

12. Wings of small aspect ratio

The inequalities of equation (37) represent the assumption that the aspect ratio is large. We now reverse the inequalities so as to consider wings of small aspect ratio. Thus

$$(y-y')^2 \ll (x-x')^2. \tag{62}$$

This fails at $x = x'$ and it is not clear how this will affect the solutions obtained, but we shall see later that the assumption is reasonable except near unswept leading edges. The downwash equation (22) now reads

$$w(x,y)/U_\infty = (1/8\pi)(\partial/\partial y) \iint_S l(x',y')[1+|x-x'|/(x-x')](y-y')^{-1} \, dx' dy'. \tag{63}$$

The term in square brackets has the value 2 for $x' < x$ and is zero for $x' > x$. This implies that the integration along x need be extended only from the leading edge, $x = x_L$, up to the plane $x = $ constant; parts of the wing behind $x' = x$ do not contribute to the downwash at $x' = x$. Hence,

$$\frac{w(x,y)}{U_\infty} = \frac{1}{4\pi} \frac{\partial}{\partial y} \int_{x_L}^{x} dx' \left[\int_{-s(x')}^{+s(x')} \frac{l(x',y')}{y-y'} \, dy' \right], \tag{64}$$

where $s(x)$ is the local semispan in the plane $x = $ constant. Performing the differentiation and changing the order of integration, we have

$$\frac{w(x,y)}{U_\infty} = -\frac{1}{4\pi} \int_{-s(x)}^{s(x)} \frac{dy'}{(y-y')^2} \left[\int_{x_L(y')}^{x} l(x',y') \, dx' \right]. \tag{65}$$

The integral

$$\int_{x_L(y')}^{x} l(x',y') \, dx' = L(x,y') = [x-x_L(y')]C_{Lx}(y') \tag{66}$$

may be considered as the load on the section at the spanwise station $y = y'$ up to the plane $x = x'$. $L/(x-x_L)$ is the sectional lift coefficient C_{Lx} up to that plane. If it is assumed that the chord load falls to zero at the leading edge, in such a way that $L(x, y)/(y \pm s(x)) \to 0$ as $y \to \mp s(x)$, we find that

$$w(x, y)/U_\infty = (1/4\pi) \int\limits_{-s(x)}^{+s(x)} \{\partial L(x, y')/\partial y'\}(y-y')^{-1}\, dy'. \qquad (67)$$

The nature of the approximation (62) may be explained from this equation. We imagine that part of the wing upstream of a plane $x =$ constant, and by comparison with equation (45) the downwash on this plane equals $2\alpha_{i0} U_\infty$. Thus this plane may be regarded as the Trefftz plane for that part of the wing upstream of it, and its general features correspond to what has been discussed in Section VII. 6, for the displacement effect of wings. We note further that the total downwash $w(x, y)$ on such a slender wing is determined solely by the streamwise vorticity as is suggested in Fig. VIII. 9 (b); in other words the bound vortices normal to the mainstream, which represent the lifting force over the wing by analogy with equation (5), do not contribute to the downwash. We may refer to the work of Eckhaus (1954) for further considerations of the mathematical aspects of this theory.

We now consider a flat wing at incidence so that $w/U_\infty = \alpha =$ constant. The solution of equation (67) is then

$$L(x, y) = 4\alpha s(x)[1-\{y/s(x)\}^2]^{\frac{1}{2}}, \qquad (68)$$

or

$$C_L(y) = 4\alpha(s/c)[1-(y/s)^2]^{\frac{1}{2}}, \qquad (69)$$

by integration up to a straight trailing edge. The local load is

$$l(x, y) = \partial L(x, y)/\partial x = 4\alpha(ds/dx)[1-\{y/s(x)\}^2]^{-\frac{1}{2}}. \qquad (70)$$

By integration over the whole wing surface, we obtain the overall lift coefficient

$$\bar{C}_L = \tfrac{1}{2}\pi A \alpha. \qquad (71)$$

Similarly the chordwise position of the centre of pressure is calculated as

$$\bar{C}_m/\bar{C}_L = (2/c_0) \int\limits_0^{c_0} x\{s(x)/s\}[d\{s(x)/s\}/dx]\, dx \qquad (72)$$

measured from the leading edge at the centre in terms of the chord c_0 there. Finally the induced incidence is, of course, constant over the span and given by

$$\alpha_i = \alpha = 2\bar{C}_L/\pi A. \qquad (73)$$

This is twice that for an elliptic wing of large aspect ratio, from equation (50), on which the induced incidence also is constant.

There are some remarkable properties of wings of small aspect ratio, which it is profitable to contrast with those of wings of large aspect ratio. Whereas the latter have always the same type of chordwise loading, namely the flat-plate loading of equation (41) and a spanwise loading which must be determined in each individual case (but which does not usually differ by very much from the elliptic distribution), the former have always the same spanwise loading, namely the elliptic loading of equation (68), and a chordwise loading which differs from the flat-plate loading and must be determined in each individual case. In both cases the local load $l(x, y)$, according to the linearized theories, tends to infinity at the leading edge, where it behaves like $(x - x_L)^{-\frac{1}{2}}$; this variation, however, is not accurate near an apex where the sweep of the leading edge is zero or changes abruptly, and where the assumptions of slenderness are no longer valid even for wings of small aspect ratio.

On slender wings with unswept trailing edges, the Kutta–Joukowski condition that $l = 0$ at the trailing edge is satisfied only when ds/dx is zero there. The induced drag of a slender wing is always given by equation (33): it is always at the minimum value, and it may be written as

$$\bar{C}_{Di} = \tfrac{1}{2}\bar{C}_L \alpha, \tag{74}$$

which was first derived by Ward (1949).

Consider now the further example of a wing with an elliptic leading edge and an unswept trailing edge:

$$s(x) = s[1 - (1 - x/c_0)^2]^{\frac{1}{2}}, \tag{75}$$

where x is measured from the leading edge of the centre section at which the chord is c_0. The local load is then

$$l(x, y) = \tfrac{1}{2}\pi A\alpha(1 - x/c_0)[1 - (1 - x/c_0)^2]^{-\frac{1}{2}}[1 - \{y/s(x)\}^2]^{-\frac{1}{2}}, \tag{76}$$

which is similar to that on the elliptic wing of large aspect ratio, shown in Fig. VIII. 11. But $\bar{C}_L$ is not equal to $\pi A\alpha$—as results from equation (51) for wings of large aspect ratio if the limit $A \to 0$ is formally taken—but only half that value, as has already been indicated in equation (71). Further, the load on the slender wing tends linearly to zero at the trailing edge whereas that of the wing of large aspect ratio tends to zero like $(x_T - x)^{\frac{1}{2}}$. Thus the centre of pressure is nearer the leading edge on the slender wing and given, in this elliptic case, by

$$[x_{cp}(y) - x_L(y)]/c(y) = 1 - \tfrac{1}{4}\pi = 0\cdot215 \tag{77}$$

for all spanwise stations; this is to be compared with the value $0\cdot25$

for the wing of large aspect ratio. The overall centre of lift of the slender wing lies at $x = \frac{1}{3}c_0$ which is at the centre of area.

Another case which has attracted considerable interest is that of the slender delta wing, whose planform is an isosceles triangle of very small aspect ratio. It was from this type of wing that the theory of slender wings by R. T. Jones (1946) originated. The assumptions of slender-body theory lead in this case to a conical flow, namely a flow in which conditions are similar in all transverse planes through the wing normal to the mainstream. This has the serious drawback that no exception can be made for the trailing edge at which, therefore, $ds/dx \neq 0$; thus the Kutta–Joukowski condition cannot be fulfilled. This may be interpreted as restricting the applicability of this theory to the region between the apex and the trailing edge, the apex itself being excepted, too, because the fundamental downwash equation (22) does not apply to cases of kinked vortex lines. A second approximation in which the Kutta–Joukowski condition is satisfied at the trailing edge has been attempted by Legras (1954). For slender delta wings,

$$s(x) = x \cot \varphi = \tfrac{1}{4}Ax, \tag{78}$$

where φ is the angle of sweep of the leading edge, so that the loading is

$$l(x, y) = A\alpha[1 - \{y/s(x)\}^2]^{-\frac{1}{2}} \tag{79}$$

by equation (70).

The conical solution for the delta wing is illustrated in Fig. VIII. 14. The suction peaks along the leading edge and the finite load at the trailing edge are especially significant for this class of wing. The chordwise loading now differs considerably from the flat-plate loading. l is constant along the centre line on which the value of C_L equals $2\bar{C}_L/\pi$, being given by equation (71); and the overall centre of lift is at two-thirds of the chord of the centre section.

If slender-body theory is applied to tapered wings with swept leading edges, streamwise tip edges and unswept trailing edges, lift arises only on the triangular front part of the wing where the local span changes with x. Streamwise vortices are generated by the front part of the wing, and they produce a downwash $\alpha_i = \alpha$, so that the rectangular rear part of the wing, being wholly covered by this vortex sheet, is automatically a stream surface and so does not need to contribute to the vortex distribution. Nevertheless, the overall lift of this class of wing is still given by equation (71) since it depends only on the maximum semispan, and not on the aspect ratio. Thus

$$L/\tfrac{1}{2}\rho U_\infty^2 = 2\pi\alpha s^2. \tag{80}$$

As the angle of sweep of the leading edge of such wings is reduced to zero, the lift becomes concentrated near the leading edge. This fundamental property of straight wings of very small aspect ratio can be

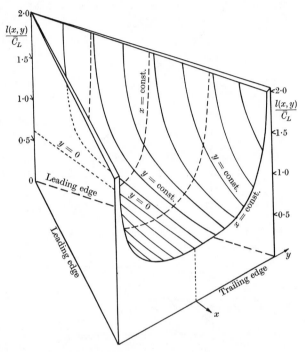

FIG. VIII. 14. The distribution of load on a slender delta wing of small aspect ratio in R. T. Jones's type of flow.

seen from equation (70), for if $s(x)$ tends to a constant value for $x > 0$, $l(x, y)$ tends to zero everywhere except at the singular leading edge $x = 0$.

A simple approximation for $l(x, y)$ which satisfies these conditions is

$$l(x, y) = C_L(y) \lim_{n \to 1} [(1/\pi n)\sin \pi n\{(c-x)/x\}^n], \tag{81}$$

for which the condition $\int_0^c l(x, y)\, dx = cC_L(y)$ of equation (23) holds since

$$\int_0^c \{(c-x)/x\}^n\, dx/c = \pi n \operatorname{cosec} \pi n. \tag{82}$$

This function is used in a method explained in Section 17, and designed to apply to wings of moderate aspect ratio. Since not only the overall lift slope, but also the chordwise loading, changes considerably on rectangular wings as the aspect ratio changes, there is still a serious gap between the theories of wings of large and of small aspect ratio.

R. T. Jones has pointed out the connexion between his theory of wings of very small aspect ratio and the flow past wings at sonic speed.

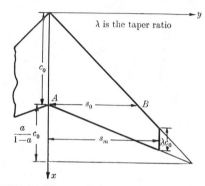

FIG. VIII. 15. The notation for a family of tapered wings.

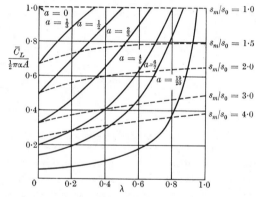

FIG. VIII. 16. The overall lift slopes of the family of tapered wings shown in Fig. VIII. 15, as calculated by Mangler (1955).

The assumption that the downwash due to a streamwise vortex line is zero upstream of the line and elsewhere equals its value at infinity downstream is reminiscent of the effect of disturbances in sonic flow. In this connexion, we may mention the work of Mangler (1955) who has given results for the family of tapered wings shown in Fig. VIII. 15. So long as the rear part of the wing behind the line AB of the figure lies wholly behind the leading edge and thus within the trailing vortex sheet of the front part, it is automatically a stream surface and so carries no load; in this case, the overall lift-curve slope is still $\frac{1}{2}\pi A$. If, however, the leading edge extends beyond the point B, lift is also experienced by the rear part of the wing from which trailing vorticity is shed. The boundary in the Trefftz plane is then in two parts, outside which the region is doubly connected; Mangler (1955), Lomax, Heaslet, and Fuller (1951), Tricomi (1951), Legendre, Eichelbrenner, and Baranoff (1952), and Mirels (1954) have all considered the ensuing mathematical complications. The lift-curve slope in such cases is less than $\frac{1}{2}\pi A$ as is shown by the examples given in Fig. VIII. 16. Stanbrook (1954) found that these results are closely approximated by

$$\bar{C}_L/\alpha = \tfrac{1}{2}\pi A[4/(2+A\tan\varphi_{\frac{1}{2}c})]$$

for $A\tan\varphi_{\frac{1}{2}c} \geqslant 2$, where $\varphi_{\frac{1}{2}c}$ is the angle of sweep of the midchord line. Mangler and Randall (1955) considered twisted wings of various planforms.

13. Infinite sheared wings

Just as with the flow past swept-back wings at zero lift, so now it is useful first to consider the character of the flow at large distances from the centre section or from any other kink. The transformation illustrated in Fig. VII. 8 is used again, so that the velocity components of the free stream are

$$\left.\begin{array}{l} U_\infty = U_\infty\cos\varphi\cos\alpha \\ V_\infty = U_\infty\sin\varphi\cos\alpha \\ W_\infty = U_\infty\sin\alpha \end{array}\right\}, \tag{83}$$

where φ is the angle of sweep of the leading edge and α the angle of incidence of the chord of each section (in streamwise planes). Such a wing can be represented by a distribution of straight bound vortices parallel to the generators of the wing. The incidence of sections perpendicular to the leading edge is $\alpha_n = W_\infty/U_\infty$. In the absence of trailing vortices on a wing of infinite span, the bound vortices alone must satisfy the boundary condition that the wing is a stream surface. Since their downwash is expressed by the incidence α_e, the boundary condition is $\alpha_n = \alpha_e\sec\varphi$. Remembering that, for the two-dimensional aerofoil, $\gamma(x) = 2U_\infty\alpha_e[(c-x)/x]^{\frac{1}{2}}$ is the solution of the downwash equation, we find for the infinite sheared wing

$$\gamma(X) = 2U_\infty\cos\varphi(\alpha_e\sec\varphi)[(c\cos\varphi-X)/X]^{\frac{1}{2}}. \tag{84}$$

In other words, $\qquad \gamma(x) = 2U_\infty\alpha_e[(c-x)/x]^{\frac{1}{2}}, \tag{85}$

which is again the two-dimensional flat-plate distribution.

With the vorticity vector swept at an angle φ, the local load is given by equation (7) as

$$l = 2\gamma \cos\varphi / U_\infty, \tag{86}$$

and so, with equation (85),

$$l(x) = 4\alpha_e \cos\varphi[(c-x)/x]^{\frac{1}{2}}. \tag{87}$$

Integration of this gives the sectional lift coefficient $C_L = 2\pi\alpha_e \cos\varphi$ which has already been given in equation (8). The sectional lift-curve slope $a_0(y)$ is given by

$$a_0 = C_L/\alpha_e = 2\pi \cos\varphi \tag{88}$$

and, in this particular case, is constant along the span.

14. The centre section of swept wings of infinite span

As in the last section, there is again an analogy with the symmetrical swept-back wing at zero lift, for no distribution of kinked vortex

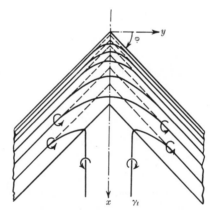

Fig. VIII. 17. A sketch illustrating the vortex lines near the centre of a plane swept wing.

lines, as shown by the broken lines in Fig. VIII. 17, can account for a constant or even a finite downwash over the whole wing. Such kinked vortex lines are not permitted in the derivation of the general downwash equation (21) or (22). They result in an infinitely large downwash on $y = 0$, which is unrealistic; a more plausible assumption would be that the vortex lines on a flat wing cut $y = 0$ perpendicularly and that some go into the wake as trailing vortices even when $A = \infty$. Nevertheless, the change in direction of the bound vortices is the principal characteristic of the centre section of all swept wings and, as a start, it is useful to consider the downwash distribution due to kinked vortices from which there is no trailing vorticity. The wing shape which corresponds to this is not flat but both cambered and twisted.

Küchemann (1952) argued that the embarrassment of the infinite downwash on the centre section due to the kinks of the vortex lines arises mainly from the mathematical fiction of an infinitely thin wing for which not only the equations of motion but also the boundary conditions are linearized. On a real wing of non-zero thickness, all these vortex lines would lie within the wing and the downwash, calculated on the surface of the wing, would be finite everywhere. In that general case, the downwash equation (21) does not apply.

It can be shown that the downwash due to a distribution of kinked vortex lines on a wing of small but non-zero thickness may conveniently be written in a general form as

$$w(x,y) = (1/2\pi)\left[\int_0^c \gamma(x')(x-x')^{-1}\,dx' + \gamma(x)\sigma(\varphi; x,y)\right]. \tag{89}$$

The function $\sigma(\varphi; x,y)$ can be determined from Biot–Savart's law, and is regular because the singularity normally associated with vortex lines has been taken out in the form of the first integral, where Cauchy's principal value must be taken. It has been found from numerical calculations that σ may be approximated by a function of φ and y only: $\sigma = \sigma(\varphi; y)$, if φ is not too large. The two values

$$\sigma(\varphi; \infty) = \sigma(0; y) = 0 \tag{90}$$

ensure that equation (89) is correct at large distances from the centre section and also in the degenerate two-dimensional case. Further, $\sigma(\varphi, 0) = \pi\tan\varphi$ gives good numerical agreement for values on the centre line $y = 0$, provided φ is not too close to $\frac{1}{2}\pi$. Somewhat similar results have been obtained by Heemert (1951).

With this approximation for σ, the shape of the centre section of a swept-back wing of infinite span and constant chord may now be calculated for a given distribution of $\gamma(x)$. For example, let the flat-plate loading,

$$l(x) = (2C_L/\pi)[(c-x)/x]^{\frac{1}{2}} \quad \text{on } y = 0, \tag{91}$$

be the required load distribution and let C_L be constant along the span so that there are no trailing vortices. Equation (86) gives

$$\gamma(x) = (U_\infty C_L/\pi)\sec\varphi[(c-x)/x]^{\frac{1}{2}} \tag{92}$$

and substitution in equation (89) gives, on $y = 0$,

$$w/U_\infty = (C_L/2\pi)\sec\varphi\{1 + \tan\varphi[(c-x)/x]^{\frac{1}{2}}\}. \tag{93}$$

With the streamline condition $w/U_\infty = dz/dx$, the coordinates of the mean line of the aerofoil section at the centre of the wing can be obtained by integration: thus

$$z_c(x)/c_0 = \sec\varphi(C_L/2\pi)\{x/c_0 + \tfrac{1}{2}\tan\varphi \cos^{-1}(1 - 2x/c_0) + \tan\varphi[(c-x)/x]^{\frac{1}{2}}\} \tag{94}$$

if $z_c(0) = 0$. At large distances from the centre line, equation (91) gives the load distribution of the flat plate $z(x) = \sec\varphi(C_L/2\pi)x$, which shape is represented by the first term in equation (94). The second and third terms in the curly bracket represent the amounts of camber and twist— both of which depend on the sweep-back—needed to counteract the effect of the kink and to produce the loading (91) characteristic of a two-dimensional flat plate. For swept-back wings, the required camber is negative. On a wing designed according to equation (94) whose shape was faired reasonably from the centre section to the tip, Küchemann (1953a) found good experimental agreement with the load distribution given in equation (91), thus confirming the adequacy of the downwash equation (89) with $\sigma = \pi\tan\varphi$.

We are normally confronted with the problem of finding the loading on a wing whose camber lines are of given shape, and for this we continue with the assumption that $\sigma = \sigma(\varphi; y)$ is an adequate approximation in equation (89). The direct problem of solving this equation for $\gamma(x)$ can be solved by using the result of Carleman (1922) that the general solution of the integral equation

$$F(x) = 2\pi w(x)/\sigma = (1/\sigma)\int_0^c \gamma(x')(x-x')^{-1}\,dx' + \gamma(x) \tag{95}$$

can be written

$$\gamma(x) = \frac{\sigma^2}{\sigma^2 + \pi^2}\,F(x) + \frac{c}{c-x}\left(\frac{c-x}{x}\right)^n - $$
$$- \frac{\sigma}{\sigma^2 + \pi^2}\left(\frac{c-x}{x}\right)^n \int_0^c F(x')\left(\frac{c-x'}{x'}\right)^{-n}\frac{dx'}{x-x'}, \tag{96}$$

where $n = (1/2\pi)\cos^{-1}[(\sigma^2 - \pi^2)/(\sigma^2 + \pi^2)]$.

For an uncambered wing, $w = \alpha_e U_\infty$ is the downwash required from all the vorticity components except the trailing vortices, if the latter are again assumed to induce a downwash which is constant along the chord, on wings of sufficiently large aspect ratio. Thus with $\sigma = \pi\tan\varphi$ at the centre section, we have

$$F = 2\alpha_e U_\infty \cot\varphi \quad \text{and} \quad n = n_0 = \tfrac{1}{2}(1 - 2\varphi/\pi). \tag{97}$$

The vorticity is then found from equation (96) to be

$$\gamma(x) = 2\alpha_e\, U_\infty \cos\varphi[(c-x)/x]^{n_0}. \qquad (98)$$

We now make the assumption that the vortex lines cut the centre line perpendicularly and apply equation (7) with $\varphi = 0$ to obtain

$$l(x,0) = 4\alpha_e \cos\varphi[(c-x)/x]^{n_0}. \qquad (99)$$

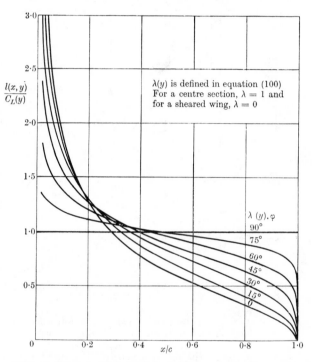

$\lambda(y)$ is defined in equation (100)
For a centre section, $\lambda = 1$ and
for a sheared wing, $\lambda = 0$

$\lambda(y).\varphi$
$90°$
$75°$
$60°$
$45°$
$30°$
$15°$
0

Fig. VIII. 18. The calculated chordwise loadings on some flat swept-back wings of infinite span, according to equation (100).

To obtain the loading at any other section, Küchemann (1952) adopted an interpolation procedure based on the fortunate fact that the loadings at the centre section, equation (99), and far away from it, equation (87), are of the same form so that only the index n need be regarded as a function of both φ and y. Thus he put

$$\left.\begin{array}{l} l(x,y) = [(1/\pi n)\sin \pi n]C_L(y)[(c-x)/x]^n \\ n(\varphi;y) = \tfrac{1}{2}[1-2\lambda(y)\varphi/\pi] \\ \lambda(y) = [1+(2\pi y/c)^2]^{\frac{1}{2}}-2\pi y/c \end{array}\right\} \qquad (100)$$

The lift-incidence relation and the sectional lift slope, a, are given, at any section, by

$$C_L = (4\pi n \cosec \pi n \cos\varphi)\alpha_e = a(\varphi; y)\alpha_e. \tag{101}$$

Typical loadings, according to equations (100), are shown in Fig. VIII. 18 while a comparison with experiments of Küchemann, Weber, and Brebner (1951) is shown in Fig. VIII. 19. The theoretical lines in

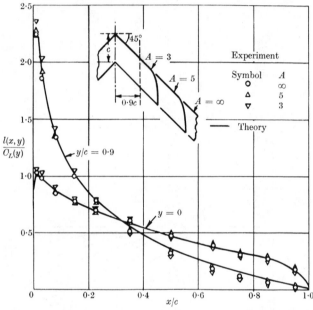

Fig. VIII. 19. A comparison between calculated and experimental chordwise loadings on some untapered wings of $45°$ sweep-back.

this last figure represent the result given by (100) modified by Weber (1953), according to the ideas of Section VII. 8, to take into account the displacement effect of the wing thickness. This experiment was made with wings which differed only in their aspect ratios, and which were specifically designed to check the assumptions made above. These imply that the aspect ratio affects primarily the distribution of trailing vorticity and hence the spanwise loading $C_L c$ but not the distribution of the load along the chord. The experimental results confirm this down to an aspect ratio as small as 3.

We note the important effect of sweep-back in shifting backwards the centre of pressure on the centre section and reducing the suction near the leading edge; this seems to follow from the bound vortices taking a short cut across the centre line, as shown in Fig. VIII. 17. The centre of pressure is given by

$$x_{cp}/c = \tfrac{1}{2}(1-n) = \tfrac{1}{4}+\lambda(y)\varphi/2\pi, \tag{102}$$

which follows from the second of equations (100) and the general relation

$$(1/c^2) \int_0^c [(c-x)/x]^n x \, dx = \tfrac{1}{2}\pi n(1-n)\operatorname{cosec} \pi n. \tag{103}$$

15. The effect of finite aspect ratio

To determine the complete loading on wings of finite span, we have now to take two factors into consideration. First, changes in downwash occur near the tips due to the disappearance of the bound vorticity at the tips; and second, the effect of trailing vorticity may no longer be ignored as in the previous two sections.

The tip effect on the bound vorticity may be allowed for by regarding the tip as the centre section of a swept wing of opposite sweep. The application of this idea to displacement effects was discussed and justified in Section VII. 9 and here we attempt no further justification for lifting wings. Equation (100) therefore is taken to give the loading near the tips, provided n now takes the value $n = \tfrac{1}{2}(1+2\lambda\varphi/\pi)$; y/c is measured inwards in the definition of λ, and c is the tip chord.

Now in considering the effect of the trailing vortices on a swept wing of large aspect ratio, we first remind ourselves of the fact that the mean downwash induced by the trailing vortices may be taken as being independent of the wing sweep for wings of given span and overall lift, provided they are so cambered and twisted that the spanwise load distribution is also independent of the sweep. We then make the assumption that this is an adequate approximation even when the loading over the swept wing is not strictly the same as on the corresponding unswept wing and, further, that the induced downwash is constant along the chord, in analogy to the result in Section 7. It is thus assumed that the equation $\alpha_i = \alpha_{i0}$ still holds even for a swept wing, provided its aspect ratio is large. It is further assumed that the remaining contributions to the downwash arise solely from the bound vortices, and that the downwash from the spanwise bound vortices, $\alpha_e U_\infty$, may be given the same values as for wings of infinite aspect ratio, again in analogy to the result in Section 9. Experiments, such as those in Fig. VIII. 19, have justified this for $\varphi = 45°$.

The downwash equation therefore is similar to that for unswept wings, equation (42), except for the fact that the sectional lift slope is no longer 2π but a which, from (101), depends on φ and y. Thus we write, analogously to (42),

$$C_L(y)/a(\varphi; y) = \alpha(y) - (1/8\pi) \int_{-s}^{s} \{d(C_L c)/dy'\}(y-y')^{-1}\, dy'. \quad (104)$$

16. General characteristics. Various drag forces

Fig. VIII. 20 illustrates some of the characteristics of the three basic solutions obtained so far. Sweep-back leads to a reduction of lift accompanied by a rearward shift of the centre of pressure in the central region and to the opposite effects in the tip regions; the effect of small aspect ratio tends to make the spanwise loading elliptic and to bring the centre of pressure forward towards the leading edge; the overall lift slope is reduced by sweep and still more so by small aspect ratio; only on the swept wing are there appreciable spanwise changes in the chordwise loading and thus in the position of the centre of pressure. These general features will occur repeatedly in the intermediate cases to be considered in more detail in succeeding sections.

Provided the aspect ratio of a wing is sufficiently large to enable a swept wing to be considered in three parts—centre region, tip region, and the middle sheared region—an approximate solution for wings of general planform may be constructed by replacing the wing by fictitious elements of wing in each of these three regions. It is a basic hypothesis which is frequently applied in the theory of wings that it is more important to assess correctly the local effect of sweep and chordwise loading than the mutual spanwise interactions. It is represented by equation (41) in the case of thin wings of large aspect ratio, and has been held valid in that case, and now it is extended to spanwise changes in wing chord and to spanwise changes in angle of sweep. Thus, in each of the three regions, the sweep and chord are assigned constant values typical of each region. It is on this basis that the curves in Fig. VIII. 20 were calculated for the swept wing.

For both straight and swept wings of large aspect ratio, the local vortex, or induced, drag may be introduced, which is obtained from the relation

$$C_{Di}(y) = \alpha_{i0}(y)C_L(y) = C_L(y)[\alpha(y) - C_L(y)/a(\varphi; y)]. \quad (105)$$

The overall induced drag is minimum for a given lift when α_{i0} is constant along the span, and for this the spanwise load distribution must be elliptic, as given in equations (28) and (48), when the overall induced drag is given by equation (33). Since α_{i0} is constant in this case, $\alpha_e = \alpha - \alpha_{i0}$ is also constant along the span of flat wings. Hence, for swept wings, $C_L = a(\varphi; y)\alpha_e$ is not constant for minimum induced drag but varies directly as the sectional lift slope, $a(\varphi; y)$, which is given by equation (101). This is a special characteristic of swept wings and a direct consequence of the different chordwise loadings along the span.

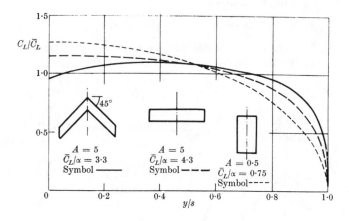

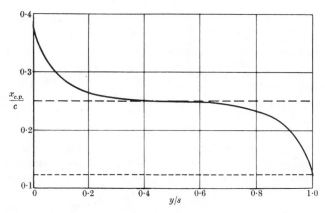

Fig. VIII. 20. The effects of aspect ratio and angle of sweep on the spanwise loading and the position of the centre of pressure, typified by three particular wings.

If the wing planform is such that the value of a_0 in the sheared region can be used as a mean value, it can be shown that

$$\left.\begin{array}{l} C_L/\overline{C}_L = a(y)\sec\varphi/a_0 \\ \overline{C}_L/\alpha = [\sec\varphi/a_0 + 1/\pi A]^{-1} \end{array}\right\}, \tag{106}$$

the latter equation including the usual result for an unswept wing of large aspect ratio.

With swept wings, the spanwise chord distribution which gives elliptic spanwise loading is not itself elliptic. The chord distribution $c(y)$ can be determined from equations (28), (104), and (106):

$$c(y)/c_0(y) = a_0 \cos\varphi/a(\varphi; y), \qquad (107)$$

where $c_0(y)$ is the elliptic planform of the unswept wing with the same aspect ratio. Such a wing is shown as A in Fig. VIII. 21.

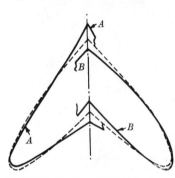

FIG. VIII. 21. A and B are planforms calculated for minimum induced drag and constant spanwise lift respectively. Their aspect ratios are 2·9 and 3·3 and the mid-chord line is swept-back by 45°. The broken line indicates an elliptic distribution of chord.

The minimum induced drag of thin wings in frictionless flow has been discussed as one part of the lift-dependent drag at supersonic speeds by R. T. Jones (1951). He showed that, for the drag to be a minimum, the downwash in the combined disturbance field (obtained by a superposition of the disturbance field of the given wing and the field in reversed flow of a wing with the same planform, cambered and twisted to have the same lift distribution in reversed flow) must be constant at all points of the wing surface. This reverse-flow theorem which is based on ideas of Munk (1919) has been introduced by Brown (1949) and has been discussed in some detail by Heaslet and Spreiter (1952).

It is of interest to consider the special case of swept wings whose local lift coefficient is constant, C_L, along the span, remembering that on unswept elliptic wings, the two conditions of constant C_L and minimum induced drag go together, which is no longer true on swept wings. The chord distribution $c(y)$ can be obtained from equation (104) by

$$C_L/a(y) = \alpha - (C_L/8\pi) \int\limits_{-s}^{s} \{dc(y')/dy'\}(y-y')^{-1}\,dy', \qquad (108)$$

which is of a similar type to Prandtl's aerofoil equation and can be solved according to the methods of Section 18 by successive approximations. Such a wing is shown as B in Fig. VIII. 21: there is a slight inverse taper in this particular case near the centre section but this does not occur for wings of smaller aspect ratio. Brebner (1954) has considered this important design problem in detail; it is raised again in Section 26.

An important characteristic of symmetrical thick swept-back wings at zero incidence was found in Sections VII. 8 and 9 to be the existence, even in inviscid flow, of a drag in the centre region and a thrust in the tip region. This effect, of course, persists when the wing is at incidence, and it may be shown that similar drag forces arise from the bound vortices. In addition, there are viscous drag forces, and to obtain a better insight into the various physical effects contributing to the drag, we write

$$C_D(y) = \Delta C_{DT}(y) + \lambda(y)[C_L(y)]^2/a(y) + C_{Di}(y) + \Delta C_{DB}(y) + C_{DF}. \quad (109)$$

The first three terms on the right-hand side arise in inviscid flow; the last two are due to viscosity effects. The first term is the normal-pressure drag due to thickness; it is proportional to $(t/c)^2$. The second term arises from the spanwise changes in chordwise loading and is related to the bound vortices. The integral of both these terms over the whole wing is zero. The third term is the vortex, or induced, drag which is related to the vorticity shed from the trailing edge. ΔC_{DB} is due to the loss of circulation caused by the boundary layer, which amounts, to a first approximation, to a reduction, $\Delta\alpha_B$, in the effective incidence so that $\Delta C_{DB} = \Delta\alpha_B C_L$. Thus the three middle terms are proportional to $(C_L)^2$. The last term represents the skin friction. The relative magnitudes of the various pressure drag forces and their distribution along the span are shown in Fig. VIII. 22, given by Küchemann, Weber, and Brebner (1951). By comparison with the usual result for unswept wings, where the first two terms do not arise and where C_{Di} is more uniform and ΔC_{DB} smaller, the effects of the three-dimensionality of the flow are shown to be very marked. In particular, the maximum local pressure drag is much higher than the mean so that the level of the latter depends on a precarious balance.

The induced drag, according to the first inviscid approximation, has been put in terms of the drag factor K in equation (34). The result of the additional terms in (109) is to increase the rate of change of $\bar{C}_D$ with $(\bar{C}_L)^2$: thus

$$\partial\bar{C}_D/\partial(\bar{C}_L)^2 > K/\pi A. \quad (110)$$

In some extreme cases such as thin highly-tapered wings, the separation near the tips leads to a resultant force which is normal to the wing surface and not inclined forward as in Fig. VIII. 9. If the separation extends along the whole loading edge,

$$\bar{C}_{Di} = \bar{C}_L \alpha, \quad (111)$$

and the drag factor, K, due to lift is then very much greater than its value calculated on the basis of unseparated inviscid flow.

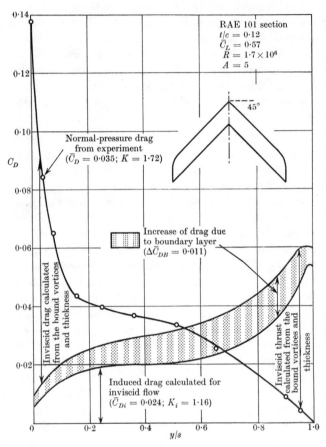

FIG. VIII. 22. The spanwise distribution of normal-pressure drag for an untapered swept-back wing.

17. Wings of general planform and moderate aspect ratio

None of the three theories which have been discussed in the preceding sections is immediately applicable to many of the most common planforms since practical values of the aspect ratio are neither very large nor very small. But they have much in common: the load distribution over the wing surface, in particular, is always approximately of the form

$$l(x,y) = \sin \pi n\, C_L(y)[(c-x)/x]^n/\pi n. \tag{112}$$

Also, $C_L(y)$ obeys equation (104) as it stands if the aspect ratio is large; while if the aspect ratio is small so that $\alpha_i = 2\alpha_{i0}$, the integral in (104) must be doubled. This suggests the development, for the general wing, of an interpolation method in which equations (104) and (112) are retained in modified form.

First, the exponent n is taken to vary with the aspect ratio of the wing so that $n = n(\varphi, y, A)$. The finite width of the trailing vortex sheet in relation to the wing chord is taken to modify the downwash α_{i0} by the so-called downwash factor ω defined by $\alpha_i = \omega\alpha_{i0}$. $\omega = 1$ for wings of large aspect ratio and $\omega = 2$ for wings of very small aspect ratio, as seen from equations (45) and (73). Such a method, following Küchemann (1952), will be described below. As shown in Section 12, it is needed mainly for, and applies best to, wings which are not highly tapered. Its purpose is not only to provide a simple numerical means for calculating the load but also to demonstrate most clearly what the effects of a small aspect ratio are.

As this method is based on a one-parameter function for the chordwise loading, the boundary condition that the wing is a stream-surface must be relaxed and can be fulfilled only in the mean over the wing chord at each spanwise station. In particular, a solution based on equation (112) throughout cannot be correct near the leading edge where l should always behave like $(x-x_L)^{\frac{1}{2}}$, but the case $A \to 0$ is at least formally included as $n \to 1$, by equation (81). Further, the downwash from the whole vortex system is again split into two contributions, one w_1 from the bound vortices, the other w_2 from the streamwise vortices. The mean value

$$(1/cU_\infty) \int_{x_L}^{x_T} w_1(x)\,dx = \alpha_e \tag{113}$$

may then be described as the effective incidence, and the mean value

$$(1/cU_\infty) \int_{x_L}^{x_T} w_2(x)\,dx = \alpha_i \tag{114}$$

as the induced incidence of the aerofoil section. The boundary condition, $\alpha = \alpha_e + \alpha_i$, remains but is only approximately satisfied by the new meanings of the symbols.

Next we notice that $\omega = 2n$ is exact for the two limiting values of n: $n = \frac{1}{2}$ is the case of infinite aspect ratio and $n = 1$ that of infinitely small aspect ratio.

The relationship between C_L and α_e is obtained by assuming that the mean downwash due to the bound vortices is not greatly altered by the fiction that they extend spanwise to infinity. Thus

$$\alpha_e = (1/2\pi c U_\infty) \int_{x_L}^{x_T} \int_{x_L}^{x_T} \left[\gamma_b(x')/(x-x') \right] dx dx' \tag{115}$$

and with $\gamma_b = \tfrac{1}{2} U_\infty l$ and l given from equation (112), this becomes

$$C_L(y)/\alpha_e = a = a_0 2n(1-\pi n \cot \pi n)^{-1}, \tag{116}$$

where the two-dimensional lift slope 2π has been replaced by the more general value a_0 which may take into account effects of thickness and viscosity.

Finally, Küchemann (1952) suggested that for unswept wings a reasonable relation between n and A is

$$n = 1 - \tfrac{1}{2}[1 + (a_0/\pi A)^2]^{-\frac{1}{2}}. \tag{117}$$

This fits in with experimental evidence. The downwash equation (104) is then modified by (40) into the form

$$C_L/a\omega = \alpha/\omega - (1/8\pi) \int_{-s}^{+s} \left[d(cC_L)/dy' \right](y-y')^{-1} dy'. \tag{118}$$

A check on the accuracy of this method has been carried out by Weber (1954b) who calculated the value of the downwash, and hence of the aerofoil shape $z(x)$, at the centre line of a rectangular wing of aspect ratio unity, assuming elliptic spanwise loading and a chordwise loading as calculated by this method. It will be seen from Fig. VIII. 23 that the deviation from a straight line is small in spite of the very simple type of loading.

For a swept wing, the same procedure of solution through equations (112) and (118) could be followed except that the sectional lift slope and n should now be given by

$$C_L/\alpha_e = a = a_0 2n \cos\varphi \operatorname{cosec} \pi n_0 [1 - \pi n(\cot \pi n - \cot \pi n_0)]^{-1}, \tag{119}$$

$$\text{and} \qquad n = 1 - \tfrac{1}{2}(1 + 2\lambda\varphi/\pi)[1 + (a_0 \cos\varphi/\pi A)^2]^{-(4+2|\varphi|/\pi)^{-1}}, \tag{120}$$

where n_0 is the corresponding value for wings of large aspect ratio, given by equation (100).

Fig. VIII. 24 shows reasonable agreement between calculated results of this method and experimental results obtained by Küchemann, Weber, and Brebner (1951). Characteristic effects of small aspect ratio become appreciable only when A is below 3 for this wing of 45° sweep-back, whereas the corresponding aspect ratio for unswept wings is about 6. In general, the effect of the aspect ratio being small is to decrease the lift for given incidence and to move the position of the centre of pressure nearer the leading edge.

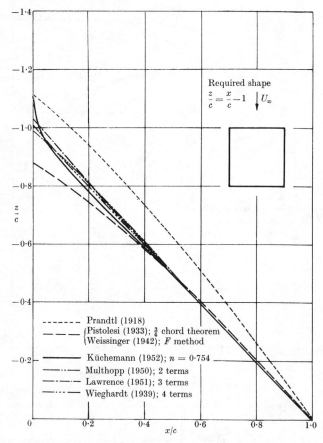

Fig. VIII. 23. Camber lines as calculated by Weber (1954b) from various theories for the centre line of a rectangular wing of aspect ratio unity.

Cranked wings, on which the angle of sweep changes abruptly at one or more spanwise stations between the centre and the tip, may also be treated by this type of method. The general effect of a crank is similar to that of a centre section and has been studied by Brebner (1953). A crank at which the sweep decreases in the outward direction shows properties normally associated with the centre section of a swept-forward wing and the load tends to be concentrated further forward

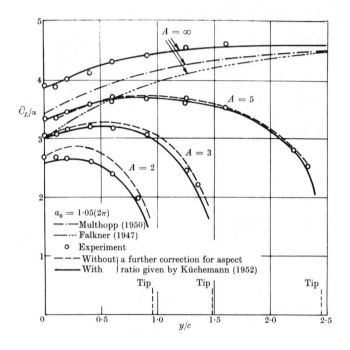

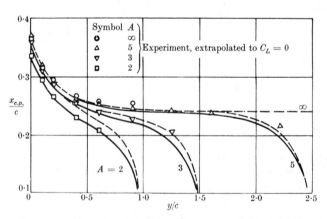

Fig. VIII. 24. A comparison between calculated and experimental spanwise distributions of lift and positions of centre of pressure for wings of constant chord and 45° sweep-back, as in Fig. VIII. 19.

towards the leading edge. This is clearly shown in Fig. VIII. 25 and may lead to premature separation and to adverse compressibility effects at high subsonic Mach numbers.

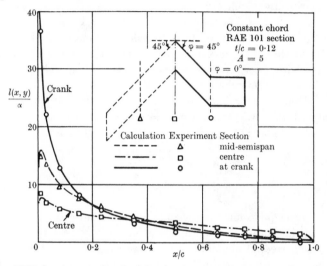

Fig. VIII. 25. A comparison between the chordwise loadings on a fully swept wing and a cranked wing.

18. Numerical methods for solving the spanwise loading equation

All the theories discussed so far lead to the same equation (118) for the spanwise loading, and often it is preferable to solve this equation numerically, to within a given error, rather than to rely on analytical approximations of whose errors one cannot be certain. It is as well to remember also that the equation itself is an approximation, and possibly in some cases a poor approximation: it is pointless to demand accurate solutions of it and so we are interested mainly in methods of routine calculation which are both quick and simple in application. The final checks on the adequacy of the basic equations and the accuracy of their solution are always by appropriate experiments.

There were numerous early attempts to solve the equation. These are reviewed by Lotz (1931a), Betz (1935), and by Kármán and Burgers (1935) among others. It may be mentioned that the first successful method, for rectangular wings, was obtained by Betz (1919), who assumed the solution to be of the type

$$C_L c/4s = \gamma_M(y) = [1-(y/s)^2]^{\frac{1}{2}} \sum_{\substack{j=0 \\ j\,\text{even}}}^{2N} \gamma_{Mj} y^j. \tag{121}$$

On the basis of this assumption Pohlhausen, in an unpublished paper, was the first to show that wings with elliptic loading possess the smallest possible induced drag, a theorem which was subsequently proved in a general way by Munk (1919), as discussed in Section 6. The factor $[1-(y/s)^2]^{\frac{1}{4}}$ ensures that the lift falls to zero at the tips in a reasonable manner, a problem that has been considered in more detail by Pfeiffer (1937). Without this factor a convergent series could not be found, and even with it convergence was not always assured and the computation of the coefficients was extremely tedious.

In reducing the problem to one in potential theory, Trefftz (1921) introduced the use of Fourier series, which proved a very fruitful approach. He defined a new variable θ by the relation

$$y = s \cos \theta \tag{122}$$

and put
$$C_L c/4s = \gamma_M(\theta) = \sum_{\mu=1}^{N} A_\mu \sin \mu\theta. \tag{123}$$

The integral equation (118) is then fulfilled at a finite number of points, N, along the span. This method was extensively used by H. Glauert (1926) who treated not only rectangular wings, but straight tapered unswept, and also twisted wings. In the course of these investigations, integrals of the type

$$I_n = \int_0^\pi \cos n\theta' \, d\theta'/(\cos \theta' - \cos \theta) = \pi \sin n\theta \operatorname{cosec} \theta \tag{124}$$

recur, n being a positive integer.

In the simple case of rectangular wings, Glauert introduced the coefficients δ and τ defined by

$$\left. \begin{array}{l} \bar{C}_{Di} = (1+\delta)\bar{C}_L^2/\pi A \quad \text{or} \quad K_i = 1+\delta, \\ \bar{\alpha}_{i0} = (1+\tau)\bar{C}_L/\pi A. \end{array} \right\} \tag{125}$$

Here $\bar{\alpha}_{i0}$ is the mean of $\alpha_{i0}(y)$ over the span. Using the relations $\alpha = \bar{\alpha}_e + \bar{\alpha}_{i0}$ and $\bar{\alpha}_e = \bar{C}_L/a_0$—the latter assuming that the sectional lift slope is constant along the span—we have

$$\bar{C}_L/\alpha = a_0/[1+(1+\tau)a_0/\pi A]. \tag{126}$$

The values of δ and τ as calculated by Glauert for rectangular wings are given in Table VIII. 1; he also calculated values for straight-tapered wings. One of the uses to which the result (126) was put by the earlier experimenters was the calculation of the two-dimensional lift slope

$a_0 = C_L/\alpha_e$ from three-dimensional experiments which gave the value of $\bar{C}_L/\alpha$. Alternatively, the equation enables $\bar{C}_L$ to be calculated for any aspect ratio if its value for a certain aspect ratio is known.

TABLE VIII. 1

Glauert's factors for rectangular wings

A/a_0	δ	τ
0·50	0·019	0·10
0·75	0·034	0·14
1·00	0·049	0·17
1·25	0·063	0·20
1·50	0·076	0·22
1·75	0·088	0·24

A reasonable variation of $C_L(y)$ near the tips of wings was not always achieved by the earlier methods and in this connexion the work of Wieselsberger (1927) and Gates (1928) may be mentioned. But all these methods have the serious inconvenience that the accuracy cannot be improved by successive approximations because to take more terms in the series requires the repetition of the whole calculation. The method of Lotz (1931a) was designed to avoid this and was based on the Fourier analysis of the load distribution, the chord distribution $c(y)$, the incidence distribution $\alpha(y)$, and the lift slope $a(y)$. Multhopp (1938a) succeeded in refining this general approach so that the solution of the full equation (118) may be computed within an hour or two with the aid of desk machines only; his method is described in detail in the following section.

19. The numerical method of Multhopp (1938a)

$(N+1)$ spanwise points are first defined by y_ν, $\nu = 0, 1, 2, ..., N$, given by

$$y_\nu = s\cos(\nu\pi/N) = s\cos\theta_\nu. \tag{127}$$

For convenience, N is assumed to be even. It is then assumed that

$$C_L c/4s = \gamma_M(\theta) = (2/N) \sum_{\mu=1}^{N-1} \gamma_{M\mu} \sum_{\lambda=1}^{N-1} \sin\lambda\theta_\mu \sin\lambda\theta \tag{128}$$

in which the coefficients $\gamma_{M\mu}$ are the values of $\gamma_M(\theta)$ at the points $y = y_\mu$ or $\theta = \theta_\mu$. Now the expression for the induced incidence α_{i0} can be written, from equations (27) and (45), as

$$\alpha_{i0}(\theta) = (1/2\pi) \int_0^\pi (d\gamma_M/d\theta')\, d\theta'/(\cos\theta' - \cos\theta). \tag{129}$$

Substituting from equation (128) into (129) and using the result (124), we find $\alpha_{i0}(\theta_\nu)$ in the form

$$\alpha_{i0}(\theta_\nu) = b_{\nu\nu}\gamma_{M\nu} - \sum_{\substack{\mu=1 \\ \mu \neq \nu}}^{N-1} b_{\nu\mu}\gamma_{M\mu} \tag{130}$$

where the coefficients have the values

$$\left.\begin{array}{ll} & b_{\nu\nu} = \tfrac{1}{4}N \operatorname{cosec}\theta_\nu \\ \text{for } |\mu-\nu| \text{ odd:} & b_{\nu\mu} = (1/N)\sin\theta_\mu(\cos\theta_\mu - \cos\theta_\nu)^{-2} \\ \text{for } |\mu-\nu| \text{ even:} & b_{\nu\mu} = 0 \end{array}\right\} \tag{131}$$

which may be tabulated once and for all, for any given value of N.

The complete span-loading equation (118) is then satisfied at all y_ν by the simultaneous equations

$$(b_{\nu\nu} + 2A\bar{c}/\omega a_\nu c_\nu)\gamma_{M\nu} = \alpha_\nu/\omega + \sum_{\substack{\mu=1 \\ \mu \neq \nu}}^{N-1} b_{\nu\mu}\gamma_{M\mu}. \tag{132}$$

In practical applications, we may reduce the numerical work involved by distinguishing between symmetrical and anti-symmetrical flows when α and c are even or odd functions of y respectively. Here, let us continue only with the symmetrical case: then $\gamma_\nu = \gamma_{N-\nu}$ and the terms in the sum in equation (132) may be arranged in pairs so that

$$\left.\begin{array}{l} (b_{\nu\nu} + 2A\bar{c}/\omega a_\nu c_\nu)\gamma_{M\nu} = \alpha_\nu/\omega + \sum_{\mu=1}^{\frac{1}{2}N} B_{\nu\mu}\gamma_{M\mu}, \quad \nu = 1, 2, ..., \tfrac{1}{2}N, \\ \text{where} \quad B_{\nu\mu} = b_{\nu\mu} + b_{\nu,N-\mu}, \quad B_{\nu\nu} = 0, \quad \text{and} \quad B_{\nu,\frac{1}{2}N} = b_{\nu,\frac{1}{2}N}. \end{array}\right\} \tag{133}$$

The values of $b_{\nu\nu}$ and $B_{\nu\mu}$ are given in Table VIII. 2 for $N = 16$.

TABLE VIII. 2

Values of Multhopp's coefficients for a symmetrical wing and $N = 16$

ν	1	2	3	4	5	6	7	8
y_ν/s	0·9808	0·9239	0·8315	0·7071	0·5556	0·3827	0·1951	0·0000
$b_{\nu\nu}$	20·5030	10·4525	7·1998	5·6568	4·8107	4·3295	4·0786	4·0000
μ				$B_{\nu\mu}$				
1	0	3·7687	0	0·1671	0	0·4070	0	0·0254
2	7·3924	0	2·8086	0	0·1872	0	0·0641	0
3	0	4·0774	0	2·2598	0	0·1960	0	0·1004
4	0·6055	0	2·8762	0	1·9523	0	0·2229	0
5	0	0·4069	0	2·2958	0	1·7976	0	0·3368
6	0·1927	0	0·3259	0	1·9975	0	1·8139	0
7	0	0·1644	0	0·3091	0	1·9254	0	3·2210
8	0·0650	0	0·0904	0	0·2025	0	1·6422	0

Values of the coefficients for higher values of N and for the asymmetrical case as well may be found in Multhopp's original paper.

The particular advantages of this numerical method are that not only are the equations for a given N in a very convenient form for iterative solution, but also the values obtained for $N = 2^p$ may be used as the initial values for $N = 2^{p+1}$. We may illustrate these features by considering the equations for $N = 8$, which are:

$$\left.\begin{array}{l}(5 \cdot 2262 + 2A\bar{c}/\omega a_1 c_1)\gamma_{M1} = \alpha_1/\omega + 1 \cdot 9142\gamma_{M2} + 0 \cdot 1464\gamma_{M4}\\(2 \cdot 1648 + 2A\bar{c}/\omega a_3 c_3)\gamma_{M3} = \alpha_3/\omega + 0 \cdot 9142\gamma_{M2} + 0 \cdot 8536\gamma_{M4}\\(2 \cdot 8284 + 2A\bar{c}/\omega a_2 c_2)\gamma_{M2} = \alpha_2/\omega + 1 \cdot 0360\gamma_{M1} + 1 \cdot 1944\gamma_{M3}\\(2 \cdot 0000 + 2A\bar{c}/\omega a_4 c_4)\gamma_{M4} = \alpha_4/\omega + 0 \cdot 1121\gamma_{M1} + 1 \cdot 5774\gamma_{M3}\end{array}\right\}. \quad (134)$$

If trial values of γ_{M2} and γ_{M4} are inserted in the first two equations, the values so obtained for γ_{M1} and γ_{M3} may be substituted in the second two equations to give improved values of γ_{M2} and γ_{M4}. Furthermore, γ_{M2} and γ_{M4} for $N = 8$ denote the same quantities as γ_{M1} and γ_{M2} for $N = 4$; the iterative solution of equations (129) can therefore conveniently be started with the values obtained from

$$\left.\begin{array}{l}(1 \cdot 4142 + 2A\bar{c}/\omega a_2 c_2)\gamma_{M2} = \alpha_2/\omega + 0 \cdot 5000\gamma_{M4}\\(1 \cdot 0000 + 2A\bar{c}/\omega a_4 c_4)\gamma_{M4} = \alpha_4/\omega + 0 \cdot 7071\gamma_{M2}\end{array}\right\}, \quad (135)$$

which are the equations for $N = 4$ in the symmetrical case, the notation for $N = 8$ being retained.

Once a solution for the $\gamma_{M\mu}$ is known, $\gamma_M(\theta)$ follows from equation (128). $\bar{C}_L$ and $\bar{C}_{Di}$ are then given by

$$\left.\begin{array}{l}\bar{C}_L = (A/s) \int_{-s}^{+s} \gamma_M \, dy = (\pi A/N) \sum_{\mu=1}^{N-1} \gamma_{M\mu} \sin \theta_\mu\\[2mm]\bar{C}_{Di} = (A/s) \int_{-s}^{+s} \gamma_M \alpha_{i0} \, dy = (\pi A/N) \sum_{\mu=1}^{N-1} \gamma_{M\mu} \alpha_{i0\mu} \sin \theta_\mu\end{array}\right\} \quad (136)$$

which are easily calculable. Values of α_{i0} can most simply be obtained from the condition $\omega\alpha_{i0} = \alpha - \alpha_e$ in the form

$$\alpha_{i0\mu} = \alpha_\mu/\omega - (2A\bar{c}/\omega a_\mu c_\mu)\gamma_{M\mu}. \quad (137)$$

A graphical solution of Multhopp's equations (128) has been described by Vandrey (1951); the circulation is represented by scales, and a pair of dividers is required, so that its application is both simple and rapid. A mechanical integrator for evaluating the integral for the downwash α_{i0} for a given spanwise load distribution was devised by Sherman (1938); this was adapted by Küchemann (1938b) to find the downwash at any point in the plane of the wing. Weissinger (1952) showed how it is possible to insert one additional pivotal point for given N at a chosen spanwise station. Multhopp's numerical method has also the advantage that it can easily be applied to calculate the loading on elastic wings as has been done, for example, by Hunn (1952).

For wings of very large aspect ratio, it may be preferable to work in terms of spanwise points which are equally spaced in y rather than in θ, and a corresponding analysis may be constructed.

20. Approximate solutions for wings with special planforms

When it was realized that the Prandtl–Lanchester theory for unswept wings of large aspect ratio is not satisfactory for other classes of wings, great efforts were made to improve and extend it to cover wings of small aspect ratio and arbitrary planform. Although much of this work has been superseded by developments which lead to simpler and more accurate solutions such as have been described in previous sections, some of the methods employed and some of the results obtained are of general interest and may have some bearing on future work. Therefore, in this section, a brief description will be given of the theoretical work which has been concentrated on wings of special planform, in particular, on rectangular wings, circular wings, elliptic wings, and triangular or delta wings. Generalized methods, based on this work and designed for arbitrary planforms and especially for swept wings, will be the subject of Section 21.

Some of the methods employ the concept of concentrated vortex lines rather than vortex sheets. If the wing and its wake are represented by a number, N, of concentrated vortex lines, the stream-surface condition applied at an equal number of points leads to N simultaneous equations for the unknown strengths of the vortex lines, and the problem is, at least in principle, approximately solved. The complexity of this type of solution when N is large has led to methods using very few vortex lines, even only a single line. These were guided mainly by the apparently successful but incorrect interpretation of Prandtl's classical aerofoil theory as a lifting-line theory and, on the whole, they are not satisfactory.

To follow up this last point, let us suppose that the chordwise vorticity is concentrated along a line. The strength Γ of this line vortex is determined from the known overall circulation of the flat-plate distribution at a given effective incidence α_e; thus from equation (24), $\Gamma = \frac{1}{2}cC_L U_\infty = \pi c\alpha_e U_\infty$. Its position is best determined by the position of the centre of pressure for the assumed chordwise loading; this is the quarter-chord point for the two-dimensional flat-plate distribution. It may be assumed, further, that the downwash at this line from the streamwise vorticity components is one-half that of an infinitely long sheet of trailing vortices. Thus for any flow whose solution is known it might for some purposes be legitimate and convenient to replace the real lifting surface by this concept of a lifting line.

Some special properties of the two-dimensional thin aerofoil unfortunately suggested the possibility of a solution being found in terms of a lifting line. Pistolesi (1933) showed that, in the case of the flat plate, the downwash at the three-quarter-chord point induced by a concentrated vortex at the quarter-chord point is the same as that produced by the theoretical chordwise distribution of vorticity given by equation (18). This is the so-called three-quarter-chord theorem. But in general neither the position of the centre of pressure nor the point at which the downwash of a concentrated vortex happens to equal the correct downwash are known in advance. Methods based on the three-quarter-chord theorem must therefore be highly suspect.

Some methods based on a lifting line have been constructed empirically with such skill that their results are reasonably good, though this must be largely fortuitous. For example, Helmbold (1942) followed by Scholz (1950) and Diederich (1951), among others, assumed elliptic spanwise loading on unswept wings. Helmbold's principal result was for the overall lift slope:

$$\bar{C}_L/\alpha = a_0/\{[1+(a_0/\pi A)^2]^{\frac{1}{2}}+a_0/\pi A\}. \tag{138}$$

By the further approximation that A may be replaced by $A\sec\varphi$ for a swept wing, this may be extended to

$$\bar{C}_L/\alpha = (a_0\cos\varphi)/\{[1+(a_0/\pi A)^2\cos^2\varphi]^{\frac{1}{2}}+(a_0/\pi A)\cos\varphi\}, \tag{139}$$

which is equivalent to Diederich's relation. Now it happens that this relation contains both the limiting cases of very large aspect ratio (equation (106)) and of very small aspect ratio (equation (71)); further it agrees very well with the results from the theory of Section 17 and from some good approximations for elliptic wings, as may be seen from Fig. VIII. 26. Thus equations (138) and (139) may be used for most purposes with some confidence.

The three-quarter-chord theorem has been used by Weissinger (1942) in two ways. In his L-method, the lift is concentrated at the quarter-chord line and the downwash from the whole vortex system is calculated on the three-quarter-chord line. In his F-method, the bound vortices are assumed to be distributed along the chord according to the two-dimensional flat-plate distribution and the downwash of the whole

vortex system is again calculated at the three-quarter-chord line. The
L-method, applied to a rectangular wing, gives

$$w/U_\infty = (s/2\pi) \int\limits_{-s}^{+s} [d(C_L c/4s)/dy']\{1+[1+A^2(y-y')^2s^{-2}]^{\frac{1}{2}}\}(y-y')^{-1}\, dy'. \tag{140}$$

We see that the limit $A \to 0$ leads correctly to $w_2/U_\infty = 2\alpha_{i0}$, a result
in favour of equation (140).

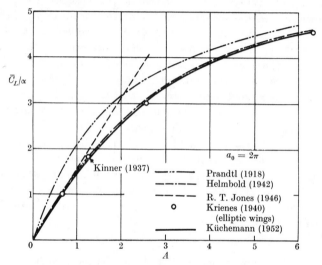

FIG. VIII. 26. The overall lift of unswept wings with elliptic spanwise
loading, as calculated by various authors.

The interpretation of the F-method is that it uses the downwash
equation in the general form of equation (21) with the load $l(x,y)$ as a
product of $C_L(y)$ and a function of x only, under the approximation that
$[(x-x')^2/c^2+\frac{1}{4}A^2(y-y')^2/s^2]^{\frac{1}{2}}$ may be replaced by $[(\frac{1}{2})^2+\frac{1}{4}A^2(y-y')^2/s^2]^{\frac{1}{2}}$.
This implies that all the chordwise distances in the vortex system are
equal to half the chord, and results in the chordwise loading of the two-
dimensional flat-plate distribution.

The practical application of the F-method is very laborious. Numerical
results are shown in Fig. VIII. 27 for the chordwise loading at the
centre line of a square plate and in Fig. VIII. 28 for the overall lift
slope of a series of rectangular wings of various aspect ratios. The
overall lift slope is generally too small by between 5 and 10 per cent
when compared with experimental results or with values calculated
from the method of Section 17. The shift of the position of the aero-

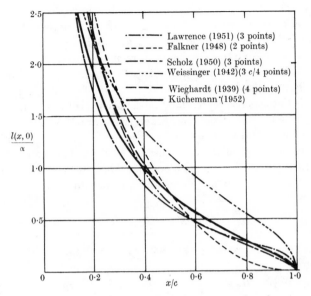

Fig. VIII. 27. The chordwise loading at the centre section of a square wing, as calculated by various authors.

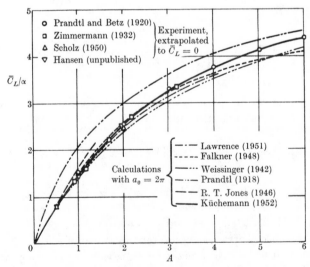

Fig. VIII. 28. A comparison between experimental and calculated values of the overall lift slope of rectangular wings.

dynamic centre with aspect ratio cannot, of course, be represented by these methods derived from Weissinger's work. Another check on the accuracy of Weissinger's method can be provided by calculating the true downwash from the load distribution it assumes and so determining the aerofoil shape. The result of this is shown, for a particular case, in Fig. VIII. 23, Pistolesi's result being the same: from this it is seen that the angle of incidence represented in the theory is too small.

Lawrence (1951) satisfies the general downwash equation for rectangular wings (22) only on the average in the spanwise direction, for each chordwise station x, in contrast to the method of Section 17 where mean values of the downwash along the chord are considered. He uses a function $G(x)$, called the parametric lift per unit chord, given by

$$dG(x)/dx = \int_{-s}^{+s} l(x, y) \, dy, \tag{141}$$

whose value, G_s, for slender wings of very small aspect ratio is known to be

$$G_s(x) = 4 \int_{-s}^{+s} [w(x, y)/U_\infty][s^2 - y^2]^{\frac{1}{2}} \, dy, \tag{142}$$

as follows from equation (68). Inserting $w(x, y)$ from equation (22) into equation (142) and integrating by parts with respect to y, we obtain

$$2\pi G_s(x)$$
$$= \int_{x_L}^{x_T} dx' \left\{ \int_{-s}^{+s} l(x', y') \, dy' \left[\int_{-s}^{+s} \frac{y}{(s^2 - y^2)^{\frac{1}{2}}} \left(1 + \frac{\{(x-x')^2 + (y-y')^2\}^{\frac{1}{2}}}{x-x'} \right) \frac{dy}{y-y'} \right] \right\}. \tag{143}$$

By evaluating the integral with respect to y approximately, Lawrence obtained his equation in the form

$$G_s(x) = \tfrac{1}{2} G(x) + \tfrac{1}{4} \int_{x_L}^{x_T} (dG/dx')[1 + \{(x-x')^2 + s^2\}^{\frac{1}{2}}(x-x')^{-1}] \, dx'. \tag{144}$$

It includes both limiting cases for very large and very small aspect ratios, but is best suited to wings of small aspect ratio, as is indicated in Figs. VIII. 23, 27, and 28, where its accuracy is good.

Another method of considerable accuracy is that of Wieghardt (1939), who applied it to a series of rectangular flat wings of small aspect ratio. The method assumes that the load $l(x, y)$ is of the form $C_L(y)g(x)$ and that the spanwise loading is elliptic. The downwash equation (22) takes the form of an integral equation for the function $g(x)$ which is solved by expanding $g(x)$ into a series of the form proposed by Birnbaum (1923) and by determining the coefficients from the boundary condition $w/U_\infty = \alpha$. Weber (1954b) has extended Multhopp's method of Section 19 to solving this integral equation, and the results are compared with others in Figs. VIII. 23 and 27. The interpolation method of Section 17 gives roughly the same values as those from Wieghardt's continuous distribution with four terms of the Birnbaum series; this indicates that, except very close to the leading edge, the function of equation (112) is evidently better suited to wings of low aspect ratio than is the Birnbaum series, which was designed to describe the properties of two-dimensional thin aerofoils.

The first attempt to improve on Prandtl's solution for rectangular wings was made by Blenk (1925), who assumed

$$\left.\begin{array}{l} l(x,y) = \sum K_n(y/s)^n[1-(y/s)^2]^{\frac{1}{2}}; \\ K_n = A_n[(c-x)/x]^{\frac{1}{2}}+B_n[x(c-x)/c^2]^{\frac{1}{2}}+C_n(1-2x/c)[x(c-x)/c^2]^{\frac{1}{2}}. \end{array}\right\} \quad (145)$$

This was the first method which went beyond the assumption that the loading is a product of a function of x and a function of y. Blenk carried out calculations for a series of flat rectangular wings, with the downwash having the prescribed value at six points on one half wing. These results showed that the lift is overestimated by Prandtl's theory, for aspect ratios of less than, say, 6; this is shown by Fig. VIII. 28.

Special attention has been given to wings of circular and elliptic planform by Kinner (1937), Kochin (1940), and Krienes (1940), while Hansen (1939) has supplemented these theoretical investigations with experiments. Both Kinner and Krienes used the concept of the acceleration potential developed by Prandtl (1936). Solutions of Laplace's equation for circular and elliptic boundaries are available in the form of Legendre and Lamé functions. They have been used extensively, but entail considerable mathematical detail, and the reader is referred to the original papers. The investigations concern both flat and cambered wings, and the elliptic wing is also considered in sideslip. Results for all the aerodynamic derivatives have been worked out and have largely been confirmed by experiment. The results are again approximate in that finite series have been used: it is therefore of some interest to compare the results with those of other methods. Fig. VIII. 26 includes a few results in a particular case.

The case of the circular plate has also been treated by Multhopp (1950) who, by a new method to be described in Section 21, found that

$\bar{C}_L/\alpha = 1.799$. Kinner had found, by taking four chordwise terms in his own method, that $\bar{C}_L/\alpha = 1.820$, whereas Multhopp showed that five terms lead to the value 1.804. The method of Section 17 gives the value 1.805. The position of the overall centre of pressure, measured from the leading edge at the centre in terms of the centre-line chord, is 0.236 from Multhopp (1950), 0.243 from Kinner (four terms), and 0.231 from the interpolation method. The spanwise loadings from the three methods agree closely.

The special case of the triangular, or delta, wing with unswept trailing edge has been treated by Garner (1948, 1949) who worked in terms of the velocity potential. Special functions for $\Delta\phi(x,y)$ are derived such that the behaviour at the leading edge is the same as on the two-dimensional flat plate; further it was assumed that the load tends to zero at the wing tips as for elliptic spanwise loading and at the trailing edge as on the two-dimensional flat plate. In the special case of a slightly cropped delta wing with a leading edge swept-back through $45°$, as shown in Fig. VIII. 29, the discontinuity in the potential function is assumed to be of the form

$$\Delta\phi/c_0 U_\infty = \phi_0 \sum_p \sum_q A_{pq}(1-x/c_0)^p(y/s)^q, \tag{146}$$

where
$$\phi_0 = \left(\frac{x^2-y^2}{c_0 x}\right)^{\frac{1}{2}}\left[1-\frac{c_0(x^2-y^2)}{3(c_0^2-y^2)x}\right]\left(1-\frac{49y^2}{36c_0^2}\right)^{\frac{1}{2}}. \tag{147}$$

In the general case of wings where both the leading and trailing edge are smooth curves, the load of the surface is represented by the double series

$$l(x,y) = \sum_{n=0}^{N} \sum_{m=1}^{M} 2C_{nm} A_m(y)\Gamma_n(\Theta), \tag{148}$$

where Θ is the usual chordwise angular coordinate related to (x,y) by

$$x = m(y)-\tfrac{1}{2}c(y)\cos\Theta, \tag{149}$$

$x = m(y)$ being the equation of the locus of the midchord points. Also,

$$\left. \begin{array}{l} \Gamma_0(\Theta) = 2\cot\tfrac{1}{2}\Theta; \qquad \Gamma_n(\Theta) = -2\sin n\Theta \quad \text{for} \quad n > 0 \\ A_m(y) = (s/c)(y/s)^{m-1}[1-(y/s)^2]^{\frac{1}{2}}. \end{array} \right\} \tag{150}$$

This form was also used by W. P. Jones (1943) and by Falkner (1943a). In common with many other practical methods, it has the disadvantage that it cannot make satisfactory allowances for discontinuous spanwise derivatives in the chord or in the local sweep.

Garner determined a numerical solution for the cropped delta wing shown in Fig. VIII. 29 by satisfying the boundary condition at sixteen points on the wing. In equation (146) p took the values 0, 1·5, 2, 3, and q the values 0, 2, 4, 6. Fig. VIII. 29 shows the chordwise loading at the centre line and compares results from other methods; it also includes results obtained from an electrical potential analyser by Redshaw (1952), which may be good except that they fail to represent the singularities at the leading edge. Such an analogue computer is a

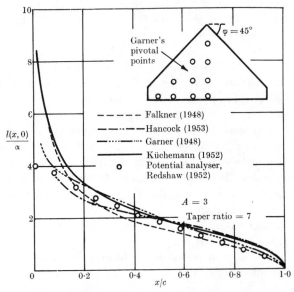

Fig. VIII. 29. The chordwise loading along the centre line of a cropped delta wing, as calculated by various authors.

very useful tool, either in the form of a network as used by Redshaw or in the form of an electrolytic tank as used, for instance, by Malavard and Duquenne (1951). It enables solutions of Laplace's equation to be obtained for very general shapes of boundary, and conditions at the boundary can be fulfilled at a considerably greater number of pivotal points than can reasonably be taken in numerical work. Detailed comparisons between the results from an analogue computer and from the numerical method of Section 17 for a rectangular wing, a swept-back wing, and a delta wing, have been given by Redshaw (1954) and show good agreement. In general, the use of a properly developed analogue computer to solve the problems considered in this chapter is to be preferred to the use of a digital machine in the solution of equations developed from a simplified mathematical theory.

21. Approximate solutions for wings of arbitrary planform

Wings of arbitrary planform have already been discussed in Section 17 in the light of the three basic theories which were the subject of Sections 9 to 13. There are, however, a number of other numerical methods by which such wings may be treated, and which assume a plane vortex sheet, small disturbances of the main stream, and the Kutta–Joukowski condition at the trailing edge. They differ by the various approximations made in the downwash equation and in the functions by which the loading is approximated. Some differ from each other only in the choice of pivotal points at which the boundary condition is fulfilled. The alternative names used for similar things by various authors—local lift force, loading potential, vortex, pressure doublet, discontinuity in the velocity potential, jump in the enthalpy, and so on—are inconvenient for the general reader. The main arguments are of a purely mathematical nature; it is inappropriate to give them here and only an account of the principal features of the various methods and of their usefulness for practical applications is given. Like all the methods so far described, those which now follow refer only to the first inviscid approximation; among other things, this makes the comparison with experimental data difficult to interpret and the complete absence of any exact solutions makes it almost impossible to assess the accuracy of any of the solutions offered.

A method which, it is believed, has been widely used for unswept wings is that due to Schrenk (1940), who assumed that the spanwise loading is given by the average chord distribution of the given wing and of an ellipse of equal area. Thus

$$C_L c / \bar{C}_L \bar{c} = \tfrac{1}{2}[c/\bar{c} + (4/\pi s)(s^2 - y^2)^{\frac{1}{2}}].$$

There is no theoretical justification of this. For swept wings, a modified formula has been suggested by Diederich (1952).

A method of Weissinger (1942), already discussed in Section 17 and closely related to that of Mutterperl (1941), used the three-quarter-chord theorem which, for swept wings, is completely unjustified. Much work has been expended on calculating influence functions and spanwise loadings in advance for Weissinger's method, by De Young and Harper (1948) and others; and Dorn and De Young (1947) compared results from Mutterperl's and Weissinger's methods with some experiments. They came to the conclusion that Weissinger's method gives results of good accuracy. This is not borne out by other results such as those in Figs. VIII. 23, 27, 28, and 30, where discrepancies appear which are greater than seem permissible for practical purposes. Later, De Young and Barling (1955) made an attempt to modify the method so as to correct such errors.

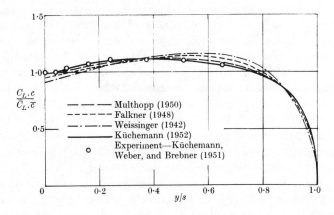

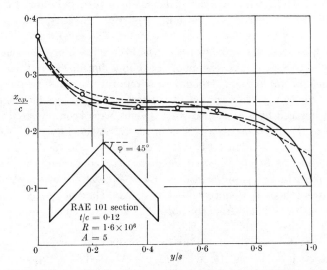

Fig. VIII. 30. A comparison between experimental and calculated spanwise loadings and positions of centre of pressure for an untapered wing of 45° sweep-back.

Another widely used method is that of Falkner (1943a). The loading function he assumes is the same as the function given in equation (148). It is replaced by concentrated vortices at a number of chordwise

positions. These discrete vortices are, in general, curved and each has its
own continuous trailing vortex system and the problem is the determination of the strength of these concentrated vortices. For this, Falkner
uses results from a two-dimensional aerofoil. For example, placing four
vortices at $\frac{1}{8}$, $\frac{3}{8}$, $\frac{5}{8}$, and $\frac{7}{8}$ of the chord, he determines their strengths by
the condition that the combined downwash of the four at the quarter-,
half-, and three-quarter-chord points is the same as the correct downwash induced by the continuous distribution. This yields as many
conditions as there are discrete vortices, and these relations are retained
also in the three-dimensional case. The next step is to divide the span
into a number of equal longitudinal strips and to replace each segment
of a vortex intercepted in this way by a rectangular horseshoe vortex,
its strength being determined by the local strength of the concentrated
vortex and thus related to the unknown coefficients in equation (148).
The wing is then covered by a rectangular lattice of vortices whose
mesh will in general vary in shape and size across the wing. There are
126 such horseshoe vortices on the wing in the standard form of the
method. The downwash due to this system of vortices is now calculated,
by the Biot–Savart law, at a number of pivotal points, each of which
is chosen at the centre of a vortex mesh. The downwash values are
thus related to the unknown coefficients in equation (148) and when
equated to αU_∞ yield a system of linear equations for these coefficients.
The main computational labour arises from the calculation of the downwash due to the 126 vortices but it is assisted by tables for the downwash induced by a horseshoe vortex which have been prepared by the
Staff of the Mathematics Division of the National Physical Laboratory
(1947) and by Lehrian (1949). The accuracy of this method has been
questioned by Schlichting and Thomas (1947) concerning the justification of retaining a two-dimensional law of equivalence when calculating
the strength of the concentrated vortices. They suggested that the
downwash calculated from the horseshoe vortices depends on the shape
of the lattice. If this is so, the convergence and the accuracy of the
approximation will be affected and an explanation given for the apparent
inconsistency of errors. Good accuracy is obtained for rectangular wings
of aspect ratio between 2 and 3, as shown in Fig. VIII. 28, but for
smaller aspect ratios the chordwise loading begins to differ from the
more accurate solutions by more than seems permissible, as is indicated
in Fig. VIII. 27. The largest errors occur on swept-back wings near the
centre and especially on untapered wings of large aspect ratio, as shown
in Figs. VIII. 24 and 30.

Schlichting and Thomas suggested an alternative to Falkner's method, which has not been worked out in detail. Thwaites (1949a) proposed another routine calculation procedure, designed to avoid both some of the complications and assumptions of Falkner's lattice theory, and also the severe restriction to trapezoidal wings of the method of Schlichting and Thomas. In this, the continuous vortex distribution along the chord is first replaced by a number of concentrated spanwise vortex lines each of which, it is assumed, may be represented by a number of linear segments; thus there is no restriction upon the shape of the planform. It is further assumed that the vorticity varies quadratically along each linear segment, so that it and its first derivative are continuous along the whole vortex line across the span. Downstream of the vortex line is a continuous distribution of trailing vorticity. Tables could be compiled for the downwash due to the typical element consisting of a finite swept vortex line, along which the vorticity varies quadratically, and of its associated trailing vorticity. This would replace Falkner's horseshoe vortex element but the actual numerical work has not yet been carried out.

Many further attempts have been made to deal with the problem of thin lifting surfaces of arbitrary planform, such as those of the Dutch school. Vooren (1952, 1953) and Leeuw, Eckhaus, and Vooren (1954) have contributed interesting methods mainly for swept wings of large aspect ratios. The method of Vooren (1953), in particular, represents a considerable advance on Weissinger's method and best positions for chordwise pivotal points are derived. The work of Truckenbrodt (1953, 1954) should also be mentioned. Garner and Acum (1952) applied Garner's method for a delta wing to a family of arrowhead wings and found the results disappointing, inasmuch as the purpose of establishing beyond question the fundamental aerodynamic characteristics of such wings was defeated by the ill-conditioned nature of the simultaneous linear equations, in spite of the considerable amount of labour expended.

The method devised by Multhopp (1950) is, in a sense, the consummation of earlier attempts but it suffers from their characteristic inadequacies. For all these methods, the computing effort is roughly proportional to the square of the number of pivotal points—or unknown parameters—and so it is imperative to find functions for the chordwise loading which depend on a minimum number of parameters. Such a function is given in equation (112) but is unsuitable for use in a method which relies on standard downwash tables. Multhopp, in common with most others, therefore resorts to the use of the first two chordwise

terms of equation (145), and goes on to show that the chordwise characteristics can be well represented if the downwash at the two points
$x/c = 0.3455$ and $x/c = 0.9045$ is suitably adjusted. This is really an
extension of the idea underlying the three-quarter-chord theorem.
Truckenbrodt (1954) in a similar way took the points $x/c = 0.25$ and
1.0. Precisely the same criticisms can be made of a method based on
two such points as were made of the three-quarter-chord theorem and
the application of such a method to swept-back wings cannot be justified
analytically. Further objections are equally inevitable, concerning, for
example, the small number of points at which the boundary condition
is satisfied and the rounding-off of the discontinuities associated with
a kink. This last point applies equally to any method employing an
interpolation function for the chord distribution, such as that given in
Section 17. However, the errors involved in the method are small for
wings of moderate sweep and moderate aspect ratio, as in the case of
Fig. VIII. 30. They are greater than seems permissible in the central
region of swept-back wing of very large aspect ratio, as in the case of
Fig. VIII. 24. They are obviously very small for unswept wings, even
if the aspect ratio is small, as in the case of Fig. VIII. 23.

22. Cambered wings

We may recall the assumptions which enabled the downwash equation
to be written in the relatively simple form (22). First, it represented
the outcome of a linearization in which both the velocity disturbances
in comparison with the stream velocity and the incidence were regarded
as small quantities. This results in the assumption that the wing and
the trailing vortex sheet lie in the plane $z = 0$. Secondly, it was
assumed that no discontinuities exist in the slope of the wing surface:
this necessarily led to the treatment of, for example, the centre section
of swept-back wings being very approximate. No further restriction
was placed on the shape of the wing.

The wing consisting of symmetrical sections, which has been the
subject of most of the previous sections, is an important practical case,
and the fact that the downwash on it due to the trailing vortices is a
function of y only, greatly aids the solution of equation (22). But for
many purposes, cambered wings are desirable; for example, the characteristics of wings at very low speeds and of swept wings at high speeds
may be improved by camber. Thus we need to consider modifications
to some of the theories of previous sections so that camber may be taken
into account.

Let us assume that the shape of the camber line is given by

$$z(x,y) = c(y)[\xi\alpha(y)-f(y)S(\xi)] \\ 0 \leqslant \xi \equiv (x-x_L)/c(y) \leqslant 1, \qquad S(0) = S(1) = 0 \Big\}, \qquad (151)$$

so that $\alpha(y)$ is the incidence of the chord and $f(y)$ is the maximum camber ratio of each section which means that the maximum value of S is unity. This form assumes that the shape of the camber line is constant across the wing or varies so little that its variations can be ignored; only on this basis is much analytical progress possible. By analogy with equation (41) we may then again take the load to be the product of a function of y and a function of ξ and write

$$l(x,y) = C_L(y)g(\xi) \\ g(1) = 0; \qquad \int_0^1 g(\xi)\,d\xi = 1 \Big\}. \qquad (152)$$

For wings of large aspect ratio, this implies that equation (27) and the relation (45) may be used to determine the induced incidence α_{i0} from the streamwise vortices, while the downwash from the bound vortices is given by equation (89). Thus, using equations (96) and (97), we find

$$w/U_\infty = \alpha_{i0}+(C_L(y)/4\pi)\sin \pi n_0 \sec \varphi\left[\pi \cot \pi n_0 g(\xi)+ \int_0^1 g(\xi')(\xi-\xi')^{-1}\,d\xi'\right]. \qquad (153)$$

Now for the camber line defined by equation (151), the stream-surface condition reads

$$w/U_\infty = \partial z/\partial x = \alpha(y)-f(y)(dS/d\xi) \qquad (154)$$

and this, combined with the downwash equation in the form (153), gives

$$F(\xi,y) = (1/\pi)\tan[\pi n_0(\varphi,y)] \int_0^1 g(\xi')(\xi-\xi')^{-1}\,d\xi'+g(\xi), \qquad (155)$$

where

$$F(\xi,y) = [4/C_L(y)]\cos \varphi \sec[\pi n_0(\varphi,y)][\alpha(y)-\alpha_{i0}(y)-f(y)(dS/d\xi)]. \qquad (156)$$

Equation (155) is again of the type considered by Carleman (1922); its solution, with the Kutta–Joukowski condition that $g(1) = 0$, is, by equation (96),

$$g(\xi) = \cos^2[\pi n_0(\varphi,y)]F(\xi,y)- \\ -\frac{1}{2\pi}\left(\frac{1-\xi}{\xi}\right)^{n_0}\sin 2\pi n_0 \int_0^1 F(\xi',y)\left(\frac{1-\xi'}{\xi'}\right)^{-n_0}\frac{d\xi'}{\xi-\xi'}. \qquad (157)$$

The condition (152) on $g(\xi)$ is now applied and the sectional lift slope

$a(y)$ is introduced from equation (101). After some calculation, it may be shown that

$$C_L(y)/a(y) = \alpha(y) + \beta(\varphi, y) - \alpha_{i0}(y), \qquad (158)$$

where

$$\beta(\varphi, y) = -\frac{\sin[\pi n_0(\varphi, y)]}{\pi n_0(\varphi, y)} f(y) \int\limits_0^1 \frac{dS}{d\xi'}\left(\frac{1-\xi'}{\xi'}\right)^{-n_0} d\xi', \qquad (159)$$

$(-\beta)$ being the no-lift angle. The integral in equation (157) depends on the shape of the camber line, $S(\xi)$, and therefore cannot be evaluated in closed form except in some simple cases. Weber (1955) has described a simple numerical method by which the integral, replaced by sums, can be evaluated with good accuracy from the given ordinates of the camber line.

The important result is that the stream-surface condition leads to the same equation for the spanwise loading as in the theory for plane wings, equation (104), the effect of the camber appearing only as a certain angle of twist given by equation (159). This is, in fact, tacitly assumed in many of the practical methods discussed in the preceding sections.

The load $l(x, y)$ itself is obtained from equations (152) and (157) in the form

$$l(x, y) = 4\cos\varphi[\alpha(y) - \alpha_{i0}(y)][(1-\xi)/\xi]^{n_0} -$$
$$- (4/\pi)f(y)\cos\varphi \sin \pi n_0\left[\pi \cot \pi n_0 \frac{dS}{d\xi} + \left(\frac{1-\xi}{\xi}\right)^{n_0} \int\limits_0^1 \frac{dS}{d\xi'}\left(\frac{1-\xi'}{\xi'}\right)^{-n_0} \frac{d\xi'}{\xi-\xi'}\right].$$
$$(160)$$

The first term on the right-hand side is clearly due to the incidence of the chord whereas the second arises from the camber. Again, the integral cannot, in general, be evaluated analytically, but Weber's method gives a good approximation for any prescribed camber line.

23. The parabolic camber

As an illustration of the equations of the previous section, let the camber line be a parabolic arc: thus $S(\xi) = 4\xi(1-\xi)$ so that

$$z(x, y)/c(y) = \alpha(y)\xi - f(y)4\xi(1-\xi). \qquad (161)$$

Equation (160) can then be integrated in closed form, and we find for the load distribution

$$l(x, y) = 4\cos\varphi[(1-\xi)/\xi]^{n_0}[\alpha(y) - \alpha_{i0}(y) + 8f(y)\{\xi - \lambda(y)\varphi/\pi\}] \qquad (162)$$

with n_0 from equation (97). The no-lift angle is then

$$-\beta = -4n_0 f = -2f(y)\{1 - 2\lambda(y)\varphi/\pi\}. \qquad (163)$$

This contains the well-known result $\beta = 2f$ for the two-dimensional aerofoil, but on swept wings β varies considerably with sweep and spanwise position. The pitching moment coefficient C_m, defined in equation (43), may also be calculated easily, in the form

$$C_m = -2\pi n_0(1-n_0)(\alpha-\alpha_{i0})\operatorname{cosec} \pi n_0 \cos\varphi -$$
$$-\tfrac{8}{3}\pi f n_0(1-n_0)(1+4n_0)\operatorname{cosec} \pi n_0 \cos\varphi. \quad (164)$$

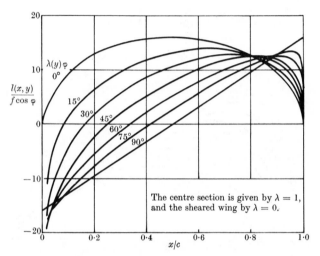

FIG. VIII. 31. The effect of sweep on the chordwise loading on a parabolic camber line.

Fig. VIII. 31 has been prepared to illustrate the effect of sweep on the chordwise loading. Since $l\sec\varphi$ and n_0 depend only on x/c and $\lambda(y)\varphi$, the figure may be used to deduce the effect of camber for any angle of sweep and at any spanwise position between the centre and the sheared part of a swept-back wing of large aspect ratio.

24. A family of camber lines of known loading

A different treatment of cambered swept wings, which leads to explicit relations for a general family of camber lines, has been given by Brebner (1952). In this case, the starting-point is a suitable load distribution and the geometric shape of the camber line is determined afterwards. Suppose, therefore, that

$$g(\xi) = (1/\pi n_0)\sin \pi n_0[(1-\xi)/\xi]^{n_0}(1-D)+(1/\pi m)\sin \pi m[(1-\xi)/\xi]^m D, \quad (165)$$

where $0 \leqslant m \leqslant 1$ and D is a parameter. This fulfils the conditions in (152). Through equations (155) and (156), a value of $dS/d\xi$ may be obtained, which becomes on integration

$$f(y)S(\xi) = -\tfrac{1}{4}DC_L\,(y)\sec\varphi\sin\pi n_0(\cot\pi m - \cot\pi n_0) \times$$

$$\times\left[\xi - (1/\pi m)\sin\pi m\int_0^\xi [(1-\xi')/\xi']^m\,d\xi'\right]. \quad (166)$$

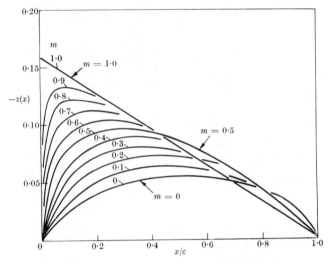

Fig. VIII. 32. Shapes of camber lines given by Brebner (1952), calculated for $C_L = 1\cdot 0$ at no sweep-back.

The integral may be put in terms of an incomplete Beta function which has not yet been tabulated in the range required here; Brebner has, however, given numerical values for $S(\xi)$ having shown that it may be put in the form

$$S(\xi) = [\xi\{\pi m\operatorname{cosec}\pi m - [(1-\xi)/\xi]^m\} - B(\xi,m)] \div B(\xi_f,m), \quad (167)$$

where ξ_f is the chordwise point of maximum camber given by

$$\left.\begin{aligned} &[(1-\xi_f)/\xi_f]^m = \pi m\operatorname{cosec}\pi m, \quad \text{with } S(\xi_f) = 1\\ \text{and} \qquad &B(\xi,m) = \int_0^\xi [(1-\xi')/\xi']^m\,d\xi' - \xi[(1-\xi)/\xi]^m \end{aligned}\right\}. \quad (168)$$

The shape is thus dependent on the parameter m only and some typical camber lines are shown in Fig. VIII. 32. Those shapes with m near unity are particularly suited for the design of aerofoils with drooped nose.

The aerodynamic properties of this family of camber lines can be determined without much difficulty. The no-lift angle, $-\beta$, comes from equation (159) while the lift coefficient is the solution of equation (158) with the value of β just found.

It can be seen from the numerical results in Fig. VIII. 33 that the no-lift angle of cambered sections varies considerably across the span

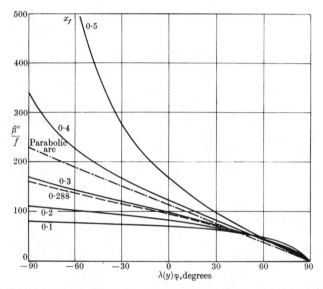

Fig. VIII. 33. The no-lift angle, $-\beta°$, for the camber lines of Brebner (1952).

of swept wings, and from this figure the no-lift angle due to camber for any spanwise position or angle of sweep may be read or interpolated. An arbitrary camber line could be roughly fitted to one of these camber lines and its characteristics deduced from the value of m so obtained. Since $\lambda < 0$ in the tip regions of a swept-back wing, the variations of β along the span may be very large on a swept wing, in contrast to unswept wings where β does not depend on y.

It has been shown by Brebner that the camber line given by $m = 0$ has some special properties. One is that on a sheared wing it gives a constant load, and it is also identical with the NACA mean line given by Abbott and Doenhoff (1949) when their parameter a is unity. Fig. VIII. 34 illustrates the loading of this particular camber line for various values of $\lambda\varphi$. The characteristic change in the chordwise loading is sometimes ascribed to an 'induced camber', and some authors have erroneously stated that this is induced by the streamwise vortices: it is, of course, caused by a change in the general direction of the bound vorticity components along the span of the wing.

Another special case is $m = \frac{1}{2}$. This is identical with the one derived in equation (94) which is needed to restore the flat-plate loading at the centre section of a swept wing.

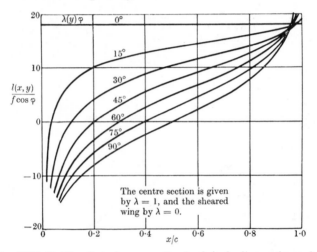

Fig. VIII. 34. The effect of sweep on the chordwise loading on the camber line which gives constant load on a sheared wing.

25. The effects of camber on wings of small aspect ratio

There is, as yet, no well-recognized theoretical approach to the study of cambered wings of small aspect ratio. Weber (1954b) has done useful work in calculating for given load distributions the shapes of the aerofoil sections at the centre line of rectangular wings of low aspect ratio. She assumed an elliptic spanwise load distribution in all cases and also the two-dimensional chordwise distribution of the flat plate. It is found that the wings must be both twisted and cambered, the camber line being not unlike a parabolic arc. The angle of twist is as much as 40°, with $7\frac{1}{2}$ per cent camber, for a rectangular wing whose aspect ratio is one-half, if an overall lift coefficient of unity is required. It is not easy to say with any accuracy what the change in the load distribution would be if the angle of twist were reduced to a more reasonable value. In general it was found, from the results for various load distributions representing various camber lines, that the shape of the camber line does not vary much with aspect ratio. The most interesting result from such calculations is that the no-lift angle increases as the aspect ratio decreases, and Weber found a simple rule

$$\beta/\beta_{A=\infty} = 1+1/4A \tag{169}$$

which has received satisfactory confirmation from experiment.

Cambered wings of very small aspect ratio have been considered by Mangler and Randall (1955) who applied the simplification (62) of slender-body theory, namely that $(y-y')^2 \ll (x-x')^2$. They calculated the loading for a family of cropped delta wings, whose camber lines are parabolic arcs. In contrast to flat slender wings, the rear rectangular part of the cambered wing carries a load which is distributed elliptically across the span.

26. Some considerations in the design of wings

The preliminary considerations in the design of a projected subsonic aircraft are, in the initial stage, dominated by factors which are not aerodynamic. But when it is reasonably clear what the purpose, range, and cruising Mach number of the aircraft are to be, it must be considered how these requirements can be met with the aerodynamic means available. At this stage, it is usually found that much the same aerodynamic performance may be achieved by various alternatives, a choice between which is made by structural and other considerations. The methods so far discussed are therefore used to determine the aerodynamic properties of a range of possible configurations. It often happens, however, that some of the main features can be fixed at an early stage, such as the aspect ratio and angle of sweep together with the required type of flow; in the consideration of these some basic problems frequently recur, which cannot readily be solved by the methods discussed so far. Here we may distinguish between three main problems:

   (i) The achievement of minimum induced drag.
   (ii) The delay or suppression of separation in other than the specified places.
   (iii) The delay of increase of drag with increase of Mach number.

For the first problem, it follows from equation (33) that the aspect ratio of the wing should be as high as is structurally practicable, and once the aspect ratio is fixed the planform should be such that the induced incidence α_{i0} is constant along the span. For unswept wings of large aspect ratio, the planform is elliptic but for swept wings, the chord distribution is given by equation (107). Such a wing has the minimum value of the induced drag for all values of C_L. If the plan-form so determined is impracticable, we may remember that for a given planform and at one particular value of C_L, the induced drag can be minimized by a suitable distribution of twist. The necessary spanwise distribution of incidence, $\alpha(y)$, is determined from equation (118) by

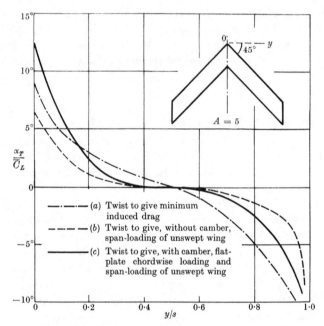

Fig. VIII. 35. The spanwise variation of the angle of twist, α_T on an untapered wing of $45°$ sweep-back under various design conditions.

inserting the minimum value of $\alpha_{i0} = \bar{C}_L/\pi A$ and the elliptic distribu-tion of C_L from equation (51). Thus

$$\alpha(y) = (\bar{C}_L/\pi A)\{\omega + [8s/a(y)c(y)][1-(y/s)^2]^{\frac{1}{2}}\}, \qquad (170)$$

where $c(y)$ is the given chord distribution.

The magnitude of the twist which might be necessary on a swept wing can be estimated by comparison with the highly-tapered swept plane wing which was found, in Section 16, to have minimum induced drag. Plan A in Fig. VIII. 21 shows a typical shape. The twist needed, according to equation (170), to give minimum induced drag at $\bar{C}_L = 1$ on an untapered wing swept-back through $45°$, is shown as curve (a) in Fig. VIII. 35; for this wing the load distribution due to incidence differs appreciably from an ellipse as we can see from Fig. VIII. 20. Obviously, the local incidence in the central region must be higher than the mean value in order to counteract the characteristic decrease in the loading there. In fact, the reduction in induced drag which can be achieved in this manner would be most unlikely to be more than 15 per cent and hardly warrants the structural complications of twist: it is often simpler to achieve the same gain by increasing the aspect ratio.

More important for practical purposes is the second problem. For example, slender wings of small aspect ratio should automatically possess elliptic spanwise loading and thus minimum induced drag, but it is seldom found that measured drag values conform to the theoretical relation $\bar{C}_{Di} = \frac{1}{2}\bar{C}_L \alpha$, given in Section 12. The reason is that separation normally occurs not only along the trailing edge, as assumed in the theory, but also along the leading edge; this implies a higher lift, as will be explained in Section XII. 8, but the drag is usually higher, too, and nearly twice the value just given. Separation of the boundary layer is particularly undesirable on swept-back wings since it is liable to occur first on the outer wings and so produce a pitching moment tending to instability; this is due to the spanwise distribution of lift having its maximum value not at the centre but farther out towards the tips, and is exacerbated by the larger suction peaks which occur near the tips as a consequence of the effect of sweep on the chordwise loading. Separation near the tips may also lead to an increase in drag, as discussed in connexion with equation (109).

We consider first the case in which, for a given planform, the camber and twist of the section shapes are required to fulfil certain conditions. If the section has a sharp leading edge, the problem of avoiding separation along the leading edge is often simpler than when the section has a rounded nose, since it may well be sufficient to specify a chordwise loading with zero load at the leading edge. For a rounded leading edge, we should need to know the effects of the wing thickness and the three-dimensional character of the boundary-layer flow over and above the effects of lift. But the calculation of the first two effects—especially as an inverse problem of design—is extremely difficult; for the moment, we assume that we can translate the viscous-flow problem into one in which the load distribution $l(x, y)$ is given.

The problem is now to determine the shape $z(x, y)$ of the aerofoil for a given load $l(x, y)$ and there is no theoretical difficulty in this since the downwash equation (22) gives w/U_∞ in terms of l, and according to linear theory this is equal to $\partial z/\partial x$. For a swept wing, the form (153) of the downwash equation may be used and Brebner (1952) has applied this to the calculation of the camber and twist on wings of moderate and large aspect ratio, using his family of camber lines discussed in Section 24. Since the downwash equals the incidence plus the local incidence of the camber line, for each section, it is possible to specify either the camber from which follow the incidence and twist, or the twist from which follows the requisite camber.

Brebner has considered, in particular, the case in which the chord-wise loading is the same for all sections and therefore equal to that in the sheared region of a wing of large aspect ratio. This is an important practical case since it also gives a good solution to the third of the three problems enumerated above, for the isobars are all parallel to the sweep. Among a number of interesting results, for details of which the original paper should be consulted, it is found that the camber line, described in Section 24 by the parameter $m = \frac{1}{2}$, is sufficient for a solution of this particular problem; both the twist and the actual magnitude of the camber can be determined simply. Fig. VIII. 35 illustrates typical results of these calculations.

A graphical method for finding the shape of a wing having an arbitrary distribution of lift has been described by Cohen (1942). Later, in an attempt at improvement, Cohen (1943) proposed another method to deal with the direct problem of calculating the load over the surface of a given wing. A solution was obtained for a 30° swept-back wing, and the characteristic change due to sweep in the spanwise loading, and in particular in the relative loss of lift in the central region, were convincingly demonstrated for the first time.

The special case of wings with uniform loading has attracted much attention, although it is by no means clear that it would be effective in preventing separation. The treatment given by Katzoff, Faison, and DuBose (1953) starts with the downwash integral (22) which can be rewritten, by the application of Gauss's theorem, in a form involving a single integral around the planform contour. Thus putting $w/U_{\infty} = \partial z/\partial x$, we have

$$\frac{\partial z}{\partial x} = -\frac{C_L}{8\pi}\left\{\int \frac{(x-x')}{[(x-x')^2+(y-y')^2]^{\frac{1}{2}}}\frac{dx'}{y-y'} + \int \frac{dy'}{[(x-x')^2+(y-y')^2]^{\frac{1}{2}}}\right\},$$
(171)

the integration to be performed around the edges of the wing. Among a number of different derivations of this equation, we mention that the uniform load can be interpreted as a uniform distribution of source doublets with axes perpendicular to the surface; it can be shown that the velocity field of such a doublet distribution is the same as that obtained from a line vortex along the boundary of the surface which is represented by equation (171). For the uniformly loaded wing of polygonal planform, the integration can be done analytically but the numerical work is still considerable even if the calculation is made only

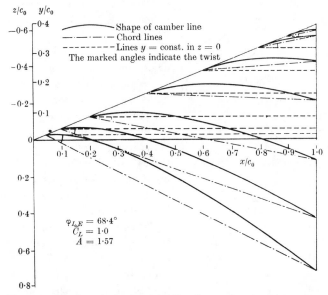

FIG. VIII. 36. The calculated camber lines for a delta wing with uniform loading over the whole surface. (Note the different scales on the axes.)

at a limited number of points. An example is shown in Fig. VIII. 36 for a delta wing of aspect ratio 1·57 having an angle of sweep of 68·4° of the leading edge. Since the method is based on the linearized downwash equation (22), it will fail at any singular section and in fact, in the example shown, the downwash tends logarithmically to infinity towards the centre line. This infinity is avoided in Brebner's theory which uses equation (153) for the downwash.

In connexion with sections at singularities in the planform, cranked wings are particularly in need of some camber and twist for, as is shown in Fig. VIII. 25, severe pressure gradients occur on a cranked flat wing. This problem has been considered in detail by Brebner (1953). Mangler and Randall (1955), on the other hand, have applied their method for cambered wings of small aspect ratio to the problem of design. In a particular calculation they showed that, on cropped delta wings with parabolic-arc camber lines, a combination of camber and twist can be found such that for a certain incidence no suction force occurs all along the leading edge, or in other words the dividing streamlines join the leading edge. If we put $\lambda = c_t/c_0$ as the taper ratio of the wing and the camber ratio τ is defined as $\tau = f/c_0$, the required angle of incidence is $\alpha = 4\tau$ and the overall lift is then

$$\bar{C}_L = \tfrac{4}{3}\pi A \tau (1+2\lambda). \qquad (172)$$

Thus, for pointed wings with $\lambda = 0$, $\bar{C}_L = \tfrac{1}{3}\pi A \alpha$ which is smaller than the value $\bar{C}_L = \tfrac{1}{2}\pi A \alpha$ for the flat wing, whereas a taper ratio of $\tfrac{1}{4}$ restores the lift at a given incidence to the same value as for the flat wing. It should be realized, therefore, that this combination of camber and twist does not normally lead to an increase of the lift at a given incidence.

The third problem, that of delaying the drag rise due to compressibility, is particularly important for swept wings because this is the declared purpose of introducing sweep. This requirement implies at least that the isobars (perhaps only on the upper surface, for a lifting wing) should be fully swept so that the three-dimensional effects of centre and tips be eliminated and sheared-wing conditions restored. To achieve this in practice, it is usually necessary to camber and twist the wing, and to choose a suitable thickness distribution for the section. But the spanwise distribution of the chord may also be used as a design parameter. This has been treated by Brebner (1954) who considered the design of the planform in relation to the spanwise load distribution. The angle of sweep of the mid-chord line is regarded as being fixed from a consideration of the performance of the aircraft at high speeds

$\varphi_{c/2} = 40°$
$A = 4.8$
$\bar{C}_L/\alpha = 3.5$

$\varphi_{c/2} = 40°$
$A = 3.0$
$\bar{C}_L/\alpha = 3.0$

$\varphi_{c/2} = 40°$
$A = 1.5$
$\bar{C}_L/\alpha = 2.0$

$\varphi_{c/2} = -40°$
$A = 3.3$
$\bar{C}_L/\alpha = 3.5$

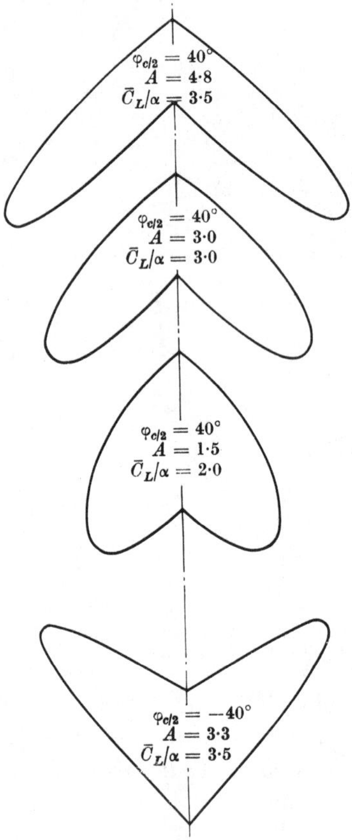

Fig. VIII. 37. Wing planforms, calculated by Brebner (1954) to give a constant spanwise distribution of lift.

and the details of the method are such that the desired spanwise lift distribution is obtained for all values of $\bar{C}_L$. Some calculated wing planforms are shown in Fig. VIII. 37. An interesting result of these calculations is that for a given angle of sweep-back there seems to be a limiting aspect ratio above which one cannot achieve a constant lift coefficient along the span; this is manifested by the chord taking negative values in the centre region. This limiting value is about $A = 20$ for $\varphi = 40°$ and $A = 10$ for $\varphi = 60°$. Further, some of the wings calculated for lesser aspect ratios show an inverse taper near the wing root, and there is a lower limiting value of the aspect ratio below which there is no inverse taper. These values of A are rather small: about $A = 2$ for $\varphi = 40°$ and $A = 1$ for $\varphi = 60°$. There is, however, a wide range of possible planforms which appear reasonable for practical purposes but it is not known to what extent wings with constant spanwise distribution of lift would be desirable in practice, or what other distributions might be preferable. Plane wings designed on this basis exhibit, of course, the characteristic variation of the chordwise loading along the span which may be counteracted by camber and twist. Brebner has shown, however, that the twist required is considerably less than for ordinary straight-tapered wings.

27. The displacement effect of thick wings

One cannot help feeling very conscious of the inadequacy of the linearization on which the whole structure of the theories described in this chapter is built. The replacement of the thick wing by an infinitely thin plate is an approximation which has long since been discarded by modern theories of two-dimensional flow. In particular, the infinite velocity at the leading edge which we have had to tolerate in nearly all the work so far is quite unrealistic, though it does, of course, indicate that on thin wings velocities tend to be high near the leading edge. If on the linearized theory a finite velocity can be obtained at the leading edge, this leads to a low maximum value of velocity on the real wing; this is often achieved by an appropriate choice of camber line and an example was given in Section 26. But the problem remains of what modifications to the general lifting-surface theory can be made to take into account the thickness distribution of the wing.

The only approach directed at the fundamental assumption of linearization has so far been made by Lighthill (1951): although this has been applied successfully to two-dimensional flow as described in Section IV. 14, and appears capable of extension, it has yet to be treated in detail for three-dimensional flow. One other method, however, is available and is capable of dealing with three-dimensional and in particular swept wings. Weber (1953, 1955), to whom it is due, super-imposes the basic singularities of source and vortex and uses successive approximations in which the effects of thickness and of incidence and camber are in turn calculated with increasing accuracy. In principle, the theory begins with a first approximation in which the streamwise

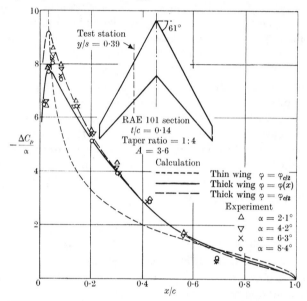

Fɪɢ. VIII. 38. A comparison between experimental and calculated chordwise distributions of load near mid-semispan of a highly swept-back wing.

velocity component on the chordline, $U(x, y)$ at $z = 0$ is expressed as the sum of a term due to the non-zero thickness, as determined in Chapter VII, and the term $\frac{1}{2}\gamma(x, y)\cos\varphi$ due to lift. Further approxima-tions concern the relation between the velocity on the chordline and the velocity on the surface of the aerofoil, and they also take account of cross-flow velocity components. The results of the theory are exact in the case of elliptic cylinders and represent good approximations for other shapes. Straight and swept wings with symmetrical and cam-bered sections can be treated, as well as aerofoils with Brebner's special family of camber lines described in Section 24. The inverse problem of designing aerofoils which have prescribed velocity distributions is also dealt with. Some gaps still remain, such as the solution of the direct problem for cambered wings of small aspect ratio and of the inverse problem for thick wings of small aspect ratio. In each individual case, at certain points along the chord the unknown quantity—the velocity increment or pressure coefficient, or the section ordinate, or the slope of the section, as the case may be—is expressed as a finite sum of the products of the given quantities and fixed coefficients which are tabulated. Thus, the practical solution requires no special computational aids and can be obtained in a few hours in any given case.

As an example, we quote the relation for the pressure coefficient on a symmetrical section at the sheared part of a swept wing

$$C_p(x) = 1 - \cos^2\alpha_e \sin^2\varphi - \left[1 + \left(\frac{S^{(2)}(\xi)}{\cos\varphi}\right)^2\right]^{-1} \times$$

$$\times \left[\cos\alpha_e[\cos\varphi + S^{(1)}(\xi)] \pm \sin\alpha_e \sec\varphi\{1 + S^{(3)}(\xi)\}\left(\frac{1-\xi}{\xi}\right)^{\frac{1}{2}}\right]^2, \quad (173)$$

where the functions $S^{(1)}$, $S^{(2)}$, $S^{(3)}$ are those defined in equation (IV. 91). The lift of the thin sheared wing, as given by equation (87), appears in the term $[(1-\xi)/\xi]^{\frac{1}{2}}$, and the angle of incidence is the effective incidence, $\alpha_e = \alpha - \alpha_i$, at the particular section. The difference between the pressure coefficients at corresponding points on the upper and lower surfaces is then given by

$$\Delta C_p = -l(\xi) = -4\cos\alpha_e \sin\alpha_e \cos\varphi \times$$

$$\times \left[1 + \frac{S^{(1)}(\xi)}{\cos\varphi}\right]\left[1 + \frac{S^{(3)}(\xi)}{\cos\varphi}\right]\left[1 + \left(\frac{S^{(2)}(\xi)}{\cos\varphi}\right)^2\right]^{-1}\left(\frac{1-\xi}{\xi}\right)^{\frac{1}{2}}. \quad (174)$$

This expression must be compared with that given in equation (81). For elliptic sections, where the terms $S^{(1)}$, $S^{(2)}$, $S^{(3)}$ can be evaluated explicitly, a further integration of ΔC_p along the chord leads directly to equation (13). Equation (174) is of some importance since it can be used to improve the values of the sectional lift slope which may have been taken in the earlier lifting-surface theories. A value of a_0 taken first from equation (13) and put in equation (119) with $\lambda = 0$, leads to yet another value in equation (174). An iteration leads to consistent values.

These results agree well with experiment, and examples have already been given in Fig. VIII. 19. Another wing is shown in Fig. VIII. 38 for which the angle of sweep is high and the section comparatively thick. The effect of thickness on the chordwise loading is noticeable. Since the wing is highly tapered, the local sweep-back $\varphi(x)$ varies along the chord. The two curves shown represent the results, first, of using the sweep-back of the mid-chord line, $\varphi_{c/2}$, in the calculations and, second, of taking the local sweep-back angle $\varphi(x)$. It appears that this effect of wing taper is not large, and can be adequately represented in this fashion. To treat such a case by a more exact method, even within the linearized theory, would involve a formidable amount of work, and would scarcely be worth while.

IX

UNIFORM FLOW PAST BODIES OF REVOLUTION

1. Introduction

ONE of the distinctions which can be made between the theories of two-dimensional flow past aerofoils, described in Chapters IV and V, and of three-dimensional flow past wings, in Chapters VII and VIII, is that the former two chapters concentrate attention on variations in stream-wise or chordwise directions, while the latter two are far more concerned with the variations in the perpendicular, spanwise direction. Now the independence of the spanwise and chordwise variations of, for example, the load on a wing is, of course, a mathematical fiction but we have discussed fully in the preceding chapters the conditions under which it is a good approximation. What was not stated quite so explicitly was the fact that this independence depends entirely on the assumptions consequent upon the wing being thin.

This last assumption is clearly quite inappropriate to a body of revolution whose thickness is, in the terminology of wings, always of the same order as its span. For this reason, we can abandon at once any hope of modifying the theories of Chapter VIII so that they become suitable for bodies of revolution. There is the single exception of slender-body theory; this theory makes no distinction between directions perpendicular to the stream direction or to the longitudinal axis of the body, and so it can validly be applied to a body of any cross-sectional shape whose longitudinal section is sufficiently slender.

For a body of revolution whose axis is parallel to a uniform stream—whose incidence, in other words, is zero—the iterative procedure of Section III. 7 presents no difficulties of principle. For the first inviscid approximation, almost the general rule is the representation of the body by distributions of singularities; although the analytical details are quite different, much of this work is analogous in its general method to that in Chapter VII for wings of zero lift. It is usually convenient to use cylindrical polar coordinates, and for a body of revolution the analysis takes on a two-dimensional form: unfortunately, however, there is nothing of comparable power and utility to the complex potential of two-dimensional flow. The mathematical functions particularly associated with axi-symmetry, and especially Legendre's functions, often occur and the reader who is not well acquainted with such functions may be guided by Jeffreys and Jeffreys (1946).

The first viscous approximation—namely, the calculation of the boundary layer—follows the methods laid down in Section II. 18, and in particular enables the drag of a body of revolution to be estimated. Here we have to assume that regions of separated flow are small; well-separated flow, such as that past shells with flat bases, is beyond the scope of this chapter. Attention therefore is confined to bodies of more or less streamline shape. Such are the analytical difficulties of studying even the flow past streamline bodies that no methods have yet been proposed for the calculation of the second inviscid approximation.

Any analogy with the flow past wings disappears as soon as the body of revolution is set at an incidence to the stream. The difficulty here lies in choosing a theoretical model. We recall that, in the inviscid flow past a wing, the trailing vorticity determines the lift on the wing. Now from the point of view of the analysis of purely inviscid flow, the trailing vorticity and hence the lift distribution on the wing can be given any value; what enables it to be determined uniquely is the Kutta–Joukowski condition of Section V. 2. This condition, as was emphasized at the time, arises from the observable physical characteristics of flow near a sharp trailing edge. But if the rear of a body has no sharp trailing edge, the Kutta–Joukowski condition cannot be applied nor has any other criterion yet been generally accepted which renders unique the distribution of concentrated vorticity in the otherwise inviscid flow. The study of the lift on bodies of revolution has therefore been based on theoretical models which do not rely on the vorticity distribution as the agency of lift, and an account of these studies is given in Sections 16–21.

Lift is, in any case, not the feature of greatest interest in the flow past bodies of revolution at incidence; usually of much more practical significance is the couple on the body which, regrettably, tends to increase the incidence. The implications of this phenomenon for the stability of the flight of a projectile are obvious, and suggest the importance of theories of oscillatory and other unsteady motions; these are, however, beyond the scope of this book.

2. The first inviscid approximation for the flow past ellipsoids of revolution

The most important of the exact solutions for potential flow past bodies of revolution are, no doubt, contained in the classical treatment of the motion of an ellipsoid of revolution, otherwise called a spheroid. This has been given in some detail by, for example, Lamb (1932) and Munk (1934), and a summary of it is given here since it introduces the use of certain techniques which have been extended to the solution of other more complicated problems.

The essence of the treatment is the use of semi-elliptic coordinates

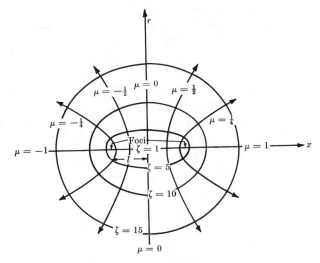

Fig. IX. 1. Diagram of the semi-elliptic system of coordinates.

(μ, ζ, θ) which are defined in terms of the cylindrical polars (r, θ, x) by the relations

$$r = l(1-\mu^2)^{\frac{1}{2}}(\zeta^2-1)^{\frac{1}{2}}, \qquad x = l\mu\zeta; \qquad \zeta \geqslant 0. \qquad (1)$$

The system of surfaces $\zeta = $ constant defines a family of confocal ellipsoids of revolution, with centre the origin; the surface $\zeta = 1$ is degenerate, being the line joining the foci $x = \pm l, r = 0$. The surfaces $\mu = $ constant, for $-1 \leqslant \mu \leqslant +1$, define an orthogonal system of confocal hyperboloids of revolution. Fig. IX. 1 illustrates the transformation. The metric for this system of coordinates is found to be

$$(ds)^2 = l^2[(d\mu)^2\{(\zeta^2-\mu^2)/(1-\mu^2)\}+$$

$$+(d\zeta)^2\{(\zeta^2-\mu^2)/(\zeta^2-1)\}+(d\theta)^2(1-\mu^2)(\zeta^2-1)]. \qquad (2)$$

Laplace's equation for the velocity potential, ϕ, may be obtained from equation (I. 87) in the form

$$\frac{\partial}{\partial\mu}\left[(1-\mu^2)\frac{\partial\phi}{\partial\mu}\right]+\frac{\partial}{\partial\zeta}\left[(\zeta^2-1)\frac{\partial\phi}{\partial\zeta}\right]+\frac{\zeta^2-\mu^2}{(1-\mu^2)(\zeta^2-1)}\frac{\partial^2\phi}{\partial\theta^2}=0. \qquad (3)$$

Solutions of this equation may be found by separation of the variables, and it may be verified by substitution that

$$\phi=\phi_{nm}K_n^m(\mu)K_n^m(\zeta)\cos(m\theta+\theta_{nm}) \qquad (4)$$

is a particular solution where ϕ_{nm} and θ_{nm} are constants. K_n^m denotes Legendre associated functions of either the first or second kind which we later distinguish as P_n^m and Q_n^m respectively. More general solutions are obtained by summing this expression for ϕ over values of n and m.

We suppose that a uniform stream, parallel to the axis $r=0$ and of speed U_∞ at infinity, is flowing past the spheroid. On the assumption that the real flow has axial symmetry, we need only consider solutions for ϕ which are independent of θ. If ϕ' is the velocity potential of the disturbance due to the spheroid,

$$\phi=U_\infty x+\phi', \qquad (5)$$

and the boundary condition on the surface becomes

$$\text{on } \zeta=\zeta_w: \qquad \partial\phi'/\partial\zeta=-U_\infty(\partial x/\partial\zeta)=-U_\infty l\mu. \qquad (6)$$

We infer that ϕ' is not only independent of θ, but linearly dependent on μ: remembering that $P_1^0(\mu)=\mu$, we are led to take $m=0$ and $n=1$ in equation (4) to find

$$\phi'=-lU_\infty(\zeta_w^2-1)^{\frac{1}{2}}P_1^0(\mu)Q_1^0(\zeta)/Q_1^1(\zeta_w) \qquad (7)$$

which, with equation (5), gives the solution to the inviscid flow. The value of ζ_w is the reciprocal of the eccentricity of the given spheroid, and $2l$ is, of course, its focal distance; the thickness-chord ratio is $t/c=(1-\zeta_w^{-2})^{\frac{1}{2}}$.

The flow over a spheroid moving laterally to its axis may be treated similarly by taking the velocity at infinity to be parallel to the z-axis, say, and of magnitude W_∞. The boundary condition for the perturbation velocity potential is then

$$\text{on } \zeta=\zeta_w: \qquad \partial\phi'/\partial\zeta=-W_\infty(\partial z/\partial\zeta)=-lW_\infty\{(1-\mu^2)/(\zeta^2-1)\}^{\frac{1}{2}}\zeta\cos\theta,$$
$$(8)$$

and it is found that

$$\phi'=-lW_\infty P_1^1(\mu)Q_1^1(\zeta)\cos\theta(1-\zeta_w^{-2})^{-\frac{1}{2}}/(dQ_1^1(\zeta_w)/d\zeta_w). \qquad (9)$$

The appropriate linear superposition of the solutions (7) and (9) yields the potential of the disturbed flow for any translational motion, combining axial and lateral movement.

The most general steady motion of a spheroid can be treated by including the effect of a rotation of constant angular velocity Ω about an axis through its centre. If this axis is $\theta = \theta_0$, it can be shown that the disturbed flow has a perturbation potential given by

$$\phi' = -\tfrac{1}{3}l^2\Omega P_2^1(\mu)Q_2^1(\zeta)\sin(\theta-\theta_0)(\zeta_w^2-1)^{-\frac{1}{2}}/(dQ_2^1(\zeta_w)/d\zeta_w). \qquad (10)$$

3. Stokes's stream function

In flows possessing axial symmetry it is often convenient to use Stokes's stream function ψ, introduced in equation (I. 13). It is related to the velocity potential by the equations

$$\partial\psi/\partial r = r\,\partial\phi/\partial x, \qquad \partial\psi/\partial x = -r\,\partial\phi/\partial r, \qquad (11)$$

in the cylindrical polar coordinates (r, θ, x). The equation for irrotational flow (I. 89) can thus be put in terms of ψ as

$$r\frac{\partial}{\partial r}\left[\frac{1}{r}\frac{\partial\psi}{\partial r}\right] + \frac{\partial^2\psi}{\partial x^2} = 0 \qquad (12)$$

for axi-symmetric flow.

The general axi-symmetric solution for the velocity potential, which is given by $m = 0$ in equation (4), is

$$\phi = \phi_{n0}K_n^0(\mu)K_n^0(\zeta), \qquad (13)$$

and to this corresponds a solution of equation (12) given by

$$\psi = [n(n+1)]^{-1}l\phi_{n0}(1-\mu^2)(\zeta^2-1)[dK_n^0(\mu)/d\mu][dK_n^0(\zeta)/d\zeta]. \qquad (14)$$

The stream function for a uniform stream of speed U_∞ parallel to the axis is $\psi = \tfrac{1}{2}U_\infty r^2 = \tfrac{1}{2}U_\infty l^2(1-\mu^2)(\zeta^2-1)$, so that the expression

$$\psi = l(1-\mu^2)(\zeta^2-1)\left[\tfrac{1}{2}U_\infty l + \sum_n \frac{\phi_{n0}}{n(n+1)}\frac{dK_n^0(\mu)}{d\mu}\frac{dK_n^0(\zeta)}{d\zeta}\right] \qquad (15)$$

represents the axial motion about a certain body of revolution whose precise shape depends on the values of ϕ_{n0}. Since on the axis $r = 0$ or $\mu = 1$ and so $\psi = 0$, the body is represented by $\psi = 0$.

For the special case of the spheroid $\zeta = \zeta_w$, equation (15) reduces to

$$\psi = \tfrac{1}{2}l^2U_\infty(1-\mu^2)(\zeta^2-1)[1-(dQ_1^0(\zeta)/d\zeta)/(dQ_1^0(\zeta_w)/d\zeta_w)]. \qquad (16)$$

Placing $\zeta = \zeta_w$ gives at once $\psi = 0$, so that this is verified to be the required solution.

4. The first inviscid approximation for the flow past a given body. Kaplan's method

Kaplan (1934) has used equation (15), with $dK_n^0/d\mu$ and $dK_n^0/d\zeta$ replaced by $dP_n^0/d\mu$ and $dQ_n^0/d\zeta$ respectively, to determine the axial flow past a body of revolution represented by

$$\zeta_w = \sum_{r=0}^{\infty} a_r \mu^r. \tag{17}$$

If the expression for the stream function given in equation (15) is written in the form

$$\psi/l(1-\mu^2)(\zeta^2-1) = \tfrac{1}{2}lU_\infty + \sum_{n=1}^{\infty} [\phi_{n0}/n(n+1)](dP_n^0(\mu)/d\mu)(dQ_n^0(\zeta)/d\zeta), \tag{18}$$

the right-hand side of this equation is zero on the body and may be expanded as a power series in μ with the help of equation (17). The coefficient of each power of μ is therefore zero and we have a set of linear equations for ϕ_{n0}. As a computational method, it is of practical value if the given shape of the body is so close to that of a spheroid that the first few terms alone of the series of equation (17) are adequate, and likewise that all but the first few constants ϕ_{n0} may be neglected.

Kaplan also describes a similar method applicable to the calculation of the transverse flow about the body of revolution, in which a set of linear equations is obtained for the coefficients ϕ_{n1} of the general expression for the corresponding perturbation potential given by

$$\phi' = \sum_n \phi_{n1} P_n^1(\mu)Q_n^1(\zeta)\cos\theta. \tag{19}$$

Since this flow is not axi-symmetric, Stokes's stream function cannot be used.

A more convenient computational method was independently suggested by Smith (1935). He approximates by taking only the first N terms in the sum in equation (18) and satisfies the equation at N chosen points on the body. This procedure avoids the necessity of making an assumption such as equation (17). The accuracy of both methods, however, is sensitive to the choice of the position of the foci of the coordinate system relative to the body. The problem of making a suitable choice is considered in Section 9. Smith's method also places a heavy responsibility on the choice of the points at which ψ is to be taken as zero. In the analogous case of the calculation of the downwash on a wing at lift, there are some criteria which enable a fairly good choice of pivotal points to be made. In the present problem, about as much as one can say is that more points should be taken round the front and back of the body than over its centre.

An alternative and later suggestion by Kaplan for the solution of the longitudinal flow involves an extension of the use of special coordinate systems of which brief details are given in the next section.

5. A method based on conformal transformation

Laplace's equation for the velocity potential in axi-symmetric flow can be written from equation (I. 88) in a form analogous to (12); thus

$$\frac{\partial}{\partial r}\left(r\frac{\partial \phi}{\partial r}\right)+\frac{\partial}{\partial x}\left(r\frac{\partial \phi}{\partial x}\right)=0 \qquad (20)$$

for $r > 0$, which may be regarded, mathematically, as the two-dimensional form of the equation

$$\nabla\cdot(r\,\nabla\phi)=0, \qquad (21)$$

valid in two-dimensional space for all values of r and x. It may be noted that we can suppose ϕ to exist for $r < 0$, by analytical continuation, as an even function of r. If a new set of two-dimensional orthogonal coordinates (ξ, η) is introduced to replace (x, r), equation (20) becomes

$$\frac{\partial}{\partial \xi}\left(\frac{rh_2}{h_1}\frac{\partial \phi}{\partial \xi}\right)+\frac{\partial}{\partial \eta}\left(\frac{rh_1}{h_2}\frac{\partial \phi}{\partial \eta}\right)=0, \qquad (22)$$

where

$$(ds)^2=(dx)^2+(dr)^2=(h_1\,d\xi)^2+(h_2\,d\eta)^2. \qquad (23)$$

In particular, if the transformation is conformal so that

$$x+ir=f(\xi+i\eta), \qquad (24)$$

where f is some specified analytic function, then $h_1 = h_2$ and equation (22) is

$$\frac{\partial}{\partial \xi}\left(r\frac{\partial \phi}{\partial \xi}\right)+\frac{\partial}{\partial \eta}\left(r\frac{\partial \phi}{\partial \eta}\right)=0. \qquad (25)$$

To Kaplan (1943) is due the method by which the upper half of the meridional section of the body—that is, the contour in the (x, r) plane—is now transformed into a segment of the real ξ-axis. This may best be done by an intermediate transformation into the circle $|Z| = R$, namely

$$x+ir=Z+\sum_{n=0}^{\infty} a_n R^{n+1}Z^{-n}, \qquad (26)$$

and then placing

$$Z=R\exp[-i(\xi+i\eta)]. \qquad (27)$$

The coefficients in the series (26) are real by virtue of the symmetry about $r = 0$ and $\eta = 0$, and may be determined by Theodorsen's method described in Section IV. 12. The transformation may then be written as

for $\eta \geqslant 0$:
$$\begin{cases} x=R[e^{\eta}\cos\xi+a_0+a_1 e^{-\eta}\cos\xi+O(e^{-2\eta})], \\ r=-R[e^{\eta}\sin\xi+a_1 e^{-\eta}\sin\xi+a_2 e^{-2\eta}\sin 2\xi+O(e^{-3\eta})], \end{cases} \quad (28)$$

with the help of equations (26) and (27).

The boundary condition satisfied at the surface by the perturbation potential is, in terms of the coordinates (ξ, η), $\partial\phi'/\partial\eta = -U_\infty(\partial x/\partial\eta)$ on $\eta = 0$; thus

$$[\partial\phi'/\partial\eta]_{\eta=0} = -U_\infty R[\cos\xi - a_1\cos\xi - 2a_2\cos 2\xi - ...], \qquad (29)$$

where U_∞ is the velocity of the body relative to the undisturbed stream, in the direction of its axis of symmetry. As $\eta \to \infty$, ϕ' tends to a constant value. The simplicity of the boundary conditions leads to an iterative process of solution of the differential equation (25) involving only simple quadratures.

The substitution of the expression for r from (28) in (25) gives the equation for the perturbation potential ϕ' in the form

$$\left(\frac{\partial^2\phi'}{\partial\xi^2} + \frac{\partial^2\phi'}{\partial\eta^2}\right)\sinh(\eta-\chi)\sin\xi + (\partial\phi'/\partial\xi)\sinh(\eta-\chi)\cos\xi +$$
$$+ (\partial\phi'/\partial\eta)\cosh(\eta-\chi)\sin\xi$$
$$= \sum_{n=1}^{\infty} b_n\,\epsilon^n \exp[-(n+1)\eta]\left\{\left(\frac{\partial^2\phi'}{\partial\xi^2} + \frac{\partial^2\phi'}{\partial\eta^2}\right)\sin(n+1)\xi +\right.$$
$$\left.+ (n+1)(\partial\phi'/\partial\xi)\cos(n+1)\xi - (n+1)(\partial\phi'/\partial\eta)\sin(n+1)\xi\right\}, \quad (30)$$

where
$$2\chi = \log a_1 \quad \text{and} \quad 2a_1^{\frac{1}{2}}b_n\,\epsilon^n = a_{n+1}. \qquad (31)$$

Likewise, the boundary condition (29) can be expressed as

$$[\partial\phi'/\partial\eta]_{\eta=0} = 2U_\infty\,Re\chi\left\{\sinh\chi\cos\xi + \sum_{n=1}^{\infty}(n+1)b_n\,\epsilon^n\cos(n+1)\xi\right\}. \qquad (32)$$

One procedure of solving equation (30), given by Kaplan (1943), puts

$$\phi' = \sum_{n=0}^{\infty}\phi_n\,\epsilon^n, \qquad (33)$$

whereupon the coefficients of like powers of ϵ on each side of the equations are equated. The equations for ϕ_0, ϕ_1, and ϕ_2 and their appropriate boundary values on $\eta = 0$ may thus be obtained without too much difficulty and Kaplan solved them by separating the new independent variables $\cos\xi$ and $\cosh(\eta-\chi)$; these enable the homogeneous left-hand side of equation (30) to be solved in terms of Legendre functions. The solution for ϕ_0 is

$$\phi_0 = -U_\infty R(e^{2\chi}-1)P_1^0(\cos\xi)Q_1^0\{\cosh(\eta-\chi)\}/Q_1^1(\cosh\chi), \qquad (34)$$

but the expression for ϕ_n becomes increasingly involved as n increases.

For the flow past an ellipsoid of revolution, $a_n = 0$ for $n \geqslant 2$ in equation (26) and so from equations (31) and (33) $\phi_n = 0$ for $n \geqslant 1$. ϕ_0, given in (34), is therefore the solution of the perturbation velocity in this case, and ξ and η can be identified with the coordinates μ and ζ of Section 2.

As an application of the general method, Kaplan considers the axial flow about a body whose meridian section is of the form of a symmetrical Joukowski profile. The resulting velocity distribution obtained is practically indistinguishable from that obtained by his method of Section 4, but the computations involved are less formidable. This particular meridian section is, of course, especially suitable to the present method; the computational advantages are less obvious for an arbitrary shape.

6. The representation of a body in longitudinal flow by distributions of singularities

The methods so far described, while possessing the advantage of accuracy, are not capable of development into simple routine procedures for the calculation of the velocity distribution on a body of prescribed shape. Methods based on the superposition of simple singular solutions have much greater potentiality in this respect; in this and subsequent sections, therefore, we discuss such methods whose similarity to earlier ones, notably those of Chapter VII, will be evident.

To start, let us consider a source at the origin of strength Q. The velocity induced by it is everywhere radial in direction and inversely proportional to the square of the radial distance in magnitude. The velocity potential and stream function are then expressed in terms of the cylindrical coordinates (r, x) by

$$\phi = -(Q/4\pi)(r^2+x^2)^{-\frac{1}{2}}, \qquad \psi = -(Qx/4\pi)(r^2+x^2)^{-\frac{1}{2}}. \tag{35}$$

The expressions obtained by differentiation with respect to x, namely

$$\phi = (Qx/4\pi)(r^2+x^2)^{-\frac{3}{2}} \quad \text{and} \quad \psi = -(Qr^2/4\pi)(r^2+x^2)^{-\frac{3}{2}}, \tag{36}$$

then refer to a source doublet whose axis lies along the x-axis. Expressions for ϕ and ψ having singularities of higher order at the origin may easily be found in terms of Legendre functions as:

$$\text{for } n > 0: \quad \begin{cases} \phi = (-1)^{n-1}n!(r^2+x^2)^{-\frac{1}{2}(n+1)}P_n^0[x(r^2+x^2)^{-\frac{1}{2}}] \\ \psi = (-1)^n(n-1)!(r^2+x^2)^{-\frac{1}{2}(n+1)}rP_n^1[x(r^2+x^2)^{-\frac{1}{2}}] \end{cases}; \tag{37}$$

$$\text{for } n < 0: \quad \begin{cases} \phi = -(r^2+x^2)^{-\frac{1}{2}(n+1)}Q_{-n-1}^0[x(r^2+x^2)^{-\frac{1}{2}}] \div (-n-1)! \\ \psi = -(r^2+x^2)^{-\frac{1}{2}(n+1)}rQ_{-n-1}^1[x(r^2+x^2)^{-\frac{1}{2}}] \div (-n)! \end{cases}. \tag{38}$$

That the axi-symmetric flow about certain closed bodies can be represented by distributions of sources and sinks was first suggested specifically by Rankine (1871) and the idea was elaborated by D. W.

Taylor (1894). A single source in a uniform stream produces a flow about the so-called Blasius–Fuhrmann half-body shown in Fig. IX. 2. The addition of a sink of equal strength downstream of the source serves to close the stream tube representing the body. For any closed body the algebraic sum of the strengths of the enclosed sources must, of course, be zero. Fuhrmann (1911) computed several bodies using continuous

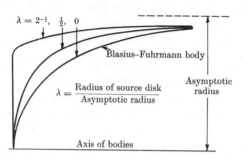

Fig. IX. 2. Shapes of half-body obtained by source disks, of different size but of equal total strength, in a uniform stream.

axial distributions of sources and sinks. Thus, if $q(x)$ is the density of the source distribution per unit length along the axis $r = 0$ in the interval $0 \leqslant x \leqslant c$, the potential and stream functions of the resulting flow are evidently given from equations (35) by

$$\phi = -\frac{1}{4\pi} \int_0^c \frac{q(t)\,dt}{[(x-t)^2+r^2]^{\frac{1}{2}}}; \qquad \psi = -\frac{1}{4\pi} \int_0^c \frac{(x-t)q(t)\,dt}{[(x-t)^2+r^2]^{\frac{1}{2}}}. \quad (39)$$

Fuhrmann employed step functions and piecewise linear variations of x for $q(x)$ and this can be shown to be equivalent to the superposition of a number of singularities of the type given by (38) with $n = -1$ and $n = -2$. For example, the potential due to a finite source-line of uniform strength is proportional to

$$\int_0^c [(x-t)^2+r^2]^{-\frac{1}{2}}\,dt = \log[\{[x^2+r^2]^{\frac{1}{2}}+x\}/\{[(x-c)^2+r^2]^{\frac{1}{2}}+(x-c)\}]$$
$$= Q_0^0[x(r^2+x^2)^{-\frac{1}{2}}] - Q_0^0[(x-c)(r^2+(x-c)^2)^{-\frac{1}{2}}]. \quad (40)$$

More recently Munzer and Reichardt (1944) have used distributions of sources to obtain bodies on which the pressure is nearly constant, so as to represent the flow past axi-symmetric cavities. The techniques they use appear appropriate only to this particular problem, but certain generalizations have been suggested by Riegels and Brandt (1944).

Another development of the use of source distributions has been initiated by Weinstein (1948) who considered shapes generated by axi-symmetric source distributions on rings, and over disks and cylinders. The fundamental solution is that for a source ring, the others being obtained by superposition. Weinstein employed an operational approach in his analysis, representing the velocity potentials and stream functions in terms of improper integrals: it may be shown, for instance, that the potential of a source ring of total strength Q, situated on $r = a$ in the plane $x = 0$, is given by

$$\phi = -(Q/2\pi^2)[x^2+(r+a)^2]^{-\frac{1}{2}}\mathbf{K}[4ar(x^2+(r+a)^2)^{-1}], \qquad (41)$$

where $\mathbf{K}$ is the complete elliptic integral of the first kind.

Although the analysis of distributions of source rings involves considerable complication, it is possible by their use to represent with good accuracy the flow past a far larger class of shapes than is possible merely with the use of axial distributions of sources. Thus, a source disk placed in a uniform stream represents the flow about a body with a much blunter nose than is obtainable by any axial distribution of sources, as was found by Tuyl (1950). This is shown in Fig. IX. 2, the total source strength being the same in the three cases.

The assumption that the flow about a certain body of revolution can be represented exactly by a distribution of sources, or of any other single type of singularity on an arbitrary surface within the body, implies the analytical continuation of the flow into the interior of the body; this is only possible if the shape of the body satisfies certain conditions. It precludes, for example, bodies with discontinuities in their surface slope. On the other hand, it has been shown by Lamb (1932) that any continuous acyclic irrotational motion of an incompressible fluid can be regarded as due to a distribution of simple sources over the boundary; in particular, therefore, a surface distribution of source rings exists which would simulate the axi-symmetric flow past any body of revolution, whatever the shape of its meridian section. The method of Kármán, outlined in the next section, is based on the representation of the flow by axial distributions of sources, whilst that of Lotz in the following section employs a less restrictive, but more involved, analysis of source rings.

7. The representation of a body by an axial distribution of sources

To determine the flow due to a specified distribution of singularities is a relatively trivial matter. The much more important practical problem—the determination of the distribution of singularities which represent the flow over a body of given axi-symmetric shape—appears first to have been assailed by Kármán (1927).

The axis of the given body is subdivided into a finite number of intervals, to each of which a source distribution of constant strength is assigned. The body is thus represented by a finite number of axial source lines. The stream function of this arrangement may be found from equation (34) by an integration for each interval and is

$$\psi = \tfrac{1}{2}U_\infty r + (1/4\pi) \sum_{k=1}^{N} q_k\{[r^2+(x-x_k-l_k)^2]^{\frac{1}{2}}-[r^2+(x-x_k)^2]^{\frac{1}{2}}\}, \quad (42)$$

where q_k is the source strength per unit length of the interval

$$x_k < x < x_k+l_k.$$

The value of ψ on the body is the same as that on the axis $r = 0$ upstream of the body, namely $\sum q_k l_k/4\pi$; in particular, it is zero if the body is closed. Thus if ψ is equated to this value at N prescribed points on the surface a set of N non-homogeneous linear equations for q_k is obtained. Kármán chose, as these points, the midpoints, $x = x_k+\tfrac{1}{2}l_k$, of the intervals; we have, however, already remarked on the necessity for a good choice of points, and one of the difficulties of this type of method, at any rate from the purely mathematical point of view, is that the errors involved in the approximations cannot be estimated accurately. Whether or not the method becomes more accurate as the number of intervals is increased depends entirely on the shape of the body. A large number of intervals involves much labour in computation which is not well spent if the body cannot be represented accurately even by a continuously varying distribution of axial sources. Nevertheless, this is the best known, and most frequently used, of the direct methods and its application to the flow over bodies at incidence is described later. Modifications to Kármán's methods have been suggested by Bilharz and Hölder (1947) and Wijngaarden (1948).

8. The representation of a body by source rings

The most important alternative method which relies on a distribution of sources is that originated by Lotz (1931b). She combines source rings which coincide with the surface, and so opens up the possibility of calculating a flow whose analytic continuation involves singularities at points other than on the axis. On the other hand, her method, although applicable to any type of body, has the practical disadvantage of requiring much greater labour in computation.

The potential for a surface distribution of sources can be obtained by superposition of a continuous distribution of ring-sources, so that using equation (41), the perturbation potential of the motion can be written as

$$\phi' = -(1/2\pi^2) \int_0^c q(t)\mathbf{K}(k^2)[(x-t)^2+(r+a)^2]^{-\frac{1}{2}} \, dt, \qquad (43)$$

where $k^2 = 4ar[(x-t)^2+(r+a)^2]^{-1}$, $q(t)$ is the source strength per unit axial length in the plane $x = t$, and $a = r_w(t)$ is the radius of the body at $x = t$. The boundary condition is

$$\partial\phi'/\partial n = -U_\infty(\partial x/\partial n). \qquad (44)$$

The calculation of the normal derivative of ϕ' from equation (43) proceeds through a limit and finally equations (43) and (44) yield an integral equation for $q(t)$: thus, with r_w regarded as a function of x,

$$q(x) = 4\pi U_\infty r_w r'_w -$$

$$- \frac{2r_w}{\pi} \int_0^c \left[2a\mathbf{D}(k^2) + \frac{[r_w-a-(x-t)r'_w]}{1-k^2}\mathbf{E}(k^2) \right] \frac{q(t)\,dt}{[(x-t)^2+(r_w+a)^2]^{\frac{3}{2}}}, \quad (45)$$

where k^2 and a are defined as before, and $\mathbf{D}(k^2)$ is the complete elliptic integral $\int_0^{\frac{1}{2}\pi} \sin^2\theta[1-k^2\sin^2\theta]^{-\frac{1}{2}} \, d\theta$. This integral equation for $q(t)$ is exact for the inviscid flow past the body of revolution.

Vandrey (1953) has done much to reduce the work involved in the numerical solution of this type of equation. He suggests an iteration scheme of the type

$$\left.\begin{array}{l} q_0(x) = \frac{1}{2}f(x), \\ n \geqslant 1: \quad q_n(x) = \frac{1}{2}q_{n-1}(x)+\frac{1}{2}f(x)+\frac{1}{2}\int q_{n-1}(t)K(x,t)\,dt \end{array}\right\} \qquad (46)$$

as being is appropriate to an integral equation of the form

$$q(x) = f(x) + \int q(t)K(x,t)\,dt, \qquad (47)$$

to which (45) plainly corresponds. The main difficulty of this scheme of iteration, which Vandrey finds rapidly convergent, lies in the evaluation of the integral which involves the complicated kernel shown in (45); to aid this evaluation, he uses an integration formula of the type

$$\int_0^c q(t)K(x,t)\,dt = \sum_m p_m q(t_m)K(x,t_m), \qquad (48)$$

for which he calculates the weighting coefficients taking proper account of the singularities in the kernel, by suitable transformation of the variable of integration t.

For full details, the reader is referred to Vandrey's paper which contains computational instructions and programmes. However, in the author's own words, 'the work is still so laborious that a single computor is likely to get tired of it'. Nevertheless, even a few iterations give high accuracy: for a spheroid, for instance, the calculated surface velocity is practically indistinguishable from the exact result given by the theory of Section 2.

The first term in equation (45) is the result from slender-body theory: it is really the result of linearizing the boundary conditions and taking them on the axis. If $S(x)$ is the cross-sectional area of the body, its displacement effect is equivalent to a source distribution given by

$$q(x) = U_\infty S'(x) = 2\pi U_\infty r_w r_w'. \tag{49}$$

This approximate result, which has been shown by Ward (1955) to be true according to linearized theory for all types of slender body and not merely bodies of revolution, is one which we shall frequently meet in later sections. Meanwhile we note that the integral in equation (45) is the exact correction to this result from slender-body theory.

9. The representation of a body by an axial distribution of doublets

Other attempts to solve the direct problem have used axial distributions of doublets: such a distribution is equivalent to a continuous one of sources, together with the addition of a discrete source at each point of discontinuity in the doublet distribution. The method is therefore of slightly greater generality than that proposed by Kármán.

The stream function describing the flow due to the axial doublet distribution of strength $Q(x)$ in $a < x < b$ may be found from equation (36) in the form

$$\psi = \tfrac{1}{2} U_\infty r^2 + r^2 \int_a^b Q(t)[r^2 + (x-t)^2]^{-\frac{3}{2}} \, dt, \tag{50}$$

the first term $\tfrac{1}{2} U_\infty r^2$ being the contribution of the uniform stream. On the axis upstream, and so on the surface, $\psi = 0$; thus the doublet strength may be found by solving an integral equation for $Q(t)$:

$$\int_a^b Q(t)[r_w^2(x) + (x-t)^2]^{-\frac{3}{2}} \, dt = -\tfrac{1}{2} U_\infty. \tag{51}$$

Of the various methods of solution of this type of equation which have been suggested, the iteration techniques due to Landweber (1951) appear to be the most satisfactory. The successive approximations, $Q_n(x)$, to the value of $Q(x)$ are constructed by using the iteration formula

$$Q_{n+1}(x) = Q_n(x) + \tfrac{1}{2}r_w^2(x)\left[\tfrac{1}{2}U_\infty + \int_a^b Q_n(t)[r_w^2(x) + (x-t)^2]^{-\frac{3}{2}}\, dt\right]. \quad (52)$$

The computations are carried out most conveniently in terms of the differences between successive approximations to $Q(x)$, which also furnish a measure of the error at each stage in the process. Two methods of integration are suggested, one semi-graphical and the other completely arithmetical, but both involve the use of Gaussian quadrature formulae.

As the first approximation to $Q(x)$, Landweber assumes it to be proportional to the cross-sectional area, $\pi r_w^2(x)$, which is equivalent to the slender-body approximation of equation (49). In application to bodies with bluff noses and tails, a slight modification to this approximation is suggested, so as to give the appropriate values to $Q(x)$ at the end-points, $x = a$ and $x = b$, of the doublet distribution. For such bodies these end-points do not coincide with the extremities of the body axis, there being a small length of the axis at the nose and at the tail over which the doublet intensity vanishes. A prior knowledge of the extent of these regions greatly increases the rate of convergence of the successive approximations, and their accuracy. Landweber shows, for instance, that if

$$r_w^2(x) = S(x) = \pi c^2[\beta_1(x/c) + \beta_2(x/c)^2 + \beta_3(x/c)^3 + O(x/c)^4], \quad (53)$$

where $x = 0$ is at the nose of the body, then a good approximation to the lower limit of the integral in equation (52) is

$$a = c\beta_1/[4 + \beta_2 + \tfrac{1}{2}\sqrt{(\beta_1\beta_3)}]. \quad (54)$$

The dominant term $a = \tfrac{1}{4}c\beta_1$ corresponds to a point half-way between the centre of curvature of the nose and the nose itself. This last result corresponds to that given by Lighthill (1951), and mentioned in Section IV. 14, in his investigation into the uniformity of convergence of expansions in powers of the thickness-chord ratio for thin aerofoils. Fig. IX. 3 compares the result of (54) and of its first term with the result of exact theory, for the particular case of the spheroid.

A knowledge of the best chordwise limits for the distribution of singularities helps the application of other methods, too, For example, it may be shown that Kaplan's early method is equivalent to the use of a source distribution of strength

$$q(x) = -2\pi \sum_{n=1}^{\infty} \phi_{n0} P_n^0(x/l) \qquad (55)$$

extending along the axis between the foci, $(\pm l, 0)$, of the semi-elliptic coordinates. To know the limits of the source distribution therefore determines the positions of the foci of the coordinate system.

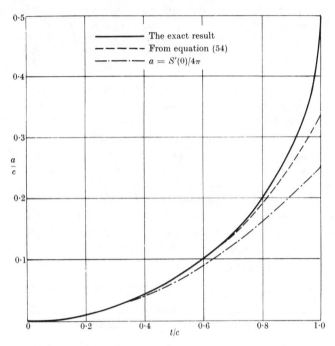

FIG. IX. 3. The distance, a, between the nose of a spheroid and the upstream end of the corresponding axial distribution of doublets.

10. The representation of a body by vortex rings

Any continuous irrotational motion, whether cyclic or not, of an incompressible fluid occupying a region extending to infinity may be regarded as due to a distribution of vortices over the interior boundaries, provided the fluid is at rest at infinity. Therefore as an alternative to source distributions we suppose that vortex rings, of strength $\Gamma(x)$ per unit length of the surface of a meridian section, cover the body. $\Gamma(x)$ is a continuous function if the surface has a continuous tangent: otherwise there will be singularities in $\Gamma(x)$. Nevertheless, the virtue of this approach, like that of Section 8, is that it can be formulated to any degree of accuracy.

One procedure involves equation (44) which expresses the fact that the component normal to the surface of the velocity induced by the vortex rings equals $[-U_\infty(\partial x/\partial n)]$. This results in an integral equation for $\Gamma(x)$ similar to equation (45); the iterative solution, given in Section 8, is, however, probably the most convenient practical method if an exact result is required.

Another equation which has been used by some authors can be obtained by applying a Green's function method to the solution of the boundary-value problem for the potential. Landweber (1951) has shown by this procedure that the integral equation for $\Gamma(x)$, the strength of the distribution of vortex rings on the surface, can be written

$$\tfrac{1}{2} \int_0^c \Gamma(t)\, r_w^2(t)\, [(x-t)^2 + r_w^2(t)]^{-\tfrac{3}{2}}(ds/dt)\, dt = -U_\infty, \tag{56}$$

with ds/dt being given by

$$ds/dt = [1 + \{r'_w(t)\}^2]^{\tfrac{1}{2}}. \tag{57}$$

The velocity on the surface of the body is then $[-\Gamma(x)]$.

An interpretation of (56) is that the velocity induced on the axis of the body by the vortex distribution equals $(-U_\infty)$. It is possible to construct an argument *a priori* showing that this must be so: an account of this is given by Milne-Thomson (1948).

In problems in which only the velocity distribution on the surface, that is $[-\Gamma(x)]$, is required, equation (56) may be solved more directly and rapidly than any of the other equations so far proposed if the iterative procedure suggested by Landweber (1951) is used. This procedure is analogous to that proposed in Section 8, for equation (45). But if the velocity field away from the body is required, then the use of vortex rings introduces no particular advantages.

11. Slender-body theory

In each of the methods so far described, any desired accuracy could be achieved in return for the expenditure of sufficient labour in computation, provided the given body was capable of being represented exactly by the particular type of singularity distribution assumed by the method. Thus numerical comparisons between the various methods mean little unless they are related to the time taken for the various calculations. Further, the computational labour is usually so great that other methods have been, and continue to be, suggested in which approximations are introduced into the analysis at an early stage, so that the work is simplified even if at the expense of rigour and ultimate accuracy. The choice of the level of compromise thus introduced will depend, of course, upon the particular application of the results envisaged by the investigator; but it often falls in favour of the simplified techniques.

The inherent approximation in nearly all the methods to which we now refer has been that the body is slender—namely, its cross-sectional area is everywhere small in comparison with the square of its length—and it has been appreciated in the course of time that all these methods can be absorbed into a generalized and rigorously developed slender-body theory. We have already met it in Section VII. 6; there its application to thick wings of no lift is similar to the work of this section for axi-symmetric bodies; and Section VIII. 12 was devoted to the theory applied to lifting wings in the form originally suggested by R. T. Jones (1946). Here a general statement of the theory is given, derived by the method of operational transforms initiated by Ward (1949) in relation to supersonic flow and extended by Adams and Sears (1953) to axi-symmetric incompressible flows.

We define the Fourier transform of the perturbation velocity potential as Φ; that is

$$\Phi \equiv \Phi(r,\theta,p) = (2\pi)^{-\frac{1}{2}} \int_{-\infty}^{\infty} \phi'(r,\theta,x)e^{ipx}\, dx. \qquad (58)$$

Laplace's equation (I. 89) in the general form for cylindrical polar coordinates then becomes

$$\frac{1}{r}\frac{\partial}{\partial r}\left(r\frac{\partial \Phi}{\partial r}\right) + \frac{1}{r^2}\frac{\partial^2 \Phi}{\partial \theta^2} = p^2\Phi \qquad (59)$$

with the boundary condition that ϕ' and $\partial\phi'/\partial x$ vanish at $x = \pm\infty$. A solution of this equation by separation of variables, including the appropriate condition at infinity, yields the expression

$$\Phi = \sum_{n=0}^{\infty} K_n(|p|r)\Phi_n(p)\cos[n\theta+\Theta_n(p)], \qquad (60)$$

where K_n is the modified Bessel function of the second kind, Φ_n and Θ_n are arbitrary functions of p, and $\Theta_0 = 0$. Now on the body surface, $|p|r$ is a small quantity of general order of magnitude r/c so that in examining the behaviour of ϕ', or of Φ, on or near the body surface we may replace K_n by its asymptotic forms

$$K_0(\epsilon) \sim [\log(2/\epsilon) - \gamma][1 + O(\epsilon^2)]$$

$$K_1(\epsilon) \sim \epsilon^{-1}[1 + O(\epsilon^2 \log \epsilon)]$$

and $\qquad K_n(\epsilon) \sim \tfrac{1}{2}(n-1)!(2/\epsilon)^n[1 + O(\epsilon^2)], \quad n \geqslant 2$

$$\left.\right\} , \qquad (61)$$

where γ is Euler's constant. These approximations are the essence of the theory and substituting the relations (61) and (60), we have as $r \to 0$:

$$\Phi \sim [1 + O(r^2 \log r)]\{[\log(2/|p|r) - \gamma]\Phi_0(p) +$$

$$+ \sum_{n=1}^{\infty} \tfrac{1}{2}(n-1)!(2/|p|r)^n \Phi_n(p)\cos[n\theta + \Theta_n(p)]\}. \quad (62)$$

To revert to the variable x, we take the inverse transform of each term which gives from (58) for $r \to 0$:

$$\phi' \sim [1 + O(r^2 \log r)]\{(1/2\pi)q(x)\log(r/2c) + \phi_0(x) +$$

$$+ \sum_{n=1}^{\infty} (r/c)^{-n}\phi_n(x)\cos[n\theta + \theta_n(x)]\}, \quad (63)$$

where $[-q(x)/2\pi]$ and $\phi_0(x)$ are the inverse transforms of $\Phi_0(p)$ and $[\log(1/|p|c) - \gamma]\Phi_0(p)$ respectively. The latter can be calculated, using the product theorem for transforms, as

$$\phi_0 = -(1/4\pi) \int_{-\infty}^{\infty} \text{sgn}(x-t)q'(t)\log|(x-t)/c| \, dt. \quad (64)$$

The functions $\phi_n(x)$ and $\theta_n(x)$, for $n \geqslant 1$, can of course be related to $\Phi_n(p)$ and $\Theta_n(p)$, but there is no purpose in finding the relations.

Equation (63) shows that the flow near the body in transverse planes $x = $ constant is a two-dimensional potential motion. In particular, the terms describing asymmetrical flow ($n \geqslant 1$) are independent of conditions up- or down-stream of the transverse plane considered, and it is these terms (or, to be precise, merely the first of these terms) which determine the flow due to a lateral motion of a slender body of revolution. The implications of this are considered in Section 14. Here we are concerned with the terms independent of θ and these do not conform to the independence principle since $\phi_0(x)$ depends on the variation of $q(x)$ for all values of x, as shown by equation (64).

Now the term $\{q(x)/2\pi\}\log(r/2c)$ in equation (63) represents a source distribution and its value in terms of the body shape may be readily found.

Let n and s be distances measured along the outward normal and along the circumference of the section of the body in a plane $x = $ constant. The boundary condition to be applied at the surface in axisymmetric flow shows that

$$\partial\phi'/\partial n = -(\partial n/\partial x)(U_\infty + \partial\phi'/\partial x) = -U_\infty(\partial n/\partial x)[1 + O(\bar{r}_w^2 \log \bar{r}_w)], \tag{65}$$

where $\bar{r}_w$ is a length characteristic of the body radius. Thus

$$\int (\partial\phi'/\partial n)\, ds = -U_\infty \int (\partial n/\partial x)\, ds = U_\infty(dS/dx), \tag{66}$$

where $S(x) = \pi r_w^2$ is the area of the cross-section. Also

$$\int (\partial\phi'/\partial n)\, ds = \int_0^{2\pi} r(\partial\phi'/\partial r)\, d\theta = q(x), \tag{67}$$

the error in both these equations being of the order $(\bar{r}_w^2/c^2)$. Thus

$$q(x) = U_\infty S'(x). \tag{68}$$

This result can of course be obtained in other ways for a body of revolution and has already been given in equation (49). We see that the source density $q(x)$ can be a discontinuous function, in which event the integral in (64) must be interpreted in the Stieltjes sense. In particular, if a body is such that $S'(x)$ is continuous, we find from (63), (64), and (68) that on or near the body surface the perturbation potential is

$$\phi' \sim [1 + O(r^2 \log r)]\frac{U_\infty}{4\pi}\left\{ \int_0^c \frac{S'(x) - S'(t)}{|x-t|}\, dt + S'(x)\log\!\left(\frac{r^2}{4x(c-x)}\right) \right\} \tag{69}$$

provided that $0 \leqslant x \leqslant c$.

In some cases, especially if the cross-sectional area of the body is given by a polynomial in x, it is convenient to express the variation of $S'(t)$ in the form of a Taylor series

$$S'(t) = \sum_{n=0}^{\infty} (1/n!)S^{(n+1)}(x)(t-x)^n, \tag{70}$$

and on the assumption that a term-by-term integration is permissible, equation (69) becomes

$$\phi' \sim -(U_\infty/4\pi) \times$$
$$\times \left[\sum_{n=1}^{\infty} (-1)^n S^{(n+1)}(x)[x^n + (c-x)^n]n \cdot n! + S'(x)\log(4x(c-x)/r^2) \right]. \tag{71}$$

The longitudinal perturbation velocity u' is then given by $\partial\phi'/\partial x$, and so

$$u' = \frac{U_\infty}{4\pi}\left\{\frac{2x-c}{x(c-x)}\,S'(x)-\left[\log\!\left(\frac{4c(c-x)}{r^2}\right)-2\right]S''(x)+\right.$$

$$\left.+\sum_{n=2}^{\infty}\frac{(-1)^n}{n!}\,S^{(n+1)}(x)I_{n+1}(x)\right\}, \quad (72)$$

where $I_n = \left(1/(n-2)\right)[x^{n-2}+(c-x)^{n-2}], \quad n > 2.$ (73)

This result was established by Laitone (1947), using an approximate method based on the axial source distribution, and later independently by Neumark (1950). There are, of course, various ways in which the results of slender-body theory may be deduced, but the value of the operational method lies in its ready extension to higher orders of accuracy.

12. The problem of design

The determination of the shape of a body of revolution, in a uniform stream parallel to its axis, having a prescribed velocity distribution on its surface is a problem which, up to now, has eluded exact solution. An approximate approach, due to Young and Owen (1943), is, however, of interest: its original treatment was based on a simplification of the early work of Kaplan, but it can now be recognized as an approximation to slender-body theory in which the longitudinal perturbation velocity on the body is written as

$$u' = -(U_\infty/2\pi)\log(2c/d)S''(x),$$ (74)

where $\tfrac{1}{2}d$ is the maximum radius of the body. The terms preserved are of order $(r^2\log r)$ on the body whereas equation (73), for instance, shows that those neglected are of order r^2. Thus the approximation is a crude one except for a quite unrealistically slender body; nevertheless it provides a very rapid means of finding the distribution of cross-sectional area corresponding to a given type of variation of u', which is at least qualitatively significant.

To this approximation the spheroid is the body of revolution on which the velocity is constant; again, in Fig. IX. 4, we show the exact surface velocity distribution—calculated from a vortex distribution—about the shape of body derived from equation (74) in which u' is assumed to be a linear function of x. The approximate method provides, at least, a guide to the shape required.

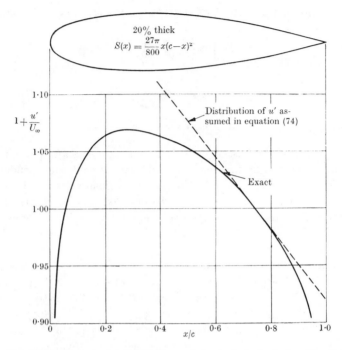

Fig. IX. 4. The velocity distribution and shape of a body designed by the method of Young and Owen (1943) to provide a uniform velocity gradient.

13. The representation of a body in lateral flow by distributions of singularities

The potential flow of a uniform stream past a body whose axis is inclined to the direction of motion can be obtained, of course, by a superposition of the two separate flows due to the resolved components of the stream in the longitudinal and lateral directions. We noticed this, in Section 2, in the solution of the flow past an ellipsoid, and in Section 4, in the expression of Kaplan for the potential of the flow past a body of arbitrary meridian section. Kaplan's method of calculating the transverse flow—namely that due to a stream perpendicular to the body axis—follows the lines of his method for longitudinal flow, and in many other methods there are treatments of the transverse flow which are analogous, in their analytical and computational development, to those of the longitudinal flow.

Whereas axi-symmetric flows can often be determined by axial distributions either of sources or of doublets whose axes lie along the axis of symmetry, transverse flows have to be represented by the super-position along the body's longitudinal axis of doublets whose axes lie in the direction of the relative transverse stream. If we take this direction as parallel to the z-axis the potential of the doublet at the origin whose axis lies in this direction is obtained from equation (35) by elementary means; thus

$$\phi = (Q/4\pi)z(x^2+y^2+z^2)^{-\frac{3}{2}} = (Q/4\pi)r\cos\theta(r^2+x^2)^{-\frac{3}{2}}. \tag{75}$$

A single doublet placed in a uniform stream parallel to the z-axis produces a spherical closed stream surface whereas a uniform distribution of such doublets along the whole of the x-axis produces a flow about an infinite circular cylinder; in any plane $x = $ constant this latter flow corresponds, of course, to that of a two-dimensional doublet. For a semi-infinite distribution of such doublets, of constant strength, along the positive x-axis,

$$\phi = (Q\cos\theta/2\pi r)[1+x(x^2+r^2)^{-\frac{1}{2}}], \tag{76}$$

which is the potential of an infinitesimal horseshoe vortex considered in Section VIII. 5 and illustrated in Fig. VIII. 8. It also exemplifies the general result, given in Section I. 21, that a vortex doublet and a source doublet are equivalent if their axes are perpendicular.

However, since only special types of body can be represented exactly by axial singularities it is better to use source rings. For the lateral flow over bodies of revolution each source ring should have a sinusoidal variation in θ of source density as indicated in equation (75). If the source strength is assumed to be $Q\cos\theta$ per unit length round the circumference of a ring of radius a in the plane $x = 0$, the potential may be calculated as

$$\phi = \frac{4Qr\cos\theta}{\pi^2[x^2+(r+a)^2]^{\frac{3}{2}}}\mathbf{C}(k^2), \tag{77}$$

where $k^2 = 4ar/[x^2+(r+a)^2]$ as before, and $\mathbf{C}(k^2)$ is the complete elliptic integral

$$\mathbf{C}(k^2) = \int_0^{\frac{1}{2}\pi} \frac{\sin^2\theta\cos^2\theta}{(1-k^2\sin^2\theta)^{\frac{3}{2}}}\,d\theta. \tag{78}$$

This is comparable with the expression for the potential of a ring of uniform strength, as given by equation (41).

Kármán's method for longitudinal flows uses a number of line sources; for lateral flows it depends on a superposition of a number of line doublets with lateral axes. From (76), the corresponding velocity potential of the lateral flow is therefore of the form

$$\phi = W_\infty r \cos\theta + \frac{\cos\theta}{2\pi r} \sum_{k=1}^{N} Q_k \left\{ \frac{x-x_k}{[r^2+(x-x_k)^2]^{\frac{1}{2}}} - \frac{x-x_k-l_k}{[r^2+(x-x_k-l_k)^2]^{\frac{1}{2}}} \right\},$$
(79)

where Q_k is the doublet intensity per unit length assigned to the segment $x_k < x < x_k+l_k$, and where the term $W_\infty r \cos\theta$ denotes the free stream potential. The velocity components v_r and u may be found in a similar form by taking the appropriate derivative of ϕ.

The boundary condition to be satisfied at the surface is that the normal component of velocity to the surface vanishes, namely,

$$\text{on } r = r_w: \quad \partial\phi/\partial n = (v_r - u r'_w)[1+(r'_w)^2]^{-\frac{1}{2}} = 0, \quad \text{or } v_r = u r'_w, \quad (80)$$

where r'_w denotes the tangent of the angle of slope of the meridian section relative to the body axis. If this condition is satisfied in one meridian section $\theta = \text{constant}$, it will evidently be satisfied at all such sections, as v_r and u both vary in direct proportion to $\cos\theta$. Thus the boundary condition may be satisfied by equating $(v_r - u r'_w)$ to zero at N points on any meridian line of the body, and this results in a set of N non-homogeneous linear equations for the N unknown values of Q_k. It should be particularly noticed that the simplicity of the boundary condition (80), in that it does not involve θ, depends entirely on the body being of revolution. For more general bodies, the analysis is bound to be much more complicated.

More accurately and in analogy with Lotz's technique for axial flow, we place a distribution of source rings, each with strength varying sinusoidally, along the axis of the body; thus from (77),

$$\phi = W_\infty r \cos\theta + (8r/\pi^2)\cos\theta \int_0^c Q(t)\mathbf{C}(k^2)[(x-t)^2+(r+a)^2]^{-\frac{3}{2}} dt$$
(81)

with $k^2 = 4ar/[(x-t)^2+(r+a)^2]$, and $a = r_w(t)$. The normal derivative of ϕ at the surface needs care in its evaluation owing to the surface singularities, but the boundary conditions (80) can be expressed as an integral equation for $Q(t)$ which is, in all essential features, similar to that in equation (45). The methods developed by Vandrey (1953) for the solution of that equation are therefore directly applicable to the one above, and involve the method of successive approximation previously described. Full computational details are to be found in Vandrey's paper.

14. The lateral flow past a slender body

We have seen that slender-body theory is applicable to the flow due to any type of motion of a slender body, and therefore in particular it will be applicable to the lateral flow past a body of revolution which satisfies the requirements of slenderness. The general expression for the perturbation potential on or near the body is given by equation (63), in which terms of order r^2/c^2 are neglected compared with unity; to an equivalent degree of approximation, the boundary condition to be satisfied at the surface is found from (80) as

$$\partial\phi'/\partial r \simeq -W_\infty \cos\theta. \tag{82}$$

Such a condition is met by supposing that in the expression for the perturbation potential all terms vanish except that involving $\cos\theta$, and so we find that, in accordance with the boundary condition,

$$\phi' \sim (W_\infty S(x)/\pi r)\cos\theta[1+O(r^2\log r)]. \tag{83}$$

This remarkable result expresses the fact that the flow may be approximated by a doublet distribution along the axis whose intensity per unit length varies locally as the cross-sectional area of the body. Equation (49) expresses a similar kind of result in longitudinal flow; in both results, the strength of the doublet distribution depends only on conditions at the point under consideration. But more than this: since in any plane normal to the body's axis, the potential of the lateral flow depends near the body only on the local shape of the surface, and is independent of upstream or downstream conditions, it may be adequately approximated, in any given transverse plane, by an appropriate two-dimensional motion about the infinite cylinder of the same local radius placed in a uniform stream.

The latter interpretation of equation (83) is of extreme practical importance, though unfortunately its validity is often seriously threatened by the effects of viscosity, especially as they affect separation.

This representation of lateral flow seems first to have been used by Munk (1934) in discussing the aerodynamic forces on airship hulls, and he derived it on the basis of physical reasoning. It has already been used in Section VIII. 11 in connexion with the Trefftz plane; and in Chapter X where slender wing-body combinations are discussed, the idea of two-dimensional flow on each transverse plane enables approximate solutions to be obtained where otherwise no solutions at all are possible.

15. The pressure distribution and forces on a body of revolution in a uniform stream

The discussion so far has concerned itself with the calculation of the first inviscid approximation to the real flow. Broadly the methods fall into two categories:

(i) Those of Lotz and Landweber lead to an integral equation which is solved to determine a distribution of sources or doublets. The velocity, and hence the pressure, on the surface is then found by an appropriate integration involving the derived distribution of singularities. This calculation is often simplified by the fact that the integrals are similar to those of the fundamental integral equation, for which a means of numerical quadrature is known.

(ii) Those of Kaplan, Kármán, and of slender-body theory derive the velocity potential, or stream function, which is written as a series of terms whose coefficients may be evaluated. The velocity on the surface is then obtained by differentiating the potential.

The only exception is the vortex distribution method, applicable to axi-symmetric flow, in which the surface velocity distribution is obtained directly as the solution of an integral equation.

It has already been remarked that a comparison of the results of the methods of Sections 4–10 is not very interesting unless the shape of the body is such that only the surface-singularity representations are capable of exact results. What is of more interest is a comparison of the results of the approximate but much more rapidly computed slender-body theory with those of exact methods. Such a comparison is tinged by the degree of slenderness of the body, but a few examples are shown in Fig. IX. 5.

The pressure distribution is derived from Bernoulli's equation which, from equation (I. 50), can be written in the form

$$(p-p_\infty)/\rho = \mathbf{V}.\nabla\phi' - \tfrac{1}{2}(\nabla\phi')^2, \tag{84}$$

where ϕ' is the perturbation velocity potential and $(-\mathbf{V})$ is the velocity vector of the free stream relative to the body. For a slender body in axi-symmetric flow we find from (63) that on or near its surface

$$C_p = (p-p_\infty)/\tfrac{1}{2}\rho U_\infty^2 = -2(u'/U_\infty)-[S'(x)/2\pi r]^2+O(r^4\log r), \tag{85}$$

where u', the perturbation longitudinal velocity, is given for instance by equation (72) to the required accuracy. Thus, in particular, the pressure coefficient on the surface of a slender spheroid is

$$C_p = (t/c)^2[4x^2/(c^2-4x^2)+2-\log(4c^2/t^2)], \tag{86}$$

where t is the maximum thickness, and the longitudinal distance x is, for once, measured from the centre of the body, rather than from the nose.

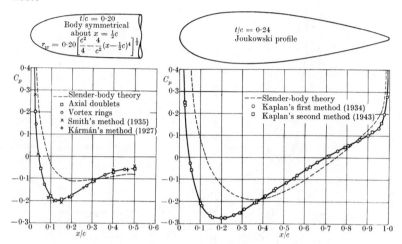

Fig. IX. 5. Some comparisons between various methods of calculating the pressure distribution on a body of revolution in a uniform stream parallel to its axis.

The exact pressure distribution for a spheroid is given from the analysis of Section 2. R. Jones (1926) found that when the stream is inclined at an angle α to the body axis, the pressure coefficient may be put in the form:

$$C_p = 1 - (1+k_2)^2 \sin^2\alpha \sin^2\theta -$$
$$-[(1+k_1)\cos\alpha\cos\beta + (1+k_2)\sin\alpha\sin\beta\cos\theta]^2, \quad (87)$$

in which

$$k_1 = -Q_1^0(\zeta_w)/\{\zeta_w(dQ_1^0(\zeta_w)/d\zeta_w)\}, \qquad k_2 = 1/(1+2k_1)$$
and
$$\zeta_w^2 = 1/(1-(t/c)^2), \qquad\qquad\qquad (88)$$

β being the meridional angle. The values of k_1 and k_2 will later be identified with the longitudinal and lateral coefficients of virtual mass, and their values are given in Table IX. 1. Q_1^0 is the Legendre associated function of the second kind. For axi-symmetric flow, equation (87) simplifies into the relation

$$C_p = 1 - (1+k_1^2)[1 + (t/c)^2 4x^2/(c^2 - 4x^2)]^{-1}. \quad (89)$$

This is compared in Fig. IX. 6 with the corresponding result in equation

(86) of slender-body theory, for three values of the thickness-chord ratio.

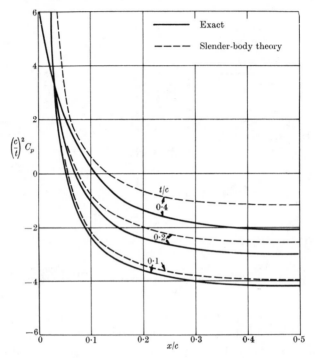

FIG. IX. 6. The pressure distribution on spheroids as given by slender-body theory compared with exact values.

If the flow is inclined at an angle α to the axis of the body, equation (83) gives the perturbation potential due to the lateral flow; thus by Bernoulli's equation (84),

$$\Delta C_p = (1-4\sin^2\theta)\sin^2\alpha - 2r'_w(x)\cos\theta\sin 2\alpha + O(\bar{r}_w^2\log\bar{r}_w), \quad (90)$$

ΔC_p being the increment in pressure coefficient due to incidence. For a spheroid at an incidence of $20°$, the chordwise distribution of ΔC_p is illustrated in Fig. IX. 7; this shows that, contrary to what might on first thoughts be expected, there is a decrease in pressure on the sides of the body. This is evident also from the typical circumferential distribution of ΔC_p shown in Fig. IX. 8.

The dominant term on the right-hand side of equation (90) is the first one, which is of unit order, and it simply describes a pressure variation proportional to that on an infinite circular cylinder. Being

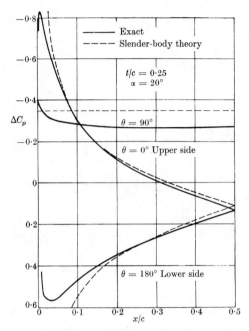

FIG. IX. 7. The chordwise distribution of the increment of pressure coefficient on a spheroid due to incidence.

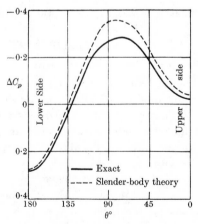

FIG. IX. 8. Circumferential distribution of ΔC_p on a spheroid at $x/c = 0.285$.

symmetrical it does not, however, contribute to any lateral force on
the body. Such a force arises from the second term; it has a magnitude
dF/dx per unit length given by

$$dF/dx = -\int_0^{2\pi} p\cos\theta\, r_w\, d\theta = \tfrac{1}{2}\rho V_\infty^2 \sin 2\alpha S'(x)[1+O(\bar{r}_w^2 \log \bar{r}_w)].$$
(91)

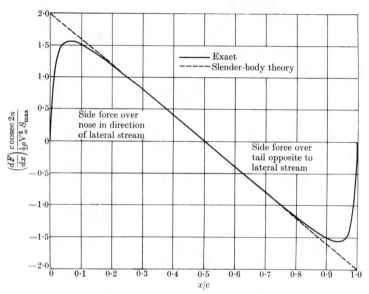

FIG. IX. 9. The distribution of side force on a spheroid.

For a spheroid the exact result appears from equation (87) that

$$dF/dx = \tfrac{1}{2}\rho V_\infty^2 \sin 2\alpha\, S'(x)[\tfrac{1}{2}(1+k_1)(1+k_2)]\cos^2\beta.$$
(92)

A comparison of the slender-body approximation with this is shown in
Fig. IX. 9. The result of slender-body theory given by equation (91)
suggests, inevitably, that the lateral force depends only on local conditions, namely on the variation of cross-sectional area; that this is incomplete is seen in the case of spheroids from equation (92) which
includes not only the local term $\cos^2\beta$, but also the term $\tfrac{1}{2}(1+k_1)(1+k_2)$
which represents an effect of overall geometry.

Now it can be seen from Table IX. 1 that for spheroids this latter
term is always near unity, varying monotonically from 1·125 for a sphere
to 1·0 for a slender body. Upson and Klikoff (1931) were led by this to
suggest that the lateral force on any body could be expressed merely as a

function of local conditions; thus as an approximation to equation (92),

$$dF/dx = \tfrac{1}{2}\rho V_\infty^2 \sin 2\alpha\, S'(x)\cos^2\beta \tag{93}$$

for a body of revolution of arbitrary shape and thickness-chord ratio. To judge by experimental evidence, this is a modification to slender-body theory in the right direction. The total side force, namely $\int_0^c (dF/dx)\,dx$, is zero according to all these calculations of potential flow.

16. Lift, drag, and moments

The absence of a lift force in the preceding calculations may seem surprising until it is recalled that the essential characteristic of finite-wing theory—the existence of vorticity—has, in Section 15, been quite ignored. There is in fact no generally accepted hypothesis for the first inviscid approximation, corresponding to that of Kutta and Joukowski, by which the action of viscosity in producing lift on a body of revolution may be explained. We shall see nevertheless in later sections that there are other methods by which it is possible to predict, with reasonable accuracy in some cases, those forces on a body which are due to the predominant action of viscosity.

But if there is no force on a body in the first inviscid approximation, there is certainly a couple. This is clear from the results of the previous section and particularly so from Fig. IX. 9. It is sometimes useful to be able to calculate this couple by considering the change of momentum of the fluid at infinity rather than by calculating the pressure distribution on the body. What now follows is a condensed account of the application of the concept of virtual mass to the calculation of the moment coefficient of a body of revolution in a uniform stream. For a more general treatment, we may refer to Lamb (1932).

We suppose that the body is moving with a constant velocity $\mathbf{V}$ in fluid otherwise at rest, and that the total momentum of the fluid is $\mathbf{M}$. Since there is no total force on the body, $\mathbf{M}$ is constant and represents the total impulse applied to the fluid by the body since the start of the motion. The couple, $\mathbf{G}$, acting on the body may be shown to be

$$\mathbf{G} = \mathbf{V} \times \mathbf{M}. \tag{94}$$

The evaluation of the momentum of the perturbed flow presents some difficulties, and our final result may be indicated by considering the kinetic energy of the perturbed field, which can be shown to be

$$T = \tfrac{1}{2}\mathbf{M}.\mathbf{V}. \tag{95}$$

Suppose $\mathbf{V}$ has components $(-U_\infty, -V_\infty, -W_\infty)$, the x-axis being the longitudinal axis of the body. T is then a homogeneous quadratic function of the velocity components, and appeal to the symmetry of the flow suggests the form

$$T = \tfrac{1}{2}m_1 U_\infty^2 + \tfrac{1}{2}m_2(V_\infty^2 + W_\infty^2). \tag{96}$$

The coefficients m_1 and m_2 depend only on the body shape and are called its longitudinal and lateral virtual mass. Thus equation (95) suggests the components of $\mathbf{M}$ as $(-m_1 U_\infty, -m_2 V_\infty, -m_2 W_\infty)$ and equation (94) then gives the couple on the body in the form

$$|\mathbf{G}| = (m_2 - m_1)\mathrm{V}_\infty^2 \sin\alpha\cos\alpha. \tag{97}$$

The direction of this moment is perpendicular to the axis of the body and the stream velocity, and is positive in the sense of the incidence increasing. The virtual masses m_1 and m_2 are usually expressed as non-dimensional coefficients, k_1 and k_2, given by

$$k_1 = m_1/\rho V, \qquad k_2 = m_2/\rho V, \tag{98}$$

where ρ is the fluid density and V the body volume. The pitching moment coefficient, about the centre of the body, is

$$C_m = \text{the couple} \div \tfrac{1}{2}\rho\mathrm{V}_\infty^2 \, V = (k_2 - k_1)\sin 2\alpha. \tag{99}$$

As we shall see, on elongated bodies the lateral virtual mass coefficient, k_2, exceeds k_1 so that the moment is generally destabilizing.

To find k_1 and k_2, we calculate the kinetic energy of the perturbed flow from a knowledge of ϕ' and compare the result with equation (96). Thus, using Gauss's theorem and $\nabla^2\phi' = 0$, we have

$$T = \tfrac{1}{2}\rho \int_{V_f} (\nabla\phi')^2 \, dV_f = \tfrac{1}{2}\rho \int_{V_f} \nabla.(\phi'\nabla\phi') \, dV_f$$

$$= \tfrac{1}{2}\rho \int_R \phi'\nabla\phi'.d\mathbf{R} - \tfrac{1}{2}\rho \int_S \phi'\nabla\phi'.d\mathbf{S}, \tag{100}$$

where V_f denotes the fluid volume, bounded on the inside by the body surface S, and on the outside by a spherical surface R. Now at large distances from the body, the sources and sinks by which it can be accurately represented have a similar effect to that of a doublet since their total strength, for a closed body, is zero. Thus $(\phi'\nabla\phi')$ decreases inversely as the fifth power of the distance from the body, and the integral over R vanishes as the radius of the sphere tends to infinity. Thus

$$T = -\tfrac{1}{2}\rho \int_S \phi'(\partial\phi'/\partial n) \, dS = -\tfrac{1}{2}\rho\mathbf{V}. \int_S \phi' \, d\mathbf{S}. \tag{101}$$

For the particular case of a spheroid, the expressions for the perturbation in equations (3) and (4) could be used to calculate the integral equation (101) and the values of k_1 and k_2 so found are given in Table IX. 1 as functions of the thickness-chord ratio.

For a slender body, equations (63) and (83) give $k_2 = 1 + O(\bar{r}_w^2 \log \bar{r}_w)$ and $k_1 = 0$; thus

$$C_m \simeq \sin 2\alpha. \qquad (102)$$

This is a result which can, of course, be obtained directly from equation (91), and which is in accordance with the particular results for a spheroid of infinitesimal thickness-chord ratio, as shown by Table IX. 1.

TABLE IX. 1

Coefficients of virtual mass for spheroids

t/c	Coefficient of longitudinal virtual mass, k_1	Coefficient of lateral virtual mass, k_2	$(k_2 - k_1)$	$\frac{1}{2}(1+k_1)(1+k_2)$
0·0	0·0000	1·0000	1·0000	1·0000
0·1	0·0207	0·9602	0·9395	1·0004
0·2	0·0591	0·8943	0·8352	1·0031
0·3	0·1054	0·8259	0·7204	1·0092
0·4	0·1563	0·7619	0·6056	1·0186
0·5	0·2100	0·7042	0·4942	1·0311
0·6	0·2657	0·6530	0·3872	1·0461
0·7	0·3230	0·6076	0·2846	1·0634
0·8	0·3812	0·5674	0·1862	1·0825
0·9	0·4402	0·5318	0·0915	1·1031
1·0	0·5000	0·5000	0·0000	1·1250

17. Comparisons between the first inviscid approximation and experiment

We should expect that for axi-symmetric flow—that is, for flow past a body of revolution at zero incidence—the first inviscid approximation would fail seriously only near the trailing edge. At high Reynolds numbers, the boundary layer is bound to separate from a bluff-ended body though for a cone- or cusp-shaped trailing edge, separation might be avoided. Fig. IX. 10 shows calculated values of the pressure coefficient over a spheroid in axi-symmetric flow, compared with values measured by R. Jones (1926). The rise in pressure sustained by the boundary layer before separation is nearly $0·4(\frac{1}{2}\rho V_\infty^2)$ and is considerably greater than could be sustained by a two-dimensional boundary layer.

The effect of the boundary layer is more marked in the flow over bodies of revolution at incidence. Fig. IX. 11 shows the calculated distribution of side force for a model of the airship 'Akron' compared

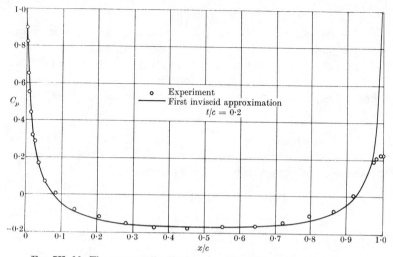

FIG. IX. 10. The pressure distribution on a spheroid in axi-symmetric flow:
a comparison between theory and experiment.

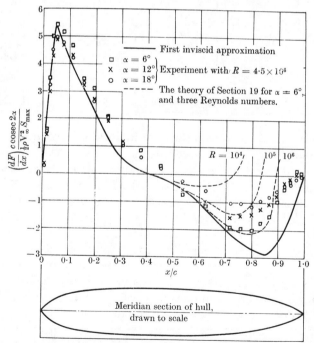

FIG. IX. 11. The distribution of side force on the airship 'Akron':
comparison between theory and experiment.

with the experimental measurements of Freeman (1932). The theory suggests a slightly smaller positive side force over the nose than actually exists, but greatly overestimates the negative side force on the tail. As a result there is, in a real flow, a resultant side force or lift which grows rapidly with increase of incidence. The comparison of the circumferential pressure distributions shown in Fig. IX. 12 at various stations

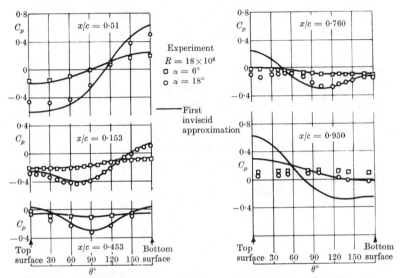

Fig. IX. 12. Circumferential distributions of pressure on the airship 'Akron': comparison between theory and experiment.

along the body shows that the side force is caused mainly by the absence of the theoretically high pressures over the top surface of the body at the tail; this, of course, suggests separation of the boundary layer over this part of the body, analogously to the case of a wing at a large incidence.

We shall have more to say about these effects of the boundary layer in the following sections. However, for the most part, the study of these effects has been aimed at providing a means of estimating the overall forces on the body, rather than their more particular effects upon the distribution of surface pressure. For the latter, we must largely rely on the potential flow.

18. Drag. The first approximation

Just as for aerofoils and wings at zero lift, so for bodies of revolution in axi-symmetric flow, the drag is composed of skin-friction drag and form drag. For a thin body with a pointed or cusped trailing edge, the skin-friction drag predominates and, for laminar flow, may be calculated by the method of Section II. 18 from a knowledge of the first inviscid approximation. For bodies with bluff ends or of projectile shape with flat bases, the form drag is a significant proportion of the total drag and should not be neglected; the calculation of the form drag in such

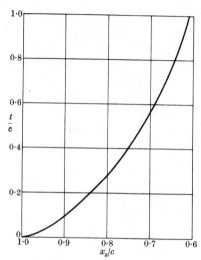

Fig. IX. 13. A theoretical assessment of the position of laminar separation on spheroids in axi-symmetric flow.

cases depends on a knowledge of the pressure at the rear but, as was pointed out in Section III. 9, we do not yet know how to predict that pressure.

Equations (II. 83) and (II. 84) refer to a boundary layer on an axi-symmetric body. The first represents the result of the transformation of Mangler (1946) and the latter equation gives the value of δ_2 for a laminar boundary layer in terms of $U(x)$, the velocity on the surface according to the first inviscid approximation. According to the criterion given in Table II. 1, separation of a laminar layer occurs near the cross-section at which $(\delta_2^2/\nu)(dU/dx) = -0\cdot090$ and Fig. IX. 13 shows the calculated position, given by $x = x_s$, of the separation line for spheroids as a function of the thickness-chord ratio. The accuracy of this prediction steadily worsens as (t/c) increases since the first inviscid approximation becomes increasingly inaccurate as the separated region increases. No adequate analysis based on equation (II. 83) has yet been proposed for turbulent boundary layers, which are therefore usually calculated from $U(x)$ by the formulae of Sections II. 5–15.

The prediction of form drag involves detailed calculations of the boundary layer and the pressure distribution within it, and neither this nor the second inviscid approximation has yet been successfully treated owing to the difficulty of the problem. But for many practical purposes, a knowledge of the total drag is sufficient, and possibly the best procedure is analogous to that given in Section V. 3.

The momentum equation for an axi-symmetric wake may be written from equation (II. 83) as

$$(U/\sigma_2)(d\sigma_2/dx) + (H+2)(dU/dx) = 0, \qquad (103)$$

in which σ_2, the momentum area of the wake, appears in place of $2r_w\delta_2$. Young (1939) assumed that $(H-1)$ varies linearly with $\log(U/U_\infty)$ where U is the velocity just outside the wake. This enables the equation to be integrated to give

$$\sigma_{2\infty}/\sigma_{2T} = (U_T/U_\infty)^{3\cdot2}, \qquad (104)$$

where subscript T denotes the tail of the body. The value of σ_{2T}, the momentum area of the boundary layer at the tail, may be given the value of $2r_w\delta_2$ at the tail as calculated by the methods just described. The total drag is given by $D = \sigma_{2\infty}\rho U_\infty^2$, so that

$$C_D = 2(U_T/U_\infty)^{3\cdot2}(\sigma_{2T}/A), \qquad (105)$$

where A is the representative area of the body.

19. Bodies at low incidence. Lift

The calculation of the boundary layer on a body of revolution at incidence presents a difficult and involved theoretical problem. It is no longer generally possible, owing to the non-linearity of the boundary-layer equations, to express the effects of the lateral flow by superposition, as in the first inviscid approximation.

Attempts at superposition have, however, been made when the incidence is assumed to be very small, although the results thus obtained are, naturally, of limited significance. Nonweiler (1955) in particular has considered this approach for laminar flow. The assumptions of slenderness and low incidence are a great simplification but to a certain extent conflict, as it appears that the magnitude of the velocity perturbations within the boundary layer due to incidence depends on the ratio $\alpha(t/c)^{-1}$ which must be small for the theory to apply. The increments of velocity are found to vary sinusoidally round the body, but

their longitudinal variation, however, is much more difficult to describe
and depends to some extent at least on the actual shape of the meridian
section.

The results are best illustrated by a study of the flow pattern in
planes perpendicular to the body axis, shown diagrammatically in Fig.
IX. 14. Over the front of the body, (a), the boundary-layer motion

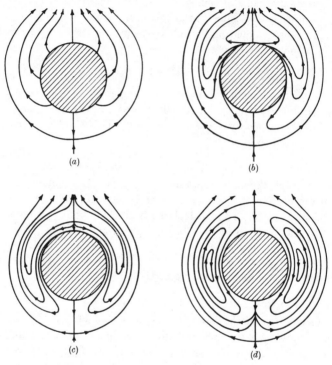

FIG. IX. 14. Sketches showing Nonweiler's theoretical predictions for the
downstream development of the streamlines in the cross-flow past a body of
revolution at small incidence.

consists of a radial outflow—due to the axi-symmetric displacement
effect—together with a retardation of the circumferential flow. Farther
downstream, this retardation becomes more marked, ultimately causing
the circumferential velocity component to reverse near the surface.
This, at first, produces the streamline pattern shown in (b), but as the
extent of the reversal increases, the radial velocity also becomes significantly modified, due to the increased defect in the flux of the circumferential flow. The modification takes the form of an induced outflow

due to incidence, in the outer strata of the boundary layer over the bottom surface; here the defect of the flux of the circumferential flow increases in the direction of the stream but a corresponding inflow occurs over the top surface of the body. Ultimately this induced inflow is sufficient to reverse the radial velocity over the top surface, and the resulting streamline pattern shows that two vortex lobes are then formed in the boundary layer on either side of the body as shown in (c) and (d).

The reversal of the circumferential flow over the rear part of a body is an important effect which can be accounted for by the suction on the bottom surface and the positive pressure over the top surface, as shown in Fig. IX. 8. The boundary-layer flow near the surface would tend to move from the high- to the low-pressure region, which is therefore in a direction opposed to the external flow. This argument may only be used with confidence for low incidences at which the separation line is still roughly in a plane perpendicular to the axis of the body: but the formation of the vortices within the boundary layer, as shown in Fig. IX. 14, may be expected to have a counterpart at higher incidences.

Fig. IX. 15. An interpretation of Fig. IX. 14 showing a similarity with the theory of slender wings.

These properties of the boundary-layer flow immediately suggest an explanation of the overall lift which we have noted from Fig. IX. 11, and which was explained then as due to the separation of the boundary layer. The pair of vortices formed over the rear of the body would induce a downwash, tending to reduce the component of the stream velocity normal to the axis of the body and so to alleviate the negative side force which exists in that region in potential flow. The analogy to a wing is clear and Fig. IX. 15 indicates the similarity between the present discussion and that in Section VIII. 12 for slender wings; for both types of flow, it appears that the centre of pressure moves steadily forward as the slenderness increases.

Nonweiler has developed his theory for low incidence to calculate the distribution of side force and his results for the 'Akron' body were incorporated in Fig. IX. 11. It will be noted that the side force appears to decrease with increase of Reynolds number; as the speed increases,

the retarded fluid is convected farther towards the tail and the characteristic flow of Fig. IX. 14 (*d*) establishes itself also nearer the tail.

In this first-order theory the interaction between viscous side-flow
and the external inviscid flow has had, naturally, to be neglected with
the result that the modification to the potential flow is overestimated;
for this reason the theory may be useful in indicating an upper limit to
the side force. To obtain a semi-empirical form for this force we may

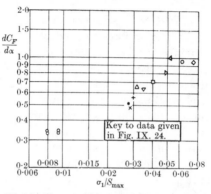

FIG. IX. 16. The rate of increase with incidence of the
side-force coefficient: experimental data, with laminar
boundary layers, to support equation (106).

argue that it is proportional to σ_1, the displacement area of the boundary
layer at the trailing edge and to the effective local incidence of the wake
there, which in turn is proportional to the body incidence α. The local
incidence appears to be also dependent on the parameter $(\sigma_1/S_{\max})$,
where $S_{\max}$ is the frontal area of the body—at least for bodies with
similar meridian sections. This suggests

$$dC_F/d\alpha = f(\sigma_1/S_{\max}),\qquad(106)$$

C_F being the side-force coefficient defined by $F = \frac{1}{2}\rho V_\infty^2 S_{\max} C_F$. Fig. IX.
16 shows a variety of experimental results which support this functional
relation tolerably well. It is suggested that equation (106) is reasonably
accurate for incidences less than 5° for bodies whose thickness-chord
ratio is less than, say, 20 per cent.

The functional relationship in equation (106) seems to hold quite
well when the boundary layer is turbulent; this is indicated by Fig. IX.
17 from which has been obtained the empirical relation

$$dC_F/d\alpha = 1 \cdot 75(A/S_{\max})R^{-1/5},\qquad(107)$$

where A is the side area of the body, and $R = V_\infty c/\nu$.

All these numerical relations are admittedly highly empirical and what is most firmly established is that, for a body of given side area, the lift decreases either as the thickness-chord ratio is decreased, or as the Reynolds number is increased. Further, all the data quoted so far refer to airship hulls. Other types of shape might well yield different results. Some tests by Lange (1941), on a family of bodies with bluff

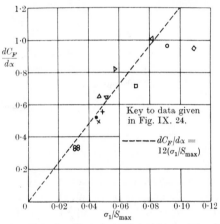

Fig. IX. 17. The rate of increase with incidence of the side-force coefficient: for turbulent layers.

spherical noses, displayed similar trends, but showed the side force to be about twice that given above.

20. Bodies at moderate incidence

We have noted that at low incidences a reversal of the cross-flow occurs where the circumferential pressure gradient reverses. This result follows from a study in which the effects of incidence are small perturbations, linear with the incidence α, to which approximation the pressure coefficient about slender bodies may be quoted from equation (90) as

$$C_p = 4\alpha r'_w(x)\cos\theta[1+O(\alpha c/t)]. \tag{108}$$

Thus the pressure gradients are reversed behind the plane of maximum diameter where $r'_w < 0$. A better approximation is obtained for slender bodies by the inclusion of the second-order term in α^2. The pressure gradient then reverses not at the plane of maximum diameter but along a line which tends towards the meridians $\theta = \pm\frac{1}{2}\pi$ as the incidence is increased. This is shown in Fig. IX. 18 for the 'Akron' hull: that the line of minimum pressure moves so rapidly towards these meridians, which are its limit as the incidence tends to $90°$, is analogous to the rapid movement towards the leading edge of the point of minimum pressure on a thin aerofoil as its incidence increases.

Allen and Perkins (1951) have conjectured that the circumferential flow will reverse along a line which would be roughly parallel to the position of minimum pressure on the hull. The results quoted in Section 19, relevant only to low incidence, are compatible with this; as the incidence increases, more and more of the flow over the top surface reverses.

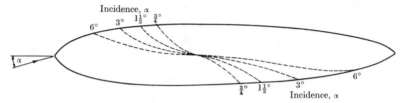

Fig. IX. 18. Some calculated loci of the positions of circumferential minimum pressure on the airship 'Akron'.

They have also remarked upon a certain analogy between the cross-flow at various stations along the body and the development with time of the flow about a circular cylinder starting from rest. Let us consider conditions in a plane of fluid which is perpendicular to the body axis and is moving with the free-stream velocity component $V_\infty \cos \alpha$. The trace of the body will be a circle, whose size will expand and contract as the plane moves along the body; this rate of change of cross-sectional area may plausibly be ignored for a slender body. The cross-flow is only aware of the circle suddenly appearing in it, and so is similar to that which would be observed for a circular cylinder suddenly introduced into a stream of velocity $V_\infty \sin \alpha$. Thus, in the flow over a body of revolution, we should be led to expect the circumferential flow to be roughly of inviscid character near the front of the body, and to exhibit farther downstream a pair of vortices. In certain conditions and principally if the Reynolds number is sufficiently high, these vortices might each in turn discharge from the body, being carried away downstream on its lee side; a new pair would form and break away, and in this way a vortex street might be formed. Relative to the body these shed vortices would appear fixed, but relative to a transverse plane moving with the fluid, the cylinder would appear to leave them behind in its lee-side wake. The length of body over which the vortex pair could remain attached would presumably become shorter as the incidence grew, because the trace of the body in the transverse plane would then move farther. On the other hand, if the Reynolds number of the cross-flow were small enough, the standing vortices might well remain stable. These ideas are illustrated in Fig. IX. 19.

The shedding of the vortices from the body surface seems inevitably to imply a separation of the boundary layer. Whilst this is no doubt true, the meaning of separation, and the indications of its presence, are

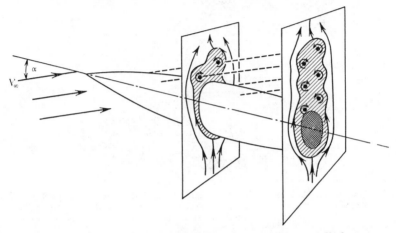

Fig. IX. 19. A sketch illustrating the cross-flow in planes perpendicular to the axis of a body of revolution at incidence.

not as clear-cut in three-dimensional as in two-dimensional flow. Here we forsake any attempt at theoretical analysis in favour of a physical explanation of what probably occurs in the boundary layer and separated region at moderate incidences. Thus we go on to extend to higher incidences the work which suggested Fig. IX. 14 and to develop the ideas of the previous section.

A valuable clue to the nature of the flow is given by the configuration of the surface streamlines, namely the limit of the streamlines as the surface is approached. These are tangential to the local direction of shear stress on the body, and can be revealed by well-known techniques of flow visualization. For incidences so low that $(\alpha c/t)$ is small, Nonweiler (1955) applied his theory to obtain stream patterns as shown in Fig. IX. 20 (a). First the circumferential component of flow reverses over the rear of the body, where a vortex pair is formed in the cross-flow; ultimately the longitudinal component also tends to reverse, on the windward side of the body in the plane of symmetry. If indeed it did so, then a nodal point of the surface streamlines would occur on the underside, where the local shear stress would vanish. This suggests that, near this point, separation would occur of a type in which the

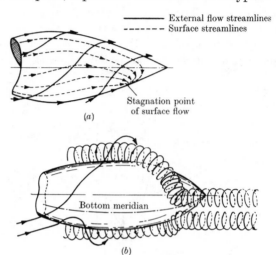

(a)

(b)

Fig. IX. 20. Sketches showing Nonweiler's theoretical predictions of the flow past a body of revolution at low incidence. (a) Side view of body showing surface flow. (b) Three-quarter view from below suggesting actual vortex formation.

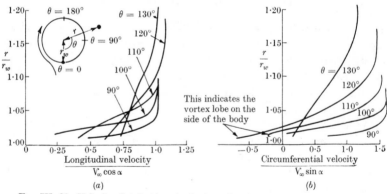

(a)   (b)

Fig. IX. 21. Velocity distributions in the boundary layer on the side of a body of revolution at moderate incidence.

vortices are shed into the wake. Fig. IX. 20 (b) illustrates this but, so far, these ideas have not been directly confirmed by experiment.

At higher incidences, of the order of t/c, experimental evidence suggests that a reversal of the longitudinal flow occurs over the sides

of the body. Fig. IX. 21 (a) gives some typical distributions of longitudinal velocity through the boundary layer, the experimental technique being unable to penetrate sufficiently close to the surface to show
positive evidence of reversal of flow. The position of the line of minimum

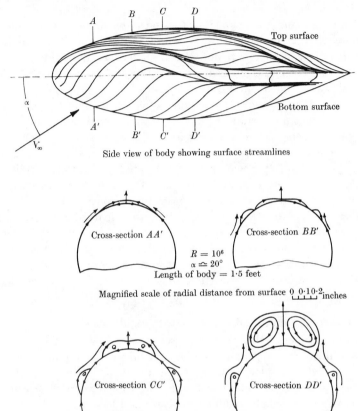

Side view of body showing surface streamlines

$R = 10^6$
$\alpha \simeq 20°$
Length of body = 1·5 feet

Magnified scale of radial distance from surface 0 0·1 0·2 inches

Development of the cross-flow

FIG. IX. 22. A schematic interpretation of experimental data. The surface
streamlines and cross-flow on a body of revolution at moderate incidence.

pressure is illustrated in Fig. IX. 18 and the circumferential flow is
generally reversed on the lee side of this line, tending to move downward, away from the upper meridian and towards this line. Experiments have, on the whole, confirmed that the line of minimum pressure
marks the edge of the vortex lobes in the circumferential flow as
indicated in Fig. IX. 21 (b); and studies of the surface flow by the

lampblack technique suggest a region of de-energized air close to, and just to the leeward side of this line. The presumed state of the flow near the surface is illustrated in Fig. IX. 22.

There are usually two distinct pairs of vortex lobes in the cross-flow; one just to the leeward side of the stagnant region (and the minimum pressure line), and another pair—often separated from it by a region of unreversed circumferential flow—whose core lies close to the upper meridian. It is of interest to note that a similar formation of two pairs of vortices is sometimes observable in the two-dimensional flow, at low Reynolds numbers, about a circular cylinder.

These regions of retarded flow have often been termed separation fronts; but it is not certain that, at any rate for moderate incidences, any fluid is being convected right away from the surface. Velocity traverses indicate that the vortex lobes remain attached to the surface at least to within 20 per cent of the body length from the tail. Certainly at higher incidences, they do in fact shed from the surface to form a vortex street above the body in the manner shown in Fig. IX. 19. Studies of the surface flow then reveal, by their marked asymmetrical patterns, the oscillatory character of the flow in this condition. It is as difficult to suggest the incidence at which this change in the character of the cross-flow occurs as to determine the onset of the comparable régime for highly-swept leading edges of wings, namely the separated vortex-flow of Fig. III. 4 (b).

21. The forces on a body at moderate incidence

We have noted earlier that the viscous cross-flow about a slender body can be likened to the starting flow about an infinite circular cylinder of the same local radius, provided that the parameter $(\alpha c/t)$ is sufficiently large. It follows that the drag associated with the flow about a circular cylinder will be manifested as a local side-force on the body and that the circumferential pressure will be roughly constant over the lee-side surface once the flow has developed, that is towards the tail. This is verified by the experimental evidence of Fig. IX. 11. If C_d is the drag coefficient of the circular cylinder, based on its diameter, then the local side force will be simply $(C_d \frac{1}{2}\rho V_\infty^2 2r_w \sin^2\alpha)$ per unit length. Integration of this expression over the length of the body gives

$$F = C_d \tfrac{1}{2}\rho V_\infty^2 A \sin^2\alpha, \tag{109}$$

where $A = \int_0^c 2r_w \, dx$ is the side area of the body.

Equation (109) indicates that, for a correlation of experimental values of F for different bodies, the expression $F/\frac{1}{2}\rho V_\infty^2 A \sin^2\alpha$ should be regarded as an important parameter and may be expected to be constant for any one body, at any rate for moderately large values of α. On the other hand, for low values of α, we see from equation (106) that the expression should vary with $1/\sin\alpha$. We are thus led to write

$$F/\tfrac{1}{2}\rho V_\infty^2 A \sin^2\alpha = a_0 \cot\alpha + \bar{C}_D, \tag{110}$$

a_0 being the lift-curve slope for a very low incidence and $\bar{C}_D$ being the cross-flow drag coefficient which becomes significant at higher incidences.

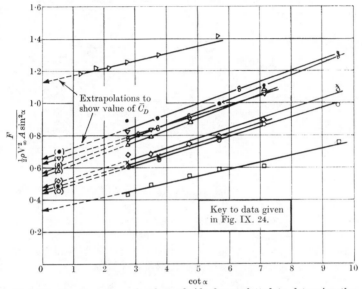

FIG. IX. 23. Experimental values of side force, plotted to determine the constants, a_0 and $\bar{C}_D$, in the relation $F/\frac{1}{2}\rho V_\infty^2 A \sin^2\alpha = a_0 \cot\alpha + \bar{C}_D$, of equation (110).

Fig. IX. 23 shows, for a number of experiments, that equation (110) is a remarkably accurate interpretation. Extrapolation of the straight lines to $\cot\alpha = 0$ indicates the value of $\bar{C}_D$ appropriate to each case. The value of a_0 shows little variation.

The value of $\bar{C}_D$ is seen to vary widely, and for purposes of prediction some criterion is necessary for its determination. If we retain for the moment the idea of the correspondence of $\bar{C}_D$ to the two-dimensional drag coefficient of a circular cylinder, then the value of $\bar{C}_D$ clearly varies with the Reynolds number of the cross-flow and the state of the boundary layer. It is very difficult to understand how this scale effect has any analogy with the flow over the body of revolution, but in view of the present vogue for the analogy we give some relevant results in Fig. IX. 24. Allen and Perkins (1951) have suggested that an allowance ought to be included for the end effects on the body by comparing the measured value of $\bar{C}_D$ with that for a finite circular cylinder of corresponding aspect ratio. Again, it could be argued, by the analogy of the development of the cross-flow along the body with that about a circular cylinder started impulsively from rest, that $\bar{C}_D$ would be less

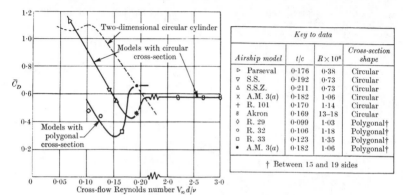

Key to data			
Airship model	t/c	$R \times 10^6$	Cross-section shape
▷ Parseval	0·176	0·38	Circular
▽ S.S.	0·192	0·73	Circular
△ S.S.Z.	0·211	0·73	Circular
× A.M. 3(a)	0·182	1·06	Circular
+ R. 101	0·170	1·14	Circular
ଃ Akron	0·169	13–18	Circular
◇ R. 29	0·099	1·03	Polygonal†
○ R. 32	0·106	1·18	Polygonal†
□ R. 33	0·123	1·35	Polygonal†
• A.M. 3(a)	0·182	1·06	Polygonal†
† Between 15 and 19 sides			

FIG. IX. 24. The dependence of the drag coefficient, $\bar{C}_D$, on the Reynolds number in the cross-flow.

than the final steady value for two-dimensional turbulent flow. But all this merely emphasizes the complexity of the problem we are attempting to rationalize and it could hardly be anticipated that a simplified theory could give any more than qualitative agreement. We therefore conclude this discussion by recalling equation (110); a good value for a_0 seems to be about 0·07 while $\bar{C}_D$ is most usually in the range $0\cdot4 < \bar{C}_D < 0\cdot7$.

Allen and Perkins (1951), and also Kelly (1954), have attempted to apply these various concepts to the prediction of the side force on projectiles with flat bases, and have thereby discovered that slender-body theory provides an adequate means of estimating the side force at low incidences. The result is, from equation (91), that the side force is given approximately by

$$F \simeq \rho V_\infty^2\, S(c)\alpha, \tag{111}$$

where $S(c)$ is the area of the base at $x = c$. This seems to be fortuitous, as of course the form of potential theory applicable to the case of separation at the base section differs radically from that leading up to equation (91). It appears, therefore, that such a separation precludes the existence of any violent change at the base in the velocity or direction of the flow, which would render slender-body theory inapplicable; consequently, the separation does not strongly influence the cross-flow upstream.

We saw earlier that the first inviscid approximation accounts for a destabilizing couple which, as a pitching moment about the centre of the body, is given in equation (99); for a slender body this reduces to equation (102), namely $C_m \doteq \sin 2\alpha$. In fact, in most applications there

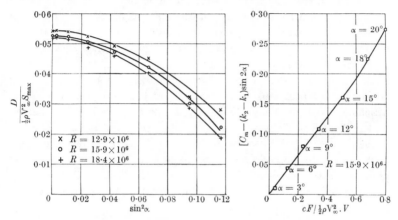

Fig. IX. 25. The drag and pitching moment about the tail of a model of the airship 'Akron', $(k_2 - k_1)$ being estimated as 0·817.

seems little point in refining these approximations for inviscid flow, as the pitching moment is considerably modified by the effects of viscosity. In the first place, the shear stresses on the body contribute to a destabilizing moment, owing to the reversal of the cross-flow. Secondly, the modification to the normal pressure distribution, which results in the side force, produces appreciable effects; the centre of pressure of the side force seems to move forward as the incidence increases, and as the cross-flow pattern becomes similar over the entire body length. However, the phenomena appear to depend on too many factors to allow any quantitative deductions to be made from the experimental measurements.

This is equally true of the prediction of the longitudinal force, and drag. At low incidences, it may be assumed that the drag varies only negligibly with incidence. At moderate incidences, there is a thrust force over the front part of the body, according to the first inviscid approximation; according to slender-body theory, the thrust force on the part of the body ahead of the section of maximum area can be calculated from equation (90) as $\frac{1}{2}\rho S_{max}V_\infty^2 \sin^2\alpha$. The effect of viscosity is to prevent this full force being exerted as a drag over the rear part of the body, and decrease of drag with incidence is invariably observed.

Typical results are shown in Fig. IX. 25 for both drag and pitching moment for the airship 'Akron'.

22. Flow past rotating bodies of revolution

A predominant characteristic of an important class of bodies of revolution—namely, projectiles—is their rotation. Shells, fired from rifled barrels, rotate about their longitudinal axis as this evidently improves the stability of their flight; rocket-propelled missiles are also often arranged to rotate for the same reason. Of the great amount of work which has been done on the problems of such rotating bodies, by far the largest part consists of the study of that branch of mechanics which deals with the unsteady motion of rigid bodies acting under given forces. Accounts of this may be found elsewhere, and the aerodynamic problems associated with the unsteady motion are outside the scope of this book. In this short section we inquire about the effect of another kind of rotation, namely, the curvature of the flight path; and by a rotating body we now mean one which rotates about some axis perpendicular to its own longitudinal axis.

We may note first that all the methods available for the analysis of the potential flow about bodies at incidence are easily applied to this problem of the flow about rotating bodies. The change of the boundary condition on the rotating body affects the details but not the principles of the methods. For example, if the body is rotating with angular velocity Ω about an axis $\theta = \theta_0$ in the plane $x = x_0$, it is simple to calculate that the perturbation potential on or near the body surface is given by slender-body theory by

$$\phi' = [(x-x_0)\Omega S(x)/\pi r]\sin(\theta-\theta_0)[1+O(r^2\log r)], \qquad (112)$$

referred to a system of coordinates fixed in the body. This solution may be superposed on that due to the longitudinal and lateral translational velocities, to give the general expression for the perturbation potential, relevant to an arbitrary motion of a body of revolution.

With a frame of axes moving with the body—the motion being specified by a translational velocity $\mathbf{V}$, relative to the undisturbed fluid, and by an angular velocity $\mathbf{\Omega}$ about the origin, referred in both instances to the instantaneous positions of the axes—the relevant form of Bernouilli's equation is

$$(p-p_\infty)/\rho = (\mathbf{V}+\mathbf{\Omega}\times\mathbf{r}).\nabla\phi'-\tfrac{1}{2}(\nabla\phi')^2\partial\phi'/\partial t, \qquad (113)$$

where **r** is the position vector of any point referred to the moving axes. Of the various kinds of quasi-steady flow, for which $\partial\phi'/\partial t = 0$, we pick out that due to the motion of the body in a circular path, so that $\mathbf{V}.\mathbf{\Omega} = 0$. Using slender-body theory we may then calculate from

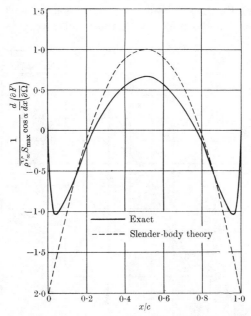

Fig. IX. 26. Theoretical chordwise distributions of side force due to rotation on a spheroid of thickness-chord ratio 0·25.

equation (113) that, if the axis of rotation is taken as the y-axis and the body incidence is α, the surface pressure coefficient is given by

$$C_p = \frac{p-p_\infty}{\frac{1}{2}\rho V_\infty^2} = \left(\frac{\Omega x}{V_\infty}+\sin\alpha\right)^2(1-4\sin^2\theta)-$$

$$-\frac{2\cos\alpha.\cos\theta}{\pi r_w(x)}\frac{d}{dx}\left[\left(\frac{\Omega x}{V_\infty}+\sin\alpha\right)S(x)\right]+O(\bar{r}_w^2\log\bar{r}_w). \quad (114)$$

With $\Omega = 0$, this reduces to the result for translational motion, given in equation (90).

R. Jones (1926) has derived the exact surface pressure distribution for a spheroid, based on the potential flow solution outlined in Section 2, and Fig. IX. 26 compares the two calculations of the chordwise distribution of side force. From equation (114) the increment of side force per unit length due to the curvature of the path is

$$d(\Delta F)/dx = \rho V_\infty \Omega \cos \alpha \{d[xS(x)]/dx\}, \qquad (115)$$

from which it follows that, to this order of approximation, the total side force is unchanged by rotation. Moreover, if the axis of rotation passes through the centre of volume, the incremental pitching moment also vanishes. On the other hand, the exact theory for a spheroid

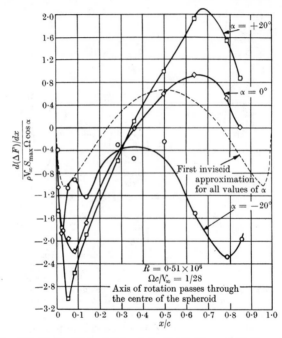

Fig. IX. 27. Experimental chordwise distributions of side force due to rotation on a spheroid of thickness-chord ratio 0·25.

predicts a non-zero resultant side force due to rotation, but this apparent disparity may easily be explained. Using arguments similar to those of Section 16, we may show that the fluid exerts a side force on the body of magnitude

$$F = -k_1 \rho V_\infty \Omega V \cos \alpha, \qquad (116)$$

and a retarding longitudinal force

$$X = k_2 \rho V_\infty \Omega V \sin \alpha, \qquad (117)$$

V being the volume of the body. The result of slender-body theory is compatible with equation (116) since k_1 may be ignored for a slender body. To the same order of accuracy we may take $k_2 = 1$, on the assumption that the body rotates about its centre of volume and so equation (117) gives a simple value for the drag due to a curved path. This is the chief effect of a motion which is not rectilinear and it may be recognized as a kind of Coriolis force exerted by the fluid on a slender body.

We should naturally expect these results to be modified by viscous effects, but the extent of the modification as shown in Fig. IX. 27 comes as a surprise. From these experiments by R. Jones (1926) it appears that the theory is most inaccurate; the side force does not even appear to be an even function of incidence. These are unexpected and unexplained effects.

X

UNIFORM FLOWS PAST JOINED BODIES

1. Introduction

THE study of fluid dynamics, and indeed of all sciences, is like a tree-trunk whose root is physical experience, drawing for its strength on our powers of observation. It stems into many branches, some leading to regions of thought far removed from the root of physical phenomena: if it were otherwise, much of its fascination would fade away. But it is as well to remember the roots, especially when we deal with the more theoretical branches of a science, and, lest we become too satisfied with the analyses in previous chapters, to remember also that real bodies are never two-dimensional, nor infinite, nor symmetrical, nor do they remain stationary in infinite streams of uniformly-moving fluid. What is more, it is a mistake to wish on the physical world these abstract properties which are as unnatural as they are simple.

The separation of variables is one of our major analytical techniques and if we mean by it something less than its strict mathematical meaning, certainly it brings with it in a physical problem the tacit assumption of the independence of the effects of these variables; and such an assumption needs to be justified by an *a posteriori* argument at the very least. When in previous chapters we have concentrated attention on fluid flows derived by abstract simplifications, we have sometimes discussed the extent to which such flows could be purposely set up in the physical world, and sometimes the extent to which they actually represent what is commonly observed. The lines of these two discussions often run together, but not when we study regions of flow whose nature clearly differs from one of our simplified ideals. Such regions are bound to occur in nearly every physical flow, for the geometrical properties of the boundaries are unlikely to be everywhere of the simplest character. The neighbourhoods of the junctions between a wing and an aircraft fuselage, or between a pipe and a strut across it, are examples of those regions external to which simple concepts may be reasonably valid, but within which more detailed, and usually more approximate, analysis is necessary.

In this chapter, we propose to consider certain special flows which, except for limited regions within them, may be considered by methods already outlined in previous chapters. Here we shall concentrate on

these excepted regions in which the effects may be thought of as interactions between two or more flows of simpler character. These effects
are commonly classified as interference effects: this term includes not
only the flows such as those mentioned in the previous paragraph but
also flows such as those of a wake over a wing, or past a biplane system,
or of a helicopter rotor near the ground. A particular kind of interference occurs when there is a common intersection of the boundaries
of the simple bodies, as with two intersecting aerofoils: the intersection
is called, by custom, the junction, and this chapter is devoted mainly
to the study of the flow in the neighbourhood of certain special kinds of
junctions.

The influence of a junction between two bodies may be felt in several
ways. First, the inviscid flow associated with each of the joining bodies
will be altered but only, we may expect, in the region of the junction.
This localized influence of the junction may, however, lead to overall
effects. Consider, as an example, an aeroplane flying at a high subsonic
speed, so that only at the junction of the wing and fuselage is the flow
locally supersonic; the associated shockwaves may nevertheless affect
the performance or stability of the whole aeroplane. Last, any local
effects of the junction on the boundary layer will inevitably be convected downstream where they may have significant influences. We
may take, as an example of this, the transition to turbulence caused
by a thin rod extending through a laminar boundary layer.

A junction may set other influences at work, but those just discussed
probably typify the two principal influences, which once again adhere
to the familiar dichotomy of potential and viscous effects. This chapter
therefore will concern itself mainly with the flow near junctions outside
the boundary layer while in Chapter XII the nature of some of the
viscous effects at a junction will be discussed. In these studies, it will
be wrong to expect a degree of accuracy similar to that obtained earlier
in more simple flows. The geometry of the physical flow will often be
simplified drastically to make some analytical treatment possible; it
will be characteristic of the theoretical work that the magnitude of the
errors arising from the simplifications cannot be estimated, though
comparison with experiment will, of course, indicate the overall sound-
ness of the analytical work.

2. The displacement flow of two intersecting unswept wings

Let us consider the first inviscid approximation for two similar
straight wings of infinite span which intersect at right angles and are

given by $y = \pm g(x)$ and $z = \pm g(x)$, $2g(x)$ being the thickness of either wing. Both wings are at zero incidence to the mainstream $(U_\infty, 0, 0)$ and are illustrated in Fig. X. 1. At large distances from the junction, the velocity distribution over one of the wings will be very close to the two-dimensional distribution, given by

$$1+u/U_\infty = [1+S^{(1)}(x)][1+\{S^{(2)}(x)\}^2]^{-\frac{1}{2}} = B\{1+S^{(1)}(x)\}, \qquad (1)$$

in the notation of Section IV. 15. It will be recalled that $[1+S^{(1)}(x)]$ is the result of linearized theory in its strict form, and that $[1+\{S^{(2)}(x)\}^2]^{-\frac{1}{2}}$,

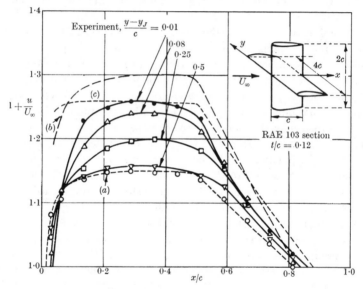

FIG. X. 1. The variation of the chordwise velocity distribution with distance from the junction of two rectangular wings.

denoted by B for convenience, is the factor usually introduced as an improvement. In Fig. X. 1, curve (a) represents equation (1) for the particular aerofoil section RAE 103. The influence of the second wing on the first steadily increases as the junction is approached and may be expected to be greatest actually on the line of intersection of the two wings. The simplest approximation for the velocity distribution at the junction would superpose the two individual displacement velocities so that the velocity increment is doubled: curve (b) in Fig. X. 1 illustrates the result of this procedure which is seen to overestimate the velocity.

Now equation (1) is derived by replacing the wing by a source distribution in the chordal plane. The source strength, $q(x)$ per unit area, is given by

$$q(x) = 2U_\infty(dg/dx). \tag{2}$$

To superpose the displacement velocities of the two wings is equivalent to taking the source distribution over the whole of the two chordal planes, $y = 0$ and $z = 0$ for $0 < x < c$, which means that the volume common for both wings is taken twice into account. We can improve on this by adding an appropriate sink distribution. The simplest approximation is a sink distribution along the axis $y = z = 0$ whose strength equals that of the source distribution which would generate a body whose cross-section $A(x)$ equals the area, at any chordwise point, common to both wings. The strength of this sink distribution, given by equation (IX. 49) according to the linearized theory, is therefore $(-U_\infty)dA(x)/dx$ per unit length along $y = z = 0$ and the induced velocity increment, in the x-direction, equals

$$-\frac{U_\infty}{4\pi} \int_0^c \frac{(x-x')}{[(x-x')^2+r^2]^{\frac{3}{2}}} \frac{dA(x')}{dx'} dx' \tag{3}$$

at a point distant r from the x-axis. On the line of intersection of the wings, $r = \sqrt{2}g(x)$ and also $A(x) = 4[g(x)]^2$. The velocity on the junction can therefore be written in the form

$$1 + \frac{u}{U_\infty} = 1 + 2[B\{1 + S^{(1)}(x)\} - 1] -$$

$$-\frac{1}{\pi} \int_0^c \frac{x-x'}{[(x-x')^2+2\{g(x)\}^2]^{\frac{3}{2}}} \frac{d[g(x')]^2}{dx'} dx'. \tag{4}$$

In most cases, the integral has to be evaluated numerically. A numerical result using equation (4) is shown by curve (c) in Fig. X. 1. Agreement with the experimental curve is as good as can be expected for such a crude theory, and the fact that the maximum velocities agree so well is particularly encouraging. It is important to note that the contribution of the sink distribution to the velocity, given by the last term in equation (4), is proportional to $(t/c)^2$: it is shown in Fig. X. 1 as the difference between curves (b) and (c). The other term in equation (4) is proportional to (t/c) and is the more important term especially for thin wings. This should be borne in mind in later sections when the sink distribution will be tacitly ignored.

The velocity increment at a section, say $y = y_0$, away from the junction of the wing $z = g(x)$ could be regarded as the sum of the increments due to (i) the wing $z = g(x)$, on its own surface, (ii) the wing $y = g(x)$, at the appropriate distance y_0 away from it, and (iii) the sink distribution along $y = z = 0$, at $(x, y_0, 0)$. Thus, according to this interpretation,

$$1 + \frac{u}{U_\infty} = 1 + [B\{1 + S^{(1)}(x)\} - 1] +$$

$$+ \frac{1}{\pi} \int_0^c \frac{dg(x')}{dx'} \frac{x - x'}{(x - x')^2 + y_0^2} \, dx' - \frac{1}{\pi} \int_0^c \frac{x - x'}{[(x - x')^2 + y_0^2]^{\frac{3}{2}}} \frac{d[g(x')]^2}{dx'} \, dx'.$$

$$(5)$$

Some experimental results are illustrated in Fig. X. 1 (in which y_J is the value of y on the junction line) and we notice that the junction has little effect at a distance greater than about half-chord. This spanwise distance is also roughly the distance over which the tip effect of a finite wing is appreciable, and altogether we might infer that the interference effects hardly vary with either of the aspect ratios provided these are greater than, say, two. For aspect ratios less than two, there may arise an interaction of the tips and the junction.

It is, of course, a general feature of a junction of the kind so far considered that the maximum velocity increment in it is greater, and by a considerable factor greater, than the maximum velocity increment on a section some distance away from it. As the stream velocity increases, therefore, effects due to the compressibility of the fluid will become noticeable first at the junctions. In addition, there will be a greater tendency for the boundary layer to separate at a junction than elsewhere, owing to the greater rise in pressure over the rear part of the junction. These effects, either singly or together, can be detrimental to the performance of an aeroplane, especially if the junction is near control surfaces, as may happen when a horizontal tail surface is combined with a vertical fin. Much of the experience gained from theoretical analysis is therefore devoted to designing junctions at which the velocity is only a little greater, if at all, than at other sections of the joined bodies.

We can see in a general way that the effect of the junction in increasing the velocity could be offset by thinning both wings near the junction. The amount of thinning required for the wings already studied can be estimated roughly from Fig. X. 1 on the assumption that the total velocity increment is roughly proportional to thickness; thus, the maximum velocity in the junction, $U/U_\infty = 1 \cdot 26$, could be reduced to that on the wings alone, $U/U_\infty = 1 \cdot 15$, by reducing the wing thickness at the junction in the ratio 0·57. The sections at other spanwise positions could be thinned by an amount similarly estimated from the curves given. On the pair of wings so obtained, the maximum velocity on each section will in fact vary slightly along the span since the introduction of thickness-taper brings with it still further effects: but the factor 0·57 indicates the extent to which the wings may have to be altered near the junction to prevent a significant increase in velocity. However, a decrease in thickness at the junction by more than, say, one-third is probably unacceptable for structural reasons, at any rate in any application to an aircraft, and we need to seek other methods of counteracting the effect of the junction on the velocity. The discussion of this problem is postponed until Section 5.

3. The displacement flow of two intersecting swept wings

In the previous section, it was assumed without any attempt at justification that the velocity increments for each of the two intersecting wings could be added, with the rather minor modification given in equation (3). This assumption may be justified by the remark that, if the wing $z = g(x)$ is replaced by the plane $z = 0$, the velocity on the other wing $y = g(x)$ is unaltered by the presence of the first.

Now this state of affairs no longer holds if one or both wings are swept. Consider first the sheared wing $y = g(x - z \tan \varphi)$ intersecting the straight wing $z = g(x)$, as illustrated in Fig. X. 2. The plane $z = 0$, to which the straight wing may for the moment be approximated, does not include streamlines of the uninterfered flow past the sheared wing, as we may see from Fig. VII. 7; thus the very presence of the straight wing has a constraining effect on the flow past the sheared wing, in addition to the effects of its thickness. If we suppose that the straight wing extends over the whole plane $z = 0$, the flow over the upper part of the sheared wing, in $z > 0$, is the same as that over half a swept-back wing whose centre section is on $z = 0$; similarly the flow over the lower part of the sheared wing corresponds to that over a swept-forward wing. The presence of the plane $z = 0$ is equivalent to the presence of a centre section on the swept wing, though a calculation based on this idea will exaggerate somewhat the effect of the presence of the wing $z = g(x)$ which only extends over $0 < x < c$.

The effect just discussed will be called, for short, the reflection effect. The velocity increment in the junction of the configuration shown in Fig. X. 2 can therefore be estimated as the sum of the increments due to (i) the undisturbed straight wing, (ii) the undisturbed sheared wing, and (iii) the reflection effect. Thus,

$$1+u/U_\infty = B[1+S^{(1)}(x)]+\{B[1+\cos\varphi\,S^{(1)}(x)]-1\}\mp B\cos\varphi f(\varphi)S^{(2)}(x)$$
(6)

for the upper and lower junctions respectively, the last term in the equation being drawn from equation (VII. 41), and B being the factor

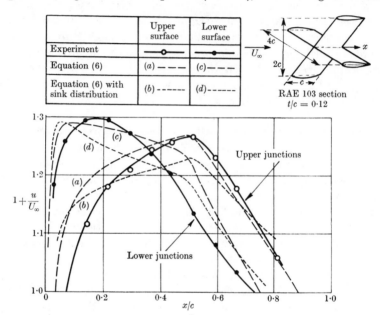

	Upper surface	Lower surface
Experiment	——○——	——●——
Equation (6)	(a) — — —	(c) — — —
Equation (6) with sink distribution	(b) - - - - - -	(d) - - - - - -

RAE 103 section
$t/c = 0.12$

Fig. X. 2. The chordwise velocity distribution in the junctions of a straight tailplane and a fin sheared through 45°.

introduced in equation (1). Fig. X. 2 shows a calculation from equation (6) with which the agreement from experimental results is reasonably good.

In other configurations, there may be two or more reflection effects. As an example, we may take the fin-tailplane of Fig. X. 3. In the upper-surface junction the velocity increment is similar to twice that at the centre section of a swept-back wing; thus

$$1+u/U_\infty = 1+2\{B[1+\cos\varphi\,S^{(1)}(x)-\cos\varphi f(\varphi)S^{(2)}(x)]-1\}. \qquad (7)$$

On the lower surface the velocity increment in the junction is similar to the sum of those on a swept-back and on a swept-forward wing, that is, to twice that of the corresponding sheared wing. Thus on the lower surface

$$1+u/U_\infty = 1+2\{B[1+\cos\varphi\,S^{(1)}(x)]-1\}. \qquad (8)$$

Numerical results from equations (7) and (8) are compared with experimental results in Fig. X. 3.

It will have been noticed that in these results we have not introduced a sink distribution, as was done in Section 2, to compensate for the duplication of the source representation of the volume common to both wings. The reason for this omission is partly that only second-order

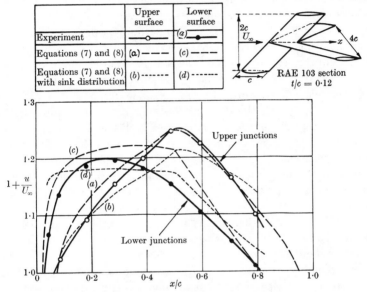

FIG. X. 3. The chordwise velocity distribution in the junctions of a swept-back tailplane and a fin sheared through 45°.

terms in (t/c) are thereby neglected, partly because it seems, in practice, not to result in consistent inaccuracy and partly because the integral in equation (4) is tedious to compute in any case. Figs. X. 2 and 3 indicate, in two particular cases, the magnitude of the neglected effect. The omission of the sink distribution and the assumption of a full reflection effect in an infinite plane doubles the possibility of error in estimating the velocity: the fact that the maximum velocity is predicted well, in the case shown in Fig. X. 3, must therefore be regarded as good fortune.

The difference between the velocity in the upper and lower junctions in a swept configuration like that shown in Fig. X. 2 might be expected to result in a lift force. This is not so, however, at any rate according to a strictly linear theory. For such a theory, the pressure increment is proportional to the velocity increment. The difference in pressure between the two surfaces is therefore proportional to the strictly linear form of the last term in equation (6) and therefore to $S^{(2)}(x)$ or dz/dx; the lift arising from this is zero, since $\int (dz/dx)\, dx$ taken round the section contour is zero. Even on a linear theory, however, there may be a local drag (or thrust) force due to the pressure distribution. This may arise from the reflection effect, since the centre section of a swept-back wing experiences a drag as described in Section VII. 8. In the configuration of Fig. X. 2 there is no overall drag, the drag from the upper junction being exactly counterbalanced by the thrust in the lower junction. But the drag for the upper-surface junctions in Fig. X. 3 amounts to twice that in the centre section of a swept-back wing. This possibility of drag demands care in design: for example, the fin-tail of Fig. X. 3 would be improved in this respect if the tail were put at the top of the fin.

The concept of the reflection effect used in this section may be applied to more general cases of wing junctions, of which three in particular may be mentioned. First, if two of the chordal planes of semi-infinite intersecting wings are not perpendicular, a further reflection effect arises which is equivalent to the effect at the centre section of a wing with dihedral. Second, when the chords of the intersecting wings are unequal, the assumption of the reflection effect is rather more accurate than in the cases considered earlier, provided we take the wing of larger chord as the reflecting plate. The drag of this type of junction, exemplified by a strut on a wing, can be appreciable. Third, chordwise vertical plates of small height mounted on a swept wing and stretching over the whole or the front part of the chord—commonly called fences —produce an effect which is in the nature of partial reflection. If the wing is swept-back, the fence causes an additional velocity on its inboard side similar to the centre effect of a swept-forward wing. If the height, H, of the fence is small, say of the same order as the maximum thickness, t, of the wing, only a proportion, ϵ_0, of the full reflection effect should be taken. Weber and Lawford (1954) have obtained the following values of ϵ_0 for a 12 per cent thick wing:

H/t	0·25	0·50	0·75
ϵ_0	0·50	0·75	0·90

the fence extending over the whole chord.

4. The displacement flow of a straight wing intersecting a body

In the flows so far considered, the reflection effect appeared as a consequence of sweep. However, since it may be thought of as being due to the image source distribution within the reflecting surface, it will appear also for straight wings when the reflecting surface is not, even approximately, plane. The junction between a wing and a fuselage is an important illustration of this. As an idealized configuration, we consider a long circular cylinder whose ends are rounded off and which is joined symmetrically to an infinite straight wing, whose span is perpendicular to the body's axis. In Fig. X. 4 is a sketch of such an arrangement.

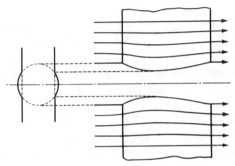

Fig. X. 4. A sketch of the streamlines near the junction of a circular cylindrical body and a straight wing.

In this flow, we should obtain a poor approximation for the velocity increment in the junction by superposing the sum of the increments due to the uninterfered body and to the uninterfered wing, in analogy to Section 2, even though the wing is straight. The reason for this is that the image source system of one half-span, which ensures that the body is a streamline, is not the source distribution representing the other half-span. Alternatively, it is instructive to consider the streamlines. In Fig. X. 4 are also shown typical streamlines close to the wing, seen in plan view, based on the assumption that the junction line between wing and body is a streamline; this assumption is well borne out by experimental observations provided the body diameter, D, is more than, say, twice the wing thickness, t. We also assume for the moment that the body is very long so that its own displacement flow is negligible near the wing. Now this streamline pattern indicates that the maximum velocity is lower at the junction than on the wing far from the junction. The difference, v_J, will depend on the ratio D/t and will decrease as the ratio D/t increases, that is, as two-dimensional conditions are approached.

An analytical treatment of this flow is difficult even if the body is taken as an infinite circular cylinder. We might try, first, to replace the part of the wing outside the body by a source distribution and fulfil the conditions on the surface of the body by an appropriate image distribution within the cylinder. But since the image of even a single source is a source-line of variable strength together with a sink-line on the axis of the body, the analysis would be extremely tedious. An alternative approach, suitable to the special case of wings of very small aspect ratio, is provided by slender-body theory in which the flow is described in terms of two-dimensional flow in planes $x =$ constant, normal to the mainstream. The general methods of Sections VII. 6 or IX. 11 could then be applied. Difficulties arise, however, in the calculation of the velocity at the junction, and this general approach has not yet been developed satisfactorily. Two more approximate methods were introduced in 1947 by Küchemann and Weber (1953*b*). In the so-called source method, a sink distribution on the body axis is superposed onto the source distribution of the isolated wing. The sink distribution takes into account that part of the wing inside the body, analogously to the procedure in Section 2; the velocity field of this distribution is proportional to the ratio between the body diameter and the chord, and also directly to the thickness-chord ratio of the wing (the body diameter remaining constant) in contrast to its square in the case of the two intersecting wings. The decrease in velocity due to the junction tends to be overestimated as may be seen from Fig. X. 5. The work of Liese and Vandrey (1942) may also be mentioned: they derived certain exact solutions which are useful as guides to the value of approximations.

But the method which, at present, seems to give the best results puts the emphasis on the waisted shape of the intersection line. If $y = y(x)$ is the projection of the intersection line on $z = 0$, a body of radius $r = y(x)$ is considered. The whole body is presumed to be waisted, and the problem is reduced to the flow past a given body of revolution. A method using vortex rings is suitable and all the usual approximations of a linear theory are made. Vortex rings in each cross-section of the circular body of strength $\gamma(x)\,dx$ are used and the required vortex distribution is represented by a sum,

$$\gamma(x) = \sum_{\nu=1}^{N} c_\nu \gamma_\nu(x), \qquad (9)$$

of suitable distributions $\gamma_\nu(x)$, chosen in a manner similar to that used by Birnbaum for thin aerofoils. The induced velocity components are

$$\mathrm{v}_x/U_\infty = \sum_{\nu=1}^{N} c_\nu(\mathrm{v}_{x\nu}/U_\infty) \qquad (10)$$

and
$$v_r/U_\infty = \sum_{\nu=1}^{N} c_\nu(v_{r\nu}/U_\infty), \qquad (11)$$

parallel and normal to the surface of the body; the functions $v_{x\nu}$ and $v_{r\nu}$ have been tabulated by Küchemann and Weber (1953b) for various

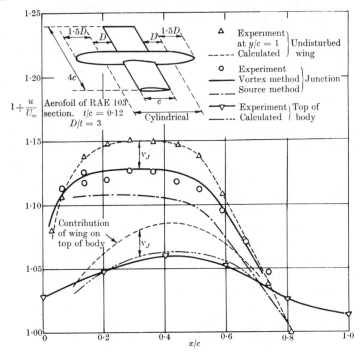

FIG. X. 5. Velocity distributions on an unswept wing joined to a cylindrical body.

values of the ratio of cylinder length to diameter. Now on the junction line, we have $dy/dx = v_y/U_\infty$ or

$$dr/dx = v_r/U_\infty. \qquad (12)$$

dr/dx is known at N suitably selected points, which determines v_r/U_∞ from equation (12) which in turn enables the coefficients c_ν to be evaluated from equation (11). Equation (10) then gives the velocity increment on the waisted body, which is taken as a good approximation to the velocity increment v_J on the junction line of the original wing-body combination.

The vortex method is alone in giving a fairly speedy and not too inaccurate solution of the inverse problem. To determine the projection of the junction line for a specified velocity distribution we proceed through equations (10), (11), and (12) in that order; and if either the shape of the body or of the wing section is given, the other may be determined.

Fig. X. 5 compares results from the two principal methods with experimental results and the vortex method seems to give the best agreement. The body in this experiment was cylindrical for one body diameter in front of the leading edge of the wing and for one diameter aft of the trailing edge, being rounded off at either end; it was therefore long enough for the velocity increment v_B near the wing due to the body alone to be negligible. The presence of the wing modifies, of course, the velocity at all points on the body and in Fig. X. 5 is shown its effect on the velocity along the straight top line of the body. This velocity was calculated in two parts; one part was regarded as induced by the complete two-dimensional wing passing through the body, and the other by a sink distribution designed to cancel the effect of the wing inside the body. If this sink distribution is located, as a simplifying approximation, on the axis of the body, its induced velocity on the top of the body is the same as that at the junction. The curve for the top of the body, in Fig. X. 5, was therefore obtained by using the value of v_J already obtained by the vortex method, and we see that there is fair agreement with experiment.

The spanwise variation of the effect of the body can most easily be calculated by the source method which gives

$$\frac{u}{U_\infty} = \frac{D}{2\pi} \int_0^c \frac{dz(x')}{dx'} \frac{x-x'}{\{(x-x')+y^2\}^{\frac{3}{2}}} \, dx', \tag{13}$$

where $z = z(x)$ is the wing section and D is the diameter of the body. As $y \to y_J$, this expression tends to v_J as given by the source method, and as $y \to \infty$, it tends to zero. In practice the interference becomes negligible at less than one chord-length away from the junction and this, except in cases of very small aspect ratio, justifies the replacement of the wing by one of infinite span.

5. The displacement flow of a swept wing intersecting a body

The complication introduced by the sweep of a wing joining a body is taken into account by the concept of the reflection effect explained in Section 3, in which a junction is regarded as the centre section of a swept wing. On such a configuration as that shown in Fig. X. 6, the velocity increment in the junction may be regarded as the sum of the increments due to:

(i) an undisturbed sheared wing, v_s;

(ii) the centre term, v_c, arising from the reflection effect;

(iii) the junction shape, v_J;

(iv) the body alone, v_B.

v_s and v_c are given by $\cos \varphi S^{(1)}(x)$ and $[-\cos \varphi f(\varphi) S^{(2)}(x)]$ respectively, in the notation of equation (VII. 41). It is usually assumed that v_J is

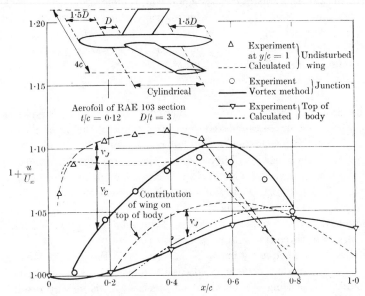

FIG. X. 6. Velocity distributions on a wing swept back through 45°, joined to a circular cylindrical body.

unaltered by the sweep of the wings, except in so far as that affects the shape of the junction on which, according to the arguments of the preceding section, v_J alone depends.

In an experiment designed to test the validity of this account of the effects of sweep, a model was constructed similar in every respect to that shown in Fig. X. 5 except that the wings, although of the same section, were swept back at an angle of 45°. This model and comparisons between the theoretical and experimental results are illustrated in Fig. X. 6; agreement is reasonably good and a number of interesting differences between the straight-wing and swept-wing flows can be noted from the two figures.

Any calculation of the velocity on the body or wing away from the junction is even more uncertain for swept than for straight wings. The method described in Section 4 may, however, be used for swept wings, and to exemplify it the velocity distribution along the top of the body already considered is shown in Fig. X. 6.

The efficacy of sweep in improving high-speed performance depends on maintaining the sweep of the isobars everywhere on the wing surface and not only on reducing maximum velocities. An effect which decreases the sweep of the isobars in any region will, therefore, be detrimental to performance. Now, the effect of a centre section is normally to reduce the sweep of the isobars, but the presence of a body offers the possibility of counteracting this. For example, the body may be designed, according to the methods of Section 4, so that

$$v_B + v_J = -v_c.$$

Alternatively, for bodies of large diameter, the shape of the junction may be taken as the calculated streamline shape of the infinite sheared wing. Some experiments made by Küchemann and Weber (1953b) have confirmed the general validity of these ideas, provided that the height of the body above the wing surface is large enough to ensure that the streamlines of the flow do not cross the intersection lines. This was one of our basic provisos: as a very rough guide, the width of the body measured at the maximum thickness of the wing in the junction should be less than three times its height above the wing.

The desirable equality between the velocity in the junction and that further out on the wing may also be achieved for a given body by modifying the wing section near the junction. This usually results in the wing being steadily thickened towards the junction.

We may now return to the problem, touched upon in Section 2, of designing a combination of two wings for which the two-dimensional velocity distribution is maintained everywhere on the wings. The solution is to enclose the junction within a body of revolution. First, this body should be so long that v_B, the velocity increment due to the body alone, is negligible; a diameter–length ratio of 0·08, say, would be good. Then its diameter should be at least, say, twice the wing thickness. A slight reduction has probably been made already in the velocity along the junction since the introduction of the three-dimensional body has the effect of removing the junction on one wing away from the other; on this argument the diameter should be as large as possible and, if the diameter–length ratio of the body is regarded as fixed, will only be restricted in practice by the limits which must be set on the length of the body. Further advantage may be gained by modifying the shape of the body-wing junctions and it is possible to design such a composite configuration on which the maximum velocity in the junction is no greater than far away from it. Working on similar lines, Kohler (1938) has shown experimentally that the drag arising from the junction of struts to a wing can be reduced considerably by suitable fairings.

Other flows to which our analysis can be applied are those near a nacelle or an external fuel tank mounted on a wing. The first is distinguished from the flow near the wing-fuselage junction in one important respect, for on one side of a nacelle on a swept wing the wing must be regarded as swept-forward while on the other side it is swept-back; as an approximation, the two sides may be treated independently. In the case of a swept-back wing with a tip-tank, the maximum velocity in the junction may, for large sweeps and if the junction has not been suitably designed, be greater than that on the wing elsewhere, since the wing must be regarded as swept-forward in the region of the junction.

In both this and the preceding section, the wing has been assumed to be symmetrically placed on the body. Further interference effects arise for other positions of the wing and these are discussed by Hartley (1949). A simple-minded estimation of the probable configuration of streamlines leads one to expect that the velocity on the surface of the wing which is on the greater arc of the body will itself be greater than that on the other surface.

6. Wings with constant spanwise lift on a fuselage at zero incidence

One approach to the consideration of a wing-fuselage combination would regard the fuselage as part of the wing and as characterized only by a large chord. This will not be followed up here since it has proved less fruitful than the alternative approach of regarding the fuselage as an infinitely-long cylindrical body. Although under this latter assumption the fuselage, if at zero incidence, coincides with streamlines of the undisturbed stream, this is no longer so when the wing is added. The singularities representing the wing could be counterbalanced by singularities inside the body to ensure that the velocity component on and normal to the surface of the body is zero, as was done in Section 4 for a wing at zero lift; but the evident complication of the three-dimensional flow explains the extreme paucity of exact solutions. There is a further difficulty: the bound vortices on the wing cannot end at the body unless we consider the unrealistic case of a wing so shaped that all the bound vortices have been shed as trailing vortices before the wing-body junction is reached. In general, the vortex lines on the wing are continued across the body, but in no simple manner. Even with the simplest representation of a wing by a single concentrated vortex, the continuation across the body of this vortex line is not a concentrated vortex along two semicircles over the circumference of the body, but a vortex distribution over the whole surface. It is not therefore surprising that the representation of the wing by vortex distributions is sometimes abandoned in favour of more convenient singularities.

An interesting exact solution for an infinite wing, represented by a concentrated vortex line, attached to a spherical body has been given by Vandrey (1937). The induced flow of a concentrated vortex includes a sphere, whose centre is on the vortex line, as a stream surface: on this is superimposed the flow of a uniform stream past a sphere which is represented by a doublet at its centre. The complete flow is then known. Although the strength of the vortex, Γ, is constant along its length, the spanwise lift distribution is not constant since the doublet induces velocity components at the wing in the direction of the stream; it may be shown that

$$C_L(y) = (\rho U_\infty \Gamma / \tfrac{1}{2}\rho U_\infty^2 c)[1 + \tfrac{1}{16}(d/|y|)^3], \qquad (14)$$

where d is the diameter of the sphere. The lift coefficient is highest in the junction and decreases outwards. The vortex induces different velocity increments on the upper and lower halves of the sphere, and from an integration of the pressure distribution it is found that the lift is constant across the diameter and equal to three-quarters of the value for the undisturbed wing. Altogether, the increment in lift on the wing due to the body is exactly balanced by the decrement on the body. It is a common effect that the body increases the loading on the wing near the junction.

Other cases, for which exact solutions have been given by Lennertz (1927) and Vandrey (1937), are those of a line vortex in combination with an infinite cylinder and with ellipsoids. Consider an infinite circular cylinder whose axis is parallel to the stream, and an infinite straight concentrated vortex passing through its axis at right angles to it. A source distribution, q, over the whole surface of the cylinder is then needed to compensate for the velocity component, $v_{n\Gamma}$, normal to the surface, induced by the line vortex. The forces on wing and body can then be determined from the singularities and their velocity field; by fairly simple arguments of symmetry, we can deduce that the velocity

in the stream direction induced by q is zero, from which it follows that
the lift on the wing is constant in the spanwise direction. The vertical
velocity component induced at the line vortex by the source distribution
is zero, which means that the line vortex can be considered as representing an untwisted wing at incidence. We have thus the simple result
that a cylindrical body at zero incidence combined with a plane wing

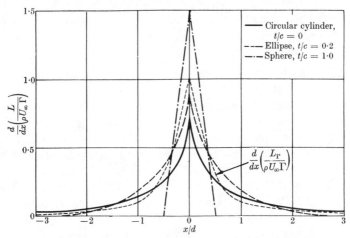

FIG. X. 7. The distribution of lift along several bodies whose axes are parallel
to a uniform stream and perpendicular to an infinite line vortex.

of infinite aspect ratio at incidence carries the same lift as would that
part of the wing which it covers, leaving the spanwise loading unaltered.
The lift on the body is distributed along its length, and arises from
the tangential velocity components induced first by the line vortex,
and second by the source distribution. The longitudinal distribution
of the lift on the body, dL/dx, is shown by the full line in Fig. X. 7,
in which $x = 0$ is the position of the vortex. This distribution differs,
of course, from that of the lift, dL_Γ/dx, due to the velocity field induced
by the concentrated vortex alone; the total value L_Γ, however, equals
L. The value of dL_Γ/dx is shown in the figure and we see that most of
the lift occurs in the region near the wing.

If the body is of finite length but again at zero incidence to the
mainstream, it may still be represented by a continuation of the line
vortex through the body and an additional source distribution over its
surface. The interaction between these singularities is again such as to
produce the same total lift force, as in the absence of the body, so long
as the body is doubly symmetrical and the concentrated vortex passes

through its centre. The upwash induced on the wing is still zero so that the line vortex may be considered to represent a plane untwisted wing. However, there must be further singularities such as a source-sink distribution along the axis to represent the body alone in the uniform stream and, as we have already seen in the case of the sphere, this affects the lift distribution over the body as well as over the wing. The streamwise distribution of the lift is shown in Fig. X. 7 for three different shapes of body; an ellipsoid of diameter–length ratio 0·20 experiences an overall lift of an amount 0·9 times the lift of that part of the wing inside the body.

7. Wings with a given spanwise distribution of lift on a fuselage at zero incidence

So far, we have considered wings which may be represented by a concentrated vortex of constant strength; in preparation for the more general case of spanwise variation of circulation we now consider the lift induced on a cylindrical body by two symmetrically-placed lifting elements each represented by a horseshoe vortex, following Lawrence and Flax (1954). If the lifting elements are not too close to the body, in terms of the body's diameter, it may be assumed that the downwash, w, induced by the lifting elements does not vary across the diameter, and that it varies only slowly in the streamwise direction. The latter assumption implies that the boundary condition, that the velocity component normal to the body surface is zero, may be satisfied by applying slender-body theory and considering the two-dimensional flow in transverse planes. This enables the source distribution over the body to be replaced by a doublet distribution along the body's axis, whose contribution to the lift on the body is found to be

$$L_1/\tfrac{1}{2}\rho U_\infty^2 = (2\Gamma\Delta y/U_\infty)(d/2y)^2, \tag{15}$$

where Δy is the span of the horseshoe vortex of strength Γ, and y is its lateral distance from the body of diameter d. There is a further contribution to the lift, arising directly from the streamwise velocity increments induced by the lifting element, and Lawrence and Flax found that this second contribution, L_2, is exactly equal to the first, L_1. They also determined the longitudinal distribution of lift with the result that the two components of lift are distributed in the same way along the body axis:

$$d(L_1/\tfrac{1}{2}\rho U_\infty^2)/dx = d(L_2/\tfrac{1}{2}\rho U_\infty^2)/dx = (\Gamma\,\Delta y/4U_\infty)d^2(x^2+y^2)^{-\tfrac{3}{2}}. \tag{16}$$

This relation shows again that the lift on the body decreases rapidly with increasing distance from the lifting element which produces it.

Using this method to determine the longitudinal distribution of lift for the simple case of a line vortex of constant strength with an infinite cylindrical body, they obtained close agreement with the exact solutions of Lennertz and of Vandrey.

When we require only the total lift on the body due to a given distribution of lift on the wing, use of the Trefftz plane leads to a simple relation. The Trefftz plane is defined in Section VIII. 11 as a transverse plane, perpendicular to the stream, far behind the wing. Its use is coupled with the assumption that trailing vortices remain parallel to the stream; with the body at zero incidence, trailing vortices lie also along the body's axis, so that the boundary in the Trefftz plane is given by the transverse section of the wing-body combination itself.

Now it is convenient to work in terms of the velocity potential, ϕ, of the disturbance. Thus

$$U = U_\infty + \partial\phi/\partial x, \tag{17}$$

and according to the usual linearized approximation the pressure coefficient due to the disturbances is given by

$$C_p = -(2/U_\infty)(\partial\phi/\partial x). \tag{18}$$

Integrating the pressure along a streamline at any given spanwise position, which according to the approximation of the present theory is a straight line parallel to the x-axis, we have

$$\int_{-\infty}^{\infty} C_p \, dx = -(2\phi_\infty/U_\infty), \tag{19}$$

since far upstream the disturbance potential is zero. The local lift force, $L(y)$, per unit span on a wing of zero dihedral is the difference between the pressures on the upper and lower surfaces and is related to the potential difference by

$$L(y)/\tfrac{1}{2}\rho U_\infty^2 = C_L(y)c(y) = \int_{-\infty}^{\infty} [-\Delta C_p(x,y)] \, dx = 2\Delta\phi/U_\infty, \tag{20}$$

where ϕ is henceforward the potential in the Trefftz plane at $x = \infty$. ϕ depends only on the two coordinates y and z, in the spanwise and vertical directions.

For a cylindrical body, $2\phi/U_\infty$ is the total force per unit length of the body circumference, directed along the normal to the body surface. The total lift on the body, L_B, is then given by

$$L_B/\tfrac{1}{2}\rho U_\infty^2 = 2 \int (\phi/U_\infty)\cos\theta \, ds, \tag{21}$$

where θ is the angle between the outward normal to the body surface and the z-axis, and s is the length of arc along the circumference.

If the lift distribution over the wing is known, then the discontinuity in the potential function at the trace of the wing in the Trefftz plane is also known from equation (20). To determine the lift distribution over the body it is sufficient to determine a potential function in the Trefftz plane which has the given discontinuity at the wing and also satisfies the condition $\partial\phi/\partial n = 0$ on the trace of the body in the Trefftz plane. This is a problem in two-dimensional potential flow; the boundary conditions are mixed since either the value of ϕ or its normal derivative is given along the boundary. In the general case the solution is still complicated, but some special cases will be treated later.

Flax (1953) and others have shown that the total lift on the body may easily be obtained from the potential difference at the wing, and that it is unnecessary to determine the potential function at the body. In the Trefftz plane, the potential function ϕ satisfies Laplace's equation in two dimensions, and if ϕ_1 is another potential function for the same region, the reciprocal relation $\oint \phi_1(\partial\phi/\partial n)\, ds = \oint \phi(\partial\phi_1/\partial n)\, ds$ is a classical result following from Green's theorem. If now the integrals are taken over the body contour (subscript B) and over the trace of the wings (subscript W), the relation can be written as

$$\oint_B \phi_1 \frac{\partial\phi}{\partial n}\, ds + \int_W \Delta\phi_1 \frac{\partial\phi}{\partial n}\, dy = \oint_B \phi \frac{\partial\phi_1}{\partial n}\, ds + \int_W \Delta\phi \frac{\partial\phi_1}{\partial n}\, dy. \qquad (22)$$

Flax takes the potential ϕ_1 to be the sum of the potential of the flow around the body at rest in a stream parallel to the z-axis with $w = -1$ at infinity, and that of a uniform stream parallel to the z-axis, with $w = +1$. At the wing $\Delta\phi_1 = 0$ since the flow is continuous outside the body, and $\partial\phi_1/\partial n = \cos\theta$ at the body. Now, $\Delta\phi$ has the given value at the trace of the wing and $\partial\phi/\partial n = 0$ at the body; thus the two integrals on the left-hand side of equation (22) are zero, and

$$\oint_B \phi \cos\theta\, ds = \int_W \Delta\phi f(y)\, dy, \qquad (23)$$

where $f(y)$ is given by $\qquad f(y) = -\partial\phi_1/\partial n \qquad\qquad (24)$

calculated on the wing at each spanwise position. With equation (21), the overall lift on the body is now obtained as

$$L_B/\tfrac{1}{2}\rho U_\infty^2 = \int (2\Delta\phi/U_\infty)f(y)\, dy = \int_W C_L(y)c(y)f(y)\, dy. \qquad (25)$$

This therefore is a general relation between the lift carried by a cylindrical body of any cross-section at zero incidence and the lift force acting on the wing.

For the special case of a wing mounted symmetrically on a circular cylinder of diameter d we find that, from (24),

$$f(y) = (2y/d)^{-2}, \tag{26}$$

and the lift on the body, from equation (25), is given as

$$L_B/\tfrac{1}{2}\rho U_\infty^2\, b\bar{c} = \int_{d/b}^{1} C_L(y)[c(y)/\bar{c}](d/2y)^2\, d(2y/b). \tag{27}$$

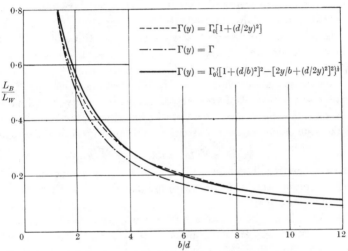

Fig. X. 8. The effect of the span and the spanwise lift distribution of a wing on the induced lift on a circular cylindrical fuselage.

It may be shown that this leads to the same result as equation (15), with $L_B = 2L_1$. To this must be added the lift on the wings given by

$$L_W/\tfrac{1}{2}\rho U_\infty^2\, b\bar{c} = \int_{d/b}^{1} C_L(y)[c(y)/\bar{c}]\, d(2y/b) \tag{28}$$

to obtain the total lift on the combination. The ratio L_B/L_W is illustrated in Fig. X. 8 for a number of different load distributions and ratios (b/d), and it is seen that the distribution of lift on the wing does not greatly affect the lift on the body.

8. The determination of the spanwise distribution of lift of a wing on a fuselage at zero incidence

To make any progress with the problem of finding the load distribution on a given wing which is attached to a given body at zero incidence, we have to retain all the assumptions of Section 7. Further, only bodies of circular cross-section and thin wings will be considered. We then have to find a vortex distribution which allows the given wing and the body to be stream surfaces, and subsequently to derive the forces on wing and body from this vortex distribution.

Now the downwash w, due to the bound vortices, may be determined to a first approximation by Prandtl's hypothesis, explained in Sections VIII. 8–9; thus at any spanwise position, $y = $ constant, the downwash is assumed to be the same as that produced by a distribution of bound vortices of infinite spanwise extent and constant strength, but with the same chordwise distribution, thus ignoring any spanwise changes. This is only valid for wings of large aspect ratio; those of small aspect ratio require different treatment. In the present problem, all this implies that the existence of the body is ignored altogether as far as the downwash on the wing of the bound vortices is concerned. The streamwise component of vorticity on the body, however, will have an effect on the wing. Following Prandtl's hypothesis, the bound vortices produce the same downwash as they would on the wing alone. Hence

$$w(y) = \alpha_e(y)U_\infty = (C_L(y)/a)U_\infty = 2\Gamma(y)/ac(y). \tag{29}$$

Here, a is the two-dimensional lift slope and equals 2π for unswept thin wings, implying that the chordwise lift distribution is that of the flat plate of infinite span.

In determining the downwash on the wing induced by the trailing vorticity, Multhopp (1941) assumed it to have half the values which are readily found from the two-dimensional flow in the Trefftz plane. This is the usual approximation of the theory of wings of large aspect ratio, and it is reasonably valid in the wing-body flow if the body is cylindrical.

In dealing with the two-dimensional vortex distribution along the wake contour in the Trefftz plane, Multhopp transforms the Trefftz plane

$$\zeta = z + iy \tag{30}$$

into the ζ_1-plane

$$\zeta_1 = z_1 + iy_1 \tag{31}$$

by the simple transformation

$$\zeta_1 = \zeta + d^2/4\zeta, \tag{32}$$

so that the boundary in the ζ_1-plane is a slit lying along the real axis. The transformation does not change the value of the potential function or the circulation $\Gamma = \Delta\phi$. The induced downwash at $x = \infty$, $y = y_1$ in the ζ_1-plane is therefore

$$w_1 = \frac{1}{2\pi} \int\limits_{-b_1/2}^{+b_1/2} \frac{d\Gamma(y_1')}{dy_1'} \frac{dy_1'}{y_1 - y_1'}, \tag{33}$$

the suffix 1 denoting values in this plane. The downwash in the physical ζ-plane is therefore

$$w = w_1 \mathscr{R}(d\zeta_1/d\zeta), \tag{34}$$

$\mathscr{R}$ denoting the 'real part of'. It may be verified that $\mathscr{R}(d\zeta_1/d\zeta)$ is related to $f(y)$ given in equation (24) by the equation

$$\mathscr{R}(d\zeta_1/d\zeta) = 1 + f(y) \tag{35}$$

which is quite generally true; for the circular body, $f(y)$ is given by equation (26).

We now have the downwash on the wing, induced by the trailing vortices, in the form

$$w(y) = \alpha_i U_\infty = \alpha_{i0} U_\infty = \frac{1+f(y)}{4\pi} \int_{-b_1/2}^{+b_1/2} \frac{d\Gamma(y_1')}{dy_1'} \frac{dy_1'}{y_1(y)-y_1'}. \tag{36}$$

The full boundary condition on the wing is that the downwash angle induced by the bound and trailing vortices together should be equal to the geometrical angle of incidence; thus

$$\alpha(y) = \alpha_e(y) + \alpha_i(y) \tag{37}$$

which, from equations (29) and (36), leads to

$$\alpha(y) = \frac{2\Gamma(y)}{ac(y)U_\infty} + \frac{1+f(y)}{4\pi U_\infty} \int_{-b_1/2}^{+b_1/2} \frac{d\Gamma(y_1')}{dy_1'} \frac{dy_1'}{y_1(y)-y_1'}. \tag{38}$$

This integral equation, which apart from the notation differs from equation (VIII. 42) only in the additional term $f(y)$, may be solved by any of the approximate numerical methods discussed in Chapter VIII.

We notice that equation (38) is generally valid for any cross-sectional shape; for a circular section the transformation (32) is particularly simple and $f(y)$ follows easily. But for other shapes, once the transformation is known, $f(y)$ follows from equation (35).

The distribution of lift which the wing induces on the body cannot be determined in the same way as the lift on the wing itself. The trailing vortices on the body cancel each other out in the ζ_1-plane, which accounts for their absence in equation (36). We therefore make use of equation (19) relating the integral of the pressure difference to the potential in the Trefftz plane. To determine the correct value of the potential along the vertical slit in the ζ_1-plane would be tedious, but a first approximation is given by

$$\phi(z_1) = \phi(z_{1J}) + (\partial\phi/\partial z_1)_J(z_1 - z_{1J}) = \phi(z_{1J}) + w_{1J}(z_1 - z_{1J}), \tag{39}$$

where the suffix J refers to the junction of the wing and body. For a circular body and a mid-wing arrangement,

$$\Delta\phi(y) = \Delta\phi(y_J) - 2w_{1J}(d^2 - 4y^2)^{\frac{1}{2}}. \tag{40}$$

The lift on the body is thus highest in the junction and decreases towards the axis. The total lift on the body can, of course, be obtained from the lift distribution already found for the wing, from equations (25) and (27).

9. The lifting wing on a fuselage at incidence

Suppose now that the body too is at an incidence, α_B, to the uniform stream. It was found in Section IX. 15 that the pressure distribution over an isolated body is such that a lift force is produced near the nose and a download near the tail; the sum of these forces is zero in inviscid flow but they combine to produce an unstable pitching moment. Now the central part of most fuselages is nearly cylindrical and sufficiently long for it to be regarded, to a good approximation, as an infinite cylinder. But since there is in fact a nose to the fuselage carrying a load, there are streamwise vortices issuing from it, and these may be said to cancel the normal velocity components which are produced by the cross-flow $w = -\alpha_B U_\infty$ in transverse planes normal to the axis of the body.

A wing attached to such a body disturbs this cross-flow, even if it is itself at zero incidence, and a lift force is produced on the wing as a consequence of the upwash from the body, which is given by

$$w_B = -\alpha_B f(y) U_\infty. \tag{41}$$

For example, if both the wing and the circular body are at the same incidence α, the wing at the junction is at a local angle of incidence of 2α. In general, this wing lift is partly carried across the body in a manner similar to that in the case of a lifting wing attached to a body at zero incidence. The streamwise extent of this wing-induced lift on the body is usually such that it does not overlap with those parts of the body where the nose and tail-loads arise; this is illustrated in Fig. X. 9.

It is usually assumed that the lift on the front of the body is not affected by the vorticity associated with the wing, and so, that it can be calculated by the methods of Chapter IX for the body alone. This assumption is supported by exact calculations by Vandrey (1937) who determined the flow past an ellipsoid up to angles of incidence of 20° with a vortex line of constant strength passing through it; the chordwise lift distribution was very nearly the same as that of the ellipsoid plus vortex line at zero incidence superposed on the asymmetric distribution of the ellipsoid alone, and the total lift was very nearly the same as if the body had been at zero incidence.

But the trailing vortices of the wing do alter the effective angle of incidence of the flow over the rear of the body, and so also the down-load. In most practical cases a downwash is produced which reduces the local angle of incidence over the rear and also the download. This is shown in Fig. X. 9 and it results in an additional lift on the body.

The pattern of vorticity is now somewhat difficult to imagine. For an isolated body, all vortex lines are closed on the body and no trailing vortices are left in the wake. But for the wing-body combination, the reduced tail-load results in some of the vortices from the front being

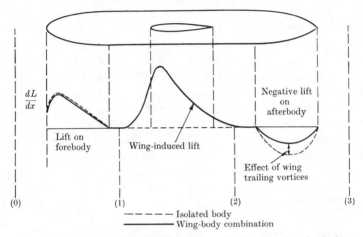

FIG. X. 9. A sketch of the lift distribution on the fuselage of a wing-body combination at incidence.

continued beyond the body into the wake, together with those from the wing-induced lift. (It is usual to ignore the effect of the bound vortices on the afterbody on the flow over the wing). These difficulties, together with the fact that the vortex lines on a very long body are inclined to the mainstream whereas the trailing vortices behind the wing are parallel to it, make the use of the Trefftz plane far downstream of uncertain value. However, experience indicates that it is the vortex system immediately behind the wing which matters most in determining the load and the Trefftz plane may therefore be taken close to the wing; experimentally, this effect is manifest in that the load on the body induced by the wing is largely independent of the length of the cylin-drical part of the body and also of the particular shape of the rear of the body, as has been shown by Weber, Kirby, and Kettle (1951) and by Lawford (1953). Thus, as far as the wing is concerned, the incidence of the body is felt only through the upwash given in equation (41); the boundary equation at the wing is therefore

$$\alpha(y) + \alpha_B f(y) = \alpha_e(y) + \alpha_i(y), \qquad (42)$$

α_e and α_i taking the same values as in equation (37). This equation may again be treated approximately by the method of Multhopp (1941) and the lift on the body induced by the wing is again given by equation (27).

The method of calculation so far described can be applied to bodies of any cross-section with any position of the wing with respect to the body axis, as long as the trace of the wing in the transformed Trefftz plane, the ζ_1-plane, can be taken as a straight line for the purpose of calculating the downwash w_1 by equation (33). The body-induced up-wash, $\alpha_B f(y)$, has been determined for non-circular bodies and for wings in off-centre positions by Multhopp (1941) and by Liess and Riegels (1942). In particular, the latter considered bodies whose cross-section is pear-shaped. The additional upwash can be higher than $\alpha_B U_\infty$ in the junction if the wing is attached to the body at a place where it is highly curved. Alternatively, it may be less on flat-sided bodies.

As the upwash induced by the body is associated with the cross-flow about the body, it is liable to be severely affected by the viscosity of the fluid. There are cases, especially at high angles of incidence, in which the cross-flow leads to separation from the sides of the body. This affects not only the load on the body itself but also the magnitude of the upwash induced by it.

A further effect of viscosity is, of course, to reduce the download on the rear of the body and, as a result, the destabilizing pitching moment is also reduced. An additional contribution to the pitching moment on the body arises from the lift induced by the wing. For practical purposes it is usually sufficient to assume that the centre of pressure of the load on the body is at the same streamwise position as that in the wing-body junction, and for a detailed discussion of the calculation of the pitching moment we refer again to the work of Multhopp (1941).

10. Some extensions of the theory of wing-body combinations at incidence

Multhopp's method of the previous section has been derived for a thin unswept wing whose chord is small compared with the wing span and with the body diameter. It is, however, capable of being extended to wings of small aspect ratio, to swept wings, and to wings whose thickness cannot reasonably be ignored. Weber, Kirby, and Kettle (1951) have carried out these extensions, a brief account of which follows.

For wings of small and moderate aspect ratio, the wing thickness is often comparable with the body diameter. If the wing is in an off-centre position or at any angle to the body axis, one effect of the non-zero thickness is to produce different shapes in the junctions on the upper and lower surfaces; this gives rise to an additional lift at and near the junction which does not change with incidence. If body and wing are represented by singularities, the sources which represent the thickness of the wing may be continued through the body, and then only those singularities which represent the part of the body outside the wing contribute to the upwash. Thus the thickness of the wing reduces the upwash induced by the body; and the effect of this on the lift distribution is only of the second order, so that a rough approximation is usually sufficient. We may assume that the upwash produced by the isolated body is reduced by a factor k, which may be taken constant along chord and span. An estimate of k is given by the ratio of the cross-sectional area of the body above and below the wing (continued through the body) and the total frontal area of the body at the position of maximum wing thickness.

If the wing is swept, the bound vortices on the wing are reflected in the body as were the source lines representing a thick wing in the case discussed in Sections 4 and 5. This primarily affects the chordwise distribution of the bound vortices and thus the sectional lift slope at spanwise stations near the body. At the wing-body junction, the chordwise loading can be taken as being approximately the same as that at the centre of a swept wing alone. According to the method of Küchemann, given in Section VIII. 17, the effect of sweep may then be taken into account by varying the sectional lift slope along the span, as on a swept wing without body. The shape of the boundaries in the Trefftz plane, according to linear theory, is unaffected by sweep.

There are several effects of small aspect ratio which modify the theory of the foregoing sections. The fundamental feature of a lifting surface of small aspect ratio is the considerable length of the streamwise vortex lines within the wing. This leads to a change in the chordwise loading and hence of the sectional lift slope. Also, the mean downwash at the wing from the trailing vortices is greater than half the value in the Trefftz plane; indeed in the limiting case, $A \to 0$, the two values are equal, as found in the theory of Section VIII. 12 and indicated in Fig. VIII. 9. In the method of Küchemann, the sectional lift slope is regarded as a function of the aspect ratio, and the downwash is increased by a factor ω, which varies from unity for $A = \infty$, to two for $A = 0$. This procedure can readily be applied to wing-body combinations.

The body-induced upwash affects only part of the wing. For a circular body the upwash decreases from its maximum value at the junction to one-ninth of this value at a distance of one diameter from the junction; since the root chord of many modern aircraft is about the same as the

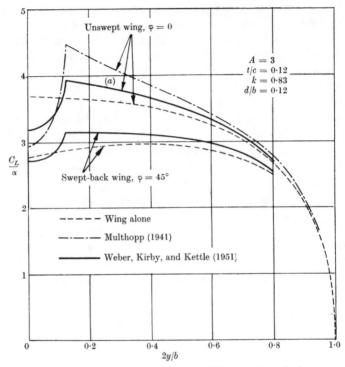

Fig. X. 10. Some spanwise distributions of lift on untapered wings on circular-cylindrical bodies in the mid-wing position.

body diameter, the part of the wing which is effectively twisted corresponds to an aspect ratio of only about unity. Ginzel (1940) has shown that, for a rectangular wing with a similarly marked spanwise change of the angle of incidence, a good approximation to the spanwise lift distribution is obtained by taking $\omega = 2$, equivalent to equating the downwash at the wing to that in the Trefftz plane; she also took the sectional lift slope corresponding to a large aspect ratio. We make use of this result by writing the local circulation $\Gamma(y)$ as a sum of the two terms Γ_W and Γ_B, where Γ_W refers to the case in which the wing is at the incidence α_W and the body at zero incidence, and Γ_B to that in which the wing is at zero incidence and the body at incidence α_B. In calculating Γ_B we take $\omega = 2$, and in calculating Γ_W a value of ω corresponding to the aspect ratio of the wing is taken.

None of these various modifications introduces any complication into Multhopp's numerical procedure for solving the downwash equation typified, in the special case of $\alpha_B = 0$, by equation (38). Some spanwise loadings calculated from the modified equation are shown in Fig. X. 10 as an illustration of the magnitude of the various effects. Experimental results, which are not shown here, lie closest to curve (a).

The pressure distribution over the wing may be calculated in the same way as was described in Section VIII. 17 for an isolated wing, by the use of the following form of the pressure difference between upper and lower surfaces; thus

$$\Delta C_p = -[\sin(\pi n)/\pi n]C_L[(c-x)/x]^n, \tag{43}$$

where n is a function of aspect ratio, angle of sweep, and the spanwise position of the point under consideration. The sectional lift then gives the chordwise distribution of pressure. Equation (43) ignores the difference between the chordwise distributions of Γ_W and Γ_B.

11. Slender-body theory

In Sections VII. 6, VIII. 12, and IX. 11, we have already described the approximation, known as the slender-body approximation, which can be made when changes in the streamwise direction are small in comparison with changes in perpendicular directions. This leads to an elegant method in which each transverse plane may be considered as a Trefftz plane for that part of the wing and body upstream of it, the part downstream having no effect.

Spreiter (1950) has applied slender-body theory to calculate the forces acting on various combinations of wings and bodies. To exemplify the

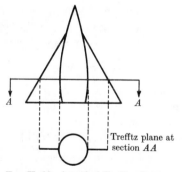

FIG. X. 11. A typical Trefftz plane on a slender wing-body combination.

procedure let us consider a thin wing with swept-back leading edge and straight trailing edge, fitted in the mid-wing position to a body of circular cross-section so that both wing and body are at an angle of incidence α to the stream. Fig. X. 11 illustrates the arrangement in which the transverse plane AA, given by $\zeta = z+iy$, can be transformed into the plane $\zeta_1 = z_1+iy_1$ by means of $\zeta_1 = \zeta+d^2(x)/4\zeta$, so that the body becomes a vertical slit and the wing a horizontal slit. The transformation therefore is somewhat different in detail from that employed by Spreiter. The flow in the transformed plane is then the same as that associated with a plane wing, and the problem is reduced to that treated by R. T. Jones (1946). The complex potential function in the Trefftz plane is found to be

$$\phi+i\psi = -\alpha U_\infty\{[\zeta+d^2(x)/4\zeta]^2+[\tfrac{1}{2}b(x)-d^2(x)/2b(x)]^2\}^{\frac{1}{2}}. \qquad (44)$$

If $x = 0$ is at the leading edge of the junction, and the body is cylindrical, the lift on the wing plus the lift on the body induced by the wing is

$$L(x,y)/\tfrac{1}{2}\rho U_\infty^2 = C_L(y)c(y) = \int\limits_0^x (-\Delta C_p)\, dx = 2[\Delta\phi(x,y)-\Delta\phi(0,y)]/U_\infty \qquad (45)$$

for the part upstream of the plane chosen. The last expression in this equation follows from equation (18).

Equations (44) and (45) are sufficient to determine the load over both wing and body since $\Delta\phi(0,y) = 0$ for the wing and

$$\Delta\phi(0,y) = 4\alpha U_\infty[\tfrac{1}{4}d^2-y^2]^{\frac{1}{2}}$$

for the body. The result of integrating equation (45) over the span is the final expression for the lift coefficient:

$$\bar{C}_{LW}+\bar{C}_{LB} = \tfrac{1}{2}\pi\alpha A[1-d^2/b^2]^2. \qquad (46)$$

We have yet to take into account the lift on the front part of the body. Here the boundary in the Trefftz plane is simply a circle and a simple application of equation (18) gives

$$\Delta C_p(x) = -4\alpha\{1-[2y/d(x)]^2\}^{\frac{1}{2}}\frac{d}{dx}(d(x)), \qquad (47)$$

from which the total lift, L_N, on the nose can be calculated as a lift coefficient referred to the wing area, including that part covered by the body; thus

$$\bar{C}_{LN} = (1/b\bar{c})\iint (-\Delta C_p)\, dxdy = \tfrac{1}{2}\pi\alpha Ad^2/b^2. \qquad (48)$$

These formulae are due to Spreiter (1950) and some of his results are reproduced in Figs. X. 12 and 13. It is seen that the body may carry a considerable part of the total load, but that the overall lift slope is always less than, or at best equal to, the lift slope of the corresponding wing without body, obtained by continuing the wing through the body. This latter value is $\tfrac{1}{2}\pi A$, as given by slender-body theory when applied to wings; this value is rather pessimistic, since non-slender wing-body

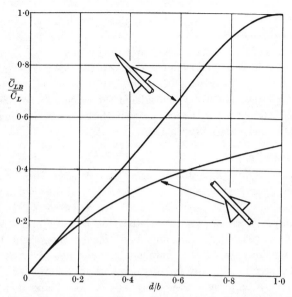

Fig. X. 12. The ratio of the lift on various slender bodies to the total lift on their combination with a swept wing.

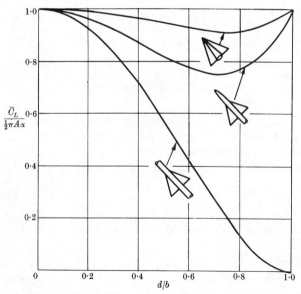

Fig. X. 13. The ratio of the total lift of various slender wing-body combinations to that on the isolated wing.

combinations often have a slightly higher overall lift than the corresponding isolated wings.

Extensions of the theory have been made by Adams and Sears (1953) who have considered the flow in the Trefftz planes behind the maximum span of the wing. For wing-body combinations which are not very slender, Lawrence (1953) has considered the calculation of the chordwise load distribution, by assuming that the spanwise loading is that resulting from slender-body theory.

12. Induced drag

Both the lift and drag forces on a body in a uniform stream are manifested by appropriate changes of velocity and pressure in the fluid as it flows from infinity upstream to infinity downstream. In the first inviscid approximation, we assume that the pressure and streamwise component of velocity are unchanged at large distances from the body, but that far downstream the components, v and w, of velocity are not necessarily zero as they are far upstream. A useful expression for the drag may then be obtained by equating the work being done by the drag force per unit time to the rate at which additional kinetic energy is accumulating downstream. As a result we have

$$D = \tfrac{1}{2}\rho \iint (v^2 + w^2)\, dy dz = \tfrac{1}{2}\rho \iint [(\partial\phi/\partial y)^2 + (\partial\phi/\partial z)^2]\, dy dz \quad (49)$$

in which ϕ, as in previous sections, is the two-dimensional velocity potential in the transverse plane far downstream. Stokes's theorem then gives

$$D = \tfrac{1}{2}\rho \int_{B,W} \phi(\partial\phi/\partial n)\, ds, \quad (50)$$

in which the integral is taken round the trace of the trailing vortices originating from both fuselage and wing, and n is the outward normal to the contour and s the length of arc along it.

This drag force is the induced drag and arises only from the trailing vorticity: if this were zero, then $\partial\phi/\partial n$ and hence the induced drag as well would be zero. The formula (50) is, of course, exact though any calculation based on it is bound to be approximate since certain simplifying assumptions concerning the spread of vorticity in the wake always have to be made.

For a wing-fuselage combination such as that shown in Fig. X. 9, we may determine the overall induced drag, $D_i = D_3$, from a consideration of planes (0) and (3), and on the assumption that the trace of the trailing vorticity in plane (3) has the same shape as a cross-section through the wing and fuselage. From equation (50) we have

$$D_i = \tfrac{1}{2}\rho \oint_B \phi_3(\partial\phi_3/\partial n)\,ds + \tfrac{1}{2}\rho \int_W \Delta\phi_3(y)w_3(y)\,dy. \tag{51}$$

Now the normal velocity component, $\partial\phi_3/\partial n$, on the trace of the body is caused by trailing vortices from the loads on the front, F, and rear, R, of the body only. Hence

$$\partial\phi_3/\partial n = (\alpha_F - \alpha_R)U_\infty \cos\theta, \tag{52}$$

where the difference between the effective angles of incidence of the front and rear of the body is approximately equal to the total induced incidence α_{iT} in the Trefftz plane at station (3) which may be approximated by a constant mean value across the diameter of the body; θ is, as before, the angle between the outward normal to the body and the z-axis. Thus we obtain from equations (51) and (52)

$$\bar{C}_{Di} = \tfrac{1}{2}\alpha_{iT}\bar{C}_{LB} + \int_{d/b}^{1} C_L(y)[c(y)/\bar{c}]\alpha_{i0}(y)\,d(2y/b), \tag{53}$$

since $\rho U_\infty \int_B \phi \cos\theta\,ds = L_B$ is the overall load on the body, and since $\Delta\phi_3 = \Gamma = \tfrac{1}{2}C_L cU_\infty$ is the local load along the span. The integral over the wing is the same as the well-known relation for the wing alone, $(w_T/2U_\infty)$ being the induced incidence α_{i0} at a wing of large aspect ratio.

We may similarly calculate the drag which arises from the front of the body and wing combined by applying equation (50) to station (2) as shown in Fig. X. 9. The downwash w_2 at the trace of the wing is

$$w_2(y) = -f(y)\alpha_F U_\infty + 2\alpha_{i0}U_\infty, \tag{54}$$

and on the body $\partial\phi_2/\partial n = \alpha_F U_\infty \cos\theta$. Since at the body $\phi_2 = \phi_F + \phi'$, where by equation (23)

$$\oint_B \phi' \cos\theta\,ds = \int_W \Delta\phi_2 f(y)\,dy, \tag{55}$$

we obtain finally

$$C_{D02} = \tfrac{1}{2}\alpha_F C_{LF} + \int_{d/b}^{1} C_L(y)[c(y)/\bar{c}]\alpha_{i0}(y)\,d(2y/b). \tag{56}$$

The drag arising from the front of the body is

$$C_{D01} = \tfrac{1}{2}\alpha_F C_{LF}. \tag{57}$$

This last relation was first derived by Ward (1949) and it implies that the resultant force is not perpendicular to the body axis but is inclined forward so that it includes a tangential component T_F along the axis. Since $D_F = \alpha N_F + T_F$, and $L_F \simeq N_F$, we have

$$T_F = -D_F = -\tfrac{1}{2}\alpha_F L_F. \tag{58}$$

This result is remarkable in so far as it differs from that obtained for lifting surfaces; for them, $C_T = -(C_L)^2/a$, so that the ratio of the suction force and the induced drag varies with the aspect ratio of the wing; with bodies, however, the diameter–length ratio—the analogue of aspect ratio—does not enter into the relation. If the suction force on a body is for some reason not realized, then equation (58) implies that the drag is doubled. It follows from equations (56) and (57) that the integral in equation (56) represents the induced drag resulting from the load on the wing together with that on the body induced by the wing. α_{i0} is found from equation (36), and the integral is performed over the wing only. This does not, of course, mean that the drag force on the body at an angle of incidence is zero. Nor is the local induced drag distributed along the wing span proportionally to $\Gamma\alpha_{i0}$, as it is for an isolated wing.

13. Minimum induced drag

As for any lifting system, the overall induced drag from equation (53) is a minimum for a given overall lift if the downwash in the Trefftz plane far downstream—say at station (3) of Fig. X. 9—is constant on the boundary in that plane. To obtain the velocity potential for this flow, sketched in Fig. X. 14, we consider first the flow in (b) and add a uniform flow of velocity $+w_T$ parallel to the z-axis so that finally in (a), $w = 0$ at $z = \infty$. The solution for the flow (b) is readily obtained, with the transformation used in Section 11. Thus we find

$$C_L(y)[c(y)/\bar{c}] = 2A(w_T/U_\infty)\{[1+d^2/b^2]^2 - [2y/b + d^2/2by]^2\}^{\frac{1}{2}}. \tag{59}$$

The parameter w_T, which is the downwash in the Trefftz plane, must now be related to the downwash α_i at the wing, where the boundary condition is given by equation (42) as before.

For the trailing vortices behind the wing, $\alpha_i = \tfrac{1}{2}\omega w_T/U_\infty$ with ω asdetermined in Section VIII. 17. The trailing vortices on the body, however, act in a twofold manner. First, they produce an upwash term at the wing proportional to $\alpha f(y)$ in equation (42). Second, they contribute to α_i; but here we encounter the difficulty that not all the streamwise vortices on the body reappear in the Trefftz plane at station (3), since some are closed through bound vortices on the rear of the body. In the absence of anything better, we assume that the vortex system on the body is such as to produce the full upwash $\alpha f(y)$

and that the trailing vortices found at station (3) can be treated in the same way as the trailing vortices from the wing, with the same value of the factor ω. Thus the boundary condition (42) may be written as

$$C_L(y) = a(y)\{\alpha[1+f(y)]-\tfrac{1}{2}\omega w_T/U_\infty\}. \tag{60}$$

The elimination of $C_L(y)$ between equations (59) and (60) gives the requisite chord distribution.

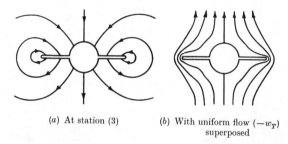

(a) At station (3)   (b) With uniform flow $(-w_T)$
superposed

FIG. X. 14. Sketches of flows in the Trefftz plane at station (3) of Fig. X. 9.

Lennertz (1927) and Pepper (1941) have determined the load distribution which gives minimum induced drag for combinations where the fuselage is an infinitely long cylinder at zero incidence. Whatever the load on the fuselage in this case, it does not contribute to the drag and the required load distribution over the wing is therefore different from that determined above. The problem is to minimize the drag on the wing, given by

$$D_i = \tfrac{1}{2}\rho \int\limits_W \Gamma(y)w_T\,dy \tag{61}$$

from equation (56), when the total load

$$L = \rho U_\infty \int\limits_W \Gamma(y)[1+f(y)]\,dy, \tag{62}$$

as given by equations (25) and (28), is specified. The methods of the calculus of variations give the condition for this to be so as

$$w_T \propto [1+f(y)].$$

Thus in this case, the downwash in the Trefftz plane is not constant, which contrasts with the case of an isolated wing for which, of course, $f(y) = 0$.

14. Some other combinations of bodies and lifting surfaces

There are some cases of practical interest in which one or more nearly plane and relatively thin surfaces, set at a small angle to the mainstream, are attached to one or more relatively long bodies of approximately circular cross-section, which may also be slightly inclined to the mainstream. Whatever the combination it may always be represented by a distribution of bound vortices over the solid surfaces and a system of streamwise vortices, partly on the solid surfaces and partly trailing behind in the wake. Always the problem is to find a relation between

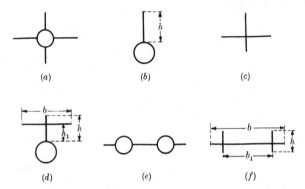

Fig. X. 15. Sketches of the transverse sections of various wing-body combinations.

the vortex distribution and the downwash induced by it; subsequently the vortex distribution must be determined by the condition that the given combination is a stream surface, which is usually interpreted in the form of an equation such as (42).

The central problem is the solution of the flow in the Trefftz plane past the body contour and the trace of the wing wake; if this can be solved, the other incidentals can at any rate be approximated. Some cases which have been treated are shown in Fig. X. 15. Case (a) is a cruciform wing-fuselage arrangement which differs in its properties from the ordinary wing-fuselage combination only if the flow conditions are asymmetric, as will occur in yaw or roll. Case (b) defines a combination which is in itself asymmetric and exemplifies the problem of a fin on a body in a sidewind. The cruciform wing combination (c), without fuselage, represents a fin-tail arrangement, which again is of interest when a sidewind is present; and case (d) adds a fuselage to this. A wake pattern like that of case (e) may occur on wings with nacelles, or on wings with tip-tanks if the two circles are at the tips of the wake. Case (f) represents the wake of a wing with vertical plates or fins, or end-plates, and may also occur behind wings with part-span vortex sheets.

The flows in the Trefftz plane are normally determined through the transformation of the whole contour into a straight slit. It is obvious that the case of a wing-fuselage combination is unique in that the circle, representing the fuselage, is easily transformed into a vertical slit on which the boundary condition is automatically fulfilled; the boundary condition on the remainder of the slit, representing the wing wake, can then be adapted to the conditions on the wing itself, in the same way as for an isolated wing. Only the case of cruciform wings, (a), can be treated in a similar way and all the other cases are much more difficult.

A computational method based on Falkner's lifting-surface theory and employing discrete horseshoe vortices has been developed by Zlotnik and Robinson (1954). This method has been applied by Queijo and Riley (1954) to various body-tailplane combinations in roll and in sideslip.

If the combination is slender, then each sketch in Fig. X. 15 represents a section through the combination itself and the boundary condition is that the contour is a streamline in a uniform stream along the z-axis with velocity $-\alpha U_\infty$. If the transformation is known the solution follows relatively simply. Slender-body theory has been applied to cruciform combinations by Spreiter (1950) and later developments have been described by Lomax and Byrd (1951) and by Bryson (1953). In most cases the aim is to find the properties of such combinations in roll and in sideslip, and often in supersonic flow as well.

For non-slender combinations the problem can be solved for the special cases in which the induced downwash in the Trefftz plane is constant along the span. Such combinations have been considered by Mangler (1938), Falkner and Darwin (1945), and Küchemann and Kettle (1951) for wings with end-plates; by Rotta (1942) for wings with single plates; by Hartley (1952) for wings with tip-tanks; by Weber (1952, 1954c) for wings with fences, fin-fuselage, and wing-nacelle arrangements; and by Weber and Hawk (1954) for fin-tail-fuselage arrangements.

In many of the cases under consideration the interference between the various components has very large effects. An example is shown in Fig. X. 16 in which β is the angle of sideslip and C_Y is the local coefficient of side force. The addition of a fuselage to a fin increases by 60 per cent the overall side force and the further addition of a tailplane may increase it still more. The corresponding distributions of side force along the span of the fin are also very different, the efficiency of the fin as a stabilizer being greatest when the tailplane is on top of the fin. This implies that the size of fin required depends on the position of the tail-plane. The effect of the position of the tailplane is illustrated in Fig. X. 17; in this the comparison with experimental results is surprisingly

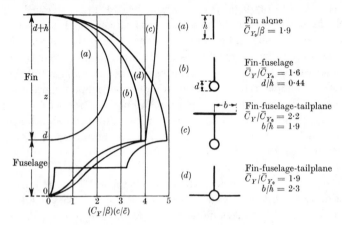

FIG. X. 16. The distribution of side force on various fin-fuselage-tailplane combinations in sideslip.

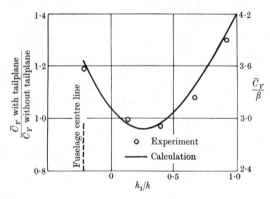

FIG. X. 17. The effect of the position of the tailplane in a fin-fuselage-tailplane combination on the side force.

good, and seems to justify the approximations in the theory. In this figure, h_1 is the height of the tailplane above the fuselage, h being the length of the fin.

Another important practical case arises from the use of boundary-layer fences, which have already been discussed in connexion with the effect of thickness, in Section 5. Weber and Lawford (1954) have determined their effect experimentally and they can cause considerable changes in both the spanwise and chordwise distribution of lift.

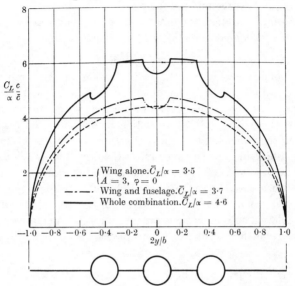

FIG. X. 18. The spanwise distribution of lift on a wing with fuselage and nacelles.

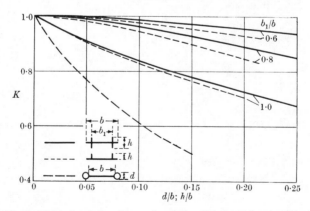

FIG. X. 19. The induced-drag factor of equation (63) for various combinations of wings and vertical plates or tip-tanks.

An example of the large effect which several bodies may have on the spanwise loading is given in Fig. X. 18. Here, the lift on the wing with fuselage and two nacelles, all of equal diameter and infinite length, is increased only to a certain extent by the change in downwash resulting from the trailing vortices; the main increase results from the upwash caused by the fuselage and nacelles.

It has been found that the induced drag may be expressed, approximately, in a form analogous to that for a wing alone:

$$\bar{C}_{Di} = K(\bar{C}_L)^2/\pi A, \qquad (63)$$

where K depends only on the configuration in the Trefftz plane. Numerical values of K are given in most of the papers mentioned earlier and Fig. X. 19 gives some examples for wings with plates and with tip-tanks where $K \leqslant 1$. The reduction in drag may be regarded as equivalent to an increase of the aspect ratio from A to A/K, and clearly can be considerable. It may even offset the form drag of the additional bodies but the effect of viscosity and separation tends to reduce the benefit, as has been shown by Salter and Jones (1955).

An equivalent formula can be derived for the overall lift, but this is a simple relation only when there are no bodies carrying forces. We may quote the result for swept wings with plates:

$$\bar{C}_L/\alpha = a_s/[1+\omega K a_s/\pi A], \qquad (64)$$

a_s being the lift curve slope of the sheared part of the wing. Again, the effect of the plates may be regarded as an increase of the aspect ratio of the wing alone by the factor $1/K$.

XI

ROTARY FLOWS

1. Introduction

THE developments in fluid dynamics which have occupied the previous chapters represent the most recent stage of a slow process of learning which has been spread, more or less evenly, over the last sixty or seventy years. This is not to belittle the influence of the great corpus of classical hydrodynamics which, for many previous decades, had been built up by some of the greatest mathematicians and physicists of their time. But nearly all the main branches of low-speed aerodynamics grew from the eventual achievement of sustained powered flight; and the problems of lift and drag, and of stability and control, were all initiated at about the beginning of this century. Within ten years, during the course of which Prandtl contributed the concept of the boundary layer, mathematical models of these problems were made which have, by and large, held good ever since.

The only completely new addition to this well-formulated body of aerodynamic theory came about through the study of the effects of compressibility (which at first ran contrary to the general rule by anticipating practical developments). Corresponding to this, the only revolutionary engineering development in aircraft practice was the gas-turbine engine.

Of all the problems associated with a gas turbine, those concerning the flow of gas form only a small part; this, however, includes a range of physical phenomena—from the intake, to the compressor, combustion chambers, turbine, and finally to the exhaust cone—which far outstrips the limits of this book. But these various types of flow within an engine have been subjected to intense study over the last twenty years or so; engine aerodynamics, as we might call these studies, is still an infant of undeveloped personality, at least as far as the theoretical side of its character is concerned, for the physical nature of many of the flows within an engine is still quite obscured by their extreme complexity. Nevertheless, engine aerodynamics has already established itself as one of the major branches of fluid dynamics.

Although the density of a gas, flowing through a compressor or a turbine, varies in practice, useful results come from analyses based on the assumptions of incompressible flow; and much knowledge has been gained by low-speed experiments which has later been applied to apparatus in which effects of compressibility are important. Theories for both radial-flow and axial-flow compressors have been developed but in this chapter we limit ourselves to the axial-flow type since it is the more important.

Even within the limitations of incompressible flow, many phenomena are as yet beyond theoretical explanation: for example, the problem of flutter—which for the wings of aircraft has long been placed on a sound theoretical footing—has yet to be conquered for the blades of compressors; again, the problem of surge, which is even more important, is still intractable. But at least one line of theoretical study, usually called actuator-disk theory, has been set off by the particular nature of flow in axial compressors and turbines, and this chapter gives an account of its fundamental theory. This theory would not enable a designer to design even the aerodynamic characteristics of a compressor, for which all kinds of empirical additions to the work of this chapter would be necessary. But the theory of the next few sections may well prove the basis of much theoretical development in the future.

2. The axial-flow compressor

A longitudinal section through the axis of an axial-flow compressor is shown diagrammatically in Fig. XI. 1. The blades, R, are thin highly-cambered wings, whose aspect ratio usually lies between 1 and 5; they are attached to the circumference of the main rotating body, B, of the compressor, their spanwise direction being radial. C is the cylindrical outer casing on which are fixed further blades, S, which are again thin highly-cambered wings whose span is radial. The moving blades, R, are called rotor blades and the fixed blades, S, stator blades; every set of blades is arranged in a ring, the circumferential spacing of the blades being roughly equal to their chord. The fluid flows in the annular space between B and C, which usually decreases in area in the downstream direction. The function of each row of rotor blades is to increase the energy of the fluid. This increase is usually manifested as an increase in pressure. At the same time, some circumferential velocity is imparted to the fluid, which it is the function of the following row of stator blades to remove. A row of rotor blades, together with the following row of stator blades, is called a stage of the compressor; ten is a typical number of stages in a compressor.

The flow through such a stage is very complicated even if the fluid is

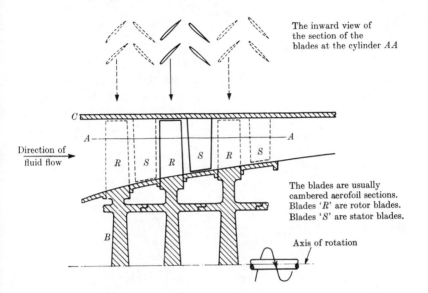

The inward view of the section of the blades at the cylinder AA

Direction of fluid flow

The blades are usually cambered aerofoil sections. Blades 'R' are rotor blades. Blades 'S' are stator blades.

Axis of rotation

Fig. XI. 1. A sketch of part of an axial-flow compressor.

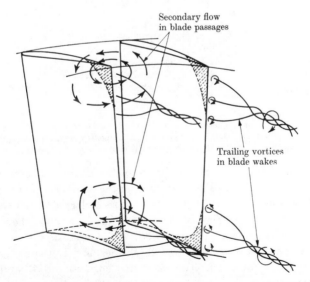

Secondary flow in blade passages

Trailing vortices in blade wakes

Fig. XI. 2. A sketch illustrating the secondary flow near two rotor blades. The shaded areas represent regions in which separation occurs owing to the secondary flow or to the effects of the boundary layers on the walls.

assumed to be inviscid. The further complications due to viscosity are
more serious than in simpler flows. The boundary layer on each blade
usually separates and its wake impinges on the rows of blades downstream. Further, there is a tendency for the boundary layer on rotor
blades to drift outwards under centrifugal forces. In addition, the
boundary layers on the walls of the flow annulus are of appreciable

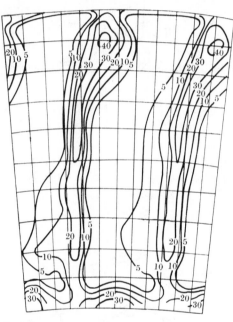

Fig. XI. 3. Typical contours of total pressure downstream of two blades.
The figures indicate the loss of total pressure as a percentage of mean dynamic
pressure at the inlet of the blade row. The measurements were made at a distance
of 0·7c downstream of the trailing edges.

thickness and their interactions with the blades cause complex secondary
flows; these often lead to separation from the blade, or from the walls
near the blade ends. A common type of secondary flow between the
blades is illustrated in Figs. XI. 2 and 3. Fig. XI. 2 shows the features
of the secondary flows, namely the flow of the annular wall boundary
layers towards the suction side of the blades, and of the mainstream
in the opposite direction. The associated spanwise flows result in a
trailing vortex sheet at the trailing edge, which rolls up. Fig. XI. 3
shows the total-pressure contours occurring downstream of the blades
in such a flow.

3. Theoretical models of flow in an annulus

To arrive at an idealized flow which might be amenable to theoretical treatment, the following simplifications have, in the past, been made. First all the effects of viscosity—drag, separation, secondary flow, and so on—which lead to a decrease of efficiency are regarded as modifications to a theory for inviscid flow, and their quantitative measures are deduced from experiments. Such experiments are also used to obtain semi-empirical rules for determining the most suitable spacing and shape of blades. Each row of blades is then replaced by the abstract concept of a plane on which the velocity vector and pressure of the fluid are discontinuous. The technical term given to this abstraction of the row of blades is actuator disk, which suggests a rotating disk composed of an infinite number of infinitesimal blades.

The present-day theory, and the methods of design, of axial-flow compressors are based on the idea of the actuator disk. Howell (1942, 1945, 1948a) is largely responsible for this theory; his papers—and that by Howell and Bonham (1950)—also consider the empirical corrections which have to be made to the results given by the simple theoretical models. Ainley and Jeffs (1946) give a valuable account of the nature of the physical flow.

This chapter concentrates, for the most part, on the theory of flow of an incompressible, inviscid fluid through an annular passage containing one or more actuator disks. No doubt, theories will eventually be developed which avoid the drastic simplification of the actuator disk. Some work on these lines has already been done. Wu (1952) has applied numerical methods to finding the pattern of streamlines through a row of blades, while the generalization of the conception of an actuator disk into a region of non-zero axial length has been considered in important papers by Marble (1948), by Marble and Michelson (1952), and by Railly (1951). It is, however, difficult to summarize these methods or to draw general conclusions, and we should refer to Horlock (1958a) for a survey of the theory of axial-flow compressors.

One of the characteristics of an actuator disk, which distinguishes the flow through it from most of the flows so far studied in this book, is its production of vorticity which fills the whole region of flow, at least downstream of the disk. When we come to establish equations of motion in Section 4, we shall need to include the effects of vorticity and shall find that its introduction demands analytical methods of solution which are not analogous to the classical methods for irrotational flow.

Rotational flow, however, may be considered independently of even the idealized actuator disk and much interest has been focused on flows in which vorticity, no longer confined to the boundary layers, plays a dominant role. Some of the characteristics of rotating fluids which only comparatively recently have become at all fully understood were anticipated in the work of G. I. Taylor (1922). Specially interesting are rotational flows in pipes, and therefore reference to flow in an unobstructed duct will be made in Section 11 of this chapter which otherwise will be devoted to problems of actuator disks.

Which properties of the flow through a duct with a single actuator disk are normally prescribed for an analytical solution? Two problems may be distinguished. First, the velocity field may be specified far upstream and downstream, and we require to know the discontinuities of velocity and pressure at the disk. There is a unique answer to this so-called design problem provided that it is assumed that the disk does not exert a radial force, or in other words that the radial velocity is continuous at the disk; and in practice most blades are designed to satisfy this assumption. The solution of this problem is considered in Sections 8 and 10. Once the discontinuities in velocity and pressure have been determined for the abstract conception of the actuator disk, the geometrical shape of the real blades is deduced, partly by the theory of cascades as summarized in Sections XII. 13–19, and partly by well-established empirical formulae. This last stage of the design problem is not considered in any detail in the following sections.

The second problem which normally arises is the determination of the effect, on a given upstream flow, of a row of blades of given geometrical characteristics. The rules of cascades to which we have just referred are usually used to deduce from the shape of the blades the direction, relative to the blades, at which the fluid leaves the row. It will be seen in Section 12 that knowledge of the so-called outlet angle is sufficient to define the flow.

The theory of actuator disks is directed principally towards the solution of one or other of these two problems, but since they refer to only a single disk an important part of the theory is devoted to the effect of two or more disks in the same duct, and of their interference. This is considered in Section 13. The fact that the flow settles down very rapidly after an actuator disk simplifies the problem of interference; it also renders valid our universal approximation that ducts may, for analytical purposes, be assumed to be infinite in length.

Finally, we need to remark that the conception of an actuator disk depends for its validity on the close spacing of the blades in a stage of a compressor. Thus the common fan—such as is found in a wind-tunnel, or in a ventilation shaft—is not included in the analysis of this chapter: the method of Thwaites (1951, 1953) may be referred to for the design and analysis of flow through ducted fans.

4. Equations of motion and some general theorems

Cylindrical polar coordinates (r, θ, z) are used, $r = 0$ being the axis of the flow, and the velocity components are (u, v, w). In the theory of the actuator disk, it will be assumed that the flow is axi-symmetric, namely that derivatives with respect to θ are zero.

The equation of continuity, from equation (I.90), becomes

$$\partial(ur)/\partial r + \partial(wr)/\partial z = 0$$

and is satisfied identically by taking, as in equation (I. 13),

$$u = -(1/r)\partial\psi/\partial z, \qquad w = (1/r)\partial\psi/\partial r, \tag{1}$$

$\psi = \psi(r, z)$ being the stream function. It was mentioned in Section I. 7 that ψ is constant on any stream surface and that the flux per unit time between the two surfaces $\psi = \psi_0$ and $\psi = \psi_1$ is $2\pi(\psi_1 - \psi_0)$. For flow in an annular region, the inner boundary is usually taken as $\psi = 0$.

If we apply Kelvin's theorem of equation (I. 54), that the circulation in a circuit moving with an inviscid fluid remains constant, to a circular cross-section of a stream surface, we have that $2\pi r v$ is constant on a stream surface. Thus

$$rv = rv_\theta = K(\psi), \tag{2}$$

K being a function of ψ only. This is a relation which is constantly used in the subsequent theory.

In the same way, from equation (I. 43) we see that the total pressure, H, is also a function of ψ only. Thus

$$H = H(\psi). \tag{3}$$

The components of vorticity are, from equation (I. 86),

$$\omega_r = -\frac{\partial v}{\partial z}; \qquad \omega_\theta = \frac{\partial u}{\partial z} - \frac{\partial w}{\partial r}; \qquad \omega_z = \frac{1}{r}\frac{\partial}{\partial r}(vr). \tag{4}$$

Now from equations (1) and (4) we obtain

$$-\omega_\theta = \frac{1}{r}\left[\frac{\partial^2\psi}{\partial z^2} + \frac{\partial^2\psi}{\partial r^2} - \frac{1}{r}\frac{\partial\psi}{\partial r}\right]. \tag{5}$$

This equation indicates the special importance of ω_θ in the theory of rotary flows, for if ω_θ is a known function of r and z, equation (5) gives the solution for ψ. This solution includes, of course, the complementary function of the equation, and the constants in this are usually chosen so that the flux of fluid within the annulus takes some prescribed value. $v = v(r)$ may meanwhile take any value, its only effect being to introduce two other components of vorticity and to affect the pressure distribution.

In view of the evident importance of ω_θ, we might seek a relation between it and other properties of the flow on which solutions could be based. In fact, a fairly simple relation exists between ω_θ, H, and (rv) which we now proceed to derive. It is best to introduce a set of orthogonal axes related to the stream surfaces. Let the coordinates be $(x_1, x_2, x_3) \equiv (n, \theta, s)$ where n is measured along the outward normal to the stream surface, θ is the azimuthal angle, and s is measured along a stream surface on a meridional plane. Elements of arc are given by $(h_1, h_2, h_3) \equiv (1, r, 1)$ at the particular point to be considered. The vorticity components are given from equation (I. 86), whence

$$\mathbf{v} \equiv (0, v_\theta, v_s) \quad \text{and} \quad \omega \equiv \left(0, \omega_\theta, \frac{1}{r} \frac{\partial}{\partial n}(rv_\theta)\right).$$

Inserting these expressions into the equation of motion which, from equation (I. 49), can be written in the form

$$\mathbf{v} \times \omega = (1/\rho)\mathrm{grad}\, H, \tag{6}$$

we obtain $\dfrac{rv_\theta}{r^2} \dfrac{\partial}{\partial n}(rv_\theta) - v_s \omega_\theta = \dfrac{1}{\rho} \dfrac{dH}{d\psi} \dfrac{\partial \psi}{\partial n} = \dfrac{1}{\rho} \dfrac{dH}{d\psi} rv_s,$

in which the fact stated in equation (3) is used. Using also equation (2), we finally obtain

$$\frac{1}{\rho} \frac{dH}{d\psi} = -\frac{\omega_\theta}{r} + \frac{rv}{r^2} \frac{d}{d\psi}(rv), \tag{7}$$

in which we have reverted to the original cylindrical polar coordinates. A second form of the equation is obtained by putting ω_θ in terms of ψ from equations (1) and (4), and is

$$\frac{1}{\rho} \frac{dH}{d\psi} = \frac{1}{r^2}\left(\frac{\partial^2 \psi}{\partial z^2} + \frac{\partial^2 \psi}{\partial r^2} - \frac{1}{r} \frac{\partial \psi}{\partial r}\right) + \frac{rv}{r^2} \frac{d}{d\psi}(rv). \tag{8}$$

This equation has come to be regarded as the fundamental equation of rotary flow and has provided the basis for most recent work. Bragg and Hawthorne (1950), to whom it is due, used it to derive an exact solution of flow through an actuator disk, while Horlock (1958b) used it to determine, approximately, the value of ω_θ at the disk in terms of the conditions far away. Long (1953) illustrated the possibility of standing waves which Fraenkel (1956), to whom is due the derivation given above of equation (7), also found in his discussion of pipe flows in the absence of any externally applied forces.

It should be mentioned that when there is an external field of force whose component in the n-direction is F_n per unit mass, a term equal to (F_n/rv_s) should be added the right-hand sides of equations (7) and (8), as was first shown by Marble and Michelson (1952).

We shall also need the equations for two-dimensional flow corresponding to equations (7) and (8). They could be derived from equation (7) by taking the limit as $r_0 \to \infty$ where $r_0 < r < r_0 + h$, the annular strip thus becoming a region between two planes. Alternatively a set of axes, (n, y, s), related to the streamlines may be taken, for which the elements of arc are $(1, 1, 1)$. The velocity is then $(0, v_y, v_s)$ and the vorticity $(0, \omega_y, \partial v_y/\partial n)$ so that the equation of motion, in the form (6), becomes
$$v_y(\partial v_y/\partial n) - v_s \omega_y = (1/\rho)(dH/d\psi)(\partial \psi/\partial n).$$

Since $\partial \psi/\partial n = v_s$,
$$v\frac{dv}{d\psi} - \omega_y = \frac{1}{\rho}\frac{dH}{d\psi}, \tag{9}$$

in which v is a function of ψ only. This, then, is the equation describing the two-dimensional flow (u, v, w) in which derivatives with respect to y are identically zero. The equation of continuity reduces to
$$\partial u/\partial x + \partial w/\partial z = 0$$
so that $u = -\partial \psi/\partial z$, $w = \partial \psi/\partial x$. The vorticity component
$$\omega_y = (du/dz - dw/dx)$$
may therefore be put in terms of ψ, and with this substitution for ω_y in equation (9) we obtain
$$\frac{\partial^2 \psi}{\partial x^2} + \frac{\partial^2 \psi}{\partial y^2} = -v\frac{dv}{d\psi} + \frac{1}{\rho}\frac{dH}{d\psi}, \tag{10}$$
which is the two-dimensional analogue of equation (8).

Certain special cases, in which ω_θ varies in a particularly simple manner, are useful. First, if the total pressure has the same value for all the streamlines in any region of flow, then, from equation (6),
$$\mathbf{v} \times \boldsymbol{\omega} = 0. \tag{11}$$

Thus, if the vorticity is not zero, the streamlines and vortex lines coincide. This type of flow sometimes occurs in practice, as for example when air is drawn from the atmosphere by an actuator disk which imparts no energy to it. Further, from equations (2) and (7), $r\omega_\theta$ is a function of ψ:
$$r\omega_\theta = \Omega_0(\psi). \tag{12}$$

This result is important since it follows that if the streamlines depart from the cylinders $r = $ constant by only a small amount, then ω_θ also will vary by only a small amount about some mean value.

The second special case arises when $rv \equiv K$ takes the same value on all the streamlines in any region. Then equation (7) gives

$$\omega_\theta/r = \Omega_1(\psi). \tag{13}$$

This, though it appears fundamentally different from equation (12), nevertheless leads to a similar argument, namely that provided the stream surfaces do not depart too much from circular cylinders, the variations in ω_θ are again small. In this case, equation (4) gives

$$\omega_r = \omega_z = 0, \tag{14}$$

which again is a common state of affairs.

These special cases help to justify what will be a general assumption in all the approximate treatment of actuator disks in subsequent sections. It will be assumed that ω_θ is a function of r only.

5. Equations for the total pressure

The equation of momentum, (I. 38),

$$Dv/Dt = \mathbf{F} - (1/\rho)\operatorname{grad} p \tag{15}$$

may be written as an energy equation by forming the dot product with $\mathbf{v}$: a slight rearrangement then gives

$$DH/Dt = \partial p/\partial t + \rho \mathbf{v} \cdot \mathbf{F}. \tag{16}$$

This equation expresses the fact that, as an element of fluid moves, the change of its total pressure is due first to time-variations of static pressure and second to the work done by the external field of force.

It is convenient, for some applications to rotary flows, to derive an equation analogous to (16) in terms of a set of axes which are rotating with the constant angular velocity $\mathbf{\Omega} = (0, 0, \Omega)$: such an equation may be used to find changes of total pressure in flow through a rotor system. The fundamental relation between time-rates of change in the two sets of axes is

$$(DA/Dt)_1 = (DA/Dt)_2 + \mathbf{\Omega} \times \mathbf{A}, \tag{17}$$

where $\mathbf{A}$ is any vector and the system 2 is rotating with an angular velocity $\mathbf{\Omega}$ relative to, and in the coordinates of, system 1. If $\mathbf{V}$ is the velocity with respect to the rotating axes, its relation to $\mathbf{v}$ is found by putting $\mathbf{A} = \mathbf{r}$ in (17); thus $\mathbf{v} = \mathbf{V} + \mathbf{\Omega} \times \mathbf{r}$. Similarly, the relation between Dv/Dt and DV/Dt is found by putting $\mathbf{A} = \mathbf{v}$. Equation (15) may then be put in terms of the velocities in the rotating system:

$$D\mathbf{V}/Dt+2\mathbf{\Omega}\times\mathbf{V}+\mathbf{\Omega}\times(\mathbf{\Omega}\times\mathbf{r}) = -(\operatorname{grad} p)/\rho+\mathbf{F}.$$

Forming the dot product with $\mathbf{V}$, we may write this as

$$(\mathbf{v}-\mathbf{\Omega}\times\mathbf{r})[D\mathbf{V}/Dt+2\mathbf{\Omega}\times\mathbf{V}+\mathbf{\Omega}\times(\mathbf{\Omega}\times\mathbf{r})]$$
$$= (\partial p/\partial t)/\rho-(\partial p/\partial t+\mathbf{V}.\operatorname{grad} p)/\rho+\mathbf{V}.\mathbf{F},$$

which may be reduced to

$$\frac{DH}{Dt} = \frac{\partial p}{\partial t}+\rho\mathbf{V}.\mathbf{F}+\rho\frac{D}{Dt}(\mathbf{v}.\mathbf{\Omega}\times\mathbf{r}). \tag{18}$$

If the flow is steady, and there are no body forces, this equation reduces to

$$\frac{DH}{Dt} = \rho\frac{D}{Dt}(\mathbf{v}.\mathbf{\Omega}\times\mathbf{r}), \tag{19}$$

so that the difference between the total pressure at two points, 1 and 2, on a stream surface referred to the axes in the rotating system is given by

$$H_2-H_1 = \rho r(v_2-v_1)\Omega. \tag{20}$$

This result has considerable practical importance, since it may be applied also to two points on either side of an actuator disk. The force exerted on the fluid by the actuator disk must be regarded as a body force $\mathbf{F}$, but on the assumption of inviscid fluid, this is normal to the relative velocity $\mathbf{V}$ and $\mathbf{V}.\mathbf{F}$ is again zero in equation (18). Equation (20) is thus true for steady flow through an actuator disk, and is a well-known turbine equation whose classical derivation we may recall. The term $\rho r(v_2-v_1)$ in the equation represents the change of angular momentum per unit volume of fluid flowing through an annulus of the disk; this corresponds to the torque exerted by the disk. The product of this torque and the angular velocity, Ω, is the work done by the disk per unit volume of fluid flowing, which is manifested in the change of total pressure of fluid.

It is worth remarking that no assumption of axial symmetry has been made to obtain equation (19); it is therefore true for quite general flows, provided they are steady and have no external forces.

6. Radial equilibrium. The pressure distribution

It is found experimentally that, in the majority of duct flows, the velocity distribution tends steadily, and fairly rapidly, to some asymptotic value away from any disturbance such as an actuator disk. In other words, all derivatives with respect to z tend to zero at infinity.

The continuity equation then gives the result that $u \to 0$ as $z \to \infty$, and the equation of motion (6) reduces to $\partial p / \partial r = \rho v^2 / r$, or

$$p = p_0 + \int_{r_h}^{r} (\rho v^2 / r) \, dr, \tag{21}$$

where p_0 is the static pressure on the inner boundary $r = r_h$.

The term 'radial equilibrium' is applied to any region of flow for which equation (21) holds, and is usefully suggestive since the equation represents the balance between the centrifugal and pressure forces.

There are exceptions to the statement that all flows tend to a state of radial equilibrium at infinity. In Section 11, for example, flows with standing waves in the z-direction are discussed; it is not necessarily always a good assumption that radial equilibrium exists far from an actuator disk, and clearly it can apply only to a duct which itself becomes parallel at its two ends.

A state of radial equilibrium may be defined by the values of $v(r)$ and $w(r)$, in terms of which ψ and H (each measured relative to some arbitrary datum) may be expressed. Conversely, $v(r)$ and $w(r)$ may be deduced from a knowledge of the variation with respect to ψ of H and $K \equiv rv$. These last two functional relationships are often used to describe the characteristics of a flow.

The primary problem in the theory of actuator disks refers to the change from one state of radial equilibrium far upstream of the disk to another far downstream. These two states are normally described by given functions $H(\psi)$ and $K(\psi)$. We then require to know the discontinuities at the disk in H and K which produce the change, the associated distribution of axial velocity w at the disk and indeed the velocity field of the whole flow.

Radial equilibrium emphasizes again the special importance of w_θ which in these special circumstances becomes, from equation (4), $\omega_\theta = -\partial w / \partial r$. The distribution of axial velocity $w(r)$ can therefore be calculated from knowledge of w_θ, the constant of integration being determined from a knowledge of the total flux through a section $z = $ constant. Further, if ω_θ is known over the whole field, equations (1) and (3) are sufficient to determine everywhere the velocity components u and w. The fundamental equation (7) is thus often regarded as an equation for ω_θ.

7. Free-vortex flow

Another common type of flow between annular walls is that in which the total pressure is constant for all streamlines far upstream. This would normally be true of any duct drawing fluid from an atmosphere at rest. In such a case, the rotary component of velocity is zero at infinity, but we proceed slightly more generally by assuming that $K = rv$ is constant, not necessarily zero. Thus with

$$dH/d\psi = dK/d\psi = 0, \tag{22}$$

equation (7) gives $\omega_\theta = 0. \tag{23}$

The simplest annular flow which satisfies the equations of continuity and of momentum, and also the special equations (22) and (23), is given by

$$u = 0; \quad v = K/r, \quad w = w_\infty, \quad p = P - \tfrac{1}{2}\rho v^2, \tag{24}$$

where K, w_∞, and P are constants. Such a flow is usually called a free-vortex flow, from the engineer's custom of referring to the flow, $u = w = 0$ and $v \propto 1/r$, as a free vortex. The term 'vortex-free' might be more appropriate since equation (24) represents the only rotary flow in which the vorticity is identically zero everywhere. The flow is in a state of radial equilibrium.

Suppose now that upstream of an actuator disk there is free-vortex flow and that the disk is such that the changes in H and K are uniform for all radial positions. Equations (22) will therefore hold downstream of the disk too, where another free-vortex flow will be established. It is, in fact, possible to design a row of blades to have this effect.

The simplicity of this solution tends to emphasize the difficulty of more general flows. The change of total pressure through an actuator disk will normally vary with r. Thus (rv) which is constant for each streamline except at a disk will vary with ψ, at any rate after the first row of blades. Thus from equation (7), ω_θ will be non-zero and so from (4) both w and u will vary with r and z.

Since, for the free-vortex flow, changes in the velocity occur only discontinuously at one or more disks, two correctly-designed disks may be placed close together without any mutual interference. This exceptional property is not shared by flows in general, and the problems of interference are discussed briefly in Section 13.

Many compressors have been designed to conform to the free-vortex flow and in Section 16 some further considerations of the flow will be discussed.

8. Approximate solutions of two-dimensional flow. Mean-value and settling-rate rules

The flow through an actuator strip, as described by equation (9), may be regarded as the state to which an annular flow tends as the radius becomes large whilst the annulus gap remains small. It has some practical interest since it corresponds to the arrangement of blades which is usually adopted in experiments on the aerodynamic characteristics of blades. Of greater interest is the fact that solutions of the two-dimensional equation exhibit, in a simple manner, some of the basic characteristics of solutions of the more complicated three-dimensional equation.

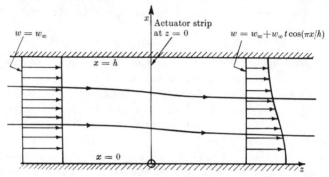

FIG. XI. 4. An illustration of flow through an actuator strip.

Let us consider therefore flow in the infinite region $-\infty < z < +\infty$, $0 \leqslant x \leqslant h$, at the section $z = 0$ of which lies a so-called actuator strip which produces discontinuities in the properties of the flow.

To begin with, let us assume the following velocity distributions at infinity which are illustrated in Fig. XI. 4.

$$z = -\infty; \quad w = w_\infty = \text{constant}, \qquad u = 0 \Big\}$$
$$z = +\infty; \quad w = w_\infty + w_\infty t \cos(\pi x/h), \quad u = 0 \Big\} . \tag{25}$$

The corresponding values of ω_y are

$$z = -\infty; \quad \omega_y = 0 \Big\}$$
$$z = +\infty; \quad \omega_y = w_\infty(\pi t/h)\sin(\pi x/h) \Big\} . \tag{26}$$

Now, upstream of the actuator strip, the vorticity is zero at infinity and so is zero in the whole upstream region. This leads to the equation

$$-\infty < z < -0, \qquad \partial^2\psi/\partial x^2 + \partial^2\psi/\partial z^2 = 0. \tag{27}$$

In the region downstream of the disk, ω_y is a function of ψ only, as follows from equation (9). The streamlines, however, are unlikely to diverge much from lines $x = $ constant, provided that the quantity t is fairly small. The approximation is therefore made, as was foreshadowed in Section 4, that ω_y is a function of x only and equal to its value at infinity downstream. Thus from (9),

$$+0 < z < +\infty, \quad \partial^2\psi/\partial x^2 + \partial^2\psi/\partial z^2 = -(w_\infty \pi t/h)\sin(\pi x/h). \quad (28)$$

The remaining boundary conditions for equations (27) and (28) are:

$$\left.\begin{array}{l}
\text{(i) } u = 0 \text{ on } x = 0 \text{ and } x = h; \\
\text{(ii) } w \equiv \partial\psi/\partial x \text{ takes the same value either side of the actuator} \\
\qquad \text{disk, } z = 0; \\
\text{(iii) } u \equiv -\partial\psi/\partial z \text{ takes the same value for } z = \pm 0, \text{ if the strip} \\
\qquad \text{is assumed to be incapable of exerting a force in the} \\
\qquad x\text{-direction.}
\end{array}\right\} \quad (29)$$

It may easily be verified that the following expressions for ψ satisfy the governing equations (27) and (28) and all the boundary conditions except, for the time being, those on the actuator disk, $z = 0$:

$$\left.\begin{array}{l}
-\infty < z < -0; \quad \psi = w_\infty x + Ae^{\lambda z}\sin(\pi x/h), \\
+0 < z < +\infty; \quad \psi = w_\infty x + (w_\infty th/\pi)\sin(\pi x/h) + Be^{\mu z}\sin(\pi x/h),
\end{array}\right\} \quad (30)$$

in which $\lambda = \pi/h$ and $\mu = -\pi/h$. As is often the case in solving equations of the type (28), particular solutions satisfying some of the boundary conditions are first written down to which are added more general solutions of Laplace's equation whose coefficients (in this case A and B) are subsequently chosen so that the remaining conditions are satisfied. The remaining conditions (ii) and (iii) in this example, at $z = 0$, may be satisfied by taking

$$A = -B = w_\infty th/2\pi. \quad (31)$$

Typical characteristics of flows past certain types of actuator disks may be extracted from this example. First, the axial velocity at the disk is given by

$$w/w_\infty = w_0/w_\infty = 1 + \tfrac{1}{2}t\cos(\pi x/h), \quad (32)$$

that is, by the mean of the velocities far upstream and far downstream. This result will be referred to as the mean-value rule. Second, the upstream velocity can be written in the form

$$-\infty < z < -0; \quad w = w_u + \tfrac{1}{2}(w_d - w_u)\exp(\pi z/h), \quad (33)$$

the suffixes u and d denoting conditions at infinity upstream and downstream respectively. This equation gives w very simply in terms of its values at infinity and of the width, h, of the duct. The equation has often been taken as an approximation to more complicated flows and will be referred to as the settling-rate rule; it is illustrated for the downstream region in Fig. XI. 5. Third, the rate of settling depends on the periodicity of the axial velocity far downstream; if the disturbance there had been proportional to $\cos(\pi x n/h)$, $n > 1$, then the exponential coefficient in equation (33) would have been $(\pi z n/h)$ and the flow would have settled more rapidly.

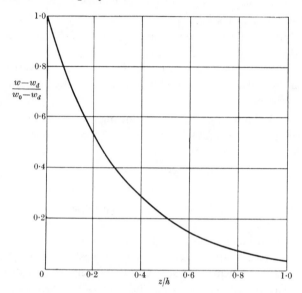

FIG. XI. 5. The settling-rate rule, giving the axial velocity w in terms of the velocity w_0 at the disk $z = 0$, and the velocity w_d at infinity.

The approximate solution of equation (9) given by equations (30) could be generalized by replacing the trigonometrical terms by sums. Thus we could write

$$
\begin{aligned}
-\infty < z < -0; \quad &\psi = w_\infty x - w_\infty t \sum A_n \exp(\lambda_n z)\sin(\pi x n/h), \\
+0 < z < +\infty; \quad &\psi = w_\infty x + w_\infty t \sum A_n \exp(-\lambda_n z)\sin(\pi x n/h) + \\
&\qquad\qquad\qquad + w_0 \sum B_n \sin(\pi x n/h),
\end{aligned}
\right\} \quad (34)
$$

as a solution of equations (27) and (28) provided $\lambda_n = n\pi/h$. The velocity distribution far downstream is then given by

$$
w = w_\infty + w_0(\pi/h) \sum n B_n \cos(\pi x n/h)
$$

and the A_n are given in terms of the B_n by the conditions (29).

It is important to recall the assumptions which led to the mean-value and settling-rate rules, namely that ω_y is a function of x only and that u is continuous at the actuator disk. Roughly, the first assumption leads to the settling-rate rule, and the second to the mean-value rule. The mean-value rule can be completely upset if the actuator strip exerts a large radial force: indeed it is possible to envisage a flow, with a suitably designed disk, in which all the adjustments between the distributions of $w(x)$ far upstream and downstream occur on one side of the disk only. The settling-rate rule would in turn be upset by a high periodicity in the x-direction of the change in $w(x)$: one can imagine a flow in which settlement occurs in any given proportion of the distance predicted by the rule. Nevertheless, in most practical applications, both rules apply with satisfactory accuracy.

While, in general, equations (34) represent only an approximate solution of the exact equations, the assumption mentioned in the preceding paragraph is exactly satisfied in the case of a linear variation of velocity at $z = +\infty$. For this case, $B_n = h/\pi n^3$ for n odd and $B_n = 0$ for n even. Conditions on the disk $z = 0$ then enable the coefficients A_n to be calculated:

$$A_n = (-h/2\pi n^3)(w_0/tw_\infty).$$

It may easily be verified that the vorticity is zero everywhere upstream of the disk, and takes a constant value downstream, and for this case, the result that the axial velocity at the disk is the mean of the velocities at infinity is exact. We note also that the settling-rate rule approximates closely to this exact solution since it is actually the settling rate of the B_1-velocity term, and this term is nine times as large as the next term, the B_3-term, which settles three times as rapidly as the B_1-term.

9. Approximate solutions of axi-symmetric flow. Mean-value and settling-rate rules

The approximation $\omega_y = \omega_y(x)$ led to a very simple solution for the actuator strip and similarly to assume $\omega_\theta = \omega_\theta(r)$ simplifies the analysis in the three-dimensional case of rotary flow. Thus from equation (5) we have, for each region of flow,

$$\partial^2\psi/\partial z^2 + \partial^2\psi/\partial r^2 - (1/r)(\partial\psi/\partial r) = rf(r), \qquad (35)$$

$f(r)$ taking the value of ω_θ appropriate to each region. For a single disk, therefore, this equation has to be solved for the two regions on either side of the disk, with the boundary conditions:

$$\left.\begin{array}{l} \text{(i)} \quad w = w_u \text{ at } z = -\infty \quad \text{and} \quad w = w_d \text{ at } z = +\infty; \\ \text{(ii)} \quad u = 0 \text{ at } r = r_t, r_h; \\ \text{(iii)} \quad u \text{ and } w \text{ continuous at the disk which is taken to be} \\ \qquad \text{at } z = 0. \end{array}\right\} \quad (36)$$

Now at infinity, where a state of radial equilibrium is assumed to exist let ψ equal ψ_∞ given by

$$\partial^2\psi_\infty/\partial r^2-(1/r)(\partial\psi_\infty/\partial r) = rf(r). \tag{37}$$

Thus if we put $\psi = \psi_\infty+\psi'$ for the whole flow, equations (35) and (37) give

$$\partial^2\psi'/\partial z^2+\partial^2\psi'/\partial r^2-(1/r)(\partial\psi'/\partial r) = 0. \tag{38}$$

By putting $\psi = g(r)\exp(k_n z/r_t)$, we find $g(r)$ in terms of the Bessel functions, J_1 and Y_1, of the first and second kind; it may easily be verified that a general solution of (38) is

$$\psi' = \sum r(r_t w_0/\lambda_n)\exp(\pm\lambda_n z/r_t)[A_n J_1(\lambda_n r/r_t)+B_n Y_1(\lambda_n r/r_t)]. \tag{39}$$

The velocity field is then given by

$$\left.\begin{aligned}
u &= \mp \sum w_0 \exp(\pm\lambda_n z/r_t)[A_n J_1(\lambda_n r/r_t)+B_n Y_1(\lambda_n r/r_t)], \\
w &= w_\infty\pm \sum w_0 \exp(\pm\lambda_n z/r_t)[A_n J_0(\lambda_n r/r_t)+B_n Y_0(\lambda_n r/r_t)]
\end{aligned}\right\}, \tag{40}$$

in which $w_\infty = w_\infty(r)$ is the solution of equation (37) for the radial-equilibrium flow at infinity.

The boundary conditions (36) now have to be satisfied. First, the conditions at infinity are automatically satisfied by the exponential terms: it is convenient to take $\lambda_n > 0$ and to choose the signs in (40) appropriately. Second, the condition on the walls of the duct leads to

$$\frac{A_n}{B_n} = -\frac{Y_1(\lambda_n r_h/r_t)}{J_1(\lambda_n r_h/r_t)} = -\frac{Y_1(\lambda_n)}{J_1(\lambda_n)}. \tag{41}$$

If we regard (r_h/r_t) as given, these equations determine both (A_n/B_n) and λ_n, the first six values of which quantities are tabulated for various values of (r_t/r_h) by Jahnke and Emde (1945). Third, the condition of continuity of u and w at the disk, $z = 0$, leads to

$$A_{nu} = -A_{nd}, \quad B_{nu} = -B_{nd}, \quad w = \tfrac{1}{2}(w_u+w_d), \tag{42}$$

the suffixes u and d denoting $z = \mp\infty$, as before. We note that the last equation gives the mean-value rule. With λ_n, A_n/B_n, and w given by equations (41) and (42), the equation (40) for w enables the values of the coefficients, A_n and B_n, to be determined by the Bessel analogue of Fourier analysis.

The summation terms in equation (40) represent what is called the perturbation velocity which, so to speak, converts the velocity at infinity into the velocity at the disk. For the particular value $r_h'/r_t = 0.45$, the first six values of λ_n are given below:

λ_n	5·84	11·49	17·22	22·9	28·6	34·3
$0.55\lambda_n$	3·22	6·32	9·48	12·61	15·72	18·88
$n\pi$	3·14	6·28	9·42	12·56	15·71	18·84

The numbers in the second and third lines of the table permit comparison of the settling rates of the two- and three-dimensional flows: comparison of equations (40) and (34) shows that the settling rates will be the same if λ_n for the three-dimensional flow is equal to $n\pi r_t/(r_t-r_h)$. Thus for $r_h/r_t = 0.45$, $0.55\lambda_n$ should be equal to $n\pi$ for equality of settling rates. The discrepancy is small, and would be smaller still for larger values of r_h/r_t.

10. Exact solutions for actuator disks

Nothing in the two previous sections enables us to estimate the error involved in the basic assumptions concerning ω_y or ω_θ. Such assumptions should naturally be checked against exact results and Bragg and Hawthorne (1950) have found some exact solutions under somewhat restricted conditions. For these it is assumed that the total pressure is constant in each of the two regions on either side of the actuator disk; namely

$$dH/d\psi = 0 \tag{43}$$

in each of the two regions of flow. It is assumed further that $K(\partial K/\partial\psi)$ is a linear function of ψ; thus

$$K(\partial K/\partial\psi) = (k^2/r_t^2)\psi, \tag{44}$$

where r_t is the constant radius of the outer wall of the annulus. Whether or not this is a reasonable assumption, or a good approximation to physical flows, will be discussed later.

Under these two assumptions, equation (8) may be written

$$\partial^2\psi/\partial z^2+\partial^2\psi/\partial r^2-(1/r)(\partial\psi/\partial r)+(k^2/r_t^2)\psi = 0 \tag{45}$$

and we may find solutions analogous to those of Section 9, of the form

$$\psi(r,z) = \psi = \psi_\infty(r)+\sum \exp(\lambda_n z)\psi_n(r), \tag{46}$$

in which
$$\psi_\infty = r(r_t w_0/k)[A_\infty J_1(kr/r_t)+B_\infty Y_1(kr/r_t)]$$
and
$$\psi_n = r[r_t w_0(k^2+r_t^2\lambda_n^2)^{-\frac{1}{2}}]\times$$
$$\times[A_n J_1(r(k^2+r_t^2\lambda_n^2)^{\frac{1}{2}}/r_t)+B_n Y_1(r(k^2+r_t^2\lambda_n^2)^{\frac{1}{2}}/r_t)]. \tag{47}$$

The constants, A_∞ and B_∞, may be chosen to satisfy whatever overall conditions at infinity may be given: for example, the mean velocity and the velocity at one other point.

The boundary conditions are similar to those given in (36). To correspond with equation (41) we have

$$\frac{B_n}{A_n} = -\frac{J_1(r(k^2+r_t^2\lambda_n^2)^{\frac{1}{2}}/r_t)}{Y_1(r(k^2+r_t^2\lambda_n^2)^{\frac{1}{2}}/r_t)} \quad \text{for } r = r_t \text{ and } r = r_h. \tag{48}$$

Again, for a given value of (r_t/r_h), there are an infinite number of values for both B_n/A_n and $(k^2+r_t^2\lambda_n^2)^{\frac{1}{2}}$, the first six values of each quantity being given by Jahnke and Emde (1945).

λ_n^2 follows from the value of this last surd, the positive value of λ_n being taken for the upstream solution and the negative value for the downstream solution, so that the perturbation terms in equation (46) vanish at infinity. The condition that u is continuous at the disk leads to

$$(\lambda_n A_n)_u = -(\lambda_n A_n)_d, \tag{49}$$

while the continuity of w leads to an identity in r which, provided the sum in equation (46) is for $n = 0$ to ∞, may be satisfied. In this way the values of A_n and B_n can be found. In particular, it can be shown that if in the first place the rotations at infinity were chosen, in equation (35), such that $k_u = k_d$, then the mean-value rule for the axial velocity at the disk holds exactly.

To illustrate the usefulness of this exact solution, Bragg and Hawthorne prescribed a flow of a character which might well be found in practice; it was defined by

$$\left. \begin{array}{l} \text{at } z = -\infty; \; u = v = 0, \, w = w_u = \text{constant} \\ \text{at } z = +\infty; \; u = 0, \, v/w_u = v_d/w_u = 0{\cdot}74(r/r_t)^2 \end{array} \right\}. \tag{50}$$

Far upstream, therefore, the flow is uniform and satisfies the condition (43); far downstream this condition, coupled with that of radial equilibrium (21), determines the value of $w_d(r)$ from the prescribed values of u and v_d in (50). v_d and w_d are illustrated by the broken line in Fig. XI. 6.

Now equations (43) and (44) define a family of velocity distributions at infinity and after a process of trial and error and with a suitable choice of the various parameters involved, it was found that one of this family, illustrated by the full line in Fig. XI. 6, fitted the prescribed velocity distributions quite well. Only the first six terms of the sums in equation (46) were used and the values of some of the parameters in this particular solution are as follows:

n	1	2	3	4	5	6
$(k^2+r_t^2\lambda_n^2)^{\frac{1}{2}}$	5·84	11·5	17·2	22·9	28·6	34·3
$(B_n/A_n)_d$	−2·31	3·86	0·89	0·126	−0·488	−1·69
$(A_n)_u$	0·0818	−0·0166	−0·0230	−0·0265	−0·0155	−0·0070
$(A_n)_d$	0·0856	−0·0167	−0·0230	−0·0265	−0·0155	−0·0070
$\lambda_n(0{\cdot}55r_t)$	3·07	6·25	9·42	12·6	15·7	18·8

$$k = 1{\cdot}740; \quad (A_\infty)_d = -1{\cdot}415; \quad (B_\infty)_d = -0{\cdot}551$$

From the last row of the table, it may be seen that λ_n is almost exactly equal to $n\pi/h$, where $h = 0\cdot55r_t$ is the radial width of the duct. Thus again we find that the rate of settling of the perturbation velocities, $\exp(\lambda_n z)$, is almost the same as $\exp(n\pi z/h)$ which was found in Section 8 for the case of the actuator strip.

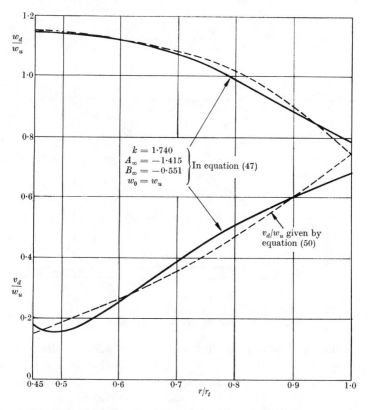

$$k = 1\cdot740$$
$$A_\infty = -1\cdot415$$
$$B_\infty = -0\cdot551 \quad\Big\} \text{ In equation (47)}$$
$$w_0 = w_u$$

v_d/w_u given by equation (50)

FIG. XI. 6. The fitting of an exact solution (shown by the full line) to a prescribed flow at infinity downstream (shown by the broken line).

In Fig. XI. 7 are shown the velocity distributions for some other sections of the duct. It is interesting that v varies so little with z; from this it follows that, since (rv) is constant on a stream surface, the stream surfaces are nearly cylindrical. A further point to notice is the rapidity with which the perturbation velocities decrease away from the disk: at a distance $z = 0\cdot1r_t$ they are already halved.

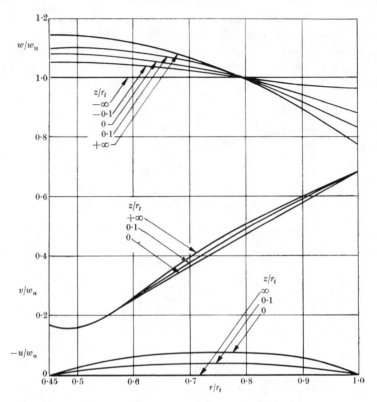

Fɪɢ. XI. 7. The distributions of velocity components across the duct at various axial positions in the flow calculated by Bragg and Hawthorne (1950).

11. Rotating flow in pipes in the absence of actuator disks

We consider in this section a cylindrical region bounded, externally only, by $r = r_t$. To begin with, we further consider only the region $z < 0$, called the upstream region, and suppose that far upstream the axial velocity w is constant and equal to w_∞, where there is also a constant angular velocity, Ω_∞, about the axis $r = 0$. Thus $v = r\Omega_\infty$; also $\psi = \frac{1}{2}w_\infty r^2$. Far upstream

$$H = p_0 + \tfrac{1}{2}\rho(w_\infty^2 + 2r^2\Omega_\infty^2) = p_0 + \tfrac{1}{2}\rho w_\infty^2 + 2\rho\Omega_\infty^2 \psi/w_\infty,$$

and $K = rv = \Omega_\infty r^2 = 2\Omega_\infty \psi/w_\infty$, where p_0 is the pressure on the axis.

If these expressions for H and K are substituted in equation (8), it becomes

$$\frac{\partial^2 \psi}{\partial z^2} + \frac{\partial^2 \psi}{\partial r^2} - \frac{1}{r}\frac{\partial \psi}{\partial r} - \frac{2\Omega_\infty^2 r^2}{w_\infty} + \frac{4\Omega_\infty^2 \psi}{w_\infty^2} = 0 \tag{51}$$

of which the particular integral is, of course, $\psi = \frac{1}{2}w_\infty r^2$, which represents the flow which has so far been defined. However, it is possible that the complementary function, ψ_1, of equation (51) represents a flow which may be superimposed on the solid rotation of the original flow, and to investigate this we put

$$\psi = \tfrac{1}{2}w_\infty r^2 + \psi_1. \tag{52}$$

The equation for ψ_1 is then, from (51),

$$\frac{\partial^2 \psi_1}{\partial z^2} + \frac{\partial^2 \psi_1}{\partial r^2} - \frac{1}{r}\frac{\partial \psi_1}{\partial r} + \left(\frac{2\Omega_\infty}{w_\infty}\right)^2 \psi_1 = 0. \tag{53}$$

Fraenkel (1956) used this equation to obtain solutions to two kinds of pipe flow. First he found the effect of a ring source on the pipe wall and was able by superposition to calculate the effect of a varying pipe radius. Secondly, he determined the disturbance due to a source on the axis; this again enabled solutions to be obtained for the pipe flow when a solid body of revolution is placed on the axis, for such a body may be represented, at least approximately, by an axial distribution of sources and sinks.

Equation (53) is analogous to (45), solutions to which have already been found: thus, from equations (47), we may write

$$\psi_1 = \exp(\lambda_n z/r_l)rJ_1[(r/r_l)\{(2\Omega_\infty r_l/w_\infty)^2 + \lambda_n^2\}^{\frac{1}{2}}] \tag{54}$$

for flows in which there are no singularities on $r = 0$. The second independent solution involving Y_1 may be included to represent a source distribution in the axis. The form of this solution attaches special importance to $z = 0$ and a complete solution involves two sets of expressions such as (54) summed over all values of n, one each for the up- and down-stream regions in which $\lambda_n \gtrless 0$ respectively. The coefficients in the two sums then have to be determined by the appropriate conditions of continuity at $z = 0$.

An important possibility arises if $2\Omega_\infty r_l/w_\infty > 3\cdot83$, which is the smallest root of J_1, for then the value of λ_n is imaginary. For large values of this rotational parameter $2\Omega_\infty r_l/w_\infty$, there is a large number of possible values of λ_n corresponding to the first so many of the infinite number of roots of the Bessel function J_1. The flow appears, therefore, not to be unique if it is rotating sufficiently fast.

Now imaginary values of λ_n imply, from equation (54), standing waves which extend to infinity both up- and down-stream, though they are of different form in the two regions by virtue of the disturbance at $z = 0$. It is generally assumed, however, that, at any rate for moderate values of $2\Omega_\infty r_t/w_\infty$, no waves occur upstream at infinity. Long (1953) has provided some experimental justification for this, by demonstrating that a body moving axially in a pipe full of rotating liquid produced no upstream effects but established waves downstream of itself. The theoretical argument most usually proposed suggests that disturbances upstream at infinity can only arise from a region of finite disturbance, but that such disturbances are convected downstream faster than they are propagated upstream within the moving fluid.

On the other hand, this assumption of no upstream disturbances seems not to be valid for very large values of $2\Omega_\infty r_t/w_\infty$. Then the fluid adjusts itself to a cylindrical flow, which does not depend on z, in preference to a flow involving waves of high frequency. This was found by G. I. Taylor (1923a) in some experiments on rotating spheres, and for a general discussion of the issues involved we may refer to Squire (1955).

It is interesting to note that in equation (47) imaginary values of λ_n can occur if k is sufficiently large. Thus there appears the possibility of standing waves in annular flow, but they have not yet been observed in experiment.

12. Approximate solutions for a single actuator disk of given geometrical characteristics

So far, our theory has concentrated on finding the velocity field everywhere when the conditions far upstream and far downstream are given, and one of the most useful results has been the emergence of the mean-value and the settling-rate rules, which are generally taken to be valid for an actuator disk which does not exert a radial force.

For a single actuator disk, the most important practical problem, however, is that of determining the flow everywhere, when the flow upstream and the geometrical characteristics of the disk are known. The two rules may be used in the treatment of this problem by a method given by Horlock (1958b); this starts with equation (20) written in the form

$$\Delta H = \rho U \Delta v, \tag{55}$$

where Δ signifies the change in value through the disk and $\mathbf{U} = \mathbf{\Omega} \times \mathbf{r}$. This value of ΔH is substituted into equation (7) to give

$$-\Delta\omega_\theta = U\Delta(dK/d\psi) - (1/r)\Delta(K\,dK/d\psi) = \Delta[(U-v)(dK/d\psi)]. \tag{56}$$

Equation (56) is regarded as giving the change in ω_θ across the disk in terms of the calculable values U and v. Assuming therefore for the moment that $\Delta\omega_\theta$ is known, we proceed as follows. The flow far upstream of the disk is in radial equilibrium and so $\omega_\theta = -\partial w_\infty/\partial r$: we then assume that ω_θ does not vary with z either upstream or downstream and so the value of ω_θ far downstream is known, from which the axial velocity distribution may be calculated, again on the assumption of radial equilibrium. Now that the axial velocity distribution is known at infinity, the mean-value and settling-rate rules determine it elsewhere.

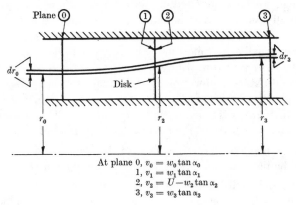

At plane 0, $v_0 = w_0 \tan \alpha_0$
1, $v_1 = w_1 \tan \alpha_1$
2, $v_2 = U - w_2 \tan \alpha_2$
3, $v_3 = w_3 \tan \alpha_3$

Fig. XI. 8. Nomenclature for approximate actuator-disk theory.

To return to the problem of solving equation (56) we use the notation shown in Fig. XI. 8. The effect of the rotating blade row is summed up by specifying the 'fluid exit angle', α_2, relative to the rotor; this angle is defined by

$$v_2 = U - w_2 \tan \alpha_2, \tag{57}$$

and it is regarded as a known function of r, being determinable from the geometry of the blade row. The inlet velocity components are connected by

$$v_1 = w_1 \tan \alpha_1, \tag{58}$$

and it is assumed that

$$v_0 = v_1 \quad \text{and} \quad v_2 = v_3 \quad \text{and} \quad w_1 = w_2. \tag{59}$$

At the disk, the ψ-derivative $d/d\psi$ equals $(1/rw_2)(d/dr)$, and so equation (56) becomes

$$\frac{dw_3}{dr} - \frac{dw_0}{dr} = \frac{\tan \alpha_2}{r} \frac{d}{dr}[r(U - \tfrac{1}{2}(w_0 + w_3)\tan \alpha_2)] -$$
$$- \frac{U - w_0 \tan \alpha_0}{\tfrac{1}{2}r(w_0 + w_3)} \frac{d}{dr}(rw_0 \tan \alpha_0). \tag{60}$$

In this equation, w_0, $\tan \alpha_0$, U, $\tan \alpha_2$ are regarded as known functions of r; if trial values of w_3 are taken in the right-hand side, (dw_3/dr) may be calculated. Integration, the constant being fixed by the equality of flux up- and down-stream, then gives a new set of values for w_3, and an iteration soon gives the solution.

If the actuator disk is a stator, then the procedure is the same except for the fact that $U = 0$.

13. Interference effects

Although we have found that the perturbation velocity decreases exponentially away from an actuator disk, as shown in Fig. XI. 5, the spacing between successive stages in an actual compressor is in fact so small that usually any one row of blades is within the perturbation region of an adjacent row. In the application of the theory of actuator disks to multi-stage compressors, two distinct problems arise.

First, in what position relative to the real row of blades shall the idealized actuator disk be placed? Horlock (1958b) has studied this problem and he calculated the effect of placing the disk

(a) in the plane of the trailing edge of the blades, and

(b) in the plane through the centre of pressure of the blade row.

In case (a) the application is relatively simple since the fluid angles at the disk on its downstream side may be taken as those determined, from cascade theory or experiment, for the blade row at its exit. Case (b) is more complicated, for the actuator disk is some distance upstream of the trailing-edge plane, whereas the fluid angles must be regarded as determined at this plane. Consequently equation (60) has to be modified to take into account the change in axial velocity between the actuator disk and the trailing-edge plane, and this modification leads to some algebraical complexity. An example of the numerical results for these two cases is shown in Fig. XI. 9. The stage was designed so that $v = 0$ at all radii before the rotor and after the stator, and for $\tan \alpha_2 = r/r_t$ where α_2 is the fluid angle (relative to the axial direction) relative to the rotor blades at the trailing-edge plane. The axial velocities have been expressed as ratios with mean axial velocity $\bar{w}$. Now the values of $w/\bar{w}$ for the actuator disks situated at the trailing-edge plane and at the centre of pressure differ by 0·08 at most, although the ratio of the axial length to the height of the blade row is 0·48, which is an unusually large value. For smaller values of this ratio, the differences in $w/\bar{w}$ are smaller. The third set of values of $w/\bar{w}$ shown in the figure came from the calculation of a radial-equilibrium theory, the basis of which is described in Section 14. Experiments by Horlock and Deverson (1958) indicate that the placing of the actuator disks at the mid-axial plane of the blades gives the best agreement between theory and experiment.

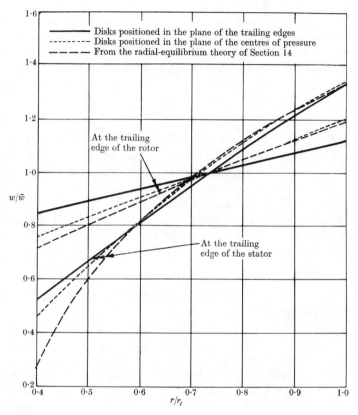

FIG. XI. 9. A comparison of the axial velocities at the trailing-edge planes of a compressor stage, given by various theories, interference effects being neglected.

The second problem, that of the interference of perturbation velocities, may be treated by an extension of methods appropriate to the case of the single disk. Two approximations are made at the outset: $u = 0$ and $\partial \omega_\theta / \partial z = 0$ except at the disks. On this basis, let us consider the effect of a change $f_n(r)$ in ω_θ at the nth actuator disk. The additional θ-vorticity will result in a change $F_n(r)$ in axial velocity far downstream given by $F_n(r) = -\int f_n(r)\, dr$, the constant of integration being chosen so that the additional flux due to $w = F_n(r)$ is zero. Thus the mean-value rule gives an additional velocity at the disk of $w = \frac{1}{2}F_n(r)$ while the settling-rate rule gives an upstream increment of $\frac{1}{2}F_n(r)\exp(\pi z/h)$ and a downstream increment of $F_n(r)[1-\frac{1}{2}\exp(-\pi z/h)]$. Here, h is the radial distance between the two walls.

The expression for the total axial velocity at any point due to a number of disks may easily be written down if these approximate results are used. Taking, for simplicity, the point required at $z = 0$, and a number of disks at the points $z = a_n$, we have

$$w = w_u + \overset{\text{upstream}}{\underset{\text{disks}}{\sum}} F_n(r)[1-\tfrac{1}{2}\exp(\pi a_n/h)] + \overset{\text{downstream}}{\underset{\text{disks}}{\sum}} F_n(r)[\tfrac{1}{2}\exp(-\pi a_n/h)].$$

$$(61)$$

Now at first sight this appears to be a linear theory of interference, in that once the effect of, say, the nth disk is calculated, it may be inserted into equation (61) independently of the effects of the other disks. This, however, is not so, since the changes in vorticity $\Delta\omega_\theta = f_n(r)$ from which $F_n(r)$ is calculated depend on the distribution of w at the nth disk, which in its turn depends on all the other disks. The insertion of an additional disk therefore would affect all the values, f_n and F_n, already obtained and so the complication of a satisfactory solution is considerable.

14. Theories based on radial equilibrium at blade edges

The approximate settling-rate rule shown in Fig. XI. 5 suggests that the flow behind a disk has settled to within about 50 per cent of its final value at a distance of about one-fifth of a blade height downstream of the actuator disk, and to within about 10 per cent at a distance of about three-quarters of a blade height downstream. For a row of blades whose axial width is comparable with the height of the blades, it appears that if the row is replaced by an actuator disk at, say, the centre of pressure, the flow has already nearly reached its final downstream condition at the plane of the trailing edge. It is therefore tempting to make the assumption that radial equilibrium exists at the plane of the trailing edge, especially as it enables great simplifications in the analysis to be made.

Cohen and White (1943) produced a theory which neglected the radial displacement of streamlines through a disk. With the nomenclature of Fig. XI. 8, $r_2 = r_0 = r$, and equation (20) becomes

$$(H_2-H_1)/\rho = \Omega r(v_2-v_1) = U(v_2-v_1). \qquad (62)$$

Next, the assumption of radial equilibrium means that $\omega_\theta = -\partial w/\partial r$ and this is taken to hold at stations (0) and (2); at these two stations, equation (7) becomes

$$
\left.
\begin{aligned}
\frac{d}{dr}\left(\frac{H_0}{\rho}\right) &= \frac{v_0}{r}\frac{d}{dr}(rv_0)+w_0\frac{dw_0}{dr} \\
\frac{d}{dr}\left(\frac{H_2}{\rho}\right) &= \frac{v_2}{r}\frac{d}{dr}(rv_2)+w_2\frac{dw_2}{dr}
\end{aligned}
\right\},
\tag{63}
$$

in which $d\psi$ has been replaced by $rw\,dr$. Elimination of the total pressures, H_0 and H_2, from equations (62) and (63) results in

$$
w_2\frac{dw_2}{dr}+\frac{1}{r}(v_2-U)\frac{d}{dr}(rv_2) = w_0\frac{dw_0}{dr}+\frac{1}{r}(v_0-U)\frac{d}{dr}(rv_0). \tag{64}
$$

Now the quantities in this equation are either to be regarded as known in any particular problem—these are w_0, v_0, $U = r\Omega$, and α_2 the fluid exit angle—or they depend on the unknown quantity w_2—and those are dw_2/dr and $v_2 = U-w_2\tan\alpha_2$. Equation (64) is therefore a first-order differential equation for w_2 which may best be solved in each particular case by a numerical iteration. At each stage of the iteration, the condition of continuity between stations (0) and (2) should, of course, be satisfied, namely

$$
\int_{r_h}^{r_t} rw_0\,dr = \int_{r_h}^{r_t} rw_2\,dr.
$$

If this analysis is applied to an intake guide-vane stator, that is, a stator row of blades upstream of which there are no other rows of blades, equation (64) reduces to

$$
w_2(dw_2/dr)+(v_2/r)(d(rv_2)/dr) = 0, \tag{65}
$$

since $U = 0$ and $dw_0/dr = 0$ in the majority of applications of such an arrangement. Also, the geometry of the blades gives a relation

$$
v_2 = w_2\tan\alpha_2, \tag{66}
$$

α_2 being known as a function of r. Elimination of v_2 between equations (65) and (66) gives

$$
(1/w_2)(dw_2/dr) = -(1/r)\sin^2\alpha_2+d(\log\cos\alpha_2)/dr,
$$

which can be integrated to give the first explicit solution, albeit approximate, for the axial velocity after a row of blades.

Cohen and White (1943) have made calculations from equation (64) for a compressor for which the fluid angles at exit to both rotor and stator blade rows are given by $\tan\alpha = 0\cdot65(r/r_m)-0\cdot35(r_m/r)$ where r_m

is the radius of the blades at mean height. This type of compressor is a 'constant reaction' design, so called from the equality of outlet angles of rotor and stator blades at a given radius. The calculations are of interest in showing how many stages are required before the so-called

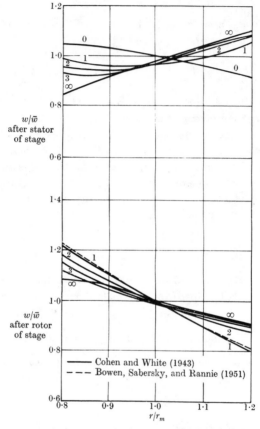

FIG. XI. 10. The variation of axial velocity with radius through successive stages of constant-reaction blading, according to radial-equilibrium theory. The stage number is indicated on each curve.

'ultimate steady state' is reached, in which flow conditions repeat themselves from stage to stage. It can be seen from Fig. XI. 10, in which are drawn the velocity distributions at the trailing-edge plane of rotors and stators, that the ultimate steady flow is nearly reached after only four stages, for this particular stage and flux.

Bowen, Sabersky, and Rannie (1951) improved upon the radial-equilibrium theory of Cohen and White by omitting the approximation $r_2 = r_0 = r$. Thus equations (62) and (63) are rewritten so that the correct value of r is taken in each term. The further relation necessary for a solution is given by the condition of continuity through the disk, namely

$$w_0 r_0 dr_0 = w_2 r_2 dr_2. \tag{67}$$

The effect of the row of blades is given by

$$v_2 = U - w_2 \tan \alpha_2, \tag{68}$$

α_2 being regarded as a known function of r. Elimination of H_2 and use of equations (62), (63), (67), and (68) gives

$$\frac{dw_2}{dr_2} = \frac{r_2}{r_0 w_0}\left[\frac{d}{dr_0}\left(\frac{H_0}{\rho}\right) - \Omega \frac{d}{dr_0}(r_0 v_0)\right]\cos^2\alpha_2 + \frac{U \sin 2\alpha_2}{r_2} -$$
$$- w_2\left[\frac{\sin^2\alpha_2}{r_2} - \frac{d}{dr_2}\log\cos\alpha_2\right]. \tag{69}$$

An approximate solution for $w_2(r_2)$ may be obtained by putting $r_0 = r_2$, for then the equation is linear and of first order in w_2. This solution can be used to give a more accurate relation between r_2 and r_0, from equation (67), which in turn could be used for a further numerical solution of (69). For an intake guide vane, $dH_0/dr_0 = 0$ and $U = v = 0$; there is then no difference between the two methods given. However, equation (69) is not only more accurate than equation (64) (taken in conjunction with (68)) but it is also rather easier to handle for numerical calculations, and so is altogether to be preferred. Clearly there is not a great difference between the results of the two methods; as an example of the latter method, the dotted line in Fig. XI. 10 may be compared with the corresponding full line.

15. The experimental verification of the various theories

The theory based on radial equilibrium has been extensively tested by experiments on annular cascades of blades and for compressors. Carter (1945) measured the speed and direction of flow and the total pressure on various radial lines downstream of a cascade placed in an annular duct through which air was drawn. These quantities were used to calculate the radial distribution of axial velocity by a method embodying the same fundamental assumption as the theory of Section 14.

At the station nearest to the blade rows, the theoretical velocity distribution was found to agree with the experimental one to within 2 or 3 per cent; this station was $0.15h$ downstream of the trailing-edge planes of the blade row, whose axial width was $0.47h$. According to the mean-value and settling-rate rules, and on the assumption that the actuator disk coincided with the mid-axial plane of the blade row, then the transition from the velocity profile far upstream to that far downstream should have been completed to within 83 per cent of the final change of velocity; this figure is made up of 50 per cent for the region upstream of the disk and 33 per cent downstream. Probably discrepancies of the order of 17 per cent of the change in axial velocity would not have been detected experimentally, and actuator-disk and radial-equilibrium theory are equally in accord with experiment here. In these early measurements the traverse planes were too far from the blade row for significant departures from radial equilibrium to be detected.

More decisive tests were, however, made by Jeffs (1954). In these, the traverse lines were only $0.24h$ away from the mid-axial planes of the blades in a single-stage compressor for which $r_h/r_t = 0.5$. In this compressor, of conventional British type, the blades were designed to give equal work input at all radial stations, provided the axial velocity was also constant across the duct. The fluid angles at exit to the blade rows, given below, were calculated from the shape of the blade by well-established rules of cascades, for which we may refer to Howell (1945).

r/r_m	0·7	0·8	1·0	1·2	1·3
α_0^0	8	17	26	30	33
α_2^0	−6	8	26	38	45
α_4^0	8	17	26	31	33

Experimental and theoretical distributions of axial velocity are shown in Fig. XI. 11, the latter being calculated by Horlock (1955). In both calculations the fluid angles at the blade-exit planes were given their design values, and not their measured values, but these values are not likely to be significantly in error if we may judge from the extensive experimental evidence which has been accumulated for compressors on the relation between fluid outlet angle and blade shape. Regions near the blade ends in which the boundary layers on the walls and the associated secondary flows create large variations of flow angle are, naturally, to be expected. The comparison given in Fig. XI. 11 shows that the actuator-disk theory is much more accurate than the radial-equilibrium theory, especially for the flow after the last stator.

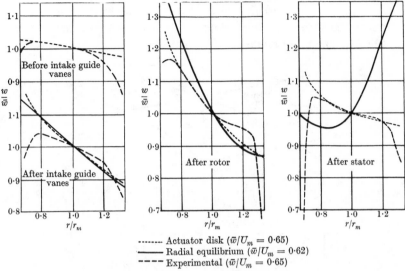

-------- Actuator disk ($\bar{w}/U_m = 0.65$)
———— Radial equilibrium ($\bar{w}/U_m = 0.62$)
- - - - Experimental ($\bar{w}/U_m = 0.65$)

Fig. XI. 11. A comparison of theoretical and experimental distributions of axial velocity in a single-stage compressor.

16. Some considerations in design

The prospect of a compressor conforming to the free-vortex flow of Section 7 is, superficially, very attractive to the designer. The flow, apart from effects of viscosity, can be predicted exactly and there should be no difficulties arising from interference between the rows of blades.

The design, in very rough outline, might proceed thus. The standard British nomenclature for the positions relative to a rotor is:

subscript	refers to
0	stationary coordinates before the rotor
1	rotating coordinates before the rotor
2	rotating coordinates after the rotor
3	stationary coordinates after the rotor.

With this nomenclature the fluid angles for a free-vortex design are:

$$\left.\begin{aligned}
\tan\alpha_0 &= \frac{v_0}{w} = \frac{K_0}{rw} \\
\tan\alpha_1 &= (U-v_0)/w = r\Omega/w - K_0/rw \\
\tan\alpha_2 &= (U-v_3)/w = r\Omega/w - K_3/rw \\
\tan\alpha_3 &= v_3/w = K_3/rw
\end{aligned}\right\}.$$

With these relations a radius must exist for which $\alpha_1 = \alpha_3$ and $\alpha_0 = \alpha_2$. This radius is usually known as the design radius and is often at or near the mean radius r_m of the annulus.

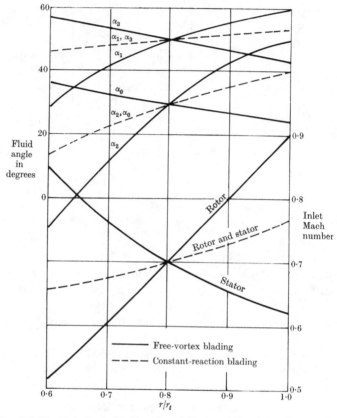

Fig. XI. 12. Variations of fluid angle and Mach number with radius for two types of blade design as calculated by Howell (1945). (Both angles and Mach numbers are relative to the blades.)

Fig. XI. 12 illustrates the fluid angles and Mach numbers of a typical compressor stage designed according the free-vortex flow. Characteristic of this flow are the large deflexions near the inner wall and the high Mach numbers near the outer wall. Both these effects are disadvantageous and, for certain design requirements, would necessitate an altogether different flow to be adopted. Recent trends, however, in the design of transonic compressors suggest that the concept of free-vortex flow will still prove useful.

Another common criterion for design is that both the total pressure and the axial velocity are constant along the span of the blades, and that also $\alpha_2 = \alpha_0$ and $\alpha_1 = \alpha_3$. This type is called a constant-reaction flow because it implies that the pressure differences across rotor and stator are equal at a given radius due to the symmetry of angles, and that the degree of reaction, defined as the ratio of the pressure rise in the rotor to the pressure rise in the whole stage, is independent of radius. The main errors implicit in this design method are that (i) interference effects are ignored together with the radial component which exists because of the changes in ω_θ through each disk, and (ii) the assumption that the axial velocity is independent of r at the first disk is inconsistent with the condition $\partial(H/\rho)/\partial r = 0$ which holds if the fluid is inspired from a free atmosphere.

However, in spite of these approximations, multistage compressors of the constant-reaction type have been designed to give high efficiencies. Provided $\alpha_2 > 0$, which is normally achieved for all radii, the value of $(H_2 - H_1)$ at the first stage is such as to make the flow into the second stage a closer approximation to the design assumptions. The virtue of this type of compressor is that Mach numbers tend to be low, as is shown in Fig. XI. 12. There is a wide variety of methods of design, based on two of the assumptions of the constant-reaction type, namely that the axial velocity everywhere and the change of total pressure at a row of blades are both independent of radius. Many are devoted to minimizing the Mach numbers in the flow, but there is little evidence to suggest that the cruder approximations lead to less-efficient compressors: even untwisted blades have been used in highly efficient compressors when Mach numbers are low. However, a less crude approximation allows for the constancy of total pressure in the fluid at entry to the rotor and assumes radial equilibrium at the planes of the trailing edge. Equation (63) becomes

$$(v/r)(dK/dr) + w\,dw/dr = 0 \quad \text{at the station (0).}$$

This equation is used to calculate $w_0(r)$ if $v_0(r)$ is regarded as prescribed, together with the total flux. $v_3(r)$ is fixed by equation (20) and hence w_3 is calculated.

XII

SOME MISCELLANEOUS TOPICS

1. Introduction

It was mentioned in the Preface that there are a number of well-defined topics in aerodynamics which by now deserve to be described as classical. Our aim has been to give an up-to-date account of those which are clearly recognizable in the titles of the eight preceding chapters. The dividing line, between what is generally accepted as belonging permanently to the development of these subjects and what is of a more temporary nature, is not always easily drawn; and there is no doubt that many flows of great interest have had to be omitted from earlier chapters. Nevertheless there are a few fringe topics which suggest themselves with special force, and it is the object of this last chapter to summarize these topics. Some of them are bound to be developed greatly in future years, and so it may be useful to indicate briefly the potentiality of the subject-matter of the following sections.

Sections 2 to 5 are devoted to the analysis of a theoretical model of the jet flap, the practical effects of which device have already been described briefly in Section VI. 20. The jet flap is, of course, more than a method of boundary-layer control: it is one of the first steps in the full integration of the lifting and propulsive systems of an aircraft. It is particularly remarkable in that it does not necessarily require a jet thrust greater than or at least equal to the aircraft weight. Other systems of producing lift will, without doubt, be developed which will depend to a much greater extent on the huge thrusts of future jet engines, but it seems likely that the principle of the jet flap will find permanent application.

Another future development which one can predict with complete confidence is the ever-increasing use of highly swept-back wings. For such wings, the assumption fundamental to Chapter VIII that the wing and the trailing vortex sheet lie in a plane is no longer acceptable; indeed we have already indicated in Section III. 6 that, for highly-swept wings, the first inviscid approximation must include some representation of a vortex sheet springing from the leading edge. The additional fact, that in reality a trailing vortex sheet for any kind of wing rolls up, also draws attention to systems in which the vorticity is not confined to a plane; a brief summary of some recent studies on non-planar vortex sheets is therefore given in Sections 6 and 8.

A recent trend in mathematical modelling of real flows attaches considerable importance to the positions on the body of the lines from which are assumed to spring the trailing vortex sheets representing the separated boundary layer. Maskell (1956) has given an account of some of the configurations which such vortex sheets might adopt. This and similar investigations may affect future methods of designing aerodynamic shapes, especially those for which separation is, for one reason or another, unavoidable; in such cases, the achievement of a steady real flow may depend on the suitable choice of the separation lines in the mathematical model. It is not yet possible to give a coherent account of these ideas.

Associated with the problem of non-planar vortex sheets is that of bubbles, of the kind used to represent certain features of real flows attributable to separation of the boundary layer. Bubbles are often used as steady-flow approximations to regions of unsteady flow, but their use nevertheless often gives a satisfactory representation of the mean flow. For two-dimensional aerofoils, some of the physical effects of separation, especially near the stall, have already been described in Section V. 14; in three-dimensional flow, these effects are naturally more complicated and Sections 9 and 10 briefly consider some of the problems involved in flows with bubbles.

Later sections, 11–22, give condensed accounts of some rather better-established theories, namely those for non-planar lifting systems such as biplanes and cascades, for the velocity field of a wing, and for non-uniformities in the flow past a wing.

These introduce the last part of this chapter in which are considered the effects of non-uniformities in mainstreams with special reference to boundary-layer flows. The Frontispiece shows how radically the displacement flow of a cylinder in the shearing flow of a boundary layer differs from that in a uniform stream. Again, the value of the experimental technique of traversing a boundary layer with a pitot tube depends on a knowledge of the interactions between the tube, the boundary, and the boundary layer. But such effects are experienced in many other important practical fields apart from aerodynamics; for example, the scouring of river beds behind piers is a consequence more of the effects of the shear in the stream than of the separation of the flow from the pier. Experimental studies are described in Sections

24–26, while Sections 27–32 summarize the theoretical investigations which have been pursued very actively in the last few years.

2. The theoretical model of a two-dimensional wing with jet flap

In Section VI. 20, it was noted that the effects of the jet flap can be put in terms of its deflexion, τ, its flux of momentum, J, and the incidence, α. The mathematical model we propose for the first approximation to the inviscid flow assumes that both the aerofoil and the jet

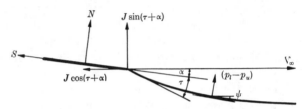

Fig. XII. 1. Scheme of notation for an aerofoil with a jet flap.

are infinitesimally thin. If the real jet contains fluid of speed v, width δ, and density ρ, the flux of momentum is $J = \rho\delta v^2$; the model of the jet is then the limit as $v \to \infty$ and $\delta \to 0$ in such a way that J remains constant. This model for the inviscid flow precludes, of course, the consideration of any mixing process between the jet and the main stream; as a consequence the flux of momentum is constant along the jet and also the jet ultimately becomes parallel to the stream. Fig. XII. 1 illustrates these ideas and the notation used.

By considering the flow of momentum in the stream direction, we see that the aerofoil experiences a thrust J, which is independent of the angle $(\tau+\alpha)$ between the jet efflux and the undisturbed stream. This thrust is manifested partly by the component $J\cos(\tau+\alpha)$ acting on the internal surfaces of the jet exit, and partly by the component $J[1-\cos(\tau+\alpha)]$ obtained as the integral of the stresses on the external surface of the aerofoil. Likewise the lift is made up of the jet reaction $J\sin(\tau+\alpha)$ together with the lift on the external surface. Thus, if the external pressures are resolved into forces N and S, normal and parallel to the chord line,

$$\left.\begin{array}{l} J[1-\cos(\tau+\alpha)] = S\cos\alpha - N\sin\alpha \\ L - J\sin(\tau+\alpha) = S\sin\alpha + N\cos\alpha \end{array}\right\}. \tag{1}$$

According to the assumption of a thin aerofoil, S is a finite non-zero force arising from the singularity at the leading edge. Unfortunately these forces S and N, and hence the lift, do not follow at once from the conventional aerofoil theory of Chapter IV, and Section 3 is devoted to their calculation.

Relationships between the velocity and pressure on either side of the jet may be obtained by considering an element of the jet. If, in Fig. V. 10, the values of velocity and pressure are such that the flow is irrotational, it may be shown that

$$u_u - u_l = \kappa J / \rho U_\infty \qquad (2)$$

and

$$p_u - p_l = -\kappa J, \qquad (3)$$

in which the upper and lower surfaces of the jet are denoted by suffixes u and l, and κ is the curvature of the jet at the point under consideration. Far downstream where κ tends to zero, the pressure and velocity become continuous across the jet.

It is interesting to calculate the reaction exerted, in the downstream direction, by the jet on the remainder of the fluid; this force is

$$-\int_0^\infty (p_u - p_l)\sin\psi \, ds = -\int_{\tau+\alpha}^0 (-\kappa J)\sin\psi \,(d\psi/\kappa) = J[1-\cos(\tau+\alpha)],$$

in which the relation (3) has been used. This, therefore, equals the thrust exerted by the fluid on the aerofoil—the aerodynamic thrust—and when we add the component $J\cos(\tau+\alpha)$ of the jet reaction on the aerofoil, we obtain the total thrust J, thus verifying the earlier result. A similar verification may be made, of course, for the lift direction.

3. The calculation of lift for the two-dimensional jet flap

The analysis will be analogous to that of Section IV. 10, in which an integral equation is formed relating the strength of the bound vortex sheet to the downwash which is specified by the slope of the aerofoil. The jet flap, however, introduces the complications of mixed boundary conditions. On the aerofoil the downwash is known; on the jet it is unknown, but is related to the vortex strength by equation (2). This equation may be rewritten as

$$x > c; \ \gamma(x) = \kappa J/\rho U_\infty \simeq -(J/\rho U_\infty)\frac{d}{dx}\left(\frac{w(x)}{U_\infty}\right), \qquad (4)$$

in which $\gamma(x)$ is the strength of the vortex sheet. The approximation for κ is justifiable if the incidence, α, of the aerofoil and τ are sufficiently small.

The analysis is further simplified by the characteristic approximation of all linearized theories, that the conditions on the aerofoil and jet may be taken on the plane $z = 0$. Remembering that we are now taking $w(x)$ as positive in the downwash direction, we recall equation (IV. 43) as

$$w(x) = -(1/2\pi) \int_0^\infty \gamma(\xi) \, d\xi/(\xi - x) \tag{5}$$

with the boundary conditions shown schematically in Fig. XII. 2:

$$0 \leqslant x \leqslant c; \quad w(x)/U_\infty = \alpha(x), \tag{6}$$

$$x = c+0; \quad w/U_\infty = \tau + \alpha(c), \tag{7}$$

$$c < x < \infty; \quad w'(x) = -2\gamma(x)/cC_J. \tag{8}$$

Equation (8) follows from equation (4), with C_J defined by

$$C_J = J/\tfrac{1}{2}\rho U_\infty^2 \, c. \tag{9}$$

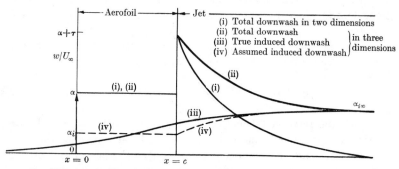

FIG. XII. 2. Distributions of vorticity and downwash on the centre chord-line of an aerofoil with jet flap, in two and three dimensions.

Equations (5)–(8) can be reduced to a single integro-differential equation

$$w(x) - (c \, C_J/4\pi) \left(\frac{x-c}{x}\right)^{\frac{1}{2}} \int_c^\infty \left(\frac{t}{t-c}\right)^{\frac{1}{2}} \frac{w'(t) \, dt}{t-x}$$

$$= (1/\pi) \left(\frac{x-c}{x}\right)^{\frac{1}{2}} \int_0^c \left(\frac{s}{c-s}\right)^{\frac{1}{2}} \frac{\alpha(s) \, ds}{s-x} \tag{10}$$

for the downwash distribution $w(x)$ over the jet $x > c$.

Spence (1956b) has obtained numerical solutions by expanding w as a Fourier cosine series in $\theta = 2 \cos^{-1}\sqrt{(c/x)}$. In the special case of a flat wing, namely $\alpha(x) = \alpha = $ constant, $\gamma(x)$ is linear in both α and τ, and the over-all lift coefficient is found in the form:

$$C_L = 2 \int_0^\infty [\gamma(x)/U_\infty] \, dx/c = \alpha(\partial C_L/\partial \alpha)_{\alpha=0} + \tau(\partial C_L/\partial \tau)_{\tau=0}. \tag{11}$$

The two derivatives are functions of C_J only, and an equation connecting them may be deduced in the following manner. Eliminating N from equations (1), we find that, correct to the second order of the small quantities τ and α,

$$S/\tfrac{1}{2}\rho U_\infty^2 c = \tfrac{1}{2}\tau^2 C_J + \tau\alpha(\partial C_L/\partial\tau)_{\tau=0} + \tfrac{1}{2}\alpha^2[2(\partial C_L/\partial\alpha)_{\alpha=0} - C_J]. \qquad (12)$$

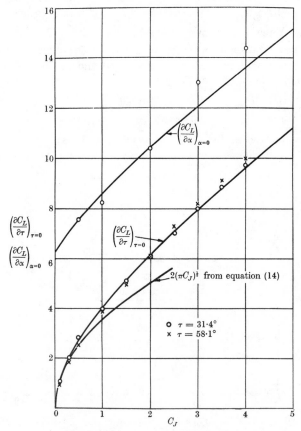

FIG. XII. 3. Calculated and experimental lift derivatives for a 12·5 per cent thick elliptic cylinder with jet flap.

Now the force S depends, of course, only on the strength of the vortex sheet actually at the leading edge, and may be shown to be

$$S = \tfrac{1}{4}\pi\rho\Big[\lim_{x\to 0} x^{\frac{1}{2}}\gamma(x)\Big]^2.$$

Thus the right-hand side of equation (12) must be a perfect square for all values of τ and α, the condition for which is

$$[(\partial C_L/\partial\tau)_{\tau=0}]^2 = 2C_J(\partial C_L/\partial\alpha)_{\alpha=0} - (C_J)^2. \qquad (13)$$

From this equation we may infer that, since $(\partial C_L/\partial\alpha)_{\alpha=0} \to 2\pi$ as $C_J \to 0$,

$$(\partial C_L/\partial\tau)_{\tau=0} \simeq 2(\pi C_J)^{\frac{1}{2}} \tag{14}$$

when C_J is small. This result is confirmed by an exact solution of equation (10) of the form

$$\tfrac{1}{2}(\pi C_J)^{-\frac{1}{2}}(\partial C_L/\partial\tau)_{\tau=0}-1 = C_J[\log(16/C_J)+\gamma]/8\pi+O(C_J\log C_J)^2,$$

where γ is Euler's constant.

Empirical expressions, which give close fits to the numerical solutions of equation (5) for values of C_J up to 10 and are consistent with equation (13), are

$$\left. \begin{array}{l} (\partial C_L/\partial\tau)_{\tau=0} = 2(\pi C_J)^{\frac{1}{2}}[1+0\cdot151(C_J)^{\frac{1}{2}}+0\cdot139C_J]^{\frac{1}{2}} \\ (\partial C_L/\partial\alpha)_{\alpha=0} = 2\pi[1+0\cdot151(C_J)^{\frac{1}{2}}+0\cdot219C_J] \end{array} \right\}. \tag{15}$$

These are plotted in Fig. XII. 3, together with experimental points obtained for a 12·5 per cent thick elliptic cylinder by Dimmock (1955).

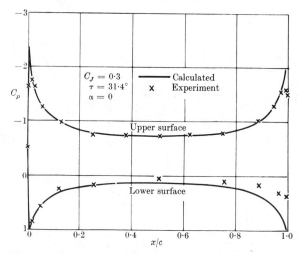

Fig. XII. 4. Experimental and calculated distributions of pressure on a 12·5 per cent thick elliptic cylinder with jet flap.

Typical pressure distributions on the same cylinder are shown in Fig. XII. 4. A feature of these, which is also found in the numerical values of $\gamma(x)$ calculated by the preceding theory, is their 'saddle-back' shape. This is, of course, characteristic of the pressure distribution on aerofoils which are not governed by the Kutta–Joukowski condition, and appears also on aerofoils fitted with the Thwaites flap described in Section VI. 10. One consequence of this is the low value of pressure near the leading edge; thus we should expect separation first to occur at a higher lift coefficient on a jet-flapped aerofoil than on a conventional one. A method of calculating the pressure distributions for given values of thrust and lift has been proposed by Küchemann (1956a).

4. The theoretical model of a three-dimensional wing with jet flap

The three-dimensional jet-flapped wing does not possess a trailing vortex sheet in the usual sense, since the jet sheet can sustain a discontinuity of pressure in addition to the discontinuity of velocity characteristic of a vortex sheet. As a consequence, some of the vortex lines, by which the combined wing and jet can be represented, lie wholly within the jet sheet.

As with the conventional wing, the total lift and thrust on the wing can be equated to the flux of downward momentum and to the excess flux of streamwise momentum through the Trefftz plane far downstream. In the case of the jet flap, however, the non-zero downwash angle $\alpha_{i\infty}$ implies a direct contribution to the downward momentum from the jet. If $\alpha_{i\infty}$ is assumed to be small and also constant across the jet sheet, the two components of the jet momentum, J, are $J\alpha_{i\infty}$ and $J(1-\tfrac{1}{2}\alpha_{i\infty}^2)$ respectively. Hence, if L and T are the total lift and thrust experienced by the wing, the contributions to the momentum relations from the flow external to the jet correspond to a reduced lift force $(L-J\alpha_{i\infty})$ and to a reduced thrust force $T = J(1-\tfrac{1}{2}\alpha_{i\infty}^2)$. The latter force is more conveniently expressed in terms of the induced drag D_i, defined as the inevitable loss of thrust, in three-dimensional compared with a two-dimensional flow with the same jet momentum; thus D_i equals $(J-T)$ and is zero in two-dimensional flow.

It may thus be argued that the external flow is the same as that for a wing alone experiencing lift and drag forces equal to $(L-J\alpha_{i\infty})$ and $(D_i-\tfrac{1}{2}J\alpha_{i\infty}^2)$ respectively, and the assumption that $\alpha_{i\infty}$ is constant across the jet sheet reduces the problem to that of minimum induced drag on a conventional wing. Thus from equation (VIII. 30), we have

$$L-J\alpha_{i\infty} = \pi\rho U_\infty^2 s^2\alpha_{i\infty}, \tag{16}$$

and, with equation (VIII. 31) as well,

$$(D_i-\tfrac{1}{2}J\alpha_{i\infty}^2)/(L-J\alpha_{i\infty}) = \tfrac{1}{2}\alpha_{i\infty}, \tag{17}$$

so that

$$D_i = \tfrac{1}{2}L\alpha_{i\infty} \tag{18}$$

just as in the case of a wing without a jet. In terms of the overall coefficients $\bar{C}_L$, $\bar{C}_{Di}$, and $\bar{C}_J$, all based on the plan area S of the wing, these relations reduce to

$$\tfrac{1}{2}\alpha_{i\infty} = \bar{C}_L/(\pi A + 2C_J) \tag{19}$$

and
$$\bar{C}_{Di} = (\bar{C}_L)^2/(\pi A + 2C_J). \tag{20}$$

The last equation emphasizes the effect of the jet in reducing the induced drag to below the minimum value, given in equation (VIII. 33), for any wing assumed to shed a plane trailing vortex sheet.

5. The calculation of lift for the three-dimensional jet flap

The conventional theory for wings of large aspect ratio needs some modification if it is to be applied to our fictitious wing whose lift is $(L - J\alpha_{i\infty})$. We may still think of an induced incidence α_i at the wing, but the increase in the downwash angle to its value $\alpha_{i\infty}$ far downstream reduces the total spanwise vorticity in the jet to $J(\tau + \alpha - \alpha_{i\infty})$. We cannot, therefore, simply use the two-dimensional solution for momentum J, deflexion τ, and incidence $(\alpha - \alpha_i)$, in which the jet vorticity is $J(\tau + \alpha - \alpha_i)$. The lift in fact depends on the downstream variation $\alpha_i(x)$ of the downwash angle. No method is known of calculating this angle but provided it is small—if, say, $(\alpha_{i\infty} - \alpha_i) \ll (\tau + \alpha)$ as is the case for sufficiently large aspect ratios—we are justified in using for $\alpha_i(x)$ an assumed distribution which will allow us to complete the calculation of $\bar{C}_L$. This is indicated in Fig. XII. 2 and by this means Maskell and Spence (1959) obtain the same expression for $\bar{C}_L$ using either of the two approximations given in equations (26) and (29) below. We go on to outline their method.

Consider the case in which τ and α, and also the sectional value of C_J, which is based on the local thrust per unit span and the local chord, are constant along the span. We assume, as indicated in the last section, that $\alpha_{i\infty}$ is independent of y and, further, that w and γ are functions of (x/c) only, so that the flow is similar at all spanwise stations. The lift coefficient, like C_J, is then the same for the whole wing as for a section.

The induced downwash $w_i(x)$ may be defined by

$$w(x) = w_i(x) - (1/2\pi) \int_0^\infty \gamma(\xi)\,d\xi/(\xi - x), \tag{21}$$

which is the three-dimensional analogue of (5). The various boundary conditions are:

$$0 \leqslant x \leqslant c; \quad w_i(x)/U_\infty = \alpha_i \quad \text{and} \quad w(x)/U_\infty = \alpha, \tag{22}$$

$$x = c+0; \quad w/U_\infty = \tau+\alpha, \tag{23}$$

$$c < x < \infty; \quad w'(x) = -2\gamma(x)/cC_J \quad \text{and} \quad w_i(x) \text{ unknown}, \tag{24}$$

$$x = \infty; \quad w/U_\infty = w_i/U_\infty = \alpha_{i\infty}. \tag{25}$$

We now introduce the first assumption to represent the unknown variation of $w_i(x)$ on $c < x < \infty$, which is that $w_i(x)$ is linearly related to $w(x)$. More precisely, by using the boundary conditions (23) and (25), we take

$$w_i(x)-w_i(\infty) = (\alpha_i-\alpha_{i\infty})[w(x)-w_i(\infty)]/(\tau+\alpha-\alpha_{i\infty}). \tag{26}$$

Equation (21) is now of the same form as equation (5), provided α in the latter equation is replaced by $(\alpha-\alpha_i)$ and C_J by

$$C_J[1-(\alpha_{i\infty}-\alpha_i)/(\tau+\alpha-\alpha_i)].$$

The lift is thus given by

$$\bar{C}_L-\alpha_{i\infty} C_J = [\tau(\partial C_L^{(2)}/\partial\tau)_{\tau=0}+(\alpha-\alpha_i)(\partial C_L^{(2)}/\partial\alpha)_{\alpha=0}], \tag{27}$$

in which the whole of the right-hand side is to be evaluated with the value of C_J just mentioned, and the superscript (2) denotes the two-dimensional case given by equations (11) and (15).

On this basis, Maskell and Spence complete the analysis by making some analytical approximations and an interesting intermediate result compares the lift in the two- and three-dimensional cases. Thus they find

$$\frac{\bar{C}_L}{\bar{C}_L^{(2)}} = \frac{A+2C_J/\pi}{A-2+(2/\pi)(\partial C_L^{(2)}/\partial\alpha)_{\alpha=0}-2\sigma} \tag{28}$$

where $\sigma = 1-2\alpha_i/\alpha_{i\infty}$, a quantity which we may expect to be small.

This equation is also found if, instead of (26), the following expression is used for the induced downwash:

$$w_i(x)-w_i(\infty) = -U_\infty(\alpha_i-\alpha_{i\infty})\{[(x-c)/x]^{\frac{1}{2}}-1\}. \tag{29}$$

In this case no approximations are needed to obtain (28) from (21).

To complete the evaluation of $\bar{C}_L$ we require a relation between $\alpha_{i\infty}$ and α_i. In the conventional case of a wing of large aspect ratio there is the familiar equation $\alpha_{i\infty} = 2\alpha_i$, and for wings of small aspect ratio $\alpha_{i\infty} = \alpha_i$. In the present case, however, no value for α_i can be deduced solely from a consideration of the downwash at infinity downstream. This is due to some of the horseshoe vortices, of which the whole vortex system is supposed to consist, originating downstream of the wing, and this suggests that α_i is less than $\frac{1}{2}\alpha_{i\infty}$, so that σ is positive. Alternatively, we can ensure that C_D given by (20) is consistent with that deduced from pressure components on the wing. This leads to the relation

$$\sigma = (1-\lambda)C_J/[\pi A\lambda-(1-\lambda)C_J], \tag{30}$$

where

$$\lambda = \alpha_{i\infty}/(\tau+\alpha) = 2\bar{C}_L/(\tau+\alpha)(\pi A+2C_J). \tag{31}$$

σ vanishes, of course, when $C_J = 0$, and since it is found to be small in all cases, a good approximation to $\bar{C}_L/C_L^{(2)}$ is given by putting $\sigma = 0$ in (28). With this approximate value of $\bar{C}_L$, (31) gives a value of λ which may then be used to give an improved value of σ for the final evaluation of $\bar{C}_L/C_L^{(2)}$.

With $C_J = 0$, the ratio $\bar{C}_L/C_L^{(2)}$ reduces to $A/(A+2)$ which, as we recall from Section VIII. 10, is the correct result for wings of large aspect ratio.

6. Wings with non-planar vortex sheets

Wing theory is difficult enough as it is, even when based on a mathematical model which assumes that the flow separates at the trailing edge only and forms a plane vortex sheet trailing behind the wing. It was realized long ago, however, that in reality such a vortex sheet deforms. When this deformation occurs behind the trailing edge of an aeroplane's unswept wing of large aspect ratio, it affects not so much the flow over the wing but primarily the flow over the rear of the fuselage and the tailplane. But if it occurs on wings of small aspect ratio, with vortex sheets originating also from the tip edges or from the leading edges, then the flow over the wing, too, is affected. Thus problems related to non-planar vortex sheets separate themselves into two different kinds: flows in which the wing is affected and those in which it is not. In both cases, the fundamental difficulty is that neither the strength of the vorticity distribution along the sheet nor its shape are known beforehand; thus all theories, in the present state of knowledge, are bound to introduce what appear to be drastic approximations. The approximations are of widely differing kinds and it is impossible here to give any general discussion of them. In the preceding section we have used one typical of problems with mixed boundary conditions: equation (26)—or (29)—makes an assumption which is not exact but it enables some mathematical analysis to be carried out which results in errors adjudged small by empirical means. The two following sections are therefore little more than guides to the literature on the two types of flow just distinguished.

7. The rolling-up of a trailing vortex sheet

We have already considered, in Section III. 4, some aspects of the rolling-up of a trailing vortex sheet. There the work of Kaden (1931) and Westwater (1936) was cited. Kaden considered the conditions along one streamwise edge with a spiral vortex sheet above it such that the shapes in different transverse planes are all similar to one another,

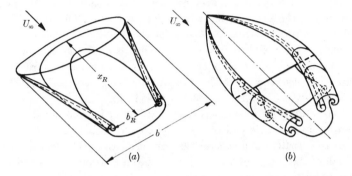

FIG. XII. 5. The rolling-up of trailing vortex sheets. (*a*) One vortex pair on an unswept wing of large aspect ratio. (*b*) Two vortex pairs on a slender wing of small aspect ratio.

no characteristic length entering the analysis. His results can be applied to the initial stages of the rolling-up of sheets behind unswept wings of large aspect ratio. Lotz and Fabricius (1937) have considered in more detail the region of transition between the initial stages and the fully rolled-up state, and Westwater calculated the deformation of an originally plane vortex sheet by considering the mathematical model of twenty concentrated line vortices of equal strength suitably placed along the span.

The distance, x_R, at which the vortex sheet may be considered as fully rolled up can only be roughly defined, as shown, for example, in Fig. XII. 5. Spreiter and Sacks (1951) have shown by similarity considerations that this distance must be of the form

$$x_R = kAb/\bar{C}_L, \tag{32}$$

and from Kaden's calculations the value of the constant for elliptic spanloading is found to be $k = 0.28$. For rectangular wings, on which more of the load is concentrated near the wing tips, the value of the constant will be smaller than 0.28, a result which might be verified intuitively by the thought that the greater the intensity of trailing vorticity near the edges of the sheet, the more rapidly will it roll up. The value of k thus depends on the planform of the wing and on the spanwise distribution of load.

Equation (32) shows that the effects of rolling-up may be particularly important for wings at high lift coefficients and for wings of small aspect ratio. We should note, however, that a single pair of vortices may be expected to result only when the vorticity leaving the wing edge is of the same sign over each half-wing. On some slender wings of small aspect ratio, the vorticity shed from part of the trailing edge may be of the opposite sign to that shed from the leading edge on the same half-wing, in which case the vortex sheet behind the trailing edge deforms in a different manner and produces two pairs of rolled-up vortices, as observed by Maltby (1958). The shape of the sheet is then not as shown in Fig. VIII. 5, but like that in Fig. XII. 5 (b).

If the trailing vortex sheet is such that it may be considered as fully rolled up into a single pair of discrete line vortices, the strength, Γ, of one of the vortices is equal to the sum of all the vorticity shed from one-half of the wing and hence equal to the circulation around the wing in the plane of symmetry. For elliptic spanloading,

$$\Gamma = 2bU_\infty \bar{C}_L/\pi A. \tag{33}$$

The distance, b_R, between the two line vortices may be fixed by the suggestion that the effective centres of the trailing vortices are left unaltered throughout the rolling-up process. Thus, again for elliptic spanloading,

$$b_R = \tfrac{1}{4}\pi b. \tag{34}$$

Each one of such a pair experiences a downwash velocity induced by the other. This can be found from the two-dimensional flow field in a transverse plane. For elliptic spanloading,

$$w/U_\infty = (4/\pi^2)(\bar{C}_L/\pi A) \tag{35}$$

which is much smaller than the corresponding value,

$$w/U_\infty = \alpha_{i\infty} = 2(\bar{C}_L/\pi A), \tag{36}$$

for the plane vortex sheet. If, however, the vortex sheet were not assumed to be held in a fixed position along the mainstream but set free, the velocity of the centres of the sheet would be only $0.43\bar{C}_L/\pi A$, which is very nearly the same as that of the vortex pair.

The flow near the centre of the spiral vortex sheets has not yet been fully investigated. In real flow, a viscous core will develop. Spreiter and Sacks (1951) estimated the radius, r_c, of this core by relating the kinetic energy of the fluid outside and inside the two cores to the induced drag coefficient which, for elliptic spanloading, is still assumed to be equal to $(\bar{C}_L)^2/\pi A$. Their estimate was

$$r_c = 0{\cdot}197b_R = 0{\cdot}155b. \tag{37}$$

It is when the tail surfaces are far removed from a wing of low aspect ratio that it is convenient, or even necessary, to use the concept of a fully rolled-up vortex sheet. For unswept wings of moderate and large aspect ratio, the rolling-up process is less significant, and methods based on the assumption of a plane vortex sheet are adequate. The effects for wings of small aspect ratio have been investigated by Owen and Maskell (1951); they also included the effect of a fuselage, the presence of which affects the strengths and positions of the vortices. This work has been extended by Owen and Anderson (1952) to include slender cruciform wing-fuselage combinations with a cruciform tail unit, set at both incidence and yaw.

An interesting phenomenon has been described by Bird (1952) in connexion with cruciform wings in the form of an X set at incidence. Far downstream the two trailing vortex sheets may be thought of as two pairs of discrete line vortices, and they interact in a manner similar to the vortex rings in the well-known phenomenon described by Helmholtz (1868). Whereas the lower pair tend to draw apart, the upper pair move toward each other and downwards. Eventually they pass down in between the lower pair and the whole process, which has been called leap-frogging, is repeated. A similar flow may occur behind one wing of small aspect ratio, such as that indicated in Fig. XII. 5 (b), where the vortex wake gives a pleated appearance. It is quite likely that this is the type of flow which Lanchester (1907) had in mind.

8. Wings with vortex sheets springing from the leading edge

We now consider those cases in which the non-planar shape of the free vortex sheets fundamentally influences the flow over the wing itself. It was in the course of attempts, made by Blenk (1925) and others, to improve on Prandtl's aerofoil theory that it was realized that some of the effects observed on wings of small aspect ratio could not be explained by any theory of lifting surfaces with plane trailing vortex sheets. The reason appeared to be that these effects are essentially non-linear. Many attempts have been made since then to establish theories for these regions of non-linear effects, and some of the earlier theories have been reviewed by Voepel (1948) and by Thieme (1954); but there is as yet no satisfactory theory. We must realize, however, that

Prandtl's is but one of many possible bases of wing theory and there can be no doubt that more comprehensive assumptions will eventually be developed for this interesting type of physical flow. Naturally, any new theory must take into account as far as possible what appear to be the most important physical characteristics, and in particular the position of the separation lines on the wing. If the ensuing surface of separation is regarded as a vortex sheet, its shape and the vorticity distribution over wing and sheet can be determined from the condition that wing and sheet are stream surfaces and that the pressure at either side of any point in the sheet is the same, so that only the wing but not the free sheet sustains differences of pressure.

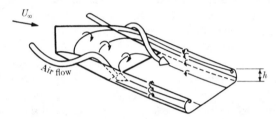

FIG. XII. 6. A sketch illustrating the separation of flow along the straight tips of a thin slender wing.

One particular case which has received some attention is that of a wing where the side edges at the wing tips are separation lines as well as the trailing edge, as sketched in Fig. XII. 6. Betz in 1939 proposed to simplify the shape of the vortex sheet as a horizontal plane behind the trailing edge and a vertical plane behind each of the tip edges. The pressure condition can then be satisfied very crudely by postulating that the vortex lines are parallel to the mainstream behind the trailing edge—as in Prandtl's theory—and are inclined at half the angle of incidence in the tip sheets, this being the mean flow direction between that on the wing and that away from the wing. The stream-surface condition can be satisfied only in the Trefftz plane and thus only the overall lift can be estimated. This has been done by Mangler (1939) and later in improved form by Küchemann (1956b), who used results obtained for wings with solid end-plates (which produce a similar trailing vortex sheet) for calculating the downwash induced by such trailing vortices. The assumption that the vortex distribution is such that the induced drag is a minimum is also made, namely that the induced downwash is taken to be constant over the wing.

With this mathematical model the height, h, of the tip vortex sheets at and behind the trailing edge of the cropped delta wing shown in Fig. XII. 6, is found to be

$$h/s = \tfrac{1}{2}\alpha[2/A - \tfrac{1}{2}\tan\varphi_L], \tag{38}$$

φ_L being the angle of sweep-back of the leading edge. The corresponding induced downwash over the wing is

$$\alpha_i = k\omega\bar{C}_L/\pi A, \tag{39}$$

where k is a function of h/s only. k has been calculated by Mangler (1939) and can be approximated by

$$k = (1+h/s)^{-1}. \tag{40}$$

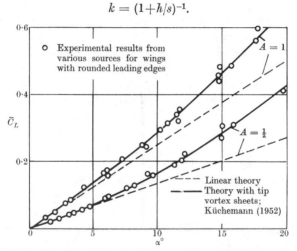

Fig. XII. 7. The effect of tip vortex sheets on the overall lift of rectangular wings of aspect ratio of $\tfrac{1}{2}$ and 1.

A particularly simple result is obtained for wings of very small aspect ratio for which the downwash factor, ω, equals 2 and $\alpha_i = \alpha$. In that case

$$\bar{C}_L = \tfrac{1}{2}\pi A\alpha + (\tfrac{1}{2}\pi - \tfrac{1}{8}\pi\tan\varphi_L)\alpha^2. \tag{41}$$

The first term is the same as that obtained from slender-body theory with trailing-edge separation only, as seen from equation (VIII. 71); the second, quadratic, term in α is typical for wings with non-planar vortex sheets.

In spite of its crude assumptions, this theory adequately predicts the overall lift on wings; Fig. XII. 7 shows some results of a similar theory extended by Küchemann (1952) to not-so-slender wings. It is clear that on slender configuration the non-linear effects predominate and indeed are the principal mechanisms by which lift is produced at all; for, since lift is associated with the trailing vorticity, vorticity shed from the trailing edge produces little lift and vorticity must be encouraged to trail from the side edges.

Another particular case which has received considerable attention is that of the slender delta wing with separation from all edges, leading to a flow as indicated in Fig. VIII. 5. The principal features of such a flow have been described by Roy (1952) and by Maskell (1955), and a large number of experimental investigations have been carried out, notably by Spreiter and Sacks (1951), Werlé (1953), Örnberg (1954), Bartlett and Vidal (1954), and Fink and Taylor (1955). In the theoretical work by Legendre (1952–3), Adams (1953), and Brown and Michael (1954), the flow is simplified by approximating the free vortex sheets by two discrete line vortices. This is found to be not altogether satisfactory and the results do not agree well with experiments. A more realistic treatment has been proposed by Roy (1956) and by Mangler and Smith (1956). The boundary conditions have been written down in general form by Mangler and Smith (1957) and for the particular case of conical flow by Legendre (1952–3). With the usual assumptions of slender-wing theory described in Section VIII. 12, the problem can be reduced to that of calculating a two-dimensional flow in which, however, the boundary conditions have no obvious physical interpretation. The method of solution by Mangler and Smith, employing continuous sheets, still depends on a number of assumptions about the behaviour near the cores of the sheets and about the shape of the sheet; but numerical results have been obtained which display most of the features experimentally observed.

The most pronounced distinctions between these non-linear flows and those assumed in slender-body theory are worth a brief description. The fact that vortex sheets spring from the leading edge implies that there is no load on the wing itself along its edge, there being none across the sheets. On the other hand, the strong vorticity above the wing draws air into the spiral sheets and induces a strong sidewash on the upper surface of the wing, directed towards the edges. This leads to a minimum in the pressures there and also in the loading across the wing. Thus the loading differs radically from that in Fig. VIII. 14. The suction maxima along the edges vanish and reappear farther inboard, as illustrated in Fig. XII. 8. This figure uses values from a greatly simplified theory given by Küchemann (1955) in which, however, the main features of the flow are retained, including the spiral motion of the air above the wing and the condition of zero load along the edge. The infinite loads at the core position $y = y_0$ are, of course,

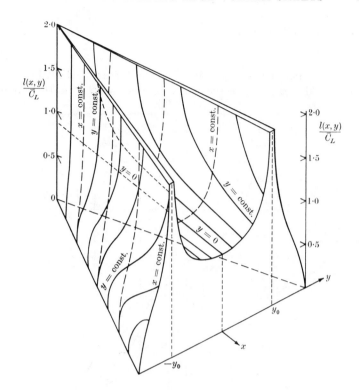

FIG. XII. 8. The distribution of load on a slender delta wing with separation at the leading edge and part-span vorticity at $y = y_0 = 0.6s$.

a result of the simplifications of the theory, and appear in a similar way in other theories of thin wings.

Another consequence of the new edge condition is that the spanwise distribution of the chord loading obeys the relation

$$d(C_L c)/d(y/s) = 0 \quad \text{when } y = \pm s, \tag{42}$$

for wings with conical flow. Thus the gradient of the spanwise distribution of load is zero at the edges, as illustrated in Fig. XII. 9. Only when the loading peaks run along the edges, namely when $y_0 = s$, does the spanloading become elliptic and tend to zero like $(s-y)^{\frac{1}{2}}$. This feature is characteristic and has been observed experimentally even for wings on which the flow is not strictly conical.

Another fundamental feature of flows with non-planar vortex sheets is that the minimum induced drag for given span and lift is no longer given by $(\bar{C}_L)^2/\pi A$. For flat wings with zero load along the leading edge, the lift force is approximately normal to the wing surface so that

$$\bar{C}_D = \bar{C}_L \alpha, \tag{43}$$

as has been pointed out by Relf (1953). But a specified lift force may be obtained at a much smaller angle of incidence than in the classical

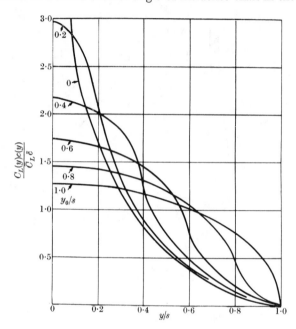

<small>Fig. XII. 9. Spanwise distributions of load, calculated for delta wings with leading-edge vortex sheets and conical flow, with loading maxima at $y = y_0$.</small>

type of flow so that $\bar{C}_L \alpha$ may well be smaller than $(\bar{C}_L)^2/\pi A$. Indeed, experimental values as low as 0·6 times $(\bar{C}_L)^2/\pi A$ have been found on unswept wings of aspect ratio one-half.

9. Wings with bubbles. Physical characteristics

If we have emphasized in the last section the possibility of separation at a leading edge inducing vortex-like motion on the upper surface of a wing, we must dispel any impression that this type of motion is characteristic of such separation. Many types of separation follow the pattern shown in Fig. I. 17, in which the external flow displays none of the characteristics of a vortex motion. It is not at all easy to establish criteria which enable a prediction to be made of whether separation at the leading edge will cause a concentration of vorticity or not. Certainly the sweep of the leading edge seems to be an important factor; but none of the theories yet proposed are capable of suggesting even the existence of a critical value of the sweep-back, let alone its actual magnitude. In experimental investigations, however, the various techniques for visualization of flow enable the general character of any given flow to be understood fairly thoroughly, and in this and the next section we consider some of the characteristics of flow past wings in which leading-edge separation does not induce concentrated vorticity in the main field of flow.

Let us consider first the familiar picture of separation in a two-dimensional flow illustrated in Fig. I. 14. Separation of the flow from a solid surface is said to begin at S, the separation point, in the sense that the fluid particles which have hitherto flowed close to the solid surface cease to do so at S. The streamline from S leaving the surface divides the flow into two regions, separating the fluid which has been in contact with the surface on the one side of S from that which has been in contact with the surface on the other side of S.

When discussing three-dimensional flows, we have to consider surfaces of separation rather than lines, and in this we follow Maskell (1955). These surfaces and, to a lesser extent, the corresponding attachment surfaces define the three-dimensional structure of the external flow since, together with the solid body itself, they provide its internal boundaries. If we are to deduce the general forms taken by the surfaces of separation, we must distinguish between two distinct kinds of path that may be followed by individual fluid particles. These can either be open, beginning at infinity upstream and ending at infinity downstream, or be closed in the interior of the fluid. All particles which originate at infinity upstream initially possess the velocity of the undisturbed stream and constitute what may be called the main flow, the streamlines of which are necessarily open. Particles which do not originate at infinity upstream must follow closed paths about which they circulate continuously. They, therefore, constitute what may be called standing eddies, which may be isolated from the main flow by closed stream surfaces. It is convenient to call any such closed region of flow a bubble —a single bubble may contain a complex system of standing eddies.

Free vortex sheets, on the other hand, are surfaces of separation with open streamlines on either side, forming the skeletons of shear layers embedded wholly in mainstream fluid. The bubble and the free vortex sheet are the main constituents in the structure of the viscous region.

They need not, and probably will not, in general occur as alternatives. We infer that the surfaces of separation can be formed in such a way that a mixed flow is possible, the free vortex sheet springing, in this case, from the surface of a bubble rather than from the solid surface itself.

To demonstrate this, we have sketched in Fig. XII. 10 the structure of possible types of flow, viewed parallel to the leading edge, in which separation is assumed to occur at and by virtue of the sharp leading

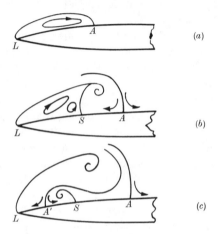

Fig. XII. 10. Sketches of various possible types of flow in sections normal to a leading edge, involving bubbles and vortex sheets.

edge L. Case (a) represents a two-dimensional state of affairs, and the main change from this to case (b) of moderate sweep is that the attachment line A is displaced from the end of the bubble where the stream surface from the edge L rejoins the surface. The latter is then replaced by a secondary separation point S. This means that some air is drawn over the top of the bubble and turned along the stream on the inside of the bubble; it necessitates the introduction of two eddies of opposite sense inside the bubble and also a free surface of separation which is, in fact, equivalent to a free vortex sheet. As the angle of sweep is increased, the attachment line A and the secondary separation line S may move farther apart, and the spiral-shaped free vortex sheet grows in size and presumably in strength. At very high angles of sweep, and according also to the details of the planform, the bubble may cease to exist altogether, the secondary separation at S leading to a secondary coiled vortex sheet underneath the primary sheet, with a secondary attachment line at A', as in case (c). It seems that, in principle, this process whereby further separation lines and vortex sheets are introduced may be continued indefinitely.

The extreme cases in this series have already been considered. Two-dimensional bubbles constantly recurred in the discussion of Chapters I to VI, and in particular their effect on the stall were considered in Section V. 14; non-planar vortex sheets have been considered in Section 8 while plane trailing vortex sheets form the basis of classical wing theory.

10. Wings with bubbles. Analytical methods

As long as the bubble-separation occurring on a wing of moderate or large aspect ratio is such that the height of the bubble and its wake are still small compared with the wing chord, the principal effect of the bubble may be regarded as a change of the sectional lift slope. The methods of Chapter VIII can then be applied except that difficulties arise when the characteristics of the section no longer vary linearly with incidence and when the bubble extends over only part of the span. In these cases, a method due to Multhopp (1938a) may be used. In this method the span-loading equation (VIII. 132) is written, with $\omega = 1$, in the form

$$\gamma_{M\nu} = (c_\nu C_{L\nu}/4s)\Big[\alpha_\nu + \sum_{\mu=1}^{N-1} b_{\nu\mu}\gamma_{M\mu} - b_{\nu\nu}\gamma_{M\nu}\Big]. \tag{44}$$

This should be interpreted as the value of C_L associated with an effective incidence $\alpha_{e\nu}$ equal to the value of the term in square brackets. Equation (44) may be regarded as a non-linear system of equations for $\gamma_{M\mu}$, which can be solved by iteration in the following manner: an approximation (p) being known, the approximation $(p+1)$ is obtained from

$$\gamma_{M\nu}^{(p+1)} = (c_\nu C_{L\nu}/4s)\Big[\alpha_\nu + \sum_{\mu=1}^{N-1} b_{\nu\mu}\gamma_{M\mu}^{(p)} - b_{\nu\nu}\gamma_{M\nu}^{(p+1)}\Big]. \tag{45}$$

It is important that the iteration is arranged so that $\gamma_{M\nu}^{(p+1)}$ occurs on the right-hand side too, because otherwise convergence is not assured.

Equation (45) can easily be solved by graphical methods on the assumption that the appropriate sectional relation between C_L and α_e is known; this may be obtained, for example, from two-dimensional experiments. The procedure is illustrated in Fig. XII. 11. Assuming that a solution $\gamma_{M\nu}^{(p)}$ is known, we can calculate the term $\Big[\alpha_\nu + \sum_{\mu=1}^{N-1} b_{\nu\mu}\gamma_{M\mu}^{(p)}\Big]$ and the point P' is thus determined. We then note that the ratio between $b_{\nu\nu}\gamma_{M\nu}^{(p+1)}$ and $C_{L\nu}^{(p+1)} = (4s/c_\nu)\gamma_{M\nu}^{(p+1)}$ is automatically independent of $\gamma_{M\nu}^{(p+1)}$. Therefore, a line can be drawn through the point P' with the slope $(-4s/c_\nu\, b_{\nu\nu})$ and the intersection of the line with the measured curve $C_L(\alpha_e)$ gives the point P from which the value of $\gamma_{M\nu}^{(p+1)}$ can be obtained. This method has been further developed by Sivells and Neely (1947), and by Sivells and Westrick (1952). In the latter paper the method is applied to wings with flaps or ailerons, for which there is a discontinuity in the spanwise direction in the effective incidence.

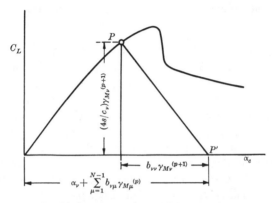

Fig. XII. 11. Graphical representation of Multhopp's equation applied to non-linear sectional lift characteristics.

Such methods are not normally adequate for swept wings where part-span separations similar to those in Fig. XII. 10 (b) may occur long before the stall. Many swept-back wings of moderate or large aspect ratio are commonly flown in conditions of complex mixed flows; for example, there may be trailing-edge separation only over the inner part of the wing, with leading-edge and trailing-edge separations over the outer parts of the wing involving bubbles and free vortex sheets. This has a profound effect on the aerodynamic characteristics of the wing.

As an illustration, let us consider the two wings of 45° sweep-back, shown in Fig. XII. 12. The main difference between them lies in the thickness–chord ratio of their sections. If the overall lift is calculated by linearized theories it is very nearly the same in the two cases owing to the combined effect of aspect ratio and wing thickness, the wing with the smaller aspect ratio having the greater thickness. Now in experiment we first distinguish the régime of flow from zero lift to point A on each curve; the predominant factor here is the unseparated boundary layer. The régime from A to B is dominated by the appearance of tip vortex sheets. These produce an increased lift slope, while the pitching moment becomes stable since the additional non-linear load appears near the tips in a rearward position. That these effects can, in fact, be explained entirely by the presence of tip vortex sheets has been shown for the thicker wing by Küchemann and Kettle (1951). It is significant that the régime of the tip vortex sheet begins at a higher

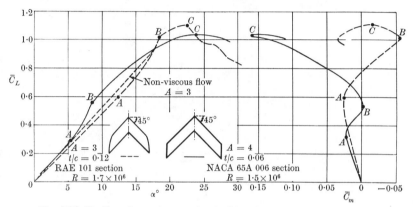

FIG. XII. 12. Experimental curves for the lift and pitching moment for two untapered wings with 45° sweep-back.

value of $\bar{C}_L$ and lasts longer for the thicker wing. The end of this régime at point B is marked by a check in the lift and by a minimum in the pitching moment. Because of the latter, the value of $\bar{C}_L$ at point B often sets a practical limit to the range of usable lift. There is a mixed bubble-vortex-sheet separation from point B onwards, which begins on the outer parts of the wings and creeps gradually inwards as the incidence is increased. It is often in the middle of this process that the maximum value of the lift is reached at point C; this stalling-point now has no particular significance, and does not mark the onset of a new type of flow.

The loss of lift due to such a separation on the outer wing is demonstrated for the thicker of these two wings in Fig. XII. 13. There must be a large amount of trailing vorticity at the boundary between that part of the wing with attached flow at the leading edge and that with separation there; and this we may call the part-span vorticity, as suggested by Küchemann (1953b). This vorticity is in the same sense as the ordinary trailing vorticity. Being closer inboard, however, it has a considerable effect on the downwash at the tailplane especially at high incidences; the effectiveness of the tailplane is therefore reduced just at that stage when it is most needed—when the wing itself becomes unstable. These separations and their consequences, therefore, have serious effects on the behaviour of swept-back wings.

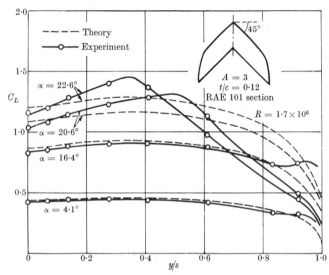

FIG. XII. 13. Some spanwise distributions of lift on an untapered wing of 45° sweep-back at high incidences as given by Küchemann, Weber, and Brebner (1951).

Little theoretical work has yet been done on swept wings with such separations. Efforts have been concentrated on finding, experimentally, means of alleviating their effects. Most devices are designed to modify the span- and chord-wise loading in such a manner as to postpone the onset of the separation to a higher lift and to retard the inward expansion of the separation once it has occurred. Fences, which are small vertical reflection plates placed on the front part of the wing in a suitable spanwise position, are typical devices and their effects have been explained theoretically by Weber (1954c) and demonstrated experimentally by Weber and Lawford (1954). Camber and twist, as well as planform modifications, can also be used with good effect, as has been explained in Section VIII. 26.

In the theoretical treatment of lifting bodies of very small aspect ratio, and arguing that on such a body the longitudinal-flow component matters much less than the cross-flow component, Betz (1935) introduced the 'cross-flow drag coefficient', C_{Dc}, which was taken to be the drag obtained on such a body in the two-dimensional flow at right angles to its axis. Hence,

$$\bar{C}_L = C_{Dc}\alpha^2 \tag{46}$$

for the lift coefficient of such a body. Taking $C_{Dc} = 2$ as an approximation, we have

$$\bar{C}_L = 2\alpha^2, \tag{47}$$

a relation which has frequently been used. The concept of the cross-flow drag has been applied in particular to bodies of revolution by Multhopp (1941), Allen and Perkins (1951), Kelly (1954), and also by Bartlett and Vidal (1954) who calculated the lift on slender wings.

Closely related to this is the theory of Bollay (1937, 1939), following suggestions by Kármán, for rectangular wings of small aspect ratio. Bollay used plane vortex sheets above the tip edges at right angles to the wing, with the vorticity vector inclined at angle $\frac{1}{2}\alpha$ to the main-stream for wings of very small aspect ratio, as in the vortex-sheet theory discussed in Section 7. But in this case, these vortex sheets are not stream surfaces but must be interpreted as representing eddies contained in bubbles, according to Küchemann (1956b). It is interesting to note that Bollay obtains again equation (47) in the limiting case of $A \to 0$, and that that result is also the same as that obtained for an inclined plate in a Newtonian fluid. We may note, also, the similarity to equation (41) which gives $\frac{1}{2}\pi\alpha^2$ in this case.

In fact, it seems unlikely that such bubbles are formed on wings and bodies of small aspect ratio. The longitudinal-flow component must surely be important and must lead to the breaking-up of any bubbles. In the few cases where the flow has been experimentally observed, vortex sheets, not bubbles, have been found.

11. Non-planar lifting systems. Biplanes and annular aerofoils

All the lifting systems so far considered have been reduced to models whose vortex sheets lie, for the most part, in a single plane. But some systems cannot possibly be approximated in this way. Of these the most prominent are biplanes and other multi-decked lifting systems for aircraft, and cascades of aerofoils whose purpose is to exert a lifting force on the stream and so to change its direction. The former are briefly considered in this section together with annular aerofoils, while Sections 13–19 are devoted to cascades.

With biplanes, we have to deal with the interaction between two lifting surfaces which are nearly parallel and more or less above one another. The problem is traditionally divided into two parts, one dealing with the interaction between the bound vortices and the other with that between the trailing vortices. The first concerns primarily the chordwise loading and the sectional characteristics; it may thus be studied as a two-dimensional problem. The aim of the second has been mainly to find the lift and drag of those cases which give minimum induced drag; this is usually attempted by the consideration of the conditions in a Trefftz plane far downstream, which again leads to a problem in two-dimensional flow.

In both cases, the difficulties are mainly of a mathematical nature in that doubly-connected regions are involved. Most investigators have used conformal transformations whereby two straight lines or aerofoil sections are transformed into two circles. Of great generality is the method of Garrick (1936) and further references may be found in a paper by Küchemann (1938a).

The case of biplanes with minimum induced drag has been solved by Munk and Prandtl, and described by Prandtl and Betz (1927). They find that, if the smallest induced drag for a given total lift $\bar{L}$ is written as

$$\bar{D}_i = \kappa \bar{L}^2 / \tfrac{1}{2}\pi\rho U_\infty^2\, b_1^2, \tag{48}$$

then the factor κ depends only on the ratios h/b and b_2/b_1; here h is the distance between the wings, and b_1 and b_2 are the two spans. Numerical values of κ are plotted in Fig. XII. 14, together with the lift ratio,

$$\lambda = L_2/(L_1+L_2). \tag{49}$$

We note that the overall induced drag of a biplane is always smaller than that of the monoplane which carries the same overall lift and which has the same span as the largest of the biplane wings. Alternatively, a monoplane of greater aspect ratio whose span is $b_1\kappa^{-\frac{1}{2}}$ carries the same lift for the same induced drag as the biplanes. The main aerodynamic advantage of a biplane is, therefore, that its span can be considerably smaller than that of the monoplane having the same lift and drag. The properties of triplanes and other multi-decked systems follow similar trends, and results for these have also been given by Prandtl (1918).

A more general method, in which the interference between bound and trailing vortices is considered together, has been proposed by Betz (1914), who replaced the wings by horseshoe vortices; and Küchemann (1938a) has given extensions of it to general systems of vortices. In this, the downwash induced by the bound vortices of one wing at the position of the other is taken into account as well as the downwash induced at one wing by the trailing vortices of the other. These down-wash angles may be treated as an angle of twist which changes along the span. A step-by-step calculation is thus possible whereby in each step Multhopp's equation for a twisted monoplane is solved. Two further terms enter the equation for the effective twist: (i) each wing produces

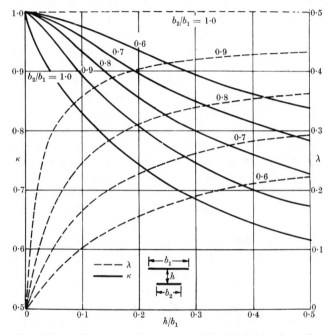

Fig. XII. 14. The induced-drag factor and the lift-division factor for biplanes.

a change, Δu, of the streamwise velocity component at the position of the other, which may be accounted for by putting

$$\Delta\alpha = \alpha(\Delta u/U_\infty), \qquad (50)$$

and (ii) each wing is in a curved flow of curvature r^{-1} caused by the other, which may be accounted for by putting

$$\Delta\alpha = c/4r = \tfrac{1}{4}c\,\partial(w/U_\infty)/\partial x. \qquad (51)$$

This was derived by H. Glauert (1926) and later by Pistolesi (1936) who showed that a plane aerofoil in a curved flow may be approximated by a cambered aerofoil in a parallel flow.

In contrast to biplanes, annular aerofoils have not been used extensively in the past—an early application was Townend's for the improvement of the flow past radial engines, as was described in Section VI. 2—but modern studies of ducted fans, as alternatives to propeller turbines, and of other sources of power and lift for vertical-take-off aircraft, suggest wide uses for annular aerofoils in the future. Their function is the control of the flow within the duct round which they form the fairing, and this is exercised mainly through the circulation set up round each section of the annular aerofoil. We may refer to Küchemann and Weber (1953a) for details of what are regarded as problems in the aerodynamics of propulsion. But for many applications, especially in the design of fairings which will not suffer seriously from the effects of separation, it is important to be able to calculate the flow due to the fairing itself. Two cases have to be considered: the first, in which the axis of the annulus is parallel to the main stream, and the second, in which the axis is tilted so that there is a resultant lift force. In both cases, the effects of the thickness of the aerofoil are usually not so significant as those of the circulation set up round each section.

According to linearized theory, a thin annular aerofoil may be represented by vortex rings lying on a circular cylinder which is analogous to the chordal plane in two-dimensional theory. When the aerofoil is at zero incidence, each vortex ring is of constant strength round its circumference, and the velocity field and stream function for such a ring have been tabulated by Küchemann (1940b). The condition that a given aerofoil is a stream surface may be satisfied at a number of points, if a series of standard vortex distributions along the cylinder are used; tables of certain standard distributions are given by Küchemann and Weber (1953a). Once the distribution of vorticity is determined, the chordwise distribution of pressure, and hence the radial force, can be calculated. The rate of flow through the aerofoil can be found from the value of the stream function at the trailing edge, where the Kutta–Joukowski condition is assumed to hold.

The thickness of an annular aerofoil may be represented by a source distribution on the chordal cylinder; this will induce components of velocity in the radial, as well as in the axial, direction and so a corresponding distribution of vortex rings must be added to maintain the condition that the aerofoil is a stream surface. Some examples of this have been calculated by Bagley, Kirby, and Marcer (1958). Calculations of the pressure distribution on annular aerofoils, both with and without thickness, have also been made by Malavard (1957), using an electrolytic-tank analogy, and Hacques (1957a, b) who have been able to consider the inverse problem of designing for a prescribed pressure distribution.

If the whole annular aerofoil is at incidence to the mainstream, it experiences an overall lifting force and, because there are now trailing vortices, an induced drag. Experiments by Muttray (1941) and Fletcher (1957) show that annular aerofoils have about twice the lift slope, and half the induced drag, of rectangular wings of the same aspect ratio, as has been shown theoretically by Weissinger (1955) and others. In Weissinger's work, a distribution of vortex rings whose strengths vary round their circumferences is used, together with the corresponding trailing vortices, and Weissinger (1957) and Bagley, Kirby, and Marcer (1958) have shown how to develop this method to calculate the pressure distributions.

12. Non-planar lifting systems. Ground interference

A problem closely related to that of the biplane arises when a lifting wing is placed near a solid plane boundary. The most common practical example occurs during the take-off or landing of an aircraft, when the height of the aircraft's wing above the ground is only of the order of its chord-length. Under these circumstances the flow past the wing can be substantially affected, especially as the wing is usually operating at a high lift coefficient with the consequent possibilities of separation and so on. The effect of the ground on the flow past the wing decreases very rapidly with increasing height and vice versa. Nevertheless, we may observe that the flight of an aircraft is necessarily accompanied by an increase in pressure over the ground, whose integral equals the weight of the aircraft. This increase of pressure is, of course, usually undetectably small; there is, however, an analogous laboratory technique, in which the lift of an aerofoil in a wind-tunnel may be deduced from measurements of the static pressure of the walls of the working section.

The ground may be replaced, for the purposes of analysis, by an image wing which is the reflection of the real wing in the ground plane. The methods mentioned in the previous section then apply; also related are problems of wind-tunnel corrections, and of aerofoils in bounded streams.

Consider first a symmetrical wing at zero incidence. If we replace the wing and its image by distributions of sources and vortices, we see at once that the sources representing the displacement flow of the image wing produce an upwash over the front part of the physical wing and a downwash over the rear part. Thus to counteract this, a vortex distribution is required, corresponding to a camber, which is such as to produce a force directed towards the ground. This phenomenon is well known to seamen who have to apply considerable rudder on two ships steaming close together with equal velocities.

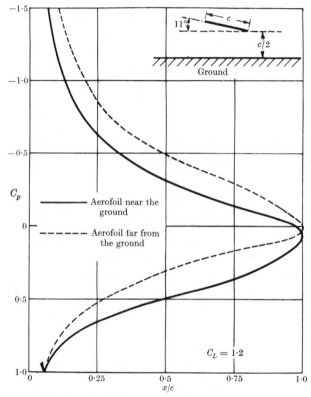

Fig. XII. 15. The effect of the ground on the pressure distribution of a two-dimensional flat plate aerofoil.

With the wing at incidence, further distributions of vortices are required which change the lift and its chordwise distribution. The latter is shown in Fig. XII. 15 for the two-dimensional case, and an important effect is on the change in the position of the aerodynamic centre due to the ground. A method of calculating the pressure distribution for any given aerofoil shape has been developed on this basis by Bagley (1959).

The analysis for two-dimensional thin aerofoils near the ground is relatively simple with the use of conformal transformations. The simplest case of a flat plate at incidence, already illustrated, has been solved by Tomotika, Nagamiya, and Takenouti (1933). Their result for the lift, L, in relation to the lift, L_0, at a large distance from the ground, is reproduced in Fig. XII. 16. The lift increases sharply as the ground is approached in what may be described as a cushioning effect which is familiar to glider pilots. Tani, Taima, and Simidu (1937) calculated the

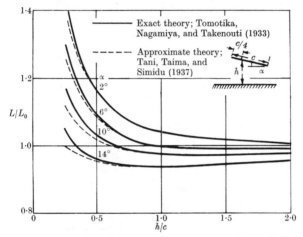

FIG. XII. 16. The effect of height on the lift on a two-dimensional flat-plate aerofoil near the ground.

lift of a two-dimensional flat plate by an approximate method involving Birnbaum's vortex distributions. This is very much simpler than the method using conformal transformation. Their results, also shown in Fig. XII. 16, are in reasonable agreement with the results from the exact method. A summary of investigations of this problem has been given by Hamal (1953).

The trailing vortices of a wing of finite span are also reflected in the ground plane. The image vortices induce an upwash at the real wing so that the total induced incidence for a wing near the ground is smaller than in an unbounded stream. This is another reason for the increase of lift near the ground, the aircraft being kept at the same incidence. The reduction of the induced incidence was first determined by Wieselsberger (1921) for wings with elliptic spanloading. Haller (1936) has calculated the load distributions which give constant downwash and thus minimum induced drag. The induced incidence and induced drag for wings of large aspect ratio can again be written in the forms

$$\alpha_{i0} = \kappa \bar{C}_L / \pi A; \qquad \bar{C}_{Di} = \kappa (\bar{C}_L)^2 / \pi A. \qquad (52)$$

The factor κ is plotted in Fig. XII. 17, from which it is seen that the difference between the minimum induced drag and that for elliptic loading is not very significant in comparison with the ground effect itself, which can be considerable.

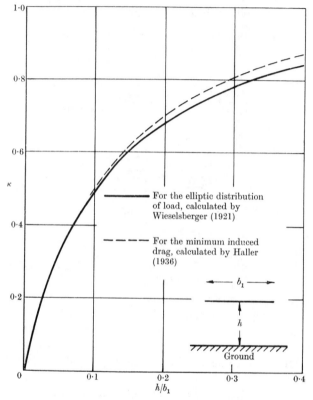

Fɪɢ. XII. 17. The effect of height on the induced-drag factor of a wing near the ground.

13. Non-planar lifting systems. Cascades

The analytical discussion of a cascade—that is, an infinite array of regularly-spaced two-dimensional aerofoils, as sketched in Fig. XII. 18 —has one or two features common to the flows of the two preceding sections. Attention is confined to the first inviscid approximation and a basic conformal transformation of a logarithmic type reduces the cascade to a single closed body. Most of the classical theories of cascades largely ignored the thickness of the individual aerofoils of the cascades, though this was remedied later. Lastly, the theory of cascades of wings of finite span is still quite undeveloped, so in the next few sections we shall not be bothered by considerations of trailing vorticity.

But the practical and physical characteristics of cascades differ greatly from those of biplanes or of wings near the ground. First, a finite flux of fluid is associated with each aerofoil of a cascade and with the forces imposed on the fluid by that aerofoil; it at once follows that cascades have the power of deflecting streams of fluid. An abrupt bend in a channel normally results in a considerable loss of energy in the fluid flowing within it; if, however, a cascade is used at the bend, this loss of energy may be reduced to a value associated only with the drag of the individual aerofoils of the cascade. Next, the fact that, in practice, a cascade is of finite span and that there are boundary layers on the boundaries at the two ends of the span leads to the flow in the cascade taking on a three-dimensional character. These so-called secondary flows have been met in previous chapters and have usually been dismissed as having little influence on the main part of the flow; however, they are often of great importance in flows in curved ducts. This is especially true of ducts which extend so far upstream of the bend that a boundary layer can no longer be distinguished, the whole region of flow being subject to the action of viscosity.

The first inviscid approximation for the flow past cascades fitted to bends in ducts must, therefore, be accepted with far greater reserve than for flow past aerofoils. And although we do not attempt any account of secondary flows in cascades, the reader is well advised to acquaint himself with them, by reference to the work of, for example, Squire and Winter (1951), of Preston (1954a), and of Hawthorne (1955).

Apart from the secondary flows, the direct effects of viscosity—influence of the boundary layer on the external flow, and their mutual interactions on closely-spaced blades—may be greater in cascades than for isolated aerofoils, since the Reynolds numbers of the former are often relatively low. This being so, the performance data of cascades used in the design of wind-tunnels or of axial compressors is usually obtained experimentally. However, at higher Reynolds numbers, say of 10^6 or more, it is possible to make rough calculations of the first viscous approximation, as may be seen from the work of Schlichting and Scholz (1951) and of Schlichting (1954), which are in reasonable agreement with experiment.

Last, we may mention the importance of theories of and experiments on cascades in their application to rotary flows. It will be recalled from Chapter XI that the idealization of the actuator disk depended for its usefulness on information concerning the fluid angles at entry and exit, and it is this information which can be yielded by the study of cascades. Current American methods of utilizing and synthesizing experimental data from cascades are contained in a comprehensive review of the aerodynamic design of axial-flow compressors, edited by Johnsen and Bullock (1956).

14. General relations for inviscid flow through a cascade

We use, without further explanation, the notation of Fig. XII. 18 in which, upstream of the cascade, the uniform flow has velocity components U_1 and W_1, the velocity V_1' is inclined at an angle

$$\alpha_1 = \tan^{-1}(W_1/U_1)$$

to the x-axis and the pressure is denoted by p_1. The corresponding downstream values are U_2, W_2, V_2', α_2, and p_2 respectively. In general, the velocity and pressure downstream differ from those upstream.

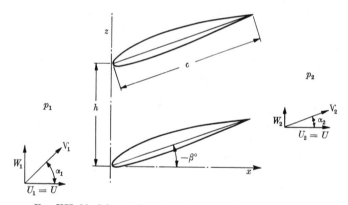

Fig. XII. 18. Scheme of notation for a two-dimensional cascade.

The regular repetition of the flow at intervals of h measured parallel to the z-axis implies that it is sufficient to consider a single interval of this height to establish the main features of the flow. First, the flux, $\rho_1 U_1 h$, of mass across a line far upstream parallel to the z-axis equals $\rho_2 U_2 h$ downstream where a uniform flow is re-established. Now for incompressible flow, $\rho_1 = \rho_2 = \rho$; hence also $U_1 = U_2 = U$ and the suffixes on both ρ and U will be omitted. The circulation Γ around each aerofoil may be found by considering a contour consisting of two streamlines, separated by a distance $z = h$, joined by lines parallel to the z-axis at large distances up- and down-stream of the aerofoil. The sum of the contributions from the two identical streamlines is zero, and so

$$\Gamma = (W_1 - W_2)h = Uh(\tan\alpha_1 - \tan\alpha_2). \tag{53}$$

The rise in static pressure through the cascade is expressed in terms of W_1, W_2, and $\bar{p}$ as

$$p_2 - p_1 = \tfrac{1}{2}\rho(W_1^2 - W_2^2) - \bar{p}, \tag{54}$$

where $\bar{p}$ is the loss in total pressure arising from viscosity. Since there

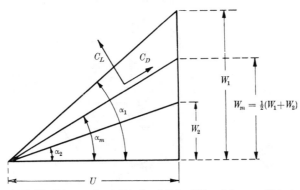

$$W_m = \tfrac{1}{2}(W_1 + W_2)$$

FIG. XII. 19. Scheme of notation for defining lift and drag coefficients on a two-dimensional cascade.

is no change of momentum parallel to the x-axis, the force per unit span on each aerofoil has a component X given by

$$X = -\tfrac{1}{2}\rho h(W_1^2 - W_2^2) + \bar{p}h = -\rho W_m \Gamma + \bar{p}h, \tag{55}$$

where W_m is the mean velocity component in the z-direction. Considering next the rate of change of momentum parallel to the z-axis, we find that the force component $Z = \rho U^2 h(\tan\alpha_1 - \tan\alpha_2) = \rho U\Gamma$. Hence in the absence of viscous losses the resultant force is $\rho\Gamma(U^2 + W_m^2)^{\frac{1}{2}}$ and acts along a line inclined at an angle $\alpha_m = \tan^{-1}(W_m/U)$ to the z-axis. We therefore define the lift and drag coefficients in terms of the components of force parallel and perpendicular to this line and of the speed $(U^2 + W_m^2)^{\frac{1}{2}}$. Thus

$$C_D = 2h\cos\alpha_m\,\bar{p}/c\rho(U^2 + W_m^2) \tag{56}$$

and

$$C_L = (2h/c)(\tan\alpha_1 - \tan\alpha_2)\cos\alpha_m - C_D\tan\alpha_m. \tag{57}$$

This scheme of notation is illustrated in Fig. XII. 19.

15. Conformal transformations for cascades

The inviscid flow past a cascade of aerofoils may be reduced to that outside a single closed body by the application of any suitable periodic transformation. Such a one is $t = \tanh(\pi\mathfrak{z}/h)$, for which points at infinity up- and down-stream in the $\mathfrak{z}$-plane become $t = \mp 1$. The uniform flow upstream is then represented by a source of strength Uh and a vortex of strength $(-W_1 h)$ at $t = -1$ and the corresponding down-stream flow at $t = 1$ consists of a sink and vortex of strengths Uh and $W_2 h$ respectively. The sum of the circulations around these points is

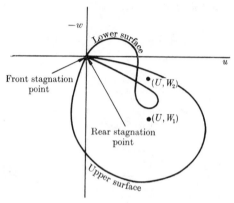

Fig. XII. 20. A typical boundary in the hodograph plane, for the flow past a cascade of aerofoils having wedge-shaped trailing edges.

equal but of opposite sign to the circulation around each aerofoil of the cascade, as shown from equation (53). For small values of h/c the leading and trailing edges of the profile in the t-plane are close to the points $t = \mp 1$ and points uniformly spaced along the chord in the $\mathfrak{z}$-plane are concentrated towards the leading and trailing edges. Due to the close proximity of $t = 1$ the flow over the rear of the aerofoil is determined mainly by the sink and vortex at this point. Thus, since the Kutta–Joukowski condition of Section V. 2 largely determines the character of the flow over the trailing edge, the values of W_2/U and of the exit angle α_2 depend mainly on the geometry of the cascade, and to a much smaller extent on the inlet angle α_1. This is an important and fortunate property of cascades, since among other things it means that variations in upstream conditions affect only slightly the per-formance of the cascade.

The representation of a cascade flow in the hodograph plane,

$$d\mathfrak{w}/d\mathfrak{z} = u - iw,$$

also leads to a single profile which in this case encloses the field of flow. Fig. XII. 20 sketches the boundary in the hodograph plane for a typical flow; only a few special flows result in a simple curve and generally the potential function is multi-valued and must be represented on a Riemann surface of two or more sheets, as is necessary in the case illustrated. The flow upstream and downstream of the cascade corresponds to singularities of the same nature and magnitude as in the t-plane but they are now located at the points $d\mathfrak{w}/d\mathfrak{z} = U - iW_1$ and $d\mathfrak{w}/d\mathfrak{z} = U - iW_2$ respectively. The further transformation of the area inside the boundary in the hodograph plane into a circular area or into a half-plane enables the flow to be calculated.

The hodograph method is useful in the design of cascade sections giving a chosen deflexion with a specified maximum velocity on the aerofoils. The Kutta–Joukowski condition is automatically satisfied by the choice of a finite boundary.

16. Flow past cascades of flat plates

The flow past a cascade of staggered flat plates may be found directly from the relation

$$\mathfrak{z}e^{i\beta} = (h/2\pi)\{e^{i\beta}\log[(1+t_1)/(1-t_1)] + e^{-i\beta}\log[(t_1+a^2)/(t_1-a^2)]\}.$$
(58)

This transforms a row of flat plates of stagger-angle β and gap h, into the circle $|t_1| = a$. The chord, c, and the radius, a, are functionally related and to determine this relationship it is most convenient to use the intermediate variable $\zeta = \xi + i\eta$ introduced by Collar (1940).

If we put $$\tanh(\pi\zeta/h) = (t_1^2 - a^2)/t_1(1 - a^2),$$ (59)

the circle $|t_1| = a$ corresponds to a cascade of flat plates all lying along the imaginary axis $\xi = 0$ at intervals of h. The length, $2f$, of these plates is a convenient parameter, and it is easy to show from (59) that

$$a = \tan(\pi f/2h).$$ (60)

Eliminating t_1 from equations (58) and (59), we find for the $(\mathfrak{z}, \zeta)$ transformation

$$\mathfrak{z}e^{i\beta} = (h/\pi)\{\cos\beta \cosh^{-1}[\sec(\pi f/h)\cosh(\pi\zeta/h)] + (i\pi\zeta/h)\sin\beta\}.$$ (61)

From this, it may be shown that the extremities of the plates in the $\mathfrak{z}$-plane are given by the following value of η:

$$\sin(\pi\eta/h) = \sin\beta \sin(\pi f/h),$$ (62)

and also that the gap-chord ratio is given by

$$\pi c/h = \cos\beta \log[(k+1)/(k-1)] + 2\sin\beta \tan^{-1}(k^{-1}\tan\beta) \left.\right\}$$
where $$k^2 = 1 + \sec^2\beta \cot^2(\pi f/h). \left.\right\}$$ (63)

f and k are thus best regarded as parameters, either of which determine the gap-chord ratio.

To find the relation between the inlet and exit angles, α_1 and α_2, we first write down the complex velocity potential in the t_1-plane, which has singularities at $t_1 = \pm 1$ identical to those in the t-plane determined in the preceding section. Thus

$$\mathfrak{w}(t_1) = \frac{Uh}{2\pi}\log\left[\frac{(t_1+1)(t_1+a^2)}{(t_1-1)(t_1-a^2)}\right] - i\frac{W_1 h}{2\pi}\log\left(\frac{t_1+1}{t_1+a^2}\right) + i\frac{W_2 h}{2\pi}\log\left(\frac{t_1-1}{t_1-a^2}\right). \tag{64}$$

Equating to zero $d\mathfrak{w}/d\zeta$, from equations (59) and (64), at the trailing edge specified by (62), we find that

$$\tfrac{1}{2}(W_1-W_2) = W_m[\tan^2(\pi f/h)+\sin^2\beta]^{\frac{1}{2}} + U\sin(\pi f/h), \tag{65}$$

which may be rewritten as

$$(\tan\alpha_1+\tan\beta)/(\tan\alpha_2+\tan\beta) = (k+1)/(k-1) \tag{66}$$

in terms of the parameter k, which in turn depends on the gap-chord ratio from equation (63). For zero stagger, $\beta = 0$, equations (63) and (66) yield

$$\tan\alpha_1 \cot\alpha_2 = \exp(\pi c/h). \tag{67}$$

In practice, gap-chord ratios are small, and so k is not much greater than unity. We therefore infer, from (66), what we have already argued in Section 15, namely that α_2 is roughly equal to $(-\beta)$ whatever the value of α_1. This is further supported by the experimental results shown later in Fig. XII. 25.

The relation (66) between the inlet and exit angles is readily extended to cascades of cambered aerofoils of non-zero thickness, but the constants in the equation are of course modified. The angle $(-\beta)$ is replaced by the angle of zero lift and k depends on the aerofoil shape as well as on the gap-chord ratio; the latter, however, remains a very important parameter. Both constants can be calculated by a method similar to that given above once the transformation of the aerofoils into plates in the ζ-plane (or into some other suitable shape) has been found. Alternatively the constants can be assessed from experimental results.

The lift coefficient in inviscid flow is found from equations (57) and (66) in the form

$$C_L = (4h/ck)\sin(\alpha_m+\beta)\sec\beta. \tag{68}$$

The variation with stagger and gap-chord ratio of the characteristics of cascades of flat plates is illustrated in Fig. XII. 21, where

$$C_L/2\pi\sin(\alpha_m+\beta) = (2h/\pi ck)\sec\beta,$$

the ratio of the lift of the aerofoil in cascade to that of an isolated plate, is plotted against the gap-chord ratio. These results for cascades of plates give a general guide to the influence of gap-chord ratio and stagger on the performance of cascades of thin symmetrical aerofoils, although differences of course arise due to the finite thickness of the aerofoils.

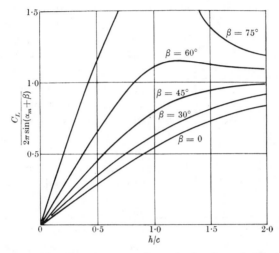

FIG. XII. 21. The effect of stagger and gap-chord ratio on the lift of a flat plate in cascade.

17. Various methods of deriving cascades of aerofoils of non-zero thickness

The flow past particular aerofoil cascades can be derived by a generalization of the process by which the isolated Joukowski aerofoils are obtained from the circle. If a transformation is known connecting a cascade of ovals with a cascade of flat plates then this transformation can be applied to the flow past larger ovals of the same group to yield aerofoils of finite thickness. The centres of these latter ovals may be displaced to produce sections with sharp trailing edges and camber. Collar (1941) has used ovals in the l-plane connected with the circle in the t_1-plane by the relation $t_1 = \tanh(\pi l/h)$, but the resulting aerofoils are found to have camber lines differing considerably from those found by experiment to give satisfactory performance. Another family of ovals has been investigated by Merchant and Collar (1941). These are derived from the flow normal to a row of equally-spaced doublets and differ little from circles even when the diameters are a considerable proportion of the gap. The resulting profiles resemble the isolated

Joukowski aerofoils and are closer to practical sections than those found by Collar, though the computation is somewhat involved.

The results derived in Section 16 for the flat-plate cascade can also be found from a consideration of the flow in the hodograph plane. The appropriate hodograph boundary is a straight line inclined at an angle β to the real axis and the potential function for the required

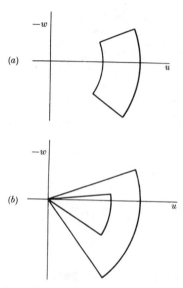

flow can readily be calculated. Other configurations in the hodograph plane have been considered by Legendre (1939) who has investigated a range of boundaries, many formed largely of circular arcs centred at the origin, which correspond to surfaces of constant pressure. The simplest type shown in Fig. XII. 22 (a) leads to sections with cusped leading and trailing edges while other forms extending to the origin, as in Fig. XII. 22 (b), give finite angles at the leading and trailing edges. These boundaries yield concave-convex sections and serve as a useful guide to the design of sections with considerable camber suitable for large deflexions of flow.

FIG. XII. 22. Some boundaries in the hodograph plane, as considered by Legendre (1939)

A logarithmic transformation converts the circular-arc boundaries into straight lines, and the subsequent application of the Schwarz–Christoffel transformation maps the area enclosed on to a half-plane where the flow can be found by the method of images.

A rather more direct method of design, based on a desired distribution of velocity on the aerofoils, has been given by Lighthill (1945a) as an extension of his method of aerofoil design described in Sections IV. 20 and 21. The details of the method are complicated and the numerical work is difficult even for a skilled computer; we therefore leave the reader to consult the original paper and that of Crooks and Howard (1954). We may, however, mention that it is more difficult in this case of cascades to choose a suitable distribution of velocity as a function of ϕ, the angle on the circle into which the cascade aerofoil is transformed, than in the case of the conventional aerofoil. This is mainly due to the fact that there is no characteristic relation for cascades analogous to $x = \frac{1}{2}c(1-\cos\phi)$ for isolated aerofoils.

Methods of calculating flows past cascades based on distributions of sources and vortices have been described by a number of authors. When the gap-chord ratio is large, it is sufficient to represent the influence of adjacent aerofoils approximately by using a limited number of discrete singularities but for small gap-chord ratios a detailed representation of the interference is required. Systematic developments of the latter type of method have been carried out, notably by Scholz (1954) and Schlichting (1955).

It is convenient in dealing with these methods to employ axes (x_1, z_1) parallel and normal to the chord-lines of the aerofoils in place of those used previously. Referred to these axes, the complex potential for a row of sources of unit strength, equally spaced at intervals of h along a line inclined to the z_1-axis at an angle β, is $\mathfrak{w} = (1/2\pi)\log \sinh[\pi e^{-i\beta}(\mathfrak{z}_1-\mathfrak{z}_1')/h]$, one of the row being situated at the point $\mathfrak{z}_1 = \mathfrak{z}_1'$. The velocity components are therefore given by

$$u - iw = (e^{-i\beta}/2h)\coth[\pi e^{-i\beta}(\mathfrak{z}_1-\mathfrak{z}_1')/h]. \tag{69}$$

Thus the total velocity field due to a distribution $g(\mathfrak{z}_1')$ of singularities along the mean line of an aerofoil of chord c becomes

$$u - iw = (e^{-i\beta}/2h) \int_0^c g(\mathfrak{z}_1')\coth[\pi e^{-i\beta}(\mathfrak{z}_1-\mathfrak{z}_1')/h]\, d\mathfrak{z}_1'. \tag{70}$$

The function $g(\mathfrak{z}_1')$, if complex, represents a distribution of both sources and vortices and therefore, with an additional term representing a uniform stream, equation (70) can be used to represent the flow past a cascade of lifting aerofoils.

The method is most easily applied to cascades of thin aerofoils of small camber when the typical approximation of calculating the induced velocities on the chord-line can be made. Changes in the shape of the camber line with gap-chord ratio and stagger for a given chordwise lift distribution are readily calculated in this way. Scholz has suggested that the difference in velocity field between the cascade and the corresponding isolated aerofoil, namely

$$(1/2h) \int_0^c g(\mathfrak{z}_1')[e^{-i\beta}\coth\{\pi e^{-i\beta}(\mathfrak{z}_1-\mathfrak{z}_1')/h\}-h/\pi(\mathfrak{z}_1-\mathfrak{z}_1')]\, d\mathfrak{z}_1',$$

should be employed for this purpose and has devised a rapid method of calculation using numerical tables for the function contained in the square brackets, computed for a wide range of values of the stagger and gap-chord ratio.

Schlichting (1954) has extended the method to the calculation of the flow past profiles of arbitrary shape and has given examples of typical results including applications to aerofoils of large camber. Isay (1953) has used a similar method for problems involving the interference between two or more adjacent aerofoil cascades and his is one of the few methods suitable for such complicated problems.

18. Various methods of solving the flow past a cascade of given aerofoils

The use of conformal transformations to find the flow past a given cascade requires (i) the reduction to a single profile according to the method of Section 15, (ii) the transformation of the resulting profile into a nearly circular boundary, and finally (iii) the transformation of the nearly circular boundary into an exact circle. The last step also arises in the calculation of the flow past an arbitrary isolated aerofoil and the methods of Chapter IV are applicable.

Howell (1948b) uses three transformations to reduce the aerofoil cascade to a nearly circular shape. The aerofoils in the $\mathfrak{z}$-plane are first transformed by $t = \tanh(\pi\mathfrak{z}/h)$ into a single boundary which usually has an S-shaped camber line, if the original cascade is staggered. The S-shaped distortion of the camber line becomes more pronounced as the gap-chord ratio is reduced and the difficulty of converting the distorted shapes obtained for small gap-chord ratios into a circle forms one of the limitations of the method. The second and third transformations are both of the familiar Joukowski type. The t-plane is then transformed to the ζ_2-plane by $t_2 = \zeta_2 + C_2^2/\zeta_2$, t_2 differing from t only in the displacement of the origin and the orientation of the axes which are chosen to give a nearly elliptic boundary in the ζ_2-plane. The constant C_2 must, of course, be chosen so that the points $t_2 = \pm 2C_2$ lie within the boundary. A similar transformation with a further change of axes produces a nearly circular boundary which is then transformed into an exact circle using Theodorsen's method of Section IV. 12. This process has been employed by Carter and Hughes (1946) for theoretical calculations of cascade performance.

An alternative method has been suggested by Garrick (1944) who uses the transformation (58) which, when applied to an aerofoil in the $\mathfrak{z}$-plane, produces a nearly circular boundary in the t_1-plane. This method avoids some of the difficulties occurring in Howell's method for small gap-chord ratios but suffers from the considerable disadvantage that t_1 cannot be expressed explicitly in terms of ζ for nonzero stagger. Thus the coordinates in the t_1-plane must be found from the aerofoil coordinates by an iterative process.

The use of the electrolytic-tank analogy originally employed by Relf (1924) provides a powerful alternative to theoretical methods for determining two-dimensional inviscid flows past cascades of arbitrary aerofoils. The analogy with inviscid flow is of course exact so that errors arise only from defects in the experimental technique, and with suitable precautions it should be possible to reduce them to negligible proportions. The application of the method to cascades has been described by Malavard (1947) and Hargest (1949) who give details of the procedure for adjusting the circulation around the aerofoils to satisfy the Kutta–Joukowski condition and for determining the corresponding direction of the downstream flow. In the direct analogy where the tank represents the flow in the physical ζ-plane, a minimum of five aerofoils is usually employed and the boundaries of the flow are represented by straight walls. This simple arrangement gives adequate accuracy since the flow is uniform at relatively short distances ahead of and behind a cascade. Alternatively, the electrolytic tank can be used to represent the flow past the appropriate boundary in either the t- or ζ-plane.

19. Some experimental results for cascades

A wide range of experimental data for different cascade configurations is now available, notably those given by Salter (1946), Carter (1948), Bogdonoff (1948), Bridle (1949), and Rhoden (1952); only a brief reference to some of the main results will be made here. The chief problem in establishing experimental data directly comparable with theoretical calculations arises from the difficulty of producing experimentally a truly two-dimensional flow. The boundary layers on the duct walls usually change in thickness as they pass through the cascade and secondary flows also arise. These effects combined can result in a considerable change in the spanwise dimension, and while they can be reduced by the application of boundary-layer control to the walls of the duct, as has been shown by Erwin and Emery (1949), they are not easily eliminated.

We pick out some results given for cascades of unit gap-chord ratio designed for axial-flow compressors and tested by Rhoden (1952). The thickness-chord ratio for the cascades is 10 per cent with the maximum thickness at $0 \cdot 3c$; the camber lines are circular arcs and defined by the

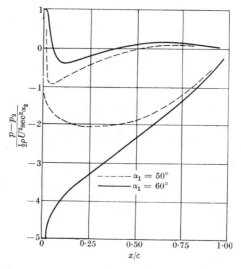

Fig. XII. 23. Chordwise distributions of pressure on a cascade
with a 40° circular-arc camber, as found by Rhoden (1952)
using an electrolytic tank.

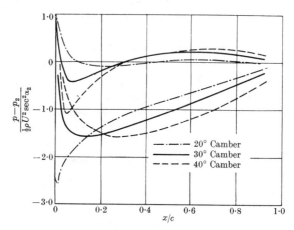

Fig. XII. 24. The effect of camber on the chordwise distribution of pressure
on a cascade.

angle $\bar{\theta}$ between the tangents to the camber line at the leading and trailing edges. Typical pressure distributions expressed in terms of the
downstream dynamic pressure are shown in Figs. XII. 23 and 24. The
first figure shows the pressure distributions found in the electrolytic

tank for two incidences for a 40°-camber cascade with a stagger angle of −38°. The main feature of these curves is the small change with incidence in the pressure distribution over the rear half of the profile, which we have remarked on before as typical of a closely-spaced cascade. The pressure gradient on the upper surface at the larger incidence indicates the approach of separation. There is an appreciable range of incidence over which unseparated flow with thin boundary layers can be expected; its extent depends, of course, on a suitable choice of camber and gap-chord ratio for the required deflexion of the stream.

The influence of camber on the load distribution along the chord for a deflexion of 20° is shown in Fig. XII. 24, compiled from tests in a cascade tunnel at a Reynolds number of 4.8×10^5. The 30°-cambered section produces an approximately uniform distribution of load and is typical of pressure distributions near the middle of the working range. This type of pressure distribution may be expected to give good performance at high Reynolds numbers but the experimental results show that at lower Reynolds numbers the sections with smaller camber are preferable since the flow does not separate so readily from their upper surfaces.

For a given deflexion of flow, the loading on each blade is proportional to the spacing so that a reduction of gap-chord ratio will reduce the adverse pressure gradients on the blades provided the ratio is not so small that the effects of the thickness of the blades predominate. The maximum allowable blade loading, without risk of separation for thin aerofoils of optimum camber, can be assessed roughly on the basis of a lift coefficient based on the dynamic pressure of the downstream flow. A value of about 1·4 can be achieved without excessive losses due to viscous effects; this value will tend to decrease as the blockage due to thickness increases.

Scale effect must be determined mainly from experiment and is often usefully interpreted in terms of the loss of total pressure through the cascade. A fairly general result is that at high Reynolds numbers, say those greater than 5×10^5, the loss coefficient is roughly constant over a wide range of incidence; for lower Reynolds numbers of the order of 10^5 there is less uniformity and for values below 10^5 the losses are considerably greater.

Fig. XII. 25 illustrates the variation in the deflexion of the flow at two Reynolds numbers for the 30°-cambered aerofoil of the previous figure, and the small variation in α_2 over the whole incidence range of

α_1 is again emphasized. The direction of the exit flow, which has been shown in Section 16 to be close to the zero-lift angle, differs appreciably from the direction of the tangent to the camber line at the trailing edge and this deviation δ can be estimated from the semi-empirical relation known as Constant's rule:

$$\delta = m\bar{\theta}(h/c)^n, \tag{71}$$

where $\bar{\theta}$ is the camber angle, and m depends on the stagger and the camber-line shape and is of the order of 0·2. Theoretical calculations

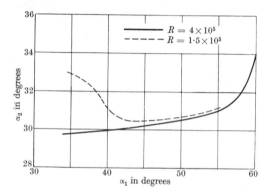

FIG. XII. 25. Experimental curves showing a typical variation of the exit angle with the inlet angle for a cascade.

show that the index n has a value close to unity and this is confirmed by experiments on turbine cascades for which β is positive. For cascades in compressors, however, a value of one-half gives better agreement with experiment, as explained more fully by Horlock (1958a).

20. The velocity field of a wing

We were concerned in Chapter X with problems of interference in which the junction of two or more bodies creates a flow significantly different from the flows past the single isolated bodies. For these flows, the effects of viscosity or of compressibility usually make themselves felt in relation to the velocity field very close to the surface; and for this and other reasons, we concentrated attention almost exclusively on the velocity distribution, in the first inviscid approximation, on the surface and not elsewhere.

Many interference effects of great practical importance, however, arise from action at a distance; possibly the most obvious is the influence of an aircraft's main wing on the flow field near a tailplane. Here the downwash of the wing alters the angle of incidence of the tailplane;

the alteration itself varies with the incidence of the wing, and this whole effect is of vital importance in the longitudinal stability of an aeroplane. This particular example also prompts a re-examination of the assumption that the trailing vorticity is confined to a plane sheet lying behind the wing, or body, parallel to the stream. The first part of the assumption—the neglect of the process of rolling-up—

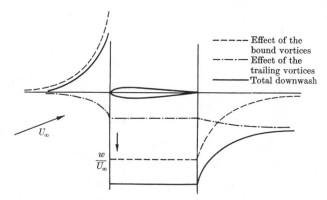

FIG. XII. 26. Qualitative variations of the induced downwash along the chord-line of the centre section of a finite wing at incidence.

probably does not lead to very serious errors except for wings of small aspect ratio, and has been further discussed in Section 7: but with regard to the second part—the neglect of the downward displacement of the sheet—there may be flows which are sensitive to the position of the sheet.

This section, therefore, reviews the methods in current use for determining the velocity field of a wing. Some of the relevant effects are illustrated in Fig. XII. 26. In the particular case of elliptic loading, the streamwise distribution of downwash at the centre section on the trailing vortex sheet may be evaluated in terms of a complete elliptic integral; and for points some way downstream, an asymptotic expansion of the integral gives

$$w/U_\infty = (2C_L/\pi A)[1+(b/2\pi x)^2]. \tag{72}$$

In the more general case of arbitrary spanwise loading Multhopp (1938b) obtained an expression for the downwash at any point on the trailing vortex sheet; thus

$$w_\nu/U_\infty = 2b_{\nu\nu}\frac{\Gamma_\nu}{bU_\infty} - \sum_{\mu=1}^{m} b_{\nu\mu}\left(1+\frac{x}{[x^2+(y_\nu-y_\mu)^2]^{\frac{1}{2}}}\right)\frac{\Gamma_\mu}{bU_\infty}, \tag{73}$$

where x and y are measured in terms of the semi-span, $\frac{1}{2}b$, and the coefficients $b_{\nu\mu}$ are those given in Table VIII. 2. This equation is convenient for rapid calculations of the downwash.

The variation of the downwash with vertical distance, $(z-z_1)$, away from the trailing vortex sheet is illustrated in Fig. XII. 27; the curves refer to conditions far downstream where the contribution of the bound

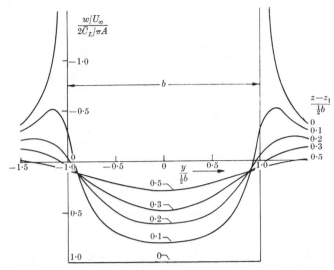

Fig. XII. 27. Spanwise distributions of downwash far behind a finite wing with elliptic loading, at various vertical distances from the trailing vortex sheet.

vorticity is negligible. On the sheet, at $z-z_1 = 0$, we notice that the downwash is constant, which shows that the special case of elliptic loading has been taken.

A first approximation to the shape of the trailing vortex sheet may be made from equation (73); a second approximation would involve the recalculation of the downwash due to the new curved vortex sheet: in fact, it would not be worth while to perform this further calculation since the assumption that the trailing vorticity lies in a sheet involves overriding inaccuracies.

Meanwhile, we note that as far as the effect on the load distribution on the wing is concerned, it appears theoretically possible to take the downward displacement of the trailing vortex sheet into account. Kármán and Burgers (1935) and Spreiter and Sacks (1951) have all made suggestions on these lines, but it is doubtful whether the increased accuracy would justify, for practical purposes, the increased computation.

It is important to take into account the displacement of the trailing vortex sheet when calculating the velocity field near a tailplane, since the downwash changes rapidly with distance from the vortex sheet, as is shown by Figs. XII. 27 and 28. The latter also indicates that on

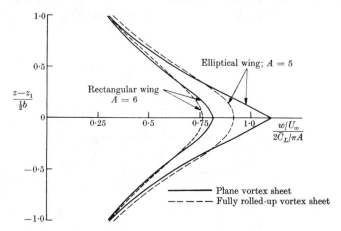

FIG. XII. 28. The variation of downwash with distance from the trailing vortex sheet, on the centre section one semi-span behind two typical wings.

each side of and close to the centre section of a plane sheet, the variation of downwash is approximately linear. These effects impose difficulties on a designer's choice of the tailplane position.

Design charts for predicting the downwash angle and wake characteristics behind plain and flapped wings have been prepared by Silverstein and Katzoff (1939), and Priestley (1945) has given a critical review of experimental data and calculation methods. Charts are also available in the series of *Data Sheets* prepared by the Royal Aeronautical Society, London.

Any effect which alters the spanwise loading, such as the deflexion of flaps, causes a corresponding change in the velocity field; in all cases, however, Multhopp's equation (73) can be applied once the spanwise loading is known. In particular, estimates of the downwash behind wings with flaps have been made by Silverstein, Katzoff, and Bullivant (1939). It frequently happens that comparatively small changes in the spanwise loading near the centre of the wing cause considerable changes in the downwash at the tail. For example, a small reduction of the chord of the wing root may change the sign of the downwash, which thus becomes an upwash. Similar effects may occur on swept-back wings of large aspect ratio.

21. Non-uniform mainstreams. The effects of spanwise variations in the stream

A type of interference, quite different from those we have studied so far, occurs when a single body, say a wing, is placed in a non-uniform

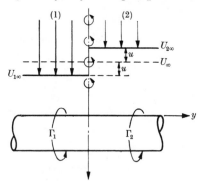

Fig. XII. 29. A sketch of an idealization of a wing in a mainstream with a spanwise discontinuity.

stream. In this section we consider an idealization of the type of flow found on wings fitted with forward airscrews, the effect of which is to place part of the span in a flow of higher velocity than the remainder. Of the many investigations into the effects of propeller slipstream, we may mention the work of Smelt and Davies (1937) and of Hartley, Spence, and Kirby (1951). A similar effect, that due to the boundary layer on the fuselage, has been studied by Mendelsohn and Polhamus (1947) and by Mair (1955). A general theory of a lifting line in non-uniform flow has been proposed by Kármán and Tsien (1945).

To illustrate the technique which can be used, we consider the simplest case in which an unswept aerofoil of infinite span lies in a stream which is divided into two regions each of constant velocity. Suppose in regions 1 and 2, the velocities are $U_{1\infty} = U_\infty + u$ and $U_{2\infty} = U_\infty - u$ as indicated in Fig. XII. 29. The two regions are then separated by a plane vortex sheet with the vorticity vector at right angles to the mainstream. This vortex sheet passes over the aerofoil and the question is: how does it affect the circulation around the aerofoil?

Vandrey (1940) has solved a linearized version of this problem when u may be assumed to be small. In the Trefftz plane far downstream, the assumption of linearization leads to the vortex sheet remaining plane and the condition that the pressure is equal on either side becomes $\phi_1 U_1 = \phi_2 U_2$, which suggests that the solution might be found in terms of a single function ϕ for which

$$\begin{aligned} \phi_1 &= \phi(1-u/U_\infty) \\ \phi_2 &= \phi(1+u/U_\infty) \end{aligned} \Bigg\}. \tag{74}$$

It can be shown that Prandtl's equation (VIII. 42) can then be written in the form, analogous to equation (VIII. 59),

$$(2/ca)\Delta\phi + \tfrac{1}{2}(\partial\phi/\partial z)_{z=+0} = \alpha(U_\infty \pm 2u) \tag{75}$$

in regions 1 and 2 respectively. This represents the flow past a fictitious wing at an incidence $(1\pm 2u/U_\infty)\alpha$ in a uniform stream of velocity U_∞: thus the change in spanwise velocity can be represented by a discontinuity of incidence (or of twist), the load distribution over the wing in the non-uniform mainstream being the same as on the fictitious wing. Vandrey has generalized the result to deal with a stream velocity which varies continuously in the spanwise direction. Thus if

$$U_\infty = V_\infty(1+\mathrm{v}(y)), \tag{76}$$

the lift distribution is obtained from the following modification to equation (VIII. 118):

$$\frac{2A\bar{c}}{ac}\frac{C_L c}{4s} = \alpha(1+2\mathrm{v}) - \frac{\omega s}{2\pi}\int_{-s}^{+s}\frac{d(C_L c/4s)}{dy'}\frac{dy'}{y-y'}. \tag{77}$$

Experiments made by Schlichting and Jacobs (1940) confirmed the validity of this theory even in cases where the non-uniformity was by no means small.

22. Non-uniform mainstreams. The effects of variations in the stream in the lift direction

Entirely different effects arise if the non-uniformity of the stream is in the lift direction—an important example occurs when the tail of an aircraft is in or near the wake of the main wing. Apart from the obvious effect of reducing the total pressure and thus affecting the forces on the tailplane, such non-uniformities also have pronounced further effects on the static pressure distribution on the tailplane.

Consider a thick symmetrical body, as in Fig. XII. 30, on which no lift force would be exerted by a uniform inviscid stream. In case (a), we could argue, roughly, that the ratio of the speed at the surface to the appropriate stream speed is the same for corresponding points on the upper and lower surfaces, but that the pressures are smaller in the region of higher speed. Thus the overall lift force tends always to be directed towards the region with the higher velocity or total pressure. In case (*b*) we see the same effect illustrated for a tailplane unsymmetrically placed in a wake or a slipstream; the reversal of the lift force, as the tail passes through the centre of the wake or slipstream, necessitates careful design.

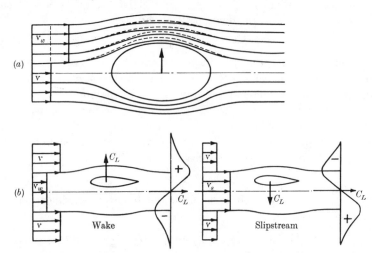

FIG. XII. 30. Sketches showing the direction of the lift force on aerofoils in streams whose velocities are non-uniform in the lift direction.

Flows such as these past a two-dimensional aerofoil have been treated by Kármán (1929) and by H. Glauert (1932). Both authors represented the aerofoil by a line vortex and their results are, therefore, rather inaccurate near the aerofoil itself. A more detailed investigation has been carried out by Ruden (1939) who replaced the aerofoil by distributions of sources and vortices and so obtained a better approximation for the boundary conditions on both the aerofoil and the surface of discontinuity of stream velocity. Ruden (1940) went on to compare his theory with experimental results and the agreement was satisfactory.

23. Non-uniform mainstreams. Bodies within boundary layers

A kind of non-uniform flow, more complicated than those considered in previous sections, occurs when bodies lie within a boundary layer. First, it is no longer adequate to idealize the flow by a discontinuity of velocity. But further, the non-uniformity of the velocity within the boundary layer is not the only feature to be accounted for; the presence of the solid surface introduces additional boundary conditions. That the velocity is zero on this surface still further distinguishes this type of flow, as does the dominant effect of viscosity. It is, however, difficult to incorporate the latter into the analysis of these complex interference flows, and it is usual to postulate a theoretical model of an inviscid fluid whose vorticity, moreover, is constant far upstream. Thus, at any rate in the mathematics, we tend to restrict attention to the inner part of the boundary layer in which the velocity gradient is roughly constant. Extensions of this model have, in fact, been considered and are described in Section 31.

The remaining sections of the book, therefore, are devoted to a description of some of the experimental and theoretical studies of such flows. In Sections 24–26 we have selected topics of particular practical importance; they include aerofoils crossing a boundary layer on a plane wall, small three-dimensional excrescences in a laminar boundary layer, and pitot tubes in boundary layers and wakes. Sections 27–32 go on to summarize the theoretical work which has concentrated on these particular flows.

24. Experiments on aerofoils and cylinders in shear flow

We consider first the flow well away from a wall on which an aerofoil is mounted. Fig. XII. 31 illustrates the flow viewed perpendicularly to

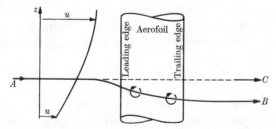

FIG. XII. 31. A sketch of the displacement of the streamlines past an aerofoil, due to shear in the mainstream.

the velocity vector far upstream. The broken line AC shows a typical streamline for the aerofoil in a uniform stream, as would occur far from the wall outside the boundary layer. Within the boundary layer, the streamlines are distorted, so that AC may be regarded as being displaced inwards to the position shown by the full line AB. This may be explained qualitatively by considering the positive gradient of total pressure in the outward, or positive-z, spanwise direction; this tends to give the fluid near the leading stagnation point on the aerofoil a component of velocity towards the wall. Thus the streamlines are displaced inwards, and at the same time a component of vorticity is introduced in the direction of the stream, as shown in the figure. The final result is a three-dimensional flow which is still more complicated near the wall.

Fig. XII. 32 is a photograph of the flow of air from left to right, past a circular cylinder projecting from a plane surface. The boundary layer separates upstream of the cylinder owing to the positive pressure gradient induced by the stagnation line on the cylinder, and in the separated region there is intense vorticity as shown by the smoke filament. In the figure, the helical filament is rotating in the clockwise sense and is moving towards the camera on its way round the front of the cylinder. Thus at the sides of the cylinder and behind it there is a component of vorticity in the direction of the undisturbed stream, leading to a downward displacement of the streamlines as shown in Fig. XII. 31. There has been little detailed experimental study of other shapes of projecting body. Already mentioned in Section 21 were the works of Mendelsohn and Polhamus (1947) who measured the pressure distribution at various spanwise positions on an aerofoil protruding normally from the wall of a wind tunnel, and of Mair (1955) who produced the spanwise velocity gradient by the wake from a flat plate mounted in the wind tunnel upstream of the aerofoil. Experiments of the same kind have been made with cascades of aerofoils, as for example those by Hawthorne and Armstrong (1955). A comprehensive visual study of such flow in cascades has been made by Herzig, Hansen, and Costello (1954).

In attempting to calculate the pressure distribution on the aerofoil in such cases, one cannot use the method of Vandrey (1940) leading to the lift equation (77), since the assumption of inviscid flow seems altogether too drastic. One could assume that the pressure coefficient, based on the local approach velocity, is constant along the span for a given chordwise position. In fact, the spanwise variation of pressure found in experiments is much smaller than that given by this simple assumption, and the lift coefficient based on a constant approach velocity varies only slightly along the span. For example, in Mair's experiments the velocity at the centre of the wake was about 14 per cent less than the velocity outside, yet the lift coefficient at the centre was only reduced by about 2 per cent. This may be explained qualitatively by saying that the spanwise component of velocity, associated with the

Fig. XII. 32. A smoke filament showing the flow in a boundary layer near the junction of a plane wall and a projecting circular cylinder. The air speed is about 5 ft sec⁻¹.

FIG. XII. 35. A smoke filament showing the flow past a long cylindrical rod, which is wholly within the boundary layer. The rod is parallel to the general flow and on the surface, and the air speed is 5 ft sec^{-1}.

streamwise vorticity indicated in Fig. XII. 31, tends to equalize the pressure along the span of the aerofoil.

The strong vorticity produced by these interference flows is responsible for the well-known effect of 'scouring' which occurs in river beds in the neighbourhood of bridge piers. The flow associated with the streamwise vorticity leads to the removal of solid material from the bottom of the river and Fig. XII. 33 shows depth contours, obtained by

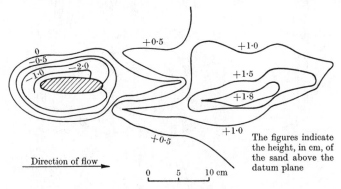

The figures indicate the height, in cm, of the sand above the datum plane

Direction of flow

0   5   10 cm

FIG. XII. 33. The scouring effect in sand of boundary-layer flow past an elliptical strut.

A. T. Ling and reproduced by Hawthorne (1954), on the sandy bottom of a laboratory water channel in the presence of a strut of elliptical section. The slight asymmetry of the contours in this case is probably caused by variation of stream velocity across the channel.

25. Experiments on excrescences in boundary layers

A photograph of a circular cylinder, taken in conditions similar to those of Fig. XII. 32, except that the height of the cylinder is now of the same order as the thickness of the boundary layer, appears as the Frontispiece. The flow itself is also similar to that in Fig. XII. 32, but the effect of the smallness of the cylinder seems to be that the smoke filament goes much nearer to it before coiling up.

Gregory and Walker (1951) made some experiments on this type of flow, as part of an investigation into the effect of very small excrescences in promoting transition from laminar to turbulent flow. They showed that the vortex seen is continuous, passing round the front of the cylinder in both directions and leading to a vortex pair trailing downstream; Fig. XII. 34 illustrates in some detail their interpretation of the flow. Pimples of even smaller height may not cause transition, but the effects of the vortex remain; they appear as a pair of closely-spaced parallel lines if the china-clay technique, introduced by Richards and Burstall (1945), is used. More recent experiments on small pimples have been made by Gregory and Walker (1957).

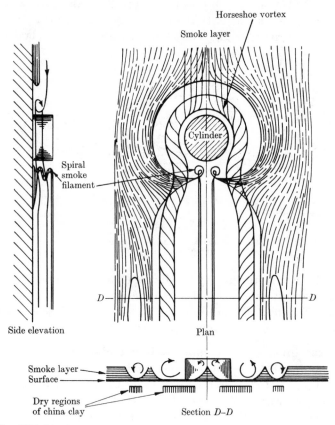

Fig. XII. 34. A representation, given by Gregory and Walker (1951), of the shear flow past a small circular cylinder on a plane, based on the observation of a layer of smoke.

26. Experiments on pitot tubes in boundary layers

An important experimental technique is the 'pitot-traverse' of a boundary layer in which the velocity distribution is deduced from the readings of total pressure recorded from a pitot tube. The velocity so deduced is, in fact, the actual fluid velocity which occurs not at the geometrical centre of the tube but at some other point which is called the effective centre of the tube. Much experimental and theoretical effort has been devoted towards determining the position of the effective centre of various shapes and sizes of pitot tube, since on this determination depends the accuracy of boundary-layer traverses. In a shear flow, it is usually found that the effective centre lies on the same side of the geometric centre as the region of higher velocity; the position of the effective centre is also affected by the proximity of a boundary. This section reviews experimental investigations on these matters, while Section 30 deals with some theoretical aspects.

Fig. XII. 35 is a photograph of a solid cylindrical rod in contact with a plane surface, taken in conditions similar to Fig. XII. 32. The thickness of the boundary layer on the plane surface is of the same order as the diameter of the rod. Since the orifice in a pitot tube has a relatively small effect on the external flow, the photograph gives an indication of the flow past a pitot tube in contact with a wall. It can be seen that a vortex is formed in front of the rod and stream-wise vorticity is generated, in the same way as in the earlier figures. There is also a downward deflexion of the streamlines approaching the front of the rod, which explains the outward displacement of the effective from the geometric centre. Similar vortex formations are observed with pitot tubes not in contact with a wall. Thus Fig. XII. 35 may be regarded as indicating qualitatively the behaviour of a pitot tube in any shear flow.

Some of the earliest experimental investigations were those of Young and Maas (1937), who used blunt-nosed pitot tubes of circular section and of different sizes to traverse the wake behind an aerofoil. The observed widths of the wake were plotted against the diameters of the pitot tubes, for several values of the total pressure of the stream. From the slopes of these curves, which were found to be the same for all total pressures, the distance d_e between the geometric and effective centres was obtained. With tubes having a ratio of internal diameter d_1 to external diameter d_0 of 0·6, it was found that $d_e/d_0 = 0·18$.

It appeared from these experiments that, for a given tube and provided the velocity gradient was roughly constant across the mouth of the tube, d_e was independent of the velocity gradient. This was a surprising result, because the displacement of the streamlines approaching the tube would not be expected to change discontinuously when the velocity gradient changed sign. In fact, more recent experiments, discussed later, indicate that d_e increases with velocity gradient, and is zero, as it surely must be, when the velocity gradient is also zero.

In experiments by MacMillan (1956) who used a pipe in which the flow was turbulent, the tubes were all blunt-nosed, of circular section, and again with $d_1/d_0 = 0.6$. For distances from the wall greater than about $2d_0$ but still well away from the centre of the pipe, it was found that the ratio d_e/d_0 was more or less constant and equal to about 0.15. This may be compared with the value 0.18 found by Young and Maas, for tubes geometrically similar.

Within a distance from the wall less than $2d_0$, MacMillan found that the value of d_e/d_0 was reduced by the proximity of the wall. An effect of this kind would be expected from consideration of a forward-facing two-dimensional step in an irrotational stream; the streamlines near the wall are displaced outwards on approaching the step. Thus the presence of the wall tends to displace the effective centre of a pitot tube towards the region of lower velocity, and so tends to reduce the displacement due to shear. The magnitude of this wall effect found by MacMillan depended on the Reynolds number $u_\tau d_0/\nu$, u_τ being the friction velocity defined in equation (I. 79). When this Reynolds number was 150, the ratio d_e/d_0 was reduced from 0.15 to 0.10 when the tube was touching the wall.

Experiments by Marson and Lilley (1956), who used pitot tubes in wakes, revealed some important effects when the pitot-tube diameter was not small compared with the width of the wake.

Experiments similar to those of MacMillan were made by Livesey (1956) using an artificially thickened turbulent boundary layer on the wall of a wind tunnel. A particularly interesting result was obtained for a pitot tube with a sharp-lipped conical nose. With this tube no displacement of the effective centre from the geometric centre could be detected, although with blunt-nosed tubes Livesey found a value of d_e in good agreement with the other experiments.

Some experiments by Davies (1958) throw further light on the paradoxical result obtained by other experimenters that d_e appears to be independent of velocity gradient. With blunt-nosed tubes, for which $d_1/d_0 = 0.6$, traversing the wakes behind bodies, he found a correlation between d_e/d_0 and a non-dimensional parameter describing the magnitude of the shear. If the velocity at the centre of the tube is U, and the oncoming stream is described by $u = U(1+2\alpha z/d_0)$, α is called the shear parameter. Fig. XII. 36 gives the experimental relation between d_e/d_0 and α, and from this we see that the values of d_e/d_0 obtained by Young and Maas and by MacMillan are approximately correct for values of α greater than about 0.2. For smaller values of α, the dis-

placement is reduced, and may be compared with the theoretical result
obtained by Hall (1956) for a sphere.

For measurements of velocity very close to the surface of a body,
Stanton, Marshall, and Bryant (1920) introduced a special form of flat
pitot tube in which the inner wall of the tube was formed by the body
itself. The position of the effective centre of such a tube can be found

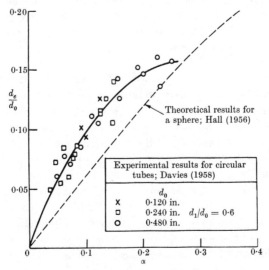

Fig. XII. 36. The variation with a shear parameter of the displacement
of the effective centre of a pitot tube.

by calibration in a pipe with laminar flow, for which the true velocity
distribution can be calculated theoretically. These measurements and
others by Fage and Falkner (1930) showed that the effective centre,
although near to the geometric centre for large tubes, moved outside
the outer lip for very small tubes.

G. I. Taylor (1938) considered the flow past such very small tubes,
for which the Reynolds numbers are also very small, and showed by
a simple dimensional analysis that the difference p between the pressure
in the tube and the static pressure in the stream should be given by

$$p = k\tau_w, \tag{78}$$

where k is a constant. Then if h and h' are the distances from the wall
to the lip of the tube and to the effective centre, it may be shown that

$$h'/h = (\nu/u_\tau h)(2k)^{\frac{1}{2}}. \tag{79}$$

Thus h' tends to take a constant value, even when h approaches zero. To determine k, Taylor made some experiments using glycerine in the annular space between two concentric cylinders, and found that $k = 1·2$ at low Reynolds numbers.

Thom (1952) used a numerical method to obtain a solution for the flow at the mouth of a two-dimensional Stanton tube at a very low Reynolds number, and found $k = 2·0$, in disagreement with Taylor's experiments. This discrepancy may have been due to differences of geometry between the two cases. His analysis also revealed a stationary eddy under the lip of the tube.

27. Theoretical considerations of displacement effect: the limited value of two-dimensional treatments

A sound quantitative theory of the shear-flow effects described in the preceding sections would be very useful, both at the low Mach numbers here discussed and still more after extension to higher Mach numbers, but it is hard to achieve. In the search for a theory, to be outlined in the remaining Sections 27 to 32, it seems reasonable to concentrate on the displacement of the effective centre of a pitot tube, because the part of the flow responsible for this displacement effect is ahead of the obstacle, so that the phenomenon is uncontaminated by the vagaries of boundary-layer separation.

In the following three sections some approaches to the problem based on two-dimensional analysis are described. These are given partly because it is interesting to consider what would happen to a 'two-dimensional pitot tube', and to other cylindrical shapes, in shear flow, and partly because the rich detail obtainable from two-dimensional analysis throws considerable light on the problem although, as we shall see, it is totally inadequate to explain the magnitude of the observed effect.

The analysis is simple because in two-dimensional flow the vortex lines are perpendicular to the plane of flow and so cannot be stretched. Hence the vorticity carried by each vortex line remains constant. In particular, when the oncoming flow is uniformly sheared, the vorticity is everywhere constant. Such an assumption of uniform shear in the oncoming flow may be not too bad an approximation to a real situation, if it gives the correct value of the vorticity on the streamlines which go near the body, since probably a different value of the vorticity on the nearly straight streamlines far from the body causes little alteration of the flow pattern.

28. The displacement effect for a circular cylinder in two-dimensional shear flow

For example, the classical solution of G. I. Taylor (1916) for a circular cylinder of radius a in a uniformly-sheared oncoming flow

$$u = U(1+\alpha z/a),$$

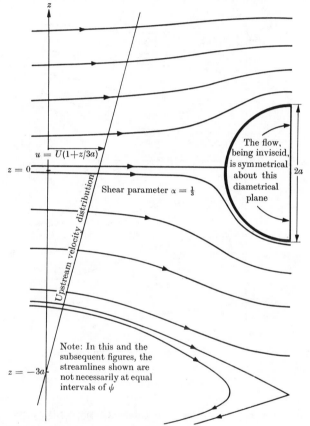

$u = U(1+z/3a)$

$z = 0$

Shear parameter $\alpha = \frac{1}{3}$

The flow, being inviscid, is symmetrical about this diametrical plane

$2a$

Upstream velocity distribution

$z = -3a$

Note: In this and the subsequent figures, the streamlines shown are not necessarily at equal intervals of ψ

Fig. XII. 37. Streamlines in the inviscid two-dimensional uniformly-sheared flow past a circular cylinder.

where the origin is at the centre of the cylinder, is given by a stream function

$$\psi = U\left(z - \frac{a^2 z}{x^2 + z^2}\right) + \frac{U\alpha}{2a}\left\{z^2 - \frac{a^4(z^2 - x^2)}{2(x^2 + z^2)^2}\right\}, \qquad (80)$$

and the streamlines for the case $\alpha = \frac{1}{3}$ are as in Fig. XII. 37. One might fear that the peculiar behaviour near the line $z = -a/\alpha$, where the assumed velocity of the oncoming flow is zero, would seriously affect the predicted flow near the cylinder. However, Fig. XII. 38 illustrates a flow with non-uniform vorticity and non-vanishing velocity, inferred by using equation (80) for $|z| < b = 1 \cdot 5a$ and by replacing z^2, the first term in the curly brackets, by $[2b|z| - b^2]$ when $|z| > b$. The oncoming flow then has uniform vorticity in $|z| < b$ and zero vorticity in $|z| > b$;

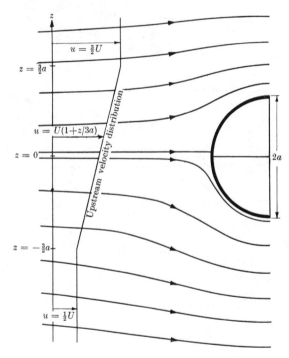

FIG. XII. 38. Approximate streamlines in a more realistic inviscid flow about a circular cylinder.

it is a shear layer. The solution has the necessary continuity of velocity required by Bernoulli's equation, and is inaccurate only in that the region of non-zero vorticity is taken bounded by the straight lines $|z| = b$ instead of the slightly curved streamlines which run into these lines at infinity. However, the flow in $|z| < b$ is the same as in Fig. XII. 37, which suggests that solutions like (80) for uniform oncoming shear are adequate for describing flow past obstacles in shear layers. In addition, flows strikingly similar to that of Fig. XII. 37 have been realized in a special Couette-flow channel by Reichardt (1954).

The dividing streamline in Fig. XII. 38 is $\psi = \frac{1}{4}\alpha Ua$ and far up-stream, by (80), this takes the form $Uz + \frac{1}{2}\alpha Uz^2/a = \frac{1}{4}\alpha Ua$, or $z = d_e$ where

$$d_e/2a = [(1 + \frac{1}{2}\alpha^2)^{\frac{1}{2}} - 1]/2\alpha. \tag{81}$$

It seems reasonable that, when used as a pitot tube, the cylinder with a fairly wide slit cut out in front would measure the stagnation pressure carried by this dividing streamline; then d_e is the displacement of the effective centre, being towards the region of higher velocity as observed for ordinary pitot tubes, but far smaller in magnitude. In practical cases in which the velocity varies by less than a factor of 2 across the diameter of the cylinder, $\alpha < \frac{1}{3}$ and the displacement d_e is given with less than 1·5 per cent error as

$$d_e/2a = \alpha/8. \tag{82}$$

This ratio of displacement to diameter is only 0·04 even in the extreme case $\alpha = \frac{1}{3}$, shown in Fig. XII. 37, and may be compared with values of from 0·15 to 0·20 which are still found experimentally for pitot tubes with considerably lower values of the shear parameter.

However, one may usefully seek the physical explanation of such effect as there is. This is evident from Fig. XII. 37 and from equation (80), in which the last term represents the images in the cylinder of all the vorticity outside it. These images exert an influence on the oncoming fluid which tends to make it turn right, with a velocity increasing as the inverse cube of the distance from the origin, as the cylinder is approached. However, the influence of the basic irrotational flow on any streamline slightly to the left of the central streamline is to make it turn left as the obstacle is approached, also with a velocity proportional to the inverse cube of the distance from the origin. For one particular streamline the effects cancel out, and this streamline remains almost exactly straight right up to where it hits the body, becoming the dividing streamline.

Actually, the images in a circular cylinder of a single vortex produce at large distances a dipole velocity field, which falls off as the inverse square of the distance; and the total field of all the image systems is quadrupole, as seen from the last term of (80), only because there is just as much vorticity behind the cylinder as ahead of it; the images of vortices behind the cylinder partly cancel those of vortices ahead of it.

It may be thought, therefore, that the presence of a wake in the real flow will mitigate this cancelling and cause a more pronounced, inverse-square effect upstream, leading to greater displacement. However, it

should be remembered that a body with a wake has itself a more pronounced effect on the basic irrotational flow upstream than an ideal
dragless body; source terms proportional to the drag must be added
to (80), producing a deflexion of streamlines near to the central streamline proportional to the inverse square of the distance from the origin.
Hence, one cannot expect much change, in the balance which determines the displacement, from the presence of a wake.

29. The displacement effect for other two-dimensional shapes in shear flow

The last result is proved conclusively if we consider the displacement
effect of an obstacle like the Rankine half-body, which is the two-
dimensional body generated by a line source in a uniform stream.
The conclusion is just the same, actually, for a two-dimensional pitot
tube, realistic in shape in all respects except its two-dimensionality.
Indeed, for all bodies ending in a semi-infinite parallel portion of external
thickness $2a$, whatever the shape of the front portion, and whether or
not they include an internal cavity, the displacement in a mainstream
$u = U(1+\alpha z/a)$ is given by

$$d_e = a[(1+\alpha^2)^{\frac{1}{2}}-1]/\alpha, \qquad (83)$$

so that it is the same as that predicted for a circular cylinder of diameter
$a\sqrt{2}$ in the same mainstream. The approximate form

$$d_e/2a = \tfrac{1}{4}\alpha \qquad (84)$$

of (83) is valid to within 1·5 per cent if $\alpha < \frac{1}{4}$.

To prove (83), we choose axes with z measured from the centre line
of the parallel portion of the obstacle. Let ψ_0 be the stream function
for the irrotational flow about the body with uniform upstream velocity
U (in the x-direction), and chosen so that $\psi_0 = 0$ is the dividing streamline. Next, for a flow with mainstream $u = U(1+\alpha z/a)$, let the stream
function be

$$\psi = \psi_0+\tfrac{1}{2}\alpha Uz^2/a+\psi_1. \qquad (85)$$

Then the flow represented by ψ_1 must be irrotational (since the vorticity
$\nabla^2\psi$ is everywhere equal to its upstream value $\alpha U/a$), and must vanish
at infinity and satisfy $\psi =$ constant on the boundary. Now, if we choose
this constant arbitrarily as $\tfrac{1}{2}\alpha Ua$, then clearly

$$\psi_1 = \tfrac{1}{2}\alpha U(a-z^2/a) \qquad (86)$$

on the boundary, so that ψ_1 is different from zero only on a finite part
of the boundary. Hence, by potential theory, ψ_1 must tend to zero at
infinity at least as rapidly as the inverse square root of the distance
from the origin. Hence the dividing streamline $\psi = \tfrac{1}{2}\alpha Ua$ becomes

$Uz+\frac{1}{2}\alpha Uz^2/a = \frac{1}{2}\alpha Ua$ at infinity upstream; thus, it is $z = d_e$ with d_e given by (83).

For shapes like Rankine half-bodies, the physical interpretation of this result is essentially the one involving images, given above for the circular cylinder, except that the competing tendencies to deviation of streamlines vary as the inverse square of the distance in this case. However, there is one rather extreme case of the result in which images play no part, and this case is sufficiently interesting to warrant detailed treatment in the next section.

30. The displacement effect of a thin-walled two-dimensional pitot tube

Consider a two-dimensional pitot tube with the difference between internal and external thicknesses vanishingly small. Then the irrotational flow is shown by Lamb (1932) to be the imaginary part of a complex potential $\mathfrak{w}$ satisfying

$$U_{\mathfrak{z}} = \mathfrak{w}-(Ua/\pi)\log(-\mathfrak{w}/Ua). \tag{87}$$

The additional stream function ψ_1, by (86), is zero at all points of the boundary, since $z = \pm a$ at all such points. Hence ψ_1 is identically zero; in other words, the irrotational flow and the shear flow can simply be added in this case, because the boundary does not get in the way of the shear flow at all.

The streamlines take the form

$$Ux = (\psi-\tfrac{1}{2}\alpha Uz^2/a)\cot[(\pi/Ua)(\psi-Uz-\tfrac{1}{2}\alpha Uz^2/a)]-$$
$$-(Ua/\pi)\log|(\psi/Ua-\tfrac{1}{2}\alpha z^2/a^2)\mathrm{cosec}[(\pi/Ua)(\psi-Uz-\tfrac{1}{2}\alpha Uz^2/a)]| \quad (88)$$

with $\psi = $ constant, and these are plotted in Fig. XII. 39 for the case $\alpha = \frac{1}{4}$. The peculiarities of the lower part of the figure can be ignored, as already discussed in connexion with Fig. XII. 37.

A difference from Fig. XII. 37 appears, however, in the details of the displacement effect. This is because no image vorticity is present; accordingly the central streamline is undisturbed, and pursues its way down the centre of the tube to infinity. The dividing streamline, whose displacement is given by equation (83), is one which in the absence of shear would find its way round and outside the upper plate of the two-dimensional pitot tube. The added shear flow, which in that neighbourhood is downstream, brings the streamline to rest at the point where, in the absence of shear, the upstream velocity would be αU.

Some discussion is needed to establish whether it is the stagnation pressure which is carried by this dividing streamline or that carried by the central streamline which the two-dimensional pitot tube would actually measure. This point is settled by removing the unrealistic assumption that the shear flow is maintained inside the pitot tube all the way to infinity. Obviously the vorticity cannot penetrate very far without being dissipated. As a rough model to estimate the effect of this, we may suppose that the vorticity is maintained inside the tube at its full

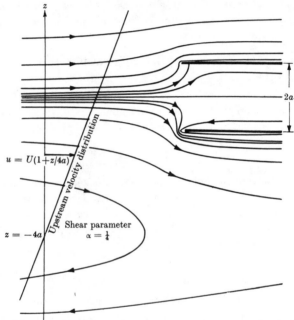

Fig. XII. 39. Streamlines in the inviscid two-dimensional uniformly sheared flow past a pitot tube with infinitesimally thin walls.

upstream value $\alpha U/a$ for, say, $x < c$, but is zero for $x > c$. Then the streamline configuration near $x = c$ can be approximated by that for the flow between infinite parallel planes with this vorticity distribution and no flow for large positive x. This is given by a stream function such that

$$
\begin{aligned}
x < c; \ \psi &= \tfrac{1}{2}\alpha U\left(\frac{z^2}{a} - a\right) + (8\alpha Ua/\pi^3) \times \\
&\times \sum_{n=0}^{\infty} (-1)^n (2n+1)^{-3} \exp[(2n+1)\pi(x-c)/2a]\cos[(2n+1)\pi z/2a] \\
x > c; \ \psi &= -(8\alpha Ua/\pi^3) \times \\
&\times \sum_{n=0}^{\infty} (-1)^n (2n+1)^{-3} \exp[-(2n+1)\pi(x-c)/2a]\cos[(2n+1)\pi z/2a]
\end{aligned}
\tag{89}
$$

and the streamlines are plotted in Fig. XII. 40. The important thing
to notice is the localization of the effect; 80 per cent of the flow turns
in the region marked by the horizontal arrows, that is, within half a
diameter of the place where the discontinuity in vorticity occurs.

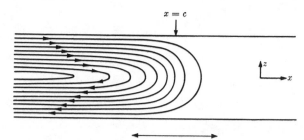

Fig. XII. 40. Steamlines in the inviscid two-dimensional flow in the infinite
channel $|z| < a$ with constant vorticity for $x < c$ and zero vorticity for $x > c$,
subject to the condition of no net volume flow along the channel.

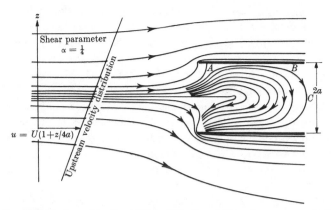

Fig. XII. 41. A combination of Figs. XII. 39 and 40 to give a more realistic
picture of the sheared flow past a two-dimensional pitot tube.

Hence, provided this place is not too close to the mouth of the tube, the
decay of vorticity probably does not greatly affect the external flow
in Fig. XII. 39, and one may get a reasonable picture of the complete
flow pattern by combining Figs. XII. 39 and 40 as in Fig. XII. 41.

Fig. XII. 41 is put forward only as a rough qualitative picture of
what might happen, but if the flow is anything like the one illustrated
then the stagnant fluid, whose pressure is measured, is in contact near
C with nearly stagnant fluid which has originated on the dividing
streamline; thus the pressure measured should be the stagnation

pressure carried by the dividing streamline, reduced by any loss that may occur between A and B due to frictional resistance. If a fraction θ of the dynamic pressure $\frac{1}{2}\rho(\alpha U)^2$ at A is dissipated between A and B, then the pressure measured will be reduced from the stagnation pressure on $z = d_e$, which is

$$p_\infty + \tfrac{1}{2}\rho U^2 (1 + \alpha d_e/a)^2 \simeq p_\infty + \tfrac{1}{2}\rho U^2 + \rho U^2 \alpha d_e/a \simeq p_\infty + \tfrac{1}{2}\rho U^2 (1 + \alpha^2),$$
(90)

to
$$p_\infty + \tfrac{1}{2}\rho U^2 \{1 + \alpha^2(1 - \theta)\}.$$
(91)

Thus, the displacement of the effective centre is

$$d_e = \tfrac{1}{2} a\alpha(1 - \theta),$$
(92)

less still than that given by (84).

It would be helpful to have a clearer idea of what determines the depth of penetration of flow into the tube. Fig. XII. 40 indicates that the flow cannot penetrate much farther than the vorticity; but conversely the vorticity can only penetrate as far as the flow will carry it without dissipation. It is also relevant that image effects cause vorticity near the upper wall to move to the right, and cause vorticity near the lower wall to move to the left. The true pattern may therefore be somewhat less symmetrical than in Fig. XII. 41, with the region of flow perhaps extending to B on the upper wall, but wetting rather less of the lower wall. Most of the dissipation of vorticity would then occur in a boundary layer between A and B; this process would probably leave a fair proportion of the kinetic energy of flow unaltered, in which case θ would be a reasonably small fraction.

We have exhibited two mechanisms which can account for a displacement effect: a streamline on the left (high-velocity) side of the geometric centre may avoid deflexion to the left round the obstacle owing to the tendency of image vorticity to move it to the right, as with a Rankine half-body; alternatively, it can enter a pitot-tube-shaped body and be forced against the left inside wall because its normal tendency to come out again is cancelled by the downstream flow within the tube associated with the original vorticity itself. For intermediate shapes such as thick-walled two-dimensional pitot tubes, both of these effects happen successively, but in a mitigated degree, and the resulting displacement is no greater, being still given by equation (83).

The arguments show clearly that two-dimensional theory cannot explain the magnitude of the pitot-tube displacement effect, and that a two-dimensional tube would have a very small displacement indeed.

Note that experimental confirmation of this is not at present available; indeed a truly two-dimensional flow of this kind would be difficult to realize. However, one is led to consider what features in the three-dimensional flow past a pitot tube could amplify the effect to the magnitude which is observed.

31. Theoretical considerations of displacement effect for three-dimensional bodies in shear flow

One principal feature stands out: in three-dimensional flow, the vorticity does not remain constant as it approaches the front of the tube. On the contrary, by the stretching of vortex lines as they pass over the tube, the vorticity builds up to much higher values near its mouth. Similarly, large concentrations of vorticity near a stagnation point were found in all the experiments on shear flow past obstacles quoted earlier in this chapter. A number of theoretical investigations have been partially successful in taking account of the effects of these concentrations of vorticity. These theories, although interesting, are much too complicated for detailed discussion here, but we may briefly summarize their results.

One important class of theories depends on the secondary-flow approximation, described by Hawthorne (1951, 1954), Hawthorne and Martin (1955), and Lighthill (1956a, 1957a). In this, the shear is regarded as slightly perturbing a primary flow with uniform velocity upstream. In the high-Reynolds-number form of these theories, which alone will be discussed here, one begins by calculating the secondary vorticity field. This is the vorticity field which would arise if the vortex lines of the upstream flow were deformed solely by the primary irrotational flow. Lighthill (1956b, 1957b) has shown that the secondary flow may be calculated as that induced by the secondary vorticity field in the presence of the obstacle—thus including the effects of image vortices.

Secondary flows can be subdivided into 'simple-shear secondary flows', in which the crude assumption of uniform upstream shear is made, as discussed in Sections 27 and 28, and 'exact-profile secondary flows', in which some more realistic upstream velocity profile is assumed. In all these theories we neglect the effects of viscosity and also the errors, of the order of the square of the shear parameter, due to regarding the vortex lines as convected by the approximate primary flow alone and not by the complete flow.

Because of the increase in vorticity as the obstacle is approached, the errors due to neglecting its square, by thus neglecting the self-convection of the vorticity, can be serious. Theories which avoid this approximation have therefore been constructed, but the mathematical difficulties are so great that this has been achieved only by making other approximations. For example, Hall (1956), by means of a special approximate assumption which enabled him to confine his calculations to the plane of symmetry, obtained terms in the first, second, and third powers of the shear parameter, corresponding to what may be called the simple-shear secondary, tertiary, and quartary flows.

An alternative type of approximation is the small-disturbance theory. This can be carried through without any assumption of small shear, for an arbitrary two-dimensional parallel flow upstream. The obstacle is represented by a distribution of sources, and the squares of disturbances to the oncoming flow are neglected. Representations of the flow due to each source have been made by Lighthill (1957c), as the Hankel transform of a certain solution of the Orr–Sommerfeld equation (in its inviscid form) for the layer in question, and by M. B. Glauert (1960) as the flow induced by a line distribution of sources whose line density is determined by solving a certain hyperbolic equation. Ordinary pitot-tube shapes are insufficiently slender for the small-disturbance approximation to be good; but, even for these, the flow at some distance from the body can be represented accurately enough as that due to a source.

This theory can be used to correct the anomalous results given by simple-shear secondary-flow theory at large distances, where the predicted secondary flow exceeds in order of magnitude the disturbances to the primary flow. This deficiency of the simple-shear theory prevents its unmodified use for the calculation of the displacement of the dividing streamline, which it predicts as becoming logarithmically infinite far upstream. The reason is that at large distances the true velocity profile is important. However, by matching the simple-shear secondary flow about a pitot tube on to an exact-profile small-disturbance solution at large distances, Lighthill (1957c) obtained a true first approximation to the displacement effect, which is a function of the actual thickness of the shear layer.

Much of the theoretical work, for example that of Hawthorne and Martin (1955), Hall (1956), and Lighthill (1956a, 1957b), has been carried out for a sphere in a shear layer. This is because the main need is to take into account the vorticity amplification produced by the three-dimensional character of the flow; the sphere, while geometrically simple, exhibits this, and, indeed, a 'spherical pitot tube' with a hole in the front of the sphere is a conceivable configuration. It may be noted that bodies like a sphere, which in inviscid flow have a doublet effect at large distances, do not, in the simple-shear secondary-flow theory, have secondary flows so large that the predicted displacement is infinite. Only the tertiary flow and higher-order approximations show this effect for the sphere, and only their contribution to the displacement depends on the exact upstream velocity profile. Hall's approximate computations of these terms are, however, suspect because they do not show this effect.

32. The displacement effect of a sphere in shear flow

We may now describe the results for a sphere, taking its radius as a, its centre as the origin, and the mainstream velocity parallel to the x-axis but varying with z. In the simple-shear theory, this variation is approximated by its tangent, say $u = U(1+\alpha z/a)$, at $z = 0$.

The simple-shear secondary vorticity field of Hawthorne and Martin (1955) and of Lighthill (1956a) is most easily described in spherical polar coordinates r, θ, λ, where

$$x = r\cos\theta, \quad y = r\sin\theta\sin\lambda, \quad z = r\sin\theta\cos\lambda. \qquad (93)$$

Then the ring vorticity ω_λ, which is $(\alpha U/a)\cos\lambda$ far upstream, is elsewhere given by

$$\omega_\lambda = (\alpha U/a)(1-a^3/r^3)^{-\frac{1}{2}}\cos\lambda, \qquad (94)$$

so that it becomes infinite, although integrably so, on the surface of the sphere. The expressions for the other components of vorticity are more complicated; but ω_θ has a similar type of infinity on the body surface, while the radial vorticity ω_r is zero there. Far downstream, there is the trailing vorticity, $\lim_{x\to\infty}\omega_x$, which varies as $(\alpha U/a)\sin\lambda$ times that function of $(r/a)\sin\theta$ which is graphed in Fig. XII. 42. Hawthorne and Martin show how this trailing vorticity may be observed in a smoke photograph.

The complete vorticity field is tabulated by Lighthill, and is illustrated by Fig. XII. 43 which shows the streamlines of the primary flow, together with the shapes of surfaces of revolution into which it distorts planes of fluid initially at right angles to the stream. This figure gives an impression of how vortex lines, which lie initially on such planes and so must remain on these surfaces of revolution, get stretched and rotated as they pass over the sphere.

Of the secondary flow itself, only the downwash, $(-w)$, on the upstream axis $\theta = \pi$ has been evaluated by Lighthill (1957b). The value

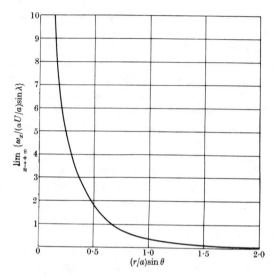

Fig. XII. 42. The secondary trailing vorticity behind a sphere of radius a in an inviscid stream with undisturbed velocity $u = U(1+\alpha z/a)$.

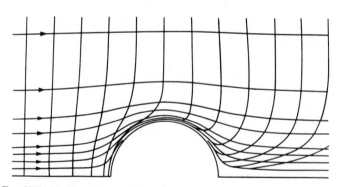

Fig. XII. 43. Streamlines of the primary, irrotational, flow about a sphere, together with the shapes of surfaces of revolution into which that flow distorts planes initially at right angles to the stream.

of $(-w/\alpha U)$ for $\theta = \pi$ is 0·97 for $r/a = 1$, namely at the stagnation-point of the primary flow, 0·33 for $r/a = \sqrt{2}$, and falls off like $\frac{5}{12}(r/a)^{-2}$ as $r/a \to \infty$. From these results, Lighthill computes the first approximation to the upstream displacement d_e of the dividing streamline as

$$d_e/2a = 0.45\alpha. \tag{95}$$

The fact that this is nearly four times as much as for the corresponding two-dimensional case given in equation (82), shows the importance of vortex-line stretching.

The downwash and displacement are found to be negligibly affected by the trailing vorticity, and indeed by all the vorticity downstream of the sphere. This indicates that inaccuracies in the solution in this region, due to boundary-layer separation, are probably unimportant. We note that asymmetric separation is not to be expected; Hall (1956) found that pressure minima on the surface streamlines are symmetrically placed. As in the two-dimensional case, the upstream vorticity makes its effect almost entirely through its images.

The experiment with which equation (95) can most suitably be compared is that of Livesey (1956) on a pitot tube with hemispherical nose, and a ratio 0·5 of internal to external diameter: the theoretical ineffectiveness of the vorticity downstream of the sphere suggests that differences of shape in this region may not matter much. Now Livesey found that $d_e/2a$ was about 0·1 in this case: Lighthill (1957b) suggests accordingly that a linear increase of $d_e/2a$ with α as in (95) may occur initially, followed by bending over to a constant value around $\alpha = \frac{1}{4}$. Negative terms due to tertiary- and quartary-flow effects, which would tend to produce this bending over, are adduced from the studies of Hall (1956) and of Lighthill (1957c). The fit is also helped by a slight increase in initial rate of rise over (95) for the pitot-tube shape, which is present because of the source-type flow which it generates far upstream; this addition takes the form $\frac{1}{8}\alpha \log(s_c/a)$, where s_c is of the order of the width of the shear layer. There is some support for these suggestions in Davies's comparison, shown in Fig. XII. 36, of his experimental results for a different shape of tube with Hall's theory. The terms additional to Hall's would steepen the theoretical curve initially and make it bend over sooner.

It may also be noted that the importance of images seems to explain the greater displacement, $d_e/2a$ being about 0·15, found with a square-fronted pitot tube, for which image vorticity would presumably be stronger. Again, Livesey's result for the sharp-lipped tube, in which by finely chamfering the front of the tube a shape approximating as closely as possible to that of Fig. XII. 41 was realized, and no measurable displacement was found, can be interpreted by noting (i) that image effects would be much smaller for this shape, and (ii) that the alternative mechanism illustrated in Figs. XII. 39 and 41 could hardly take their place since vortex lines cannot readily penetrate into the tube in the three-dimensional case.

From the discussion of the last two sections, it is clear that we are still far from a satisfactory theory of three-dimensional shear flows, but that, nevertheless, some progress is being made. The reader of this book may even consider this to be true of fluid dynamics as a whole.

REFERENCES AND AUTHOR INDEX

THE following list is not a bibliography of incompressible aerodynamics. It consists only of those works to which reference is made in the text. It is, however, intended to serve also as an author index.

The numbers in square brackets refer to the pages on which the references appear.

The full titles, and addresses of origin, of all the journals and periodicals quoted in this list are given in Current Paper 444 of the Aeronautical Research Council, London.

ABBOTT, I. H., and DOENHOFF, A. E. VON (1949). *Theory of wing sections.* McGraw-Hill, New York. [141, 357]

ACKERET, J. (1938). Probleme des Flugzeugantriebs in Gegenwart und Zukunft. *Schweiz. Bauztg.* **112**, *1.* [218]

ACUM, W. E. A. *See* Garner and Acum (1952).

ADAMS, MacC. (1953). Leading-edge separation from delta wings at supersonic speeds. *J. aero. Sci.* **20**, *430.* [514]

ADAMS, MacC., and SEARS, W. R. (1953). Slender-body theory—review and extension. *J. aero. Sci.* **20**, *85.* [268, 270, 273, 386, 454]

AINLEY, D. G., and JEFFS, R. A. (1946). Analysis of the air flow through 4 stages of half-vortex blading in an axial compressor. *Rep. Memor. aero. Res. Coun., Lond. 2383.* [467]

ALEXANDER, A. J. *See* Williams and Alexander (1957).

ALLEN, D. N. DE G., and SOUTHWELL, R. V. (1955). Relaxation methods applied to determine the motion, in two dimensions, of a viscous fluid past a fixed cylinder. *Quart. J. Mech.* **8**, *129.* [104]

ALLEN, H. J., and PERKINS, E. W. (1951). A study of the effects of viscosity on flow over slender inclined bodies of revolution. *Rep. nat. adv. Comm. Aero., Wash. 1048.* [410, 416, 523]

ANDERSON, R. G. *See* Owen and Anderson (1952).

ANDERSON, S. B., QUIGLEY, H. C., and INNIS, R. C. (1956). Flight measurements of the low-speed characteristics of a 35° swept-wing airplane with blowing-type boundary-layer control on the trailing-edge flaps. *Res. Memor. nat. adv. Comm. Aero., Wash. A56G30.* (Available at TIL, Min. Supply, Lond. as *NACA/TIL/5258.*) [251]

APELT, C. J. (1957). Some studies of fluid flow at low Reynolds numbers. Thesis, Oxford Univ. [104]

ARMSTRONG, A. H. (1954). Drag coefficients of wedges and cones in cavity flow. Unpublished report, Min. Supply, Lond. [175]

ARMSTRONG, A. H., and DUNHAM, J. H. (1953). Axisymmetric cavity flow. Unpublished report, Min. Supply, Lond. [175]

ARMSTRONG, W. D. *See* Hawthorne and Armstrong (1955).

ATKINS, P. B. *See* Keeble and Atkins (1951).

ATTINELLO, J. S. (1955). Wing lift augmentation methods for the improvement of low speed performance of high speed aircraft. *Proc. golden anniversary meeting Soc. Automot. Engrs, N.Y.* [251]

BAGLEY, J. A. (1959). The pressure distribution on two-dimensional wings near the ground. Unpublished report, Min. Supply, Lond. [528]

BAGLEY, J. A., KIRBY, N. B., and MARCER, P. J. (1958). A method of calculating the velocity distribution on annular aerofoils in incompressible flow. *Rep. aero. Res. Coun., Lond. 20597.* [526, 527]

BAGLEY, J. A. *See* Brebner and Bagley (1952).

BARANOFF, V. A. *See* Legendre, Eichelbrenner, and Baranoff (1952).

BARLING, W. H. *See* De Young and Barling (1955).

BARTLETT, G. E., and VIDAL, R. J. (1954). Experimental investigation of influence of edge shape on the aerodynamic characteristics of low-speed-ratio wings at low speeds. *Rep. Cornell aero. Lab., N.Y. 62.* [514, 523]

BATCHELOR, G. K. (1953). *The theory of homogeneous turbulence.* Cambridge University Press. [5, 55]

BATCHELOR, G. K., and DAVIES, R. H. (Editors) (1955). *Surveys in mechanics.* Cambridge University Press. *See* Squire (1955).

BATSON, A. S. *See* Bryant, Halliday, and Batson (1950).

BEASLEY, J. A. *See* Spence and Beasley (1958).

BERG, B. VAN DEN. *See* Bergh and Berg, van den (1958).

BERGH, H., and BERG, B. VAN DEN (1958). On the visualization of laminar boundary layer oscillations and the transition to turbulent flow. *Z. angew. Math. Phys.* **9b,** *97.* [56]

BETZ, A. (1914). Die gegenseitige Beeinflussung zweier Tragflächen. *Z. Flugwiss.* **5,** *235.* [524]

BETZ, A. (1919). Beiträge zur Tragflügeltheorie mit besonderer Berücksichtigung des einfachen rechteckigen Flügels. Diss. Göttingen Univ. (Available in abbreviated form in *Beihefte Z. Flugtech.* (1920) **2,** *1.*) [335]

BETZ, A. (1932). Singularitätenverfahren zur Bestimmung der Kräfte und Momente auf Körper in Potentialströmungen. *Ingen.-Arch.* **3,** *454.* [282]

BETZ, A. (1935). Applied airfoil theory. Section J in Durand, W. F. (1935). *Aerodynamic Theory* **4.** Springer-Verlag, Berlin. [309, 335, 522]

BETZ, A. (1940). Sonderaufgaben der aerodynamischen Forschung. *Schr. dtsch. Akad. Luftfahrtf.* [275]

BETZ, A. (1948). *Konforme Abbildung.* Springer-Verlag, Berlin. [269]

BETZ, A. (1950). Wie entsteht ein Wirbel in einer wenig zähen Flüssigkeit? *Naturwissenschaften* **37,** *193.* [97, 294]

BETZ, A. *See* Prandtl and Betz (1920), (1927).

BILHARZ, H., and HÖLDER, E. (1947). *ForschBer. dtsch. Luftfahrtf.* **1169/1.** (Translated as 'Calculation of the pressure distribution of bodies of revolution in the subsonic flow of a gas. Part I: Axi-symmetric flow'. *Tech. Memor. nat. adv. Comm. Aero., Wash. 1153.* [380]

BIRD, J. D. (1952). Visualisation of flow fields by use of a tuft grid technique. *J. aero. Sci.* **19,** *481.* [511]

BIRKHOFF, G. (1950). *Hydrodynamics: a study in logic, fact and similitude.* Princeton University Press. [152]

BROWN, C. E. (1949). The reversibility theorem for thin airfoils in subsonic and supersonic flow. *Tech. Notes nat. adv. Comm. Aero., Wash. 1944.* [328]

BROWN, C. E., and MICHAEL, W. H. (1954). Effect of leading-edge separation on the lift of a delta wing. *J. aero. Sci.* **21**, *690.* [514]

BROWN, C. E., and MICHAEL, W. H. (1955). On slender delta wings with leading edge separation. *Tech. Notes nat. adv. Comm. Aero., Wash. 3430.* [100]

BRUYNES, H. (1951). Fluid mixing device. U.S. Patent 2,558,816. [211]

BRYANT, C. N. *See* Stanton, Marshall, and Bryant (1920).

BRYANT, L. W., HALLIDAY, A. S., and BATSON, A. S. (1950). Two-dimensional control characteristics. *Rep. Memor. aero. Res. Coun., Lond. 2730.* [197]

BRYANT, L. W., and WILLIAMS, D. H. (1925). An investigation of the flow of air around an aerofoil of infinite span (with an Appendix by G. I. Taylor, F.R.S.). *Rep. Memor. aero. Res. Coun., Lond. 989. See* Taylor (1925).

BRYSON, A. E. (1953). Stability derivatives for a slender missile with application to a wing-body-vertical-tail configuration. *J. aero. Sci.* **20**, *297.* [459]

BULLIVANT, W. K. *See* Silverstein, Katzoff, and Bullivant (1939).

BULLOCK, R. O. *See* Johnsen and Bullock (1956).

BURGERS, J. M. *See* Kármán and Burgers (1935).

BURI, A. (1931). Eine Berechnungsgrundlage für die turbulente Grenzschicht bei beschleunigter und verzögerter Grundströmung. *Diss. eidgen. tech. Hochsch., Zürich 652.* [80, 81]

BURROWS, D. L. *See* Braslow, Burrows, Tetervin, and Visconti (1951); Loftin and Burrows (1949).

BURROWS, D. L., and SCHWARTZBERG, M. A. (1952). Experimental investigation of an NACA 64A010 airfoil section with 41 suction slots on each surface for control of laminar boundary layer. *Tech. Notes nat. adv. Comm. Aero., Wash. 2644.* [242]

BURSTALL, F. H. *See* Richards and Burstall (1945).

BUSEMANN, A. (1928). Profilmessungen bei Geschwindigkeiten nahe der Schallgeschwindigkeit. *Jb. wiss. Ges. Flugtech. (Luftf.) 95.* [275]

BUTLER, S. F. J. (1955). Current tests on laminar-boundary-layer control by suction through perforations. *Rep. Memor. aero. Res. Coun., Lond. 3040.* [231]

BYRD, P. F. *See* Lomax and Byrd (1951).

CARLEMAN, T. (1922). Sur la résolution de certaines équations integrales. *Ark. Mat. Astr. Fys.* **16**, *26.* [322, 353]

CARMICHAEL, B. H. (1954). Suction-stabilised boundary layers. *Aeronaut. Engng Rev.* **13** (2), *36.* [232]

CARTER, A. D. S. (1945). Vortex wind tunnel-test on various vortex flows. *Rep. Power Jets R1063.* [493]

CARTER, A. D. S. (1948). Some tests on compressor cascades of related aerofoils having different positions of maximum camber. *Rep. Memor. aero. Res. Coun., Lond. 2694.* [541]

CARTER, A. D. S., and HUGHES, H. P. (1946). Theoretical investigation into the effects of profile shape on the performance of aerofoils in cascade. *Rep. Memor. aero. Res. Coun., Lond. 2384.* [540]

CHIARULLI, P., and FREEMAN, J. C. (1948). Stability of the boundary layer. *Tech. Rep. H.Q. Air Materiel Command, Dayton, Monograph VI, F-TR/1197 —IA.* [230]

CROOKS, P. V., and HOWARD, W. (1954). Low speed tests on three aerofoil cascades designed for prescribed surface velocity distributions. *Rep. aero. Res. Lab., Melbourne ME76.* [538]

CURLE, N. (1956). Unsteady two-dimensional flows with free boundaries. *Proc. Roy. Soc.* A, **235**, *375.* [175]

CURLE, N., and SKAN, S. W. (1957). Approximate methods for predicting separation properties of laminar boundary layers. *Aeronaut. Quart.* **8**, *257.* [63]

CURTIS, A. R. (1949). Note on the application of Thwaites's numerical method for the design of cambered aerofoils. *Rep. Memor. aero. Res. Coun., Lond. 2665.* [143]

CURTIS, A. R. *See* Gregory and Curtis (1950).

DANNENBERG, R. E., and WEIBERG, J. A. (1953). Effect of type of porous surface and suction velocity distribution on the characteristics of a 10·5 per cent thick airfoil with area suction. *Tech. Notes nat. adv. Comm. Aero., Wash. 3093.* [224]

DANNENBERG, R. E., and WEIBERG, J. A. (1955). Exploratory investigations of an airfoil with area suction applied to a porous, round trailing edge fitted with a lift-control vane. *Tech. Notes nat. adv. Comm. Aero., Wash. 3498.* [228]

DANNENBERG, R. E. *See* Weiberg and Dannenberg (1954).

DARWIN, C. (1953). Note on hydrodynamics. *Proc. Camb. phil. Soc.* **49**, *342.* [259]

DARWIN, C. *See* Falkner and Darwin (1945).

DAVIDSON, I. M. (1956). The jet flap. *J.R. aero. Soc.* **60**, *25.* [229, 252]

DAVIES, H. *See* Smelt and Davies (1937).

DAVIES, P. O. A. L. (1958). The behaviour of a pitot tube in transverse shear. *J. Fluid Mech.* **3**, *441.* [556, 557]

DAVIES, R. H. *See* Batchelor and Davies (Editors) (1955).

DEVEREUX, A. N. *See* Pankhurst, Raymer, and Devereux (1948).

DEVERSON, E. C. *See* Horlock and Deverson (1958).

DE YOUNG, J., and BARLING, W. H. (1955). Correction of additional span loading computed by the Weissinger seven-point method for moderately tapered wings of high aspect ratio. *Tech. Notes nat. adv. Comm. Aero., Wash. 3500.* [349]

DE YOUNG, J., and HARPER, C. W. (1948). Theoretical symmetric span loading at subsonic speeds for wings having arbitrary planform. *Rep. nat. adv. Comm. Aero., Wash. 921.* [348]

DE YOUNG, J. *See* Dorn and De Young (1947).

DHAWAN, S. (1952). Direct measurements of skin friction. *Tech. Notes nat. adv. Comm. Aero., Wash. 2567.* [71]

DIEDERICH, F. W. (1951). A planform parameter for correlating certain aerodynamic characteristics of swept wings. *Tech. Notes nat. adv. Comm. Aero., Wash. 2335.* [341]

DIEDERICH, F. W. (1952). A simple approximate method for calculating spanwise lift distribution and aerodynamic influence coefficients at subsonic speeds. *Tech. Notes nat. adv. Comm. Aero., Wash. 2751.* [348]

DIEHL, Z. W. *See* Klebanoff and Diehl (1951).

DIMMOCK, N. A. (1955). An experimental introduction to the jet flap. *Curr. Pap. aero. Res. Coun., Lond. 344.* [504]

Dods, J. B., and Watson, E. C. (1956). The effects of blowing over various trailing-edge flaps on an NACA 0006 airfoil section, comparisons with various types of flaps on other airfoil sections, and an analysis of flow and power relationships for blowing systems. *Res. Memo. nat. adv. Comm. Aero., Wash. A56C01.* (Available at TIL. Min. Supply, Lond. as *NACA/TIL/5107.*) [250]

Doenhoff, A. E. von. (1940). Investigation of the boundary layer about a symmetrical airfoil in a wind tunnel of low turbulence. *Wartime Rep. nat. adv. Comm. Aero., Wash. L–507.* [182]

Doenhoff, A. E. von, and Tetervin, N. (1943). Determination of general relations for the behaviour of turbulent boundary layers. *Rep. nat. adv. Comm. Aero., Wash. 772.* [76, 85]

Doenhoff, A. E. von. See Abbott and Doenhoff (1949).

Dorn, N. H. van, and De Young, J. (1947). A comparison of three theoretical methods of calculating span load distribution on swept wings. *Tech. Notes nat. adv. Comm. Aero., Wash. 1476.* [348]

Douglas, O. (1947). A series of low-drag aerofoils embodying a new camber-line. *Rep. Memor. aero. Res. Coun., Lond. 2494.* [143]

DuBose, H. C. See Katzoff, Faison, and DuBose (1953).

Duncan, W. J. See Young (1952).

Dunham, J. H. See Armstrong and Dunham (1953).

Duquenne, R. See Malavard and Duquenne (1951).

Durand, W. F. See Betz (1935); Kármán and Burgers (1935); Munk (1934); Prandtl (1935).

Dutton, R. A. (1958). The effects of distributed suction on the development of turbulent boundary layers. *Rep. aero. Res. Coun., Lond. 20036.* [91]

Dyke, M. D. van (1954). Subsonic edges in thin wing and slender body theory. *Tech. Notes nat. adv. Comm. Aero., Wash. 3343.* [262]

Eckhaus, W. (1954). On the theory of oscillating airfoils of finite span in subsonic flow. *Rep. nat. LuchtvLab., Amsterdam F153.* [314]

Eckhaus, W. See Leeuw, Eckhaus, and Vooren (1954).

Ehlers, F. See Walz and Ehlers (1947).

Eichelbrenner, E. A. See Legendre, Eichelbrenner, and Baranoff (1952).

Eisenberg, P. (1950). On the mechanism and prevention of cavitation. *Rep. Taylor Model Basin, Wash. 712.* [107, 108]

Emde, F. See Jahnke and Emde (1945).

Emery, J. C. See Erwin and Emery (1949).

Emmons, H. W. (1951). The laminar-turbulent transition in a boundary layer, Part I. *J. aero. Sci. 18, 490.* [52]

Erwin, J. R., and Emery, J. C. (1949). Effect of tunnel configuration and testing technique on cascade performance. *Rep. nat. adv. Comm. Aero., Wash. 1016.* [541]

Eskinazi, S., and Yeh, H. (1956). An investigation on fully developed turbulent flows in a curved channel. *J. aero. Sci. 23, 23.* [57]

Eyre, R. C. W. See Fail, Lawford, and Eyre (1957).

Fabricius, W. See Lotz and Fabricius (1937).

Fage, A. (1938). Profile and skin-friction aerofoil drags. *Rep. Memor. aero. Res. Coun., Lond. 1852.* [58, 180]

FAGE, A. (1943). The smallest size of spanwise surface corrugation which affects boundary-layer transition on an aerofoil. *Rep. Memor. aero. Res. Coun., Lond. 2120.* [50]

FAGE, A., and FALKNER, V. M. (1930). An experimental determination of the intensity of friction on the surface of an aerofoil. *Proc. Roy. Soc.* A, *129, 378.* [557]

FAGE, A., and FALKNER, V. M. (1931). Further experiments on the flow around a circular cylinder. *Rep. Memor. aero. Res. Coun., Lond. 1369.* [168]

FAGE, A., and JOHANSEN, F. C. (1927). On the flow of air behind an inclined flat plate of infinite span. *Rep. Memor. aero. Res. Coun., Lond. 1104.* [106]

FAGE, A., and SARGENT, R. F. (1944). Design of suction slots. *Rep. Memor. aero. Res. Coun., Lond. 2127.* [242]

FAGE, A., and SIMMONS, L. F. G. (1925). An investigation of the air-flow pattern in the wake of an aerofoil of finite span. *Rep. Memor. aero. Res. Coun., Lond. 951.* [95]

FAIL, R., LAWFORD, J. A., and EYRE, R. C. W. (1957). Low speed experiments on the wake characteristics of flat plates normal to an airstream. *Rep. Memor. Aero. Res. Coun., Lond. 3120.* [18]

FAISON, M. F. *See* Katzoff, Faison, and DuBose (1953).

FALKNER, V. M. (1943a). The calculation of the aerodynamic loading on surface on any shape. *Rep. Memor. aero. Res. Coun., Lond. 1910.* [346, 349]

FALKNER, V. M. (1943b). The resistance of a smooth flat plate with turbulent boundary layer. *Aircr. Engng, 15, 169.* [75, 85]

FALKNER, V. M. (1947). The solution of lifting plane problems by vortex lattice theory. *Rep. Memor. aero. Res. Coun., Lond. 2591.* [334]

FALKNER, V. M. (1948). Calculated loadings due to incidence of a number of straight and swept-back wings. *Rep. Memor. aero. Res. Coun., Lond. 2596.* [343, 347, 349]

FALKNER, V. M., and DARWIN, C. (1945). The design of minimum drag tip fins. *Rep. Memor. aero. Res. Coun., Lond. 2279.* [459]

FALKNER, V. M. *See* Fage and Falkner (1930, 1931).

FAVRE, A. (1936). Mécanique expérimentale des fluides. Un nouveau procédé hypersustentateur : l'aile à paroi d'extrados mobile. *C. R. Acad. Sci., Paris, 202, 634.* [215]

FEDIAEVSKI, K. (1936). *Rep. centr. aerohydro. Inst., Moscow, 282.* (Translated as 'Turbulent boundary layer of an aerofoil'. *Tech. Memor. nat. adv. Comm. Aero., Wash. 822.*) [82, 83]

FINK, P. T., and TAYLOR, J. (1955). Some low speed experiments with 20° delta wings. *Rep. aero. Res. Coun., Lond. 17854.* [514]

FLATT, J. (1955). Some experiments in the application of boundary layer control. *Proc. golden anniversary meeting Soc. Automot. Engrs. N.Y.* [251]

FLAX, A. H. (1953). Integral relations in the linearized theory of wing-body interference. *J. aero. Sci. 20, 483.* [442]

FLAX, A. H., and LAWRENCE, H. R. (1951). The aerodynamics of low aspect-ratio wings and wing-body combinations. *Proc. 3rd anglo-amer. aero. Conf. R. aero. Soc. 363.* [301]

FLAX, A. H. *See* Lawrence and Flax (1954).

FLETCHER, H. S. (1957). Experimental investigation of lift, drag and pitching moment of five annular aerofoils. *Tech. Notes nat. adv. Comm. Aero., Wash. 4117.* [527]

GLAUERT, M. B. (1947). The application of the exact method of aerofoil design. *Rep. Memor. aero. Res. Coun., Lond.* 2683. [145, 146, 147, 236, 245, 248]

GLAUERT, M. B. (1957). The flow past a rapidly rotating circular cylinder. *Proc. Roy. Soc.* A, **242**, *108*. [217]

GLAUERT, M. B. (1959). The method of images in shear flow. To be published in *J. Fluid Mech.* [568]

GLAUERT, M. B., WALKER, W. S., and GREGORY, N. (1948). Wind-tunnel tests on a thick suction aerofoil with a single slot. *Rep. Memor. aero. Res. Coun., Lond.* 2646. [245]

GOLDSTEIN, S. (Editor) (1938). *Modern developments in fluid dynamics.* Clarendon Press, Oxford. [8, 55, 80, 82, 85, 215]

GOLDSTEIN, S. (1952). Approximate two-dimensional aerofoil theory. Parts I–VI. *Curr. Pap. aero. Res. Coun., Lond.* 68–73. [128, 140, 141]

GOLDSTEIN, S. (1948). Low-drag and suction aerofoils. *J. aero. Sci.* **15**, *189*. [142]

GÖRTLER, H. (1940). Über eine dreidimensionale Instabilität laminarer Grenzschichten an konkaven Wanden. *Nachr. Ges. Wiss. Göttingen*, **1**, *1*. [49]

GÖRTLER, H. (1957). A new series for the calculation of steady laminar boundary layer flows. *J. Math. Mech.* **6**, *1*. (Tables of universal functions for the series with directions for use, in German, are available as *Ber. dtsch. Vers. Luftfahrt, Mulheim, 34.*) [63]

GÖTHERT, B. (1941). Ebene und räumliche Strömung bei hohen Unterschallgeschwindigkeiten. *Jb. dtsch. Luftfahrtf.* **1**, *156*. [264]

GÖTHERT, B. (1942). Hochgeschwindigkeitsmessungen an einem Pfeilflügel. *Ber. Lilienthal-Ges. Luftfahrtf.* **156**, *30*. [280]

GRAY, W. E. (1952). The effect of wing sweep on laminar flow. Unpublished communication. [50]

GREEN, G. (1828). Essay on electricity and magnetism. *Mathematical Papers 3.* Cambridge University Press (1871). [43]

GREENHILL, G. (1910). Report on the theory of a streamline past a plane barrier. *Rep. Memor. aero. Res. Coun., Lond. 8.* [149]

GREENING, J. R. *See* Richards, Walker, and Greening (1944).

GREGORY, N. (1947). Note on Sir Geoffrey Taylor's criterion for the rate of boundary-layer suction at a velocity discontinuity. *Rep. Memor. aero. Res. Coun., Lond.* 2496. [245]

GREGORY, N., and CURTIS, A. R. (1950). A comparison of three thick, symmetrical, multi-slot suction aerofoils. *Curr. Pap. aero. Res. Coun., Lond.* 20. [239]

GREGORY, N., PANKHURST, R. C., and WALKER, W. S. (1950). Wind-tunnel tests on the prevention of boundary-layer separation by distributed suction at the rear of a thick aerofoil, NPL 153. *Rep. Memor. aero. Res. Coun., Lond.* 2788. [227]

GREGORY, N., STUART, J. T., and WALKER, W. S. (1955). On the stability of three-dimensional boundary layers, with application to the flow due to a rotating disc. *Proc. Symp. boundary layer effects Aerodyn., Nat. Phys. Lab.* Also available as *Phil. Trans.* A, **248**, *155*. [49]

GREGORY, N., and WALKER, W. S. (1946). Further wind-tunnel tests on a 30 per cent symmetrical suction aerofoil with a movable flap. *Rep. Memor. aero. Res. Coun., Lond.* 2287. [245]

HARTREE, D. R. (1939a). A solution of the boundary layer equation for Schubauer's observed pressure distribution for an elliptic cylinder. *Rep. Memor. aero. Res. Coun., Lond. 2427.* [63]

HARTREE, D. R. (1939b). A solution of the laminar boundary layer equation for retarded flow. *Rep. Memor. aero. Res. Coun., Lond. 2426.* [63]

HAWK, A. C. *See* Weber and Hawk (1954).

HAWTHORNE, W. R. (1951). Secondary circulation in fluid flow. *Proc. Roy. Soc. A, 206, 374.* [567]

HAWTHORNE, W. R. (1954). The secondary flow about struts and aerofoils. *J. aero. Sci. 21, 588.* [553, 567]

HAWTHORNE, W. R. (1955). Rotational flow through cascades. *Quart. J. Mech. 8, 266.* [531]

HAWTHORNE, W. R., and ARMSTRONG, W. D. (1955). Rotational flow through cascades. Part II: the circulation about the cascades. *Quart. J. Mech. 8, 280.* [552]

HAWTHORNE, W. R., and MARTIN, M. E. (1955). The effect of density gradient and shear on the flow over a hemisphere. *Proc. Roy. Soc. A, 232, 184.* [567, 568, 569]

HAWTHORNE, W. R. *See* Bragg and Hawthorne (1950).

HEAD, M. R. (1957). An approximate method of calculating the laminar boundary layer in two-dimensional incompressible flow. *Rep. Memor. aero. Res. Coun., Lond. 3123.* [90]

HEAD, M. R., JOHNSON, D., and COXON, M. (1955). Flight experiments on boundary-layer control for low drag. *Rep. Memor. aero. Res. Coun., Lond. 3025.* [230]

HEAD, M. R. *See* Jones and Head (1951).

HEASLET, M. A., and SPREITER, J. R. (1952). Reciprocity relations in aerodynamics. *Rep. nat. adv. Comm. Aero., Wash. 1119.* [328]

HEASLET, M. A. *See* Lomax, Heaslet, and Fuller (1951).

HEEMERT, A. VON (1951). A generalization of Prandtl's equation. *Rep. nat. LuchtvLab., Amsterdam F. 76.* [321]

HELMBOLD, H. B. (1942). Der unverwundene Ellipsenflügel als tragende Fläche. *Jb. dtsch. Luftfahrif. 1.* [341, 342]

HELMHOLTZ, H. VON (1858). Über Integrale der hydrodynamischen Gleichungen, welche den Wirbelbewegungen entsprechen. *J. reine angew. Math. 55, 25.* [296]

HELMHOLTZ, H. VON (1868). Über discontinuierliche Flüssigkeitsbewegungen. '*Mber*' *K. Akad. Wiss., Berlin 23, 215.* [106, 154, 511]

HERZIG, H. Z., HANSEN, A. G., and COSTELLO, G. R. (1954). A visualization study of secondary flows in cascades. *Rep. nat. adv. Comm. Aero., Wash. 1163.* [552]

HEUGHAN, D. M. (1953). An experimental study of a symmetrical aerofoil with a rear suction slot and a retractable flap. *J.R. aero. Soc. 57, 627.* [248]

HJELTE, F. *See* Holme and Hjelte (1953).

HOLDER, D. W. *See* Pankhurst and Holder (1952).

HÖLDER, E. *See* Bilharz and Hölder (1947).

HOLME, O., and HJELTE, F. (1953). On the calculation of the pressure distribution on three-dimensional wings at zero incidence in incompressible flow. *Aero. tech. Notes K. tek. Högsk., Stockholm 23.* [264, 289]

IGLISCH, R. (1944). Exakte Berechnung der laminaren Grenzschicht an der längs-angeströmten ebenen Platte mit homogener Absaugung. *Schr. dtsch. Akad. Luftfahrtf. 8ᴮ, 1.* (Translated as 'Exact calculation of laminar boundary layer in longitudinal flow over a flat plate with homogeneous suction'. *Tech. Memor. nat. adv. Comm. Aero., Wash. 1205* (1949).) [63]

INNIS, R. C. *See* Anderson, Quigley, and Innis (1956).

ISAY, W. H. (1953). Beitrag zur Potentialströmung durch axiale Schaufelgitter. *Z. angew. Math. Mech. 33, 397.* [540]

JACOBS, E. N. (1931). The aerodynamic characteristics of 8 very thick airfoils from tests in the variable density wind tunnel. *Rep. nat. adv. Comm. Aero., Wash. 391.* [28]

JACOBS, W. *See* Schlichting and Jacobs (1940).

JAHNKE, E., and EMDE, F. (1945). *Tables of Functions.* Dover Publications, New York. [480, 482]

JEFFREYS, B. S. *See* Jeffreys and Jeffreys (1946).

JEFFREYS, H., and JEFFREYS, B. S. (1946). *Methods of mathematical physics.* Cambridge University Press. [26, 370]

JEFFS, R. A. (1954). The low speed performance of a single stage of twisted constant section blades at a diameter ratio of 0·5. *Rep. aero. Res. Coun., Lond. 17081.* [494]

JEFFS, R. A. *See* Ainley and Jeffs (1946).

JOHANSEN, F. C. *See* Fage and Johansen (1927).

JOHNSEN, I. A., and BULLOCK, R. O. (Editors) (1956). Aerodynamic design of axial flow compressors, 2. *Rep. Memor. nat. adv. Comm. Aero., Wash. E56B03a.* (Available at TIL. Min. Supply, Lond. as *NACA/TIL/5508.*) [532]

JOHNSON, D. *See* Head, Johnson, and Coxon (1955).

JONES, B. M. (1936). Measurement of profile drag by the pitot-traverse method. *Rep. Memor. aero. Res. Coun., Lond. 1688.* [180]

JONES, B. M., and HEAD, M. R. (1951). The reduction of drag by distributed suction. *Proc. 3rd anglo-amer. aero. Conf. R. aero. Soc. 199.* [230]

JONES, D. S. (1955). Note on the steady flow of a fluid past a thin aerofoil. *Quart. J. Math. 6, 4.* [124]

JONES, J. P. (1957). The calculation of the paths of vortices from a system of vortex generators and a comparison with experiment. *Curr. Pap. aero. Res. Coun., Lond. 361.* [212]

JONES, R. (1926). Distribution of normal pressures on a prolate spheroid. *Rep. Memor. aero. Res. Coun., Lond. 1061.* [395, 401, 419, 421]

JONES, R. *See* Salter and Jones (1955).

JONES, R. T. (1946). Properties of low-aspect-ratio pointed wings at speeds below and above the speed of sound. *Rep. nat. adv. Comm. Aero., Wash. 835.* [268, 316, 342, 343, 386, 452]

JONES, R. T. (1947). Subsonic flow over thin oblique airfoils at zero lift. *Tech. Notes nat. adv. Comm. Aero., Wash. 1340.* [280]

JONES, R. T. (1951). The minimum drag of thin wings in frictionless flow. *J. aero. Sci. 18, 75.* [328]

JONES, R. T. (1956). Some recent developments in the aerodynamics of wings for high speeds. *Z. Flugwiss. 4, 257.* [94]

JONES, W. P. (1943). Theoretical determination of the pressure distribution on a finite wing in steady motion. *Rep. Memor. aero. Res. Coun., Lond. 2145.* [346]

KELLY, M. W., and TOLHURST, W. H. (1954). The use of area suction to increase the effectiveness of a trailing-edge flap on a triangular wing of aspect ratio 2. *Res. Memor. nat. adv. Comm. Aero., Wash. A54A25.* (Available at TIL, Min. Supply, Lond. as *NACA/TIL/4149.*) [249]

KELLY, M. W., and TUCKER, J. H. (1956). Wind-tunnel tests of blowing boundary-layer control with jet pressure ratios up to 10 on the trailing-edge flaps of a 35° sweptback wing airplane. *Res. Memor. nat. adv. Comm. Aero., Wash. A56G19.* (Available at TIL, Min. Supply, Lond. as *NACA/TIL/5298.*) [251]

KELLY, M. W. *See* Cook, Holzhauser, and Kelly (1953).

KELVIN, LORD (1869). On vortex motion. *Math. and Phys. Pap. 4, 13.* [296]

KEMPF, G. (1929). Neue Ergebnisse der Widerstandsforschung. *Werft, Reed., Hafen 10 (11), 234* and *10 (12), 247.* [71, 74]

KETTLE, D. J. *See* Küchemann and Kettle (1951); Weber, Kirby, and Kettle (1951).

KEUNE, F. (1938). Die ebene Potentialströmung um allgemeine dicke Tragflügel-profile. *Jb. dtsch. Luftfahrtf. 1, 13.* [124]

KEUNE, F. (1952). Low aspect ratio wings with small thickness at zero lift in subsonic and supersonic flow. *Aero. tech. Notes K. tek. Högsk., Stockholm 21.* [272, 287]

KEUNE, F. (1953). On the subsonic, transonic and supersonic flow around low aspect ratio wings with incidence and thickness. *Aer. tech. Notes K. tek. Högsk., Stockholm 28.* [273]

KEUNE, F., and OSWATITSCH, K. (1953). Nichtangestellte Körper kleiner Spann-weite in Unter- und Überschallströmung. *Z. Flugwiss. 1, 137.* [268]

KIMBER, K. W. *See* Preston, Gregory, and Kimber (1946).

KINNER, W. (1937). Die kreisförmige Tragfläche auf potentialtheoretischer Grund-lage. *Ingen-Arch. 8, 47.* (Unpublished translation, Min. Supply, Lond.) [342, 345]

KIRBY, D. A. *See* Hartley, Spence, and Kirby (1951); Weber, Kirby, and Kettle (1951).

KIRBY, N. B. *See* Bagley, Kirby, and Marcer (1958).

KIRCHHOFF, G. (1869). Zur Theorie freier Flüssigkeitsstrahlen. *J. reine angew. Math. 70, 289.* [106, 154]

KLANFER, L. *See* Owen and Klanfer (1953).

KLANFER, L., and OWEN, P. R. (1953). The effect of isolated roughness on boundary layer transition. Unpublished communication. [51]

KLEBANOFF, P. S., and DIEHL, Z. W. (1951). Some features of artificially thickened fully developed turbulent boundary layers with zero pressure gradient. *Tech. Notes nat. adv. Comm. Aero., Wash. 2475.* [68]

KLEBANOFF, P. S. *See* Schubauer and Klebanoff (1950), (1955).

KLIKOFF, W. A. *See* Upson and Klikoff (1931).

KOCHIN, N. E. (1940). Teoriya kryla konechnogo razmakha krugovoi formui v plane. *Prikl. Math. Mekh., Leningr. 4, 3.* (Translated as 'Theory of wing of circular planform'. *Tech. Memor. nat. adv. Comm. Aero., Wash. 1324.*) [345]

KOHLER, M. (1938). Windkanalversuche an Strebenknotenpunkten. *Luftfahrt-forsch. 15, 143.* [437]

KRIENES, K. (1940). Die elliptische Tragfläche auf potentialtheoretischer Grund-lage. *Z. angew. Math. Mech. 20, 65.* [342, 345]

KRÜGER, W. (1946). Wind tunnel investigations on a 35° sweptback wing. Unpublished translation, Min. Supply. Lond. [280]

KÜCHEMANN, D. (1938a). Berechnung der Auftriebsverteilung über die einzelnen Flügel eines Doppeldeckers. *Luftfahrtforsch.* **15**, *543*. [524]

KÜCHEMANN, D. (1938b). Note on Sherman's integrator for evaluating the downwash from a span-loading curve. *J. aero. Sci.* **5**, *312*. [339]

KÜCHEMANN, D. (1940a). Bemerkung über den Einfluß des Seitenverhältnisses auf den Zusammenhang von Normalkraft und Tangentialkraft eines Tragflügels. *Z. angew. Math. Mech.* **20**, *290* and (1942) **22**, *304*. [311]

KÜCHEMANN, D. (1940b). Tables for the stream function and the velocity components of a source ring and a vortex ring. Unpublished translation, Min. Supply, Lond. (Originally published in *Jb. dtsch. Luftfahrtf.* **1**, *547*.) [526]

KÜCHEMANN, D. (1947). Design of wing junction, fuselage and nacelles to obtain the full benefit of sweptback wings at high Mach number. *Rep. aero. Res. Coun., Lond. 11035.* [280]

KÜCHEMANN, D. (1952). A simple method of calculating the span and chordwise loading on straight and swept wings of any given aspect ratio at subsonic speeds. *Rep. Memor. aero. Res. Coun., Lond. 2935.* [321, 323, 331, 332, 333, 334, 342, 343, 347, 349, 513]

KÜCHEMANN, D. (1953a). The distribution of lift over the surface of swept wings. *Aeronaut. Quart.* **4**, *261*. [322]

KÜCHEMANN, D. (1953b). Types of flow on swept wings with special reference to free boundaries and vortex sheets. *J.R. aero. Soc.* **57**, *683*. [205, 226, 521]

KÜCHEMANN, D. (1955). A non-linear lifting-surface theory for wings of small aspect ratio with edge separations. *Rep. aero. Res. Coun., Lond. 17769.* [514]

KÜCHEMANN, D. (1956a). A method for calculating the pressure distribution over jet-flapped wings. *Rep. Memor. aero. Res. Coun., Lond. 3036.* [505]

KÜCHEMANN, D. (1956b). Der nichtlineare Auftriebsanstieg von Rechteckflügeln sehr kleines Seitenverhältnisses. *Z. Flugwiss.* **4**, *70*. [512, 523]

KÜCHEMANN, D., and KETTLE, D. J. (1951). The effect of endplates on swept wings. *Curr. Pap. aero. Res. Coun., Lond. 104.* [459, 521]

KÜCHEMANN, D., and WEBER, J. (1953a). *Aerodynamics of propulsion.* McGraw-Hill, New York. [526]

KÜCHEMANN, D., and WEBER, J. (1953b). The subsonic flow past swept wings at zero lift without and with body. *Rep. Memor. aero. Res. Coun., Lond. 2908.* [278, 280, 281, 283, 285, 432, 433, 436]

KÜCHEMANN, D., WEBER, J., and BREBNER, G. G. (1951). Low speed tests on wings of 45° sweep. *Rep. Memor. aero. Res. Coun., Lond. 2882.* [324, 329, 332, 349, 522]

KUTTA, M. W. (1902). Auftriebskräfte in strömenden Flüssigkeiten. *Ill. aero. Mitt.* **6**, *133*. [94]

LBL. See Rosenhead (Editor) (1961 ?).

LACHMANN, G. V. (1921). Die unterteilte Profilform. *Flugsport* **1**, *2*. [207, 208]

LACHMANN, G. V. (1955). Boundary layer control. *J.R. aero. Soc.* **59**, *163*. [231, 242]

LACHMANN, G. V., GREGORY, N., and WALKER, W. S. (1952). Handley Page laminar flow wing with porous strips: details of model and wind tunnel tests at N.P.L. *Rep. aero. Res. Coun., Lond. 14794.* [242]

LAGERSTROM, P. A., COLE, J. D., and TRILLING, L. (1949). Problems in the theory of viscous compressible fluids. *Rep. Cal. Inst. Tech.* [26]

LAITONE, E. V. (1947). The subsonic flow about a body of revolution. *Quart. appl. Math.* **5**, *227.* [389]

LAMB, H. (1932). *Hydrodynamics* (6th edn.). Cambridge University Press. [26, 35, 41, 43, 154, 371, 379, 399, 563]

LANCHESTER, F. W. (1907). *Aerodynamics.* Constable, London. [95, 511]

LANCHESTER, F. W. (1908). *Aerodonetics.* Constable, London. [293]

LANDWEBER, L. (1951). The axially symmetric potential flow about elongated bodies of revolution. *Rep. Taylor Model Basin, Wash. 761.* [382, 385]

LANGE, G. (1941). Kraftmessungen und Druckverteilungsmessungen an 8 Rümpfen. *ForschBer. dtsch. Luftfahrtf. 1516.* (Translated as 'Force and pressure distribution measurements on eight fuselages'. *Tech. Memor. nat. adv. Comm. Aero. Wash. 1194.*) [409]

LAUFER, J. (1950). Investigations of turbulent flow in a two-dimensional channel. *Tech. Notes nat. adv. Comm. Aero., Wash. 2123.* [55, 57]

LAUFER, J. (1953). The structure of turbulence in fully-developed pipe flow. *Tech. Notes nat. adv. Comm. Aero., Wash. 2954.* [55]

LAURMANN, J. A. *See* Robinson and Laurmann (1956).

LAWFORD, J. A. (1953). Low speed wind tunnel measurements of the lift on a 45° sweptback half wing and cylindrical body. Unpublished report, Min. Supply, Lond. [447]

LAWFORD, J. A. *See* Fail, Lawford, and Eyre (1957); Weber and Lawford (1954).

LAWRENCE, H. R. (1951). The lift distribution on low aspect ratio wings at subsonic speeds. *J. aero. Sci.* **18**, *683.* [306, 333, 343, 344]

LAWRENCE, H. R. (1953). The aerodynamic characteristics of low aspect ratio wing-body combinations in steady subsonic flow. *J. aero. Sci.* **20**, *541.* [454]

LAWRENCE, H. R., and FLAX, A. H. (1954). Wing-body interference at subsonic and supersonic speeds. Survey and new developments. *J. aero. Sci.* **21**, *289.* [440]

LAWRENCE, H. R. *See* Flax and Lawrence (1951).

LEATHEM, J. G. (1916). On two-dimensional fields of flow, with logarithmic singularities and free boundaries. *Phil. Mag.* **31**, *190.* [156]

LEEUW, J. H. de, ECKHAUS, W., and VOOREN, A. I. VAN DE (1954). The solution of the generalised Prandtl equation for swept wings. *Rep. nat. LuchtvLab., Amsterdam F156.* [351]

LEGENDRE, R. (1939). Trace des ailettes pour fluides à densité constante. *Bull. Ass. tech. marit.* **43**, *173.* [538]

LEGENDRE, R. (1952–3). Écoulement au voisinage de la pointe avant d'une aile à forte flèche aux incidences moyennes. *Rech. aero.* **30**, *3*; **31**, *3*; **35**, *3.* (Translated as *Rep. aero. Res. Coun., Lond. 16796.*) [100, 514]

LEGENDRE, R., EICHELBRENNER, E. A., and BARANOFF, V. A. (1952). Écoulement transsonique autour d'ailes à forte flèche. *Publ. Off. nat. Étud. aéro. 53.* [319]

LEGRAS, J. (1954). La seconde approximation de l'aile élancée en écoulement subsonique. *Rech. aero.* **42**, *17.* [316]

LEHRIAN, D. E. (1949). An extension of the calculation of the complete downwash in three dimensions, due to a rectangular vortex. *Rep. Memor. aero. Res. Coun., Lond. 2771.* [350]

LENNERTZ, J. (1927). Beitrag zur theoretischen Behandlung des gegenseitigen Einflusses von Tragfläche und Rumpf. *Z. angew. Math. Mech.* **7,** *17.* [438, 457]

LERAY, J. (1935). Les problèmes de représentation conforme de Helmholtz, théorie des sillages et des proues. *Comment. math. helvet.* **8,** *149* and *250.* [166, 175]

LEVI-CIVITÀ, T. (1907). Scie e leggi di resistenzia. *R. C. Circ. mat. Palermo* **23,** *1.* [158, 169]

LEWY, H. *See* Garabedian, Lewy, and Schiffer (1952).

LIESE, J., and VANDREY, F. (1942). Theoretische Untersuchungen über die Druckverteilung eines Mitteldeckers in der Nähe des Rumpf-Flügelüberganges. *Jb. dtsch. Luftfahrtf.* **1,** *326.* [432]

LIESS, W., and RIEGELS, F. (1942). Bemerkungen zum Rumpfeinfluß. *Jb. dtsch. Luftfahrtf.* **1,** *366.* [448]

LIGHTHILL, M. J. (1945a). A mathematical method of cascade design. *Rep. Memor. aero. Res. Coun., Lond. 2104.* [538]

LIGHTHILL, M. J. (1945b). A new method of two-dimensional aerodynamic design. *Rep. Memor. aero. Res. Coun., Lond. 2112.* [143, 236]

LIGHTHILL, M. J. (1945c). A note on cusped cavities. *Rep. Memor. aero. Res. Coun., Lond. 2328.* [151]

LIGHTHILL, M. J. (1945d). A theoretical discussion of wings with leading-edge suction. *Rep. Memor. aero. Res. Coun., Lond. 2162.* [236]

LIGHTHILL, M. J. (1945e). Notes on the deflection of jets by insertion of curved surfaces, and on the design of bends in wind tunnels. *Rep. Memor. aero. Res. Coun., Lond. 2105.* [156]

LIGHTHILL, M. J. (1951). A new approach to thin aerofoil theory. *Aeronaut. Quart.* **3,** *193.* [130, 365, 383]

LIGHTHILL, M. J. (1953). On boundary layers and upstream influence. Part I: A comparison between subsonic and supersonic flows. *Proc. Roy. Soc. A,* **217,** *344.* [150]

LIGHTHILL, M. J. (1956a). Drift. *J. Fluid Mech.* **1,** *31.* [259, 567, 568, 569]

LIGHTHILL, M. J. (1956b). The image system of a vortex element in a rigid sphere. *Proc. Camb. phil. Soc.* **52,** *317.* [567]

LIGHTHILL, M. J. (1957a). Corrigenda to 'Drift'. *J. Fluid Mech.* **2,** *311.* [567]

LIGHTHILL, M. J. (1957b). Contribution to the theory of the Pitot-tube displacement effect. *J. Fluid Mech.* **2,** *493.* [567, 568, 569, 571]

LIGHTHILL, M. J. (1957c). The fundamental solution for small steady three-dimensional disturbances to a two-dimensional parallel shear flow. *J. Fluid Mech.* **3,** *113.* [568, 571]

LILLEY, G. M. *See* Marson and Lilley (1956).

LIVESEY, J. L. (1956). The behaviour of transverse cylindrical and forward facing total pressure probes in transverse total pressure gradients. *J. aero. Sci.* **23,** *949.* [556, 571]

LOCK, R. C. (1946). Profile drag calculations for low drag wings with cusped trailing edges. *Rep. Memor. aero. Res. Coun., Lond. 2419.* [185]

LOFTIN, L. K., and BURROWS, D. L. (1949). Investigations relating to the extension of laminar flow by means of boundary-layer suction through slots. *Tech. Notes nat. adv. Comm. Aero., Wash. 1961.* [239, 242]

LOMAX, H., and BYRD, P. F. (1951). Theoretical aerodynamic characteristics of a family of slender wing-tail body configurations. *Tech. Notes nat. adv. Comm. Aero., Wash. 2554.* [459]

LOMAX, H., HEASLET, M. A., and FULLER, F. B. (1951). Integrals and integral equations in linearised wing theory. *Rep. nat. adv. Comm. Aero., Wash. 1054.* [319]

LONG, R. R. (1953). Steady motion around a symmetrical obstacle moving along the axis of a rotating fluid. *J. Met.* **10,** *197.* [470, 486]

LOTZ, I. (1931a). Berechnung der Auftriebsverteilung beliebig geformter Flügel. *Z. Flugtech.* **22,** *189.* [335, 337]

LOTZ, I. (1931b). The calculation of the potential flow past airship bodies in yaw. *Tech. Memor. nat. adv. Comm. Aero., Wash. 675.* [380]

LOTZ, I., and FABRICIUS, W. (1937). Die Berechnung des Abwindes hinter einen Tragflügel bei Berücksichtigung des Aufwickelns der Unstetigkeitsfläche. *Luftfahrtforsch.* **14,** *552.* [509]

LUDWIEG, H. (1945). Verbesserung der kritischen Machzahl von Tragflügeln durch Pfeilung. *Betz Festschr. Göttingen.* (Unpublished translation, Min. Supply, Lond.) [264]

LUDWIEG, H., and TILLMANN, W. (1949). Untersuchungen über die Wandschub-spannung in turbulenten Reibungsschichten. *Ingen.-Arch.* **17,** *288.* (Translated as 'Investigations of the wall-shearing stress in turbulent boundary layers'. *Tech. Memor. nat. adv. Comm. Aero., Wash. 1285.*) [57, 72, 76, 78, 79, 80, 86]

MAAS, J. N. *See* Young and Maas (1937).

MACMILLAN, F. A. (1956). Experiments on pitot-tubes in shear flow. *Rep. Memor. aero. Res. Coun., Lond. 3028.* [556]

McCULLOUGH, G. B., and GAULT, D. E. (1948). An experimental investigation of an NACA 63_1–012 airfoil section with leading-edge suction slots. *Tech. Notes nat. adv. Comm. Aero., Wash. 1683.* [234]

McCULLOUGH, G. B., and GAULT, D. E. (1951). Examples of three representative types of airfoil section stall at low speed. *Tech. Notes nat. adv. Comm. Aero., Wash. 2502.* [102, 203]

McCULLOUGH, G. B., NITZBERG, G. E., and KELLY, J. A. (1951). Preliminary investigation of the delay of turbulent flow separation by means of wedge-shaped bodies. *Res. Memor. nat. adv. Comm. Aero., Wash. A50L12.* (Available at TIL, Min. Supply, Lond. as *NACA/TIL/2632.*) [211, 212]

MAGNUS, G. (1853). Über die Abweichung der Geschosse u. auffallende Erscheinungen bei rotirenden Körpern. *Ann. Phys., Lpz.* **88,** *1.* [215]

MAIR, W. A. (1955). The distribution of pressure on an aerofoil in a stream with a spanwise velocity gradient. *Aeronaut. Quart.* **6,** *1.* [548, 552]

MALAVARD, L. C. (1947). The use of rheo-electrical analogies in certain aerodynamic problems. *J.R. aero. Soc.* **51,** *734.* [541]

MALAVARD, L. C. (1957). Recent developments in the method of the rheo-electric analogy applied to aerodynamics. *J. aero. Sci.* **24,** *321.* [526]

MALAVARD, L. C., and DUQUENNE, R. (1951). Étude des surfaces portantes par analogies rhéoélectriques. *Rech. aero.* **23,** *3.* [347]

MALTBY, R. L. (1958). A visualization technique for flows separating from highly swept edges. *J.R. aero. Soc.* [510]

MANGLER, K. W. (1938). Die Auftriebsverteilung am Tragflügel mit Endscheiben. *Luftfahrtforsch.* **14**, *564*. (Translated as *Rep. aero. Res. Coun., Lond. 3414.*) [459]

MANGLER, K. W. (1939). Der kleinste induzierte Widerstand eines Tragflügels mit kleinem Seitenverhältnis. *Jb. dtsch. Luftfahrtf.* **1**, *140*. [512, 513]

MANGLER, K. W. (1946). Compressible boundary layers on bodies of revolution. *Rep. aero. Res. Coun., Lond. 9740.* [91, 404]

MANGLER, K. W. (1955). Calculation of the pressure distribution over a wing at sonic speed. *Rep. Memor. aero. Res. Coun., Lond. 2888.* [318, 319]

MANGLER, K. W., and RANDALL, D. G. (1955). Calculation of the load distribution over a wing with arbitrary camber and twist at sonic speed. *Rep. Memor. aero. Res. Coun., Lond. 3102.* [319, 359, 363]

MANGLER, K. W., and SMITH, J. H. B. (1956). A theory of slender delta wings with leading edge separation. *Rep. aero. Res. Coun., Lond. 18757.* [514]

MANGLER, K. W., and SMITH, J. H. B. (1957). Calculation of the flow past slender delta wings with leading edge separation. *Rep. aero. Res. Coun., Lond. 19634.* [100, 514]

MARBLE, F. E. (1948). The flow of a perfect fluid through an axial turbo-machine with prescribed blade loading. *J. aero. Sci.* **15**, *473*. [467]

MARBLE, F. E., and MICHELSON, I. (1952). Analytical investigation of some three-dimensional flow problems in turbo-machines. *Tech. Notes nat. adv. Comm. Aero., Wash. 2614.* [467, 471]

MARCER, P. J. *See* Bagley, Kirby, and Marcer (1958).

MARSHALL, D. *See* Stanton, Marshall, and Bryant (1920).

MARSON, G. B., and LILLEY, G. M. (1956). The displacement effect of pitot tubes in narrow wakes. *Rep. Coll. Aero. Cranfield 107.* (Available also as *Rep. aero. Res. Coun., Lond. 19137.*) [556]

MARTIN, M. E. *See* Hawthorne and Martin (1955).

MARUHN, K. (1941). Druckverteilungsrechnungen an elliptischen Rümpfen und in ihrem Außenraum. *Jb. dtsch. Luftfahrtf.* **1**, *135*. [271]

MASKELL, E. C. (1951). Approximate calculation of the turbulent boundary layer in two-dimensional incompressible flow. *Rep. aero. Res. Coun., Lond. 14654.* [80, 81, 86, 87]

MASKELL, E. C. (1955). Flow separation in three dimensions. *Rep. aero. Res. Coun., Lond. 18063.* [291, 514, 517]

MASKELL, E. C. (1956). The significance of flow separation in the calculation of a general fluid flow. Unpublished communication. [499]

MASKELL, E. C., and SPENCE, D. A. (1959). A theory of the jet flap in three dimensions. *Proc. Roy. Soc. A*, **251**, *407*. [506]

MASKELL, E. C. *See* Owen and Maskell (1951).

MENDELSOHN, R. A., and POLHAMUS, J. F. (1947). Effect of the tunnel-wall boundary layer on test results of a wing protruding from a tunnel wall. *Tech. Notes. nat. adv. Comm. Aero., Wash. 1244.* [548, 552]

MERCHANT, W., and COLLAR, A. R. (1941). Flow of an ideal fluid past a cascade of blades. *Rep. Memor. aero. Res. Coun., Lond. 1893.* [537]

MICHAEL, W. H. *See* Brown and Michael (1954), (1955).

MICHELSON, I. *See* Marble and Michelson (1952).

MILNE-THOMSON, L. M. (1948). *Theoretical aerodynamics.* Macmillan & Co., London. [385]

MILNE-THOMSON, L. M. (1949). *Theoretical hydrodynamics* (2nd edn.). Macmillan & Co., London. [149, 154, 159]

MIRELS, H. (1954). Aerodynamics of slender wings and wing-body combinations having swept trailing edges. *Tech. Notes. nat. adv. Comm. Aero., Wash. 3105.* [319]

MITCHNER, M. (1954). Propagation of turbulence from an instantaneous point disturbance. *J. aero. Sci.* **21**, *350.* [52]

MORTON, W. B. (1913). On the displacements of the particles and their paths in some cases of two-dimensional motion of a frictionless liquid. *Proc. Roy. Soc.* A, **89**, *106.* [259]

MULTHOPP, H. (1938a). Die Berechnung der Auftriebsverteilung von Tragflügeln. *Luftfahrtforsch.* **15**, *153.* (Translated as *Rep. aero. Res. Coun., Lond. 8516.*) [337, 338, 519]

MULTHOPP, H. (1938b). The calculation of the downwash behind wings. *Luftfahrtforsch.* **15**, *463.* [545]

MULTHOPP, H. (1941). Zur Aerodynamik des Flugzeugrumpfes. *Luftfahrtforsch.* **18**, *52.* (Translated as 'Aerodynamics of the fuselage', *Tech. Memor. nat. adv. Comm. Aero., Wash. 1036,* and *Rep. aero. Res. Coun., Lond. 5263.*) [444, 448, 450, 523]

MULTHOPP, H. (1948). On the maximum lift coefficient of aerofoil sections. *Rep. aero. Res. Coun., Lond. 12115.* [204]

MULTHOPP, H. (1950). Methods for calculating the lift distribution of wings (subsonic lifting surface theory). *Rep. Memor. aero. Res. Coun., Lond. 2884.* [302, 333, 334, 345, 346, 349, 351]

MUNK, M. M. (1919). Isoperimetrische Aufgaben aus der Theorie des Fluges. *Diss. Göttingen Univ.* (See also *Rep. nat. adv. Comm. Aero., Wash. 191* (1924).) [303, 328, 336]

MUNK, M. M. (1922). General theory of thin wing sections. *Rep. nat. adv. Comm. Aero., Wash. 142.* [121]

MUNK, M. M. (1924). The aerodynamic forces on airship hulls. *Rep. nat. adv. Comm. Aero., Wash. 184.* [268]

MUNK, M. M. (1934). Fluid mechanics, Part II. Section C in Durand, W. F. (1934). *Aerodynamic Theory,* **1.** Springer-Verlag, Berlin. [371, 393]

MUNZER, H., and REICHARDT, H. (1944). Rotationally symmetric source-sink bodies with predominantly constant pressure distributions. Unpublished translation, Min. Supply, Lond. [378]

MUSKHELISHVILI, N. J. (1946). *Singular integral equations* (2nd edn. translated by J. R. M. Radok, 1953). P. Noordhoff Ltd., Groningen, Holland. [122, 309]

MUTTERPERL, W. (1941). The calculation of span load distribution on sweptback wings. *Tech. Notes nat. adv. Comm. Aero., Wash. 834.* [348]

MUTTRAY, H. (1941). Über die Anwendung des Impulsverfahrens zur unmittelbaren Ermittlung des Profilwiderstandes bei Windkanaluntersuchungen. *ForschBer. dtsch. Luftfahrtf. 824/3.* [527]

NAGAMIYA, T. *See* Tomotika, Nagamiya, and Takenouti (1933).

NEEDHAM, J. R. *See* Nuber and Needham (1948).

NEELY, R. H. *See* Sivells and Neely (1947).

NEHARI, Z. (1952). *Conformal mapping.* McGraw-Hill, New York. [153]

NEUMARK, S. (1947). Velocity distribution on straight and sweptback wings of small thickness and infinite aspect ratio at zero incidence. *Rep. Memor. aero. Res. Coun., Lond. 2713.* [280, 283]

NEUMARK, S. (1950). Velocity distribution on thin bodies of revolution at zero incidence in incompressible flow. *Rep. Memor. aero. Res. Coun., Lond. 2814.* [389]

NEUMARK, S., and COLLINGBOURNE, J. (1949). Velocity distribution on untapered sheared and swept-back wings of small thickness and finite aspect ratio at zero incidence. *Rep. Memor. aero. Res. Coun., Lond. 2717.* [264, 288]

NEUMARK, S., and COLLINGBOURNE, J. (1951). Velocity distribution on thin tapered wings with fore-and-aft symmetry and spanwise constant thickness ratio at zero incidence. *Rep. Memor. aero. Res. Coun., Lond. 2858.* [288]

NEUMARK, S., COLLINGBOURNE, J., and YORK, E. J. (1955). Velocity distributions on thin tapered arrowhead and delta wings with spanwise constant thickness ratio at zero incidence. *Rep. Memor. aero. Res. Coun., Lond. 3008.* [288]

NEWBY, K. W. (1955). The effects of taper on the supervelocities on three-dimensional wings at zero incidence. *Rep. Memor. aero. Res. Coun., Lond. 3032.* [289]

NEWTON, I. (1671). A letter of Mr. Isaac Newton, Professor of the Mathematics in the University of Cambridge, containing his new theory about light and colour. *Phil. Trans. 6, 3075.* [215]

NICKEL, K. (1952). Über spezielle Tragflügelsysteme. *Ingen.-Arch. 20, 363.* [304]

NISI, H., and PORTER, A. W. (1923). On eddies in air. *Phil. Mag. 46, 754.* [31]

NITZBERG, G. E. *See* McCullough, Nitzberg, and Kelly (1951).

NONWEILER, T. (1955). A theoretical study of the boundary layer flow and side force on inclined slender bodies. *Rep. Coll. Aero. Cranfield 115.* [405, 411]

NUBER, R. J., and NEEDHAM, J. R. (1948). Exploratory wind-tunnel investigation of the effectiveness of area suction in eliminating leading-edge separation over an NACA 64₁A212 airfoil. *Tech. Notes. nat. adv. Comm. Aero., Wash. 1741.* [224]

ÖRNBERG, T. (1954). A note on the flow around delta wings. *Aero. tech. Notes K. tek. Högsk., Stockholm 38.* [514]

OSWATITSCH, K. *See* Keune and Oswatitsch (1953).

OWEN, P. R., and ANDERSON, R. G. (1952). Interference between the wings and the tail surfaces of a combination of slender body, cruciform wings and cruciform tail set at both incidence and yaw. *Rep. aero. Res. Coun., Lond. 15317.* [511]

OWEN, P. R., and KLANFER, L. (1953). On the laminar boundary layer separation from the leading edge of a thin aerofoil. *Curr. Pap. aero. Res. Coun., Lond. 220.* [99, 203]

OWEN, P. R., and MASKELL, E. C. (1951). The interference between the wings and the tailplane of a slender wing-body-tailplane combination. *Rep. aero. Res. Coun., Lond. 14483.* [511]

OWEN, P. R. *See* Klanfer and Owen (1953); Young and Owen (1943).

PANKHURST, R. C., and GREGORY, N. (1952). Power requirements for distributed suction for increasing maximum lift. *Curr. Pap. aero. Res. Coun., Lond. 82.* [219, 222]

PANKHURST, R. C., and HOLDER, D. W. (1952). *Wind-tunnel technique*. Pitman, London. [61]

PANKHURST, R. C., RAYMER, W. G., and DEVEREUX, A. N. (1948). Wind-tunnel tests of the stalling properties of an 8 per cent thick symmetrical section with nose suction through a porous surface. *Rep. Memor. aero. Res. Coun., Lond. 2666.* [222]

PANKHURST, R. C., and SQUIRE, H. B. (1952). Calculated pressure distributions for the RAE 100–104 aerofoil sections. *Curr. Pap. aero. Res. Coun., Lond. 80.* See also further pressure distributions given in *Rep. aero. Res. Coun., Lond. 19907* (1958). [142]

PANKHURST, R. C., and THWAITES, B. (1950). Experiments on the flow past a porous circular cylinder fitted with a Thwaites flap. *Rep. Memor. aero. Res. Coun., Lond. 2787.* [220, 226, 227]

PANKHURST, R. C. *See* Gregory, Pankhurst, and Walker (1950); Relf, Pankhurst, and Walker (1954).

PASAMANICK, J., and SELLERS, T. B. (1950). Full-scale investigation of boundary-layer control by suction through leading-edge slots on a wing-fuselage configuration having 47·5° leading-edge sweep with and without flaps. *Res. Memor. nat. adv. Comm. Aero., Wash. L50B15.* (Available at TIL. Min. Supply, Lond. as *NACA/TIL/2373*.) [235]

PEARCEY, H. H. *See* Tanner, Pearcey, and Tracy (1954).

PEPPER, P. A. (1941). Minimum induced drag in wing-fuselage interference. *Tech. Notes nat. adv. Comm. Aero., Wash. 812.* [457]

PERKINS, E. W. *See* Allen and Perkins (1951).

PERSH, J. *See* Rupert and Persh (1951).

PFEIFFER, W. (1937). Das Verhalten der Auftriebsverteilung eines Tragflügels an singulären Stellen des Flügelumriß- und Anstellwinkelverlaufs. *Luftfahrtforsch.* **14**, 494. [336]

PFENNINGER, W. (1946). Untersuchungen über Reibungsverminderungen an Tragflügeln, insbesondere mit Hilfe von Grenzschichtabsaugung. *Mitt. Inst. Aerodyn. Zürich. 13.* (Translated as 'Investigations on reductions of friction on wings, in particular by means of boundary layer suction'. *Tech. Memor. nat. adv. Comm. Aero., Wash. 1181.*) [239, 241]

PFENNINGER, W. (1949). Experiments on a laminar suction aerofoil of 17 per cent thickness. *J. aero. Sci.* **16**, 227. [239, 241]

PFENNINGER, W. (1952). Experiments with laminar flow in the inlet length of a tube at high Reynolds numbers with and without boundary-layer suction. *Rep. Northrop Aircr.* [242]

PIERCY, N. A. V., PRESTON, J. H., and WHITEHEAD, L. G. (1938). The approximate prediction of skin friction and lift. *Phil. Mag.* **26**, 791. [200]

PINKERTON, R. M. (1936). Calculated and measured pressure distributions over the mid-span section of N.A.C.A. 4412 airfoil. *Rep. nat. adv. Comm. Aero., Wash. 563.* [196]

PISTOLESI, E. (1933). Considerazioni sul problema del bi-plane. *Aerotecnica, Rome* **13**, 185. [333, 341]

PISTOLESI, E. (1936). Sul problema dell' ala rotante. *Mem. Accad. Lincei* **6**, 23. [525]

POISSON-QUINTON, P. (1948). Theoretical and experimental research on boundary-layer control. *Proc. 7th Int. Congr. appl. Mech.* **2**, 365. [251]

PRESTON, J. H., GREGORY, N., and RAWCLIFFE, A. G. (1948). The theoretical estimation of power requirements for slot-suction aerofoils, with numerical results for two thick Griffith-type sections. *Rep. Memor. aero. Res. Coun., Lond. 2577.* [219, 220, 246]

PRESTON, J. H., and SWEETING, N. E. (1943). The experimental determination of the boundary layer and wake characteristics of a simple Joukowski aerofoil with particular reference to the trailing edge region. *Rep. Memor. aero. Res. Coun., Lond. 1998.* [184]

PRESTON, J. H., SWEETING, N. E., and COX, D. K. (1945). The experimental determination of the boundary layer and wake characteristics of a Piercy 1240 aerofoil, with particular reference to the trailing edge region. *Rep. Memor. aero. Res. Coun., Lond. 2013.* [184]

PRESTON, J. H. *See* Piercy, Preston, and Whitehead (1938).

PRIESTLEY, E. (1945). An investigation of wake and downwash behind wings and wing-body combinations without flaps or propellers. *Rep. aero. Res. Coun., Lond. 8600.* [547]

PRITCHARD, J. L. (1957). The dawn of aerodynamics. *J.R. aero. Soc.* **61,** *152.* [115]

QUEIJO, M. J., and RILEY, D. R. (1954). Calculated subsonic span loads and resulting stability derivatives of unswept and 45° sweptback tail surfaces in sideslip and in steady roll. *Tech. Notes nat. adv. Comm. Aero., Wash. 3245.* [459]

QUIGLEY, H. C. *See* Anderson, Quigley, and Innis (1956).

RAILLY, J. W. (1951). The flow of an incompressible fluid through an axial turbo-machine with any number of rows. *Aeronaut. Quart.* **3,** *133.* [467]

RANDALL, D. G. *See* Mangler and Randall (1955).

RANKINE, W. J. M. (1871). On the mathematical theory of streamlines, especially those with four foci and upwards. *Phil. Trans.* **161,** *267.* [377]

RANNIE, W. D. *See* Bowen, Sabersky, and Rannie (1951).

RASPET, A. (1952). Boundary-layer studies on a sailplane. *Aeronaut. Engng Rev.* **11** (6), *52.* [231]

RAWCLIFFE, A. G. (1947). Suction-slot ducting design. *Rep. Memor. aero. Res. Coun., Lond. 2580.* [242]

RAWCLIFFE, A. G. *See* Preston, Gregory, and Rawcliffe (1948).

RAYLEIGH, Lord (1877). On the irregular flight of a tennis ball. *Messeng. Math.* **7,** *14.* (Reprinted in *Scientific Papers,* **1,** *343* (1899). Cambridge University Press.) [215]

RAYLEIGH, Lord (1880). On the stability or instability of certain fluid motions I. *Proc. Lond. math. Soc.* **11,** *57.* (Reprinted in *Scientific Papers,* **1,** *474* (1899). Cambridge University Press.) [49]

RAYMER, W. G. *See* Pankhurst, Raymer, and Devereux (1948).

REDSHAW, S. C. (1952). The determination of the pressure distribution over an aerofoil surface by means of an electrical potential analyser. *Rep. Memor. aero. Res. Coun., Lond. 2915.* [347]

REDSHAW, S. C. (1954). The use of an electrical potential analyser for the calculation of the pressures on lifting surfaces. *Aeronaut. Quart.* **5,** *163.* [347]

REGENSCHEIT, B. (1946). Messungen am Absaugeklappenflügel NACA 23015 mit 10% und 15% Klappentiefe. *ForschBer. dtsch. Luftfahrtf. 1763.* (Unpublished translation, Min. Supply, Lond.) [249]

REGENSCHEIT, B., and SCHRENK, H. (1947). Versuche mit Absaugeklappenflügeln verschiedener Profilwölbung und Wölbungslage. *ForschBer. dtsch. Luftfahrtf. 1061.* (Unpublished translation, Min. Supply, Lond.) [249]

REICHARDT, H. (1946). The laws of cavitation bubbles at axially symmetric bodies in a flow. *Rep. aero. Res. Coun., Lond. 10049.* [108, 109]

REICHARDT, H. (1954). Über die Umströmung zylindrischer Körper in einer geradlinigen Couetteströmung. *Mitt. Max Planck Inst.* **9.** [560]

REICHARDT, H. See Munzer and Reichardt (1944).

REISSNER, E. (1944). On the general theory of thin airfoils for non-uniform motion. *Tech. Notes nat. adv. Comm. Aero., Wash. 946.* [301]

RELF, E. F. (1924). An electrical method for tracing streamlines in the two-dimensional motion of a perfect fluid. *Phil. Mag.* **6,** *535.* [541]

RELF, E. F. (1953). Note on the drag of thin aerofoils. *Rep. aero. Res. Coun., Lond. 15582.* [516]

RELF, E. F., PANKHURST, R. C., and WALKER, W. S. (1954). The use of pitot tubes to measure skin friction on a flat plate. *Rep. aero. Res. Coun., Lond. 17025.* [72]

REYNOLDS, O. (1895). On the dynamical theory of incompressible viscous fluids and the determination of the criterion. *Phil. Trans.* A, **186,** *123.* [55]

RHODEN, H. G. (1952). Effects of Reynolds number on the flow of air through cascades of axial flow compressor blades. *Rep. Memor. aero. Res. Coun., Lond. 2919.* [541, 542]

RIABOUCHINSKY, D. (1920). On steady fluid motion with free surfaces. *Proc. Lond. math. Soc.* **19,** *206.* [109, 151, 172]

RICHARDS, E. J., and BURSTALL, F. H. (1945). The 'china-clay' method of indicating transition. *Rep. Memor. aero. Res. Coun., Lond. 2126.* [554]

RICHARDS, E. J., WALKER, W. S., and GREENING, J. R. (1944). Tests on a Griffith aerofoil in the 13 ft × 9 ft wind tunnel. *Rep. Memor. aero. Res. Coun., Lond. 2148.* [243]

RICHARDS, E. J., WALKER, W. S., and TAYLOR, C. R. (1945). Wind-tunnel tests on a 30 per cent suction wing. *Rep. Memor. aero. Res. Coun., Lond. 2149.* [244]

RIEBE, J. M. (1955). A correlation of two-dimensional data on lift coefficient available with blowing-, suction-, slotted-, and plain-flap high-lift devices. *Res. Memor. nat. adv. Comm. Aero., Wash. L55D29a.* (Available at TIL, Min. Supply, Lond. as *NACA/TIL/4844.*) [250]

RIECKE, E. (1888). Beiträge zur Hydrodynamik. *Nachr. Ges. Wiss. Göttingen 347.* [259]

RIEGELS, F. (1948). Das Umströmungsproblem bei inkompressiblen Potentialströmungen. *Ingen.-Arch.* **16,** *373* and **17,** *94.* [131]

RIEGELS, F., and BRANDT, M. (1944). Stream functions and velocity fields of space distributions of sources, and their use in determining the profile and pressure distribution of axially symmetric bodies, with examples. *Untersuch. Mitt. dtsch. Luftfahrtf. 3106.* [378]

RIEGELS, F., and WITTICH, H. (1942). Zur Berechnung der Druckverteilung von Profilen. *Jb. dtsch. Luftfahrtf.* **1,** *120.* [131]

RIEGELS, F. See Liess and Riegels (1942).

RILEY, D. R. *See* Queijo and Riley (1954).

ROBERTS, H. E. *See* Smith, A. M. O., and Roberts (1947).

ROBINSON, A., and LAURMANN, J. A. (1956). *Wing theory.* Cambridge University Press. [111]

ROBINSON, S. W. *See* Zlotnik and Robinson (1954).

ROCK, D. H. *See* Gilbarg and Rock (1945).

ROSENHEAD, L. (Editor) (1961 ?). *Laminar boundary layers.* Clarendon Press, Oxford. [1, 7, 8, 12, 21, 24, 61, 100]

ROSHKO, A. (1955). On the wake and drag of bluff bodies. *J. aero. Sci.* **22**, *124*. [105]

ROTT, N., and CRABTREE, L. F. (1952). Simplified laminar boundary layer calculations for bodies of revolution and for yawed wings. *J. aero. Sci.* **19**, *553*. [91]

ROTTA, J. (1942). Luftkräfte am Tragflügel mit einer seitlichen Scheibe. *Ingen.-Arch.* **13**, *119*. [459]

ROUTLEDGE, N. A. *See* Spence and Routledge (1956).

ROY, M. (1952). Caractères de l'écoulement autour d'une aile en flèche accentuées. *C. R. Acad. Sci., Paris*, **26**, *159*. [294, 514]

ROY, M. (1956). Sur la théorie de l'aile en delta.—Tourbillons d'apex et nappes en cornet. *Rech. aero.* **56**, *3*. [514]

RUDEN, P. (1939). Theorie des Tragflügelprofiles in der Nachbarschaft sprunghafter Gesamtdruckänderungen. (Strahl und Windschatten mit Rechteckprofil.) *Jb. dtsch. Luftfahrtf.* **1**, *98*. [550]

RUDEN, P. (1940). Windkanalmessungen über den Windschatteneinfluß auf Rechtecktragflügel mit symmetrischen Profil. *Jb. dtsch. Luftfahrtf.* **1**, *204*. [550]

RUPERT, K. F., and PERSH, J. (1951). A procedure for calculating the development of turbulent boundary layers. *Tech. Notes nat. adv. Comm. Aero., Wash.* *2478*. [85]

SABERSKY, R. H. *See* Bowen, Sabersky, and Rannie (1951).

SACKS, A. H. *See* Spreiter and Sacks (1951).

SAFFMAN, P. G. (1956). On the rise of small air bubbles in water. *J. Fluid Mech.* **1**, *249*. [31]

SALTER, C. (1946). Experiments on thin turning vanes. *Rep. Memor. aero. Res. Coun., Lond. 2469*. [541]

SALTER, C., and Jones, R. (1955). Tests on a swept-back wing and body with endplates and wing tip tanks in the compressed air tunnel. *Curr. Pap. aero. Res. Coun., Lond. 196*. [462]

SARGENT, R. F. *See* Fage and Sargent (1944).

SARNECKI, A. J. *See* Black and Sarnecki (1958).

SCHIFFER, M. *See* Garabedian, Lewy, and Schiffer (1952).

SCHLICHTING, H. (1954). Problems and results of investigations on cascades flow. *J. aero. Sci.* **21**, *163*. [532, 540]

SCHLICHTING, H. (1955). Berechnung der reibungslosen inkompressiblen Strömung für ein vorgegebenes ebenes Schaufelgitter. *ForschHeft Ver. dtsch. Ingen., Berlin*, **21**, *447*. [539]

SCHLICHTING, H., and JACOBS, W. (1940). Experimentelle Untersuchungen über den Tragflügel in inhomogener Strömung. *Jb. dtsch. Luftfahrtf.* **1**, *81*. [549]

SCHLICHTING, H., and SCHOLZ, N. (1951). Über die theoretische Berechnung der Strömungsverluste eines ebenen Schaufelgitters. *Ingen.-Arch.* **19**, *42*. [532]

SCHLICHTING, H., and THOMAS, H. H. B. M. (1947). Note on the calculation of the lift distribution of swept wings. *Rep. aero. Res. Coun., Lond. 11300.* [350]

SCHMIDT, H. (1937). Strenge Lösungen zur prandtlschen Theorie der tragenden Linie. *Z. angew. Math. Mech.* **17**, *101*. [309]

SCHMIDT, H. (1938). Vorbemerkungen zu einer Reihe von Mitteilungen über Ergebnisse der prandtlschen Tragflügeltheorie. *Luftfahrtforsch.* **15**, *219*. [309]

SCHOENHERR, K. E. (1932). Resistance of a flat surface moving through a fluid. *Trans. Soc. nav. Archit., N.Y.* **40**, *279*. [74]

SCHOLZ, N. (1950). Beiträge zur Theorie der tragenden Fläche. *Ingen.-Arch.* **18**, *84*. [341, 343]

SCHOLZ, N. (1954). Strömungsuntersuchungen am Schaufelgittern: Teil II: Ein Berechnungsverfahren zum Entwurf von Schaufelgitterprofilen. *ForschHeft Ver. dtsch. Ingen., Berlin,* **20**, *442*. [539]

SCHOLZ, N. See Schlichting and Scholz (1951).

SCHRENK, H. See Regenscheit and Schrenk (1947).

SCHRENK, O. (1935). Versuche mit Absaugeflügeln. *Luftfahrtforsch.* **12**, *10*. [249]

SCHRENK, O. (1940). Ein einfaches Näherungsverfahren zur Ermittlung von Auftriebsverteilungen längs der Tragflügelspannweite. *Luftwissen.* **7**, *118*. (Translated as 'A simple approximation method for obtaining the spanwise lift distribution'. *Tech. Memor. nat. adv. Comm. Aero., Wash. 948.*) [348]

SCHUBAUER, G. B. (1954). Turbulent processes as observed in boundary layer and pipe. *J. appl. Phys.* **25**, *188*. [55, 56, 59]

SCHUBAUER, G. B., and KLEBANOFF, P. S. (1950). Investigation of separation of the turbulent boundary layer. *Rep. nat. adv. Comm. Aero., Wash. 1030.* [58, 72, 76, 77, 79, 82, 83, 85, 86]

SCHUBAUER, G. B., and KLEBANOFF, P. S. (1955). Contributions on the mechanics of boundary layer transition. *Tech. Notes nat. adv. Comm. Aero., Wash. 3489.* (Also available in *Proc. Symp. boundary layer effects Aerodyn., nat. phys. Lab.*) [52, 54]

SCHUBAUER, G. B., and SKRAMSTAD, H. K. (1943). Laminar boundary layer oscillations and transition on a flat plate. *Rep. nat. adv. Comm. Aero., Wash. 909.* [48]

SCHUH, H. (1954). On calculating incompressible turbulent boundary layers with arbitrary pressure distribution. *Aero. tech. Notes K. tek. Högsk., Stockholm 41.* [81, 86, 87]

SCHULTZ-GRUNOW (1940). Neues Reibungswiderstandsgesetz für glatte Platten. *Luftfahrtforsch.* **17**, *8*. (Translated as 'New frictional resistance law for smooth plates'. *Tech. Memor. nat. adv. Comm. Aero., Wash. 986.*) [69, 70, 74, 75, 79]

SCHWARTZBERG, M. A., and BRASLOW, A. L. (1952). Experimental study of the effects of finite disturbances and angle of attack on the laminar boundary layer of an NACA 64A010 airfoil with area suction. *Tech. Notes nat. adv. Comm. Aero., Wash. 2796.* [230]

SCHWARTZBERG, M. A. *See* Burrows and Schwartzberg (1952).

SEARS, W. R. *See* Adams and Sears (1953).

SELLERS, T. B. *See* Pasamanick and Sellers (1950).

SERRIN, J. (1952). Uniqueness theorems for two free boundary problems. *Amer. J. Math.* **74**, 492. [175]

SHAW, R. A. (1956). An explanation of vortex shedding on the basis of pusles travelling at the speed of sound. *Rep. aero. Res. Coun., Lond.* 18455. [105]

SHERMAN, A. (1938). An integrator for evaluating the downwash from a span-loading curve. *J. aero. Sci.* **5**, 148. [339]

SILVERSTEIN, A., and KATZOFF, S. (1939). Design charts for predicting down-wash angles and wake characteristics behind plain and flapped aerofoils. *Rep. nat. adv. Comm. Aero., Wash.* 648. [547]

SILVERSTEIN, A., KATZOFF, S., and BULLIVANT, W. K. (1939). Downwash and wake behind plain and flapped aerofoils. *Rep. nat. adv. Comm. Aero., Wash.* 651. [547]

SIMIDU, S. *See* Tani, Taima, and Simidu (1937).

SIMMONS, L. F. G. *See* Fage and Simmons (1925).

SIVELLS, J. C., and NEELY, R. H. (1947). Method for calculating wing charac-teristics by lifting line theory using non-linear section lift data. *Rep. nat. adv. Comm. Aero., Wash.* 865. [520]

SIVELLS, J. C., and WESTRICK, G. C. (1952). Method for calculating lift distribu-tions for unswept wings for flaps or ailerons by use of non-linear section lift data. *Rep. nat. adv. Comm. Aero., Wash.* 1090. [520]

SKAN, S. W. *See* Curle and Skan (1957).

SKRAMSTAD, H. K. *See* Schubauer and Skramstad (1943).

SMELT, R., and DAVIES, H. (1937). Estimation of increase in lift due to slip-stream. *Rep. Memor. aero. Res. Coun., Lond.* 1788. [548]

SMITH, A. M. O., and GAMBERONI, N. (1956). Transition, pressure gradient, and stability theory. *Rep. Douglas Aircr. ES26380.* [51]

SMITH, A. M. O., and ROBERTS, H. E. (1947). The jet airplane utilizing boundary-layer air for propulsion. *J. aero. Sci.* **14**, 97. [242]

SMITH, D. W., and WALKER, J. H. (1958). Skin friction measurements in incom-pressible flow. *Tech. Notes nat. adv. Comm. Aero., Wash.* 4231. [71]

SMITH, J. H. B. *See* Mangler and Smith (1956), (1957).

SMITH, R. H. (1935). Longitudinal potential flow about an arbitrary body of revolution with application to the airship 'Akron'. *J. aero. Sci.* **3**, 26. [374, 395]

SOUTHWELL, R. V., and VAISEY, G. (1946). Fluid motions characterised by 'free' streamlines. *Phil. Trans.* **240**, 117. [151]

SOUTHWELL, R. V. *See* Allen and Southwell (1955).

SPENCE, A. *See* Hartley, Spence, and Kirby (1951).

SPENCE, D. A. (1954). Prediction of the characteristics of two-dimensional aero-foils. *J. aero. Sci.* **21**, 577. [102, 190, 191, 196, 197]

SPENCE, D. A. (1956a). The development of turbulent boundary layers. *J. aero. Sci.* **23**, 3. [81, 86, 87]

SPENCE, D. A. (1956b). The lift coefficient of a thin, jet-flapped wing. *Proc. Roy. Soc. A*, **238**, 46. [502]

TAKENOUTI, Y. *See* Tomotika, Nagamiya, and Takenouti (1933).

TANI, I., TAIMA, M., and SIMIDU, S. (1937). The effect of ground on the aerodynamic characteristics of a monoplane wing. *Rep. aero. Res. Inst. Tokyo 156.* [529]

TANNER, L. H., PEARCEY, H. H., and TRACY, C. M. (1954). Vortex generators: their design and their effects on turbulent boundary layers. *Rep. aero. Res. Coun., Lond. 16487.* [212]

TAYLOR, C. R. *See* Richards, Walker, and Taylor (1945).

TAYLOR, D. W. (1894). On ship-shape forms. *Trans. Instn nav. Archit., Lond.* **35**, *385.* [378]

TAYLOR, G. I. (1916). Motion of solids in fluids when the flow is not irrotational. *Proc. Roy. Soc.* A, **93**, *99.* [559]

TAYLOR, G. I. (1922). The motion of a sphere in a rotating liquid. *Proc. Roy. Soc.* A, **102**, *180.* [468]

TAYLOR, G. I. (1923a). Experiments on the motion of solid bodies in rotating fluids. *Proc. Roy. Soc.* A, **104**, *213.* [486]

TAYLOR, G. I. (1923b). Stability of a viscous liquid contained between two rotating cylinders. *Phil. Trans.* A, **223**, *289.* [31, 49]

TAYLOR, G. I. (1925). *See* Bryant and Williams (1925). [180]

TAYLOR, G. I. (1938). Measurements with a half-pitot tube. *Proc. Roy. Soc.* A, **166**, *476.* [557]

TAYLOR, H. D. (1947). The elimination of diffuser separation by vortex generators. *Rep. United Aircr. Corp. R–4012–3.* [211]

TAYLOR, J. *See* Fink and Taylor (1955).

TAYLOR-RUSSELL, A. J. *See* Titchener and Taylor-Russell (1957).

TEMPLE, G. (1943). Vorticity transport and the theory of the wake. *Rep. aero. Res. Coun., Lond. 7118.* [33, 192]

TETERVIN, N. (1944). A method for the rapid estimation of turbulent boundary layer thicknesses for calculating profile drag. *Wartime Rep. nat. adv. Comm. Aero., Wash. L16.* [182, 185, 187]

TETERVIN, N. *See* Braslow, Burrows, Tetervin, and Visconti (1951); Doenhoff and Tetervin (1943).

THEODORSEN, T. (1932.) Theory of wing sections of arbitrary shape. *Rep. nat. adv. Comm. Aero., Wash. 411.* [125]

THIEME, H. (1954). Über strömungstechnische Grundlagen zur Bestimmung von Steuereigenschaften. *Schiff und Hafen*, **9**, *510.* [511]

THOM, A. (1931). Experiments on the flow past a rotating cylinder. *Rep. Memor. aero. Res. Coun., Lond. 1410.* [215]

THOM, A. (1933). The flow past circular cylinders at low speeds. *Proc. Roy. Soc.* A, **141**, *651.* [104]

THOM, A. (1952). The flow at the mouth of a Stanton pitot. *Rep. Memor. aero. Res. Coun., Lond. 2984.* [558]

THOMAS, H. H. B. M. *See* Schlichting and Thomas (1947).

THWAITES, B. (1945a). A method of aerofoil design. *Rep. Memor. aero. Res. Coun., Lond. 2166* and *2167.* [142]

THWAITES, B. (1945b). A new family of low-drag wings with improved C_L-ranges. *Rep. Memor. aero. Res. Coun., Lond. 2292.* [141]

THWAITES, B. (1946). A theoretical discussion of high-lift aerofoils with leading-edge porous suction. *Rep. Memor. aero. Res. Coun., Lond. 2242.* [222, 224]

THWAITES, B. (1947a). The production of lift independently of incidence. *Rep. Memor. aero. Res. Coun., Lond. 2611.* (See also *J.R. aero. Soc.* **52**, *117* (1948).) [221, 226, 227]

THWAITES, B. (1947b). On the design of aerofoils for which the lift is independent of the incidence. *Rep. Memor. aero. Res. Coun., Lond. 2612.* [147, 229]

THWAITES, B. (1949a). A continuous vortex line method for the calculation of lift on wings of arbitrary planform. *Rep. aero. Res. Coun., Lond. 12082* and *12389.* [351]

THWAITES, B. (1949b). Approximate calculation of the laminar boundary layer. *Aeronaut. Quart.* **1**, *245.* [62, 82]

THWAITES, B. (1949c). The development of laminar boundary-layers under conditions of continuous suction, Part II. Approximate methods of solution. *Rep. aero. Res. Coun., Lond. 12699.* [90]

THWAITES, B. (1951). A note on the design of ducted fans. *Aeronaut. Quart.* **3**, *173.* [469]

THWAITES, B. (1953). A note on the performance of ducted fans. *Aeronaut. Quart.* **4**, *179.* [469]

THWAITES, B. (1954). A note on Küchemann's aerofoil. *Rep. aero. Res. Coun., Lond. 17158.* [158]

THWAITES, B. *See* Hurley and Thwaites (1951); Pankhurst and Thwaites (1950).

TIETJENS, O. G. *See* Prandtl and Tietjens (1931).

TILLMANN, W. *See* Ludwieg and Tillmann (1949); Wieghardt and Tillmann (1944).

TITCHENER, I. M., and TAYLOR-RUSSELL, A. J. (1957). Experiments on the growth of vortices in turbulent flow. *Curr. Pap. aero. Res. Coun., Lond. 316.* [36]

TOLHURST, W. H. *See* Kelly and Tolhurst (1954).

TOMOTIKA, S., NAGAMIYA, T., and TAKENOUTI, Y. (1933). The lift on a flat plate placed near a plane wall with special reference to the effect of the ground upon the lift of a monoplane aerofoil. *Rep. aero. Res. Inst. Tokyo 97.* [529]

TOWNEND, H. C. H. (1929). Reduction of drag of radial engines by the attachment of rings of aerofoil section, including interference experiments of an allied nature with some further applications. *Rep. Memor. aero. Res. Coun., Lond. 1267.* [208]

TOWNEND, H. C. H. (1931). A study of slots, rings and boundary-layer control by blowing. *J.R. aero. Soc.* **35**, *711.* [208]

TOWNSEND, A. A. (1949). Momentum and energy diffusion in the turbulent wake of a cylinder. *Proc. Roy. Soc. A,* **197**, *124.* [55]

TOWNSEND, A. A. (1951). The structure of the turbulent boundary layer. *Proc. Camb. phil. Soc.* **47**, *375.* [55]

TOWNSEND, A. A. (1954). On the turbulent boundary layer on a flat plate of finite width. *Rep. aero. Res. Coun., Lond. 16618.* [71]

TOWNSEND, A. A. (1956). *The structure of turbulent shear flow.* Cambridge University Press. [5, 55]

TRACY, C. M. *See* Tanner, Pearcey, and Tracy (1954).

TREFFTZ, E. (1921). Prandtlsche Tragflächen- und Propeller-Theorien. *Z. angew. Math. Mech.* **1**, *206.* [311, 336]

TRICOMI, F. G. (1951). The airfoil equation for a double interval. *Z. angew. Math. Phys.* **2**, *402.* [319]

TRILLING, L. *See* Lagerstrom, Cole, and Trilling (1949).

TRUCKENBRODT, E. (1952). Ein Quadraturverfahren zur Berechnung der laminaren und turbulenten Reibungschicht bei ebener und rotationssymmetrischer
Strömung. *Ingen.-Arch.* **20**, *211*.   [81, 84, 86]

TRUCKENBRODT, E. (1953). Tragflächentheorie bei inkompressibler Strömung.
Jb. wiss. Ges. Flugtech. (Luftf.) 40.   [351]

TRUCKENBRODT, E. (1954). Experimentelle und theoretische Untersuchungen an
symmetrisch angeströmten Pfeil- und Deltaflügeln. *Z. Flugwiss.* **2**, *185*.
[351, 352]

TSIEN, H. S. *See* Kármán and Tsien (1945).

TUCKER, J. H. *See* Kelly and Tucker (1956).

TUYL, A. VAN (1950). Axially symmetric flow around a new family of half-bodies.
Quart. appl. Math. **7**, *399*.   [379]

ULRICH, W. (1944). Theoretische Untersuchungen über die Widerstandsersparnis
durch Laminarhaltung mit Absaugung. *Ber. Inst. Aero. tech. Hochsch.*,
Braunschweig 44/8. (Translated as 'Theoretical investigation of drag reduction by maintaining the laminar boundary layer by suction'. *Tech. Memor.
nat. adv. Comm. Aero., Wash. 1121.*)   [230]

UPSON, R. H., and KLIKOFF, W. A. (1931). Application of practical hydrodynamics
to airship design. *Rep. nat. adv. Comm. Aero., Wash. 405*.   [398]

URSELL, F. (1949). Notes on the linear theory of incompressible flow round symmetrical swept back wings at zero lift. *Aeronaut. Quart.* **1**, *101*.   [280]

VAISEY, G. *See* Southwell and Vaisey (1946).

VANDREY, F. (1937). Zur theoretischen Behandlung des gegenseitigen Einflusses
von Tragflügel und Rumpf. *Luftfahrtforsch.* **14**, *347*.   [438, 446]

VANDREY, F. (1940). Beitrag zur Theorie des Tragflügels in schwach inhomogener,
paralleler Strömung. *Z. angew. Math. Mech.* **20**, *148*.   [548, 552]

VANDREY, F. (1951). Graphical solution of Multhopp's equations for the lift
distribution of wings. *Curr. Pap. aero. Res. Coun., Lond. 96*.   [339]

VANDREY, F. (1953). A method for calculating the pressure distribution of a
body of revolution moving in a circular path through a perfect fluid. *Rep.
Admir. Res. Lab. ARL/R3/G/HY/12/2*. (Available also as *Rep. aero. Res.
Coun., Lond. 16655.*)   [381, 392]

VANDREY, F. *See* Liese and Vandrey (1942).

VIDAL, R. J. *See* Bartlett and Vidal (1954).

VILLAT, H. (1920). Aperçus théoriques sur la résistance des fluides. *Collection
Scientia*. Gauthier-Villars, Paris.   [159]

VISCONTI, F. *See* Braslow, Burrows, Tetervin, and Visconti (1951).

VOEPEL, H. (1948). Tests on wings of small aspect ratio. *Rep. aero. Res. Coun.,
Lond. 12450*.   [511]

VOOREN, A. I. VAN DE (1952). The generalization of Prandtl's equation for yawed
and swept wings. *Rep. nat. LuchtvLab., Amsterdam F121*.   [351]

VOOREN, A. I. VAN DE (1953). An approach to lifting surface theory. *Rep. nat.
LuchtvLab., Amsterdam F129*.   [351]

VOOREN, A. I. VAN DE. *See* Leeuw, Eckhaus, and Vooren (1954).

WAGNER, F. (1943). Development of boundary-layer control on the Arado 232
wing. Unpublished translation, Min. Supply, Lond.   [251]

WEBER, J., and HAWK, A. C. (1954). Theoretical load distributions on fin-body-tailplane arrangements in a sidewind. *Rep. Memor. aero. Res. Coun., Lond. 2992*. [459]

WEBER, J., KIRBY, D. A., and KETTLE, D. J. (1951). An extension of Multhopp's method of calculating the spanwise loading of wing-fuselage combinations. *Rep. Memor. aero. Res. Coun., Lond. 2827*. [447, 448, 450]

WEBER, J., and LAWFORD, J. A. (1954). The reflection effect of fences at low speed. *Rep. Memor. aero. Res. Coun., Lond. 2977*. [430, 460, 522]

WEBER, J. *See* Küchemann and Weber (1953a), (1953b); Küchemann, Weber, and Brebner (1951).

WEIBERG, J. A., and DANNENBERG, R. E. (1954). Section characteristics of an NACA 0006 airfoil with area suction near the leading edge. *Tech. Notes nat. adv. Comm. Aero., Wash. 3285*. [224]

WEIBERG, J. A. *See* Dannenberg and Weiberg (1953), (1955).

WEINSTEIN, A. (1948). On axially symmetric flows. *Quart. appl. Math.* **5**, *429*. [379]

WEINSTEIN, A. (1949). Non-linear problems in the theory of fluid motion with free boundaries. *Proc. Symp. appl. Math.* **1**, *1*. [150, 175]

WEISSINGER, J. (1942). Über die Auftriebsverteilung von Pfeilflügeln. *ForschBer. dtsch. Luftfahrtf. 1553*. (Translated as 'The lift distribution of swept-back wings'. *Tech. Memor. nat. adv. Comm. Aero., Wash. 1120*.) [333, 341, 343, 348, 349]

WEISSINGER, J. (1952). Über die Einschaltung zusätzlicher Punkte beim Verfahren von Multhopp. *Ingen.-Arch.* **20**, *163*. [339]

WEISSINGER, J. (1955). Zur Aerodynamik des Ringflügels *1*. Die Drückverteilung dünner, fast drehsymmetrischer Flügel in Unterschallströmung. *Ber. dtsch. VersAnst. Luftfahrt, Mülheim 2*. (See also *Z. Flugwiss*. (1956) **4**, *141*.) [527]

WEISSINGER, J. (1957). Zur Aerodynamik des Ringflügels *3*. Der Einfluß der Profildicke. *Ber. dtsch. VersAnst. Luftfahrt, Mülheim 42*. (Translated into English in *Mitteilungen No. 6* of the Institut für angewandte Mathematik der Technischen Hochschule, Karlsruhe.) [527]

WERLE, H. (1953). Visualisation en tunnel hydrodynamique. *Rech. aero.* **33**, *3*. [514]

WESTRICK, G. C. *See* Sivells and Westrick (1952).

WESTWATER, F. L. (1936). Rolling up of the surface of discontinuity behind an aerofoil of finite span. *Rep. Memor. aero. Res. Coun., Lond. 1692*. [97, 509]

WHITE, E. M. *See* Cohen and White (1943).

WHITEHEAD, L. G. *See* Piercy, Preston, and Whitehead (1938).

WHITTAKER, E. T., and WATSON, G. N. (1927). *Modern analysis* (4th edn.). Cambridge University Press. [26]

WIEGHARDT, K. (1939). Über die Auftriebsverteilung des einfachen Rechteckflügels über die Tiefe. *Z. angew. Math. Mech.* **19**, *256*. (Translated as 'Chordwise load distribution of a simple rectangular wing'. *Tech. Memor. nat. adv. Comm. Aero., Wash. 963*.) [333, 343, 344]

WIEGHARDT, K., and TILLMANN, W. (1944). Zur turbulenten Reibungsschicht bei Drückanstieg. *Untersuch. Mitt. dtsch. Luftfahrtf. 6617*. (Translated as 'On the turbulent friction layer for rising pressure'. *Tech. Memor. nat. adv. Comm. Aero., Wash. 1314*.) [79]

WIESELSBERGER, C. (1921). Über den Flugwiderstand in der Nähe des Bodens. *Z. Flugtech.* **12**, *145*. [529, 530]

WIESELSBERGER, C. (1927). Theoretische Untersuchungen über die Querrunderwirkungen beim Tragflügel. *Rep. aero. Res. Inst. Tokyo*, **30**, *421*. [337]

WIJNGAARDEN, A. VAN (1948). Écoulement potentiel autour d'un corps de révolution. *Colloq. int. Cent. nat. Rech. sci.* **14**, *72*. [380]

WILLIAMS, D. H. *See* Bryant and Williams (1925).

WILLIAMS, J. (1949). Summary of experimental lift data for wings with suction or blowing at trailing-edge flaps or with suction through nose slots. *Aero. Notes nat. phys. Lab. 175.* [249]

WILLIAMS, J. (1950a). Some improvements on the design of thick suction aerofoils. *Curr. Pap. aero. Res. Coun., Lond. 31.* [146, 147]

WILLIAMS, J. (1950b). Some investigations on thin nose-suction aerofoils. *Rep. Memor. aero. Res. Coun., Lond. 2693.* [236, 246]

WILLIAMS, J. (1955). An analysis of data on blowing over trailing-edge flaps for increasing lift. *Curr. Pap. aero. Res. Coun., Lond. 209.* [250]

WILLIAMS, J. (1958). British research on boundary-layer control for high lift by blowing. *Z. Flugwiss.* **6**, *143*. [250, 251]

WILLIAMS, J., and ALEXANDER, A. J. (1957). Some exploratory three-dimensional jet-flap experiments. *Aeronaut. Quart.* **8**, *21*. [254]

WINTER, K. G. *See* Squire and Winter (1951).

WITTICH, H. *See* Riegels and Wittich (1942).

WOODS, L. C. (1953). Unsteady cavitating flow past curved obstacles. *Curr. Pap. aero. Res. Coun., Lond. 149.* [175]

WOODS, L. C. (1954). Compressible subsonic flow in two-dimensional channels with mixed boundary conditions. *Quart. J. Mech.* **7**, *263*. [173, 174]

WOODS, L. C. (1955a). The design of two-dimensional aerofoils with mixed boundary conditions. *Quart. appl. Math.* **13**, *139*. [170]

WOODS, L. C. (1955b). Two-dimensional flow of a compressible fluid past given curved obstacles with infinite wakes. *Proc. Roy. Soc.* A, **227**, *367*. [160, 161, 164, 167, 175]

WOODS, L. C. (1955c). Unsteady plane flow past curved obstacles with infinite wakes. *Proc. Roy. Soc.* A, **229**, *152*. [175]

WOODS, L. C. (1956). Generalized aerofoil theory. *Proc. Roy. Soc.* A, **238**, *358*. [172]

WU CHUNG-HUA (1952). A general theory of three-dimensional flow in subsonic and supersonic turbo-machines of axial, radial, and mixed-flow types. *Tech. Notes nat. adv. Comm. Aero., Wash. 2604.* [467]

YEH, H. *See* Eskinazi and Yeh (1956).

YORK, E. J. *See* Neumark, Collingbourne, and York (1955).

YOUNG, A. D. (1939). The calculation of the total and skin friction drags of bodies of revolution at zero incidence. *Rep. Memor. aero. Res. Coun., Lond. 1874.* [405]

YOUNG, A. D. (1947). The aerodynamic characteristics of flaps. *Rep. Memor. aero. Res. Coun., Lond. 2622.* [209]

YOUNG, A. D. (1952). Stalling and the spin. See Chapter II of Duncan, W. J. (1952). *The principles of the control and stability of aircraft.* Cambridge University Press. [205]

YOUNG, A. D. (1953). Calculation of the profile drag of aerofoils and bodies of revolution at supersonic speeds. *Rep. Coll. Aero. Cranfield 73.* (Available also as *Rep. aero. Res. Coun., Lond. 15970.*) [75]

YOUNG, A. D., and MAAS, J. N. (1937). The behaviour of a pitot tube in a transverse total-pressure gradient. *Rep. Memor. aero. Res. Coun., Lond. 1770.* [555]

YOUNG, A. D., and OWEN, P. R. (1943). Simplified theory for streamlined bodies of revolution, and its application to the development of high speed low drag shapes. *Rep. Memor. aero. Res. Coun., Lond. 2071.* [389, 390]

YOUNG, A. D. *See* Squire and Young (1938).

ZAAT, J. A. (1951). Revised methods for routine calculations of laminar and turbulent boundary layers in two-dimensional incompressible flows. *Rep. nat. LuchtvLab., Amsterdam F79.* [86]

ZARANTONELLO, E. H. *See* Birkhoff and Zarantonello (1957).

ZIMMERMANN, C. H. (1932). Characteristics of Clark Y airfoils of small aspect ratio. *Rep. nat. adv. Comm. Aero., Wash. 431.* [343]

ZLOTNIK, M., and ROBINSON, S. W. (1954). A simplified mathematical model for calculating aerodynamic loading and downwash for midwing wing-fuselage combinations with wings of arbitrary planform. *Tech. Notes nat. adv. Comm. aero., Wash. 3057.* [459]

SUBJECT INDEX

The conventions adopted in this index are as follows:

MAIN HEADINGS are printed in capitals. If a main heading is divided into sub-headings, it occupies a whole line to itself.

SUB-HEADINGS are printed in lower case beneath their main heading and are not inset.

Subdivisions of a sub-heading are printed in lower case following their sub-heading and are inset.

Within the index, a reference to a main heading is indicated by the use of a capital initial letter, and to a sub-heading by a lower-case initial. No references are made to subdivisions of sub-headings.

The word '*see*' indicates a necessity; the words '*see also*' imply a recommendation.